CrossWinds
Golf Club

- 27 Hole Golf Course
- Practice Facilities
- Weekly League Play
- Scenic Topography
- State of the Art Clubhouse
- Banquet Facility
- Bar and Grill
- Corporate & Private Outings

For more information, call 508-830-1199
or visit us at golfcrosswinds.com
424 Long Pond Road, Plymouth, MA

#15

#16

#17

#18

It's hard to keep your head down with vistas like this

18-HOLE CHAMPIONSHIP
GOLF COURSE

9-HOLE PAR 3 GOLF COURSE

STATE-OF-THE-ART PRACTICE FACILITY

WILLOWCREEK GOLF ACADEMY

PRIVATE LESSONS & CLINICS

TRAINED PGA PROFESSIONALS

COVERED AND HEATED
OUTDOOR HITTING BAYS

INNER CLUB MEMBERSHIPS

GOLF TOURNAMENTS AND OUTINGS

INDOOR GOLF SIMULATORS

DINING & ENTERTAINMENT

LEGACY BALLROOM &
CONFERENCE CENTER

ELEGANT ACCOMMODATIONS

At Atkinson Resort & Country Club we pride ourselves in delivering a friendly and comfortable experience to all. As a leader in New England Golf, Hospitality, and Dining, our facility exemplifies an experience like no other Take advantage of our public Golf Course, tucked within 420 acres of secluded beauty in southern New Hampshire.

Serving the public seven days a week.

ATKINSON
RESORT & COUNTRY CLUB

85 COUNTRY CLUB DRIVE • ATKINSON, NH 03811 • (603) 362-8700 • WWW.ATKINSONRESORT.COM

PLAY BETTER GOLF

ENJOY THE ULTIMATE IN GAME IMPROVEMENT WITH THE ULTIMATE IN CUSTOM FITTING

- Dial-in your equipment and your game with a custom fitting at the Callaway Performance Center (CPC) at Golf & Ski Warehouse in Hudson.

- One of just 17 CPC's in the nation, the Hudson CPC features Callaway's proprietary cutting-edge fitting technology that is used to fit PGA Tour Staff Professionals Phil Mickelson and Ernie Els.

- High-speed cameras capture ten thousand images per second of your club head pre and post impact and the resulting ball flight.

- Experience the ultimate in game improvement. Schedule your Callaway Performance Center fitting in Hudson today! Call **603-595-8484**.

Callaway Performance Center Fitting SCHEDULE

Driver Fitting . . . . $100 . . . . 1 hour
Iron Fitting . . . . . $100 . . . . 1 hour
Full Set Fitting . . . $150 . . . . 1 ½ hours
Putter Fitting . . . . $50 . . . . . ½ hour

A 50% credit of your fitting fee will be applied to a related purchase within 30 days of your fitting session.

Learn more at:
www.golfskiwarehouse.com/cpc

Route 3A Hudson, NH
603-595-8484
Open Daily • No NH Sales Tax
golfskiwarehouse.com
Other stores in Greenland and West Lebanon, NH, and in Scarborough, Maine.

TOWNSEND RIDGE
COUNTRY CLUB

- 18 HOLE GOLF COURSE
- UPSCALE RESTAURANT
- MEMBERSHIPS & LEAGUES
- PROFESSIONAL STAFF

- INDOOR GOLF SIMULATORS
- PICTURESQUE SETTING
- FORMAL CELEBRATIONS
- HOLIDAY & CORPORATE EVENTS

For More Information Please Contact
978.597.8400 or visit us at www.townsendridge.com

NEW ENGLAND GOLFGUIDE®

THE DIRECTORY FOR GOLF IN NEW ENGLAND

2014

Six States. 675 Courses. One Book.™

Working in the cranberry bogs –
Southers Marsh Golf Club, Plymouth, MA

Welcome to our **25th year** of providing New England's most complete listing of information on private and public courses in Connecticut, Maine, Massachusetts, New Hampshire, Rhode Island, and Vermont. Reader comments welcome and encouraged. Visit us online.

Callarose, LLC
464 Common Street Suite 358
Belmont, MA 02478
www.newenglandgolfguide.com
Sales: (508) 330-6007 Administration: (214) 417-7469

NEW ENGLAND
GOLFGUIDE® 2014

Publisher:	The MRS Company
Editor:	Mike Suvalle
Owner:	Callarose, LLC
Book and Web Designer:	Adam Katz, www.atomikdesignstudio.com
Web Tech Development:	Mike Regan, Empire Software
Contributors:	Christina Ricci

Website: www.newenglandgolfguide.com

Course Ratings by Steve Dailey, Gene Goldstein, Mark Hall, PGA, Jim Martone, Glenn McIntyre, Frank Procopio, and Dennis Walch.

Special thanks to Adam Katz, Mike Regan, Atty. Michael MacClary of Burns & Levinson, LLP, Marcia MacClary, Derick Fors, Johnny Cleanthes, Bo MacClary, Stephen Martin, Dennis Walch, Joe Pisco

ISBN 13: 978-0-9848908-1-1
Printing by Marquis Book Printing, Montmagny, Quebec.

The *New England GolfGuide* is an annual, printed in the winter of each year.

New England GolfGuide, its advertisers, and contributors do not assume liability for any inaccuracies within these pages. **Every effort has been made to contact each course listed by mail and phone to verify and update the latest information. All prices, scorecards and distances, slopes and ratings, and coupon offers are subject to change or revocation by the course at any time.** We go to print in January, and many courses do not announce 2014 rates or other changes until just before opening in the Spring. We apologize for any errors that may appear and appreciate hearing any corrections for the next edition. You may also send corrections to editor@newenglandgolfguide.com.

For continual updates throughout the year, new coupons and offers, and a listing of corrections, please visit Newenglandgolfguide.com frequently.

Welcome to 2014

As we enter our 25th year we would like to thank all of our advertisers for their support throughout the years.

According to Editor Mike Suvalle and Owner Callarose, LLC, the 2014 Guide is the biggest and best ever providing even more coupons, information, stories and articles that readers will enjoy.

Special features in the 2014 Guide:
- **Private Course Section**
- **Coupon For A Free Warrior Golf Club** (*shipping not included*)
- **Entry into a drawing for a full set of Adams graphite golf clubs and golf bag**

Continuing Features in the 2014 Guide:
- **Updated Course Ratings**
- **Top Rated Courses for 2014**
- **Top 50 Golfing Values in New England**
- **Coupons worth over $5,000** (*More 4 for 3 coupons than ever before*)

Charity Golf Events

Our "Hit the Green" and "Hit the Fairway" programs have raised more than $100,000 for charities and golf courses throughout New England in 2009 through 2013 and promise to be even more successful in 2014. Special pricing for sunglasses, golf balls and *New England GolfGuides* are available for your events.

E-Mail Blasts

Our expanded e-mail blast program enables golf courses and advertising partners to connect directly with a captive and interested audience. The database is regularly refreshed and represents thousands of potential customers that have purchased golf-related items.

For information on any of these programs contact us at (508) 330-6007.

Thanks for your continued support.

Please visit us at www.newenglandgolfguide.com.

If we have made any mistakes or failed to report thoroughly, please let us know. We pride ourselves on listening to our readers. Contact us at info@newenglandgolfguide.com.

Contents

YOUR GUIDE TO THE GOLFGUIDE

Finding the Courses

Features

Featured Courses For 2014

92-441   The Golf Courses

The Extras: Coupons & Offers

The Course Listings

GB RTE 495

SE MA CAP

CTR WES MA

NH

RI

VT

N ME

S ME

NE CT

SW CT

Index to Public Golf Courses

ALPHABETICALLY BY STATE & COURSE

Connecticut

Maine

Massachusetts

Massachusetts cont'd.

New Hampshire

Rhode Island

Vermont

Driving Range Directory

Connecticut Driving Ranges by Town

Mountain-View Golf Driving Range	2061 Berlin Turnpike, Berlin 06037	(860) 828-5358
Woodhaven Country Club	275 Miller Road, Bethany 06524	(203) 393-3230
Stony Hill Long Drive	46 Stony Hill Road, Bethel 06801	(203) 778-2777
Mar-Lea Miniature Golf Range	244 Boston Turnpike, Bolton 06043	(860) 649-7023
Golf Quest Family Sports Center	1 Sandout Road, Brookfield 06804	(203) 775-3556
Burlington Golf Center & Practice	Rural Route 4, Burlington 06013	(860) 675-7320
Chesire Academy Of Golf	1550 Highland Avenue, Cheshire 06410	(203) 271-1403
Colchester Driving Range	160 Old Hebron Road, Colchester 06415	(860) 537-4653
Rockpile Driving Range	113 Rock Hall Road, Colebrook 06021	(860) 379-5161
Torza's Professional Golf Center	98 Sebethe Drive, Cromwell 06416	(860) 632-1132
Meadowridge Golf Center	20 North Road, East Windsor 06088	(860) 623-9500
Pleasant View Golf Park	110 North Street, Enfield 06082	(860) 763-4202
Tunxis Fore	1024 Farmington Ave., Farmington 06032	(860) 674-8924
Great Brook Golf Center	850 Route 84, Groton 06340	(860) 448-0938
East Hartford Golf Center	55 Hillside Avenue, Hartford 06106	(860) 282-7809
Goodwin Golf Course	1130 Maple Avenue, Hartford 06114	(860) 956-3601
Toll Gate Golf Range	590 Torrington Road, Litchfield 06759	(860) 496-4653
Klein's Golf Range	391 Durham Road, Madison 06443	(203) 245-1139
Golf Center Of Manchester	60 Progress Drive, Manchester 06040	(860) 646-6479
Club Golf	109 Adams Street, Manchester 06040	(860) 645-6363
Highland Ridge Golf Range	87 Highland Road, Mansfield Center 06250	(860) 423-9494
Indian Springs Golf Club	132 Mack Road, Middlefield 06455	(860) 349-8109
Newfield Golf Driving Range	500 Newfield Street, Middletown 06457	(860) 347-1750
Stanley Golf Club	245 Hartford Road, New Britain, CT 06053	(860) 827-8570
Connecticut Golf Center	562 Danbury Road, New Milford 06776	(860) 354-0012
Only Game In Town	275 Valley Service Road, New Haven 06473	(203) 239-4653
Golf Training Center	145 Main Street, Norwalk 06851	(203) 847-8008
Malerba's Golf Driving Range	650 New London Turnpike, Norwich 06360	(860) 889-5770
CherryStones	218 Shore Road, Old Lyme 06371	(860) 434-1721
Prospect Golf Driving Range	144 Waterbury Road, Prospect 06712	(203) 758-4121
Belmont's Ridgefield Golf Range	824 Ethan Allen Highway, Ridgefield 06877	(203) 431-8989
Golf Center of Connecticut	784 River Road, Shelton 06484	(203) 929-6500
Pleasant View Golf Center	452 South Road, Somers 06071	(860) 749-5868
Golf Quest Family Sports Center	125 Jude Lane, Southington 06489	(860) 621-3663
Raceway Golf Club	252 E. Thompson Road, Thompson 06277	(860) 923-9591
Rockledge Golf Shop & Driving	289 S. Main Street, West Hartford 06107	(860) 521-3156
Brown's Driving Range	1847 Poquonock Avenue, Windsor 06095	(860) 688-1745

Maine Driving Ranges by Town

Roy's Golf Center	2514 Turner Road, Auburn 04210	(207) 782-2801
XL Indoor/Outdoor Golf	620 Hammond Street, Bangor 04401	(207) 848-5850
Long Shot Golf Center	305 Bath Road, Brunswick 04011	(207) 725-6377
Vokes' Mini-Strokes	Bar Harbor Road, Ellsworth 04605	(207) 667-9519
Tee 'Em Up Golf Center	Route 100, Gray 04039	(207) 657-4653
Sugarloaf Sports & Fitness Center	Sugarloaf Access Road, Kingfield 04947	(207) 237-2000
College Street Driving Range	601 College Road, Lewiston 04240	(207) 786-7818

T's Golf	Range Way & Route 202, Manchester 04351	(207) 621-8633
Fore Season Golf	1037 Forest Avenue, Portland 04103	(207) 797-8835
Riverside Municipal Golf Course	1158 Riverside St., Portland 04103	(207) 797-3524
Cascade Golf Range	Rural Route 1, Saco 04072	(207) 282-3524
Mountain View Golf Range	Route 109, Sanford 04073	(207) 324-0436
Nonesuch River Golf Club	304 Gorham Road, Scarborough 04074	(207) 883-0007
Pine Ridge Golf Center	Route 15, Box 4660, Sedgwick 04676	(207) 359-6788
Tee Shots	1126 N. Berwick Road, Wells 04090	(207) 646-2727
Tee 'N Tee Golf Land	27 Bridgton Road, Westbrook 04092	(207) 797-6753
Sonny's Driving Range	108 Cove Hill Road, Winterport 04496	(207) 223-5242

Massachussetts Driving Ranges by Town

Crestview Country Club	281 Shoemaker Lane, Agawam 01001	(413) 786-2593
Mushy's Driving Range	369 Main Street, Agawam 01001	(413) 786-6672
Sarkisian Driving Range	153 Chandler Road, Andover 01810	(978) 688-5522
Atlantic Golf Center	754 Newport Ave, Attleboro 02703	(508) 761-5484
McGolf Driving Range	541 Southbridge Street, Auburn 01501	(508) 832-0557
South Meadow Golf Range	317 South Street, Berlin 01503	(978) 838-2333
Sun 'n' Air Driving Range	210 Conant Street, Danvers 01923	(978) 774-8180
McGolf Limited	150 Bridge Street, Dedham 02026	(781) 326-9616
Ridder Golf Course	300 Oak Street, East Bridgewater 02333	(781) 447-6613
Falmouth Country Club	630 Carriage Shop Rd., East Falmouth 02536	(508) 548-3211
Fenway Golf Range & Pitch	112 Allen Street, East Longmeadow 01028	(413) 525-6495
Easthampton Golf	103 Northampton St., Easthampton 01027	(413) 529-2300
Groton Country Club	94 Lovers Lane, Groton 01450	(978) 448-2564
Groveland Fairways	156 Main Street, Groveland 01834	(978) 373-2872
Western Mass Family Golf Center	294 Russell Street, Hadley 01035	(413) 586-2311
Garrison Par 3 Golf Center	660 Hilldale Avenue, Haverhill 01832	(978) 374-9380
Pine Crest Golf Club	212 Prentice Street, Holliston 01746	(508) 429-9871
Hyannis Golf Club	Route 132, Hyannis 02601	(508) 362-2606
Tee Time Driving Range	New Report Turnpike, Ipswich 01938	(978) 356-6599
Lancaster Golf Center	138 Old Union Turnpike, Lancaster 01523	(978) 537-8922
Bakers Driving Range & Golf	658 South Main Street, Lanesboro 01237	(413) 443-6102
Stone Meadow Golf	675 Waltham Street, Lexington 02173	(781) 863-0445
Lakeview Driving Range	449 Whalom Road, Lunenburg 01462	(978) 345-7070
Sagamore Spring Golf Club	1282 Main Street, Lynnfield 01940	(781) 334-3151
Mendon Driving Range	Route 16, Mendon 01756	(508) 478-6295
Whirlaway Sports Center	500 Merrimack Street, Methuen 01844	(978) 688-8356
Lakeville Golf Practice Range	10 Rock Street, Middleboro 02346	(508) 947-1865
Golf Country	160 S. Main Street, Middleton 01949	(978) 774-4476
Paradise Springs Golf	25 Lonergan Road, Middleton 01949	(978) 750-4653
Quaboag Valley Mini-Golf	15 Hospital Road, Monson 01057	(413) 283-4388
Natick Golf Learning Center	218 Speen Street, Natick 01760	(508) 651-2406
Airport Golf Driving Range	582 Kelley Boulevard, N. Attleboro 02760	(508) 643-2229
Pappas Indoor Golf & Baseball	70 Princeton Street, N. Chelmsford 01863	(978) 251-3933
Caddy Shack	900 State Road, N. Dartmouth 02747	(508) 991-7976
East Coast Golf Academy	333 SW Cutoff, Northborough 01532	(508) 842-3311
Golf Learning Center	19 Leonard Street, Norton 02766	(508) 285-4500
Sandbaggers Practice Range	829 Washington St., Pembroke 02339	(781) 826-1234
Holly Ridge Golf Club	121 Country Club Road, Sandwich 02563	(508) 428-5577
Seekonk Driving Range	1977 Fall River Avenue, Seekonk 02771	(508) 336-8074
Southborough Golf	20 Turnpike Road, Southborough 01772	(508) 480-9992

Massachussetts Driving Ranges by Town (continued)

Easton Country Club	265 Purchase Street, S. Easton 02375	(508) 238-2500
Coles River Family Fun Center	358 G.A.R. Highway, Swansea 02777	(508) 675-8767
Max's Country Golf	383 Middlesex Road, Tyngsboro 01879	(978) 649-2020
Golf Masters	2250 Providence Highway, Walpole 02081	(508) 668-8222
Bryant Farm Driving Range	123 Sandwich Road, Wareham 02571	(508) 295-8773
Rotary Driving Range	Route 9, Westborough 01581	(508) 366-5327
East Mountain Country Club	1458 E Mountain Road, Westfield 01085	(413) 568-1539
Golf Acres	319 Union Street, Westfield 01085	(413) 568-1075

New Hampshire Ranges by Town

Souhegan Woods Golf Club	65 Thornton Ferry Road, Amherst 03031	(603) 673-0200
White Mountain Country Club	3 Country Club Lane, Ashland 03217	(603) 536-2227
Candia Woods Golf Links	313 South Road, Candia 03034	(603) 483-2307
Beaver Meadow Golf Course	1 Beaver Meadow Street, Concord 03301	(603) 224-2828
Twin Pines Driving Range	Route 125, Epping 03042	(603) 679-9911
Driving Range	Route 124, Greenville 03048	(603) 878-1324
Legends Golf & Family	18 Legends Drive, Hooksett 03106	(603) 627-0099
World Golf Cup Center	4 Friel Golf Road, Hudon 03051	(603) 598-3838
Funspot	Rural Route 3, Laconia 03246	(603) 366-4377
Lisbon Village Country Club	Bishop Road, Lisbon 03585	(603) 838-6004
John Cain Golf Club	Unity Road, Newport 03773	(603) 863-7787
Sagamore Golf Club	North Road, North Hampton 03862	(603) 964-8393
Campbell's Scottish Highlands	72 Brady Avenue, Salem, NH 03079	(603) 896-5000
Lochmere Golf & Country Club	Rural Route 3, Tilton 03276	(603) 528-4653
Fore-U Golf Center	298 Plainfield Road, West Lebanon 03784	(603) 298-9702

Rhode Island Driving Ranges by Town

Narragansett Driving Range	1141 Boston Neck Road, Narragansett 02882	(401) 284-0005
Smithfield Driving Range	661 Douglas Pike, Smithfield 02917	(401) 231-3726
Green Meadows Golf	117 Dunns Corner Road, Westerly 02891	(401) 322-9888

Vermont Driving Ranges by Town

Mt. Anthony Country Club	180 Country Club Drive, Bennington 05201	(802) 447-7079
Essex Country Club	332 Old Stage Road, Essex Junction 05451	(802) 879-3232
Practice Tee	Route 7A, Manchester 05254	(802) 362-3100
Arrowhead Golf Course	350 Muray Avenue, Milton 05468	(802) 893-0234
Mount Snow Golf Club	Country Club Road, Mount Snow 05356	(802) 464-4254
Proctor Pittsford Country Club	Corn Hill Road, Pittsford 05763	(802) 483-9379
St. Johnsbury Country Club	Route, St. Johnsbury 05819	(802) 748-9894
Stratton Mountain	Rural Route 1, Stratton Mountain 05155	(802) 297-4114
Basin Harbor Club	Basin Harbor Road, Vergennes 05491	(802) 475-2309
Blush Hill Country Club	Blush Hill Road, Waterbury 05676	(802) 244-8974

The Top New England Golf Courses

The following is the 2014 list of the very best golf courses in New England. To make this cut, a course has to earn a *New England GolfGuide* ✪✪✪½ star rating or greater. Of the 663 public courses covered in this book, only 15 percent make it on this list.

We determine ratings using a uniform set of criteria and compiled by our experienced multi-state rating team. We also take reader feedback seriously and incorporate your comments when appropriate. It is our view that providing you with current and accurate course rating information will only add to your golfing pleasure. In the spirit of constant improvement, we continue to enhance our Course Rating Methodology as well as expand the use of our popular Value Rating™.

Course Rating–The course ratings are based on a 1 to 5 star scale. For example, we reserve the 5-star (✪✪✪✪✪) rating for only a handful of the clearly outstanding courses followed by ✪✪✪✪ for excellent, ✪✪✪ for very good, ✪✪ for good and ✪ for average and below. As an added enhancement, we also include ½ star ratings to help distinguish the unique characteristics of one course from another.

The *New England GolfGuide* rating uses criteria which include:

1. **Course layout.** Is it interesting and varied? How many of the holes are memorable? Is the course challenging but also fair? Would this course present an interesting and different challenge every time you played it?

2. **Course Condition.** What are the average conditions of the tees, fairways, rough, hazards, and greens? What is the overall level of maintenance and attention to detail? How mature is the course?

3. **Course Staff, Facilities, and Restrictions.** How helpful and courteous is the staff? Are there adequate amenities? Are there any restrictions that would detract from the golfing experience and are walkers allowed?

4. **Golfer Feedback.** We view this as an important means of gaining insight into the courses of New England. As in years past we strongly encourage you to provide us with your assessment of the courses you have played. Your feedback provides additional support for our ratings.

2014 NEGG
Top Rated Courses

(18-hole, non-par 3 courses, based on star ratings and rater feedback).

5 Star Courses ✪✪✪✪✪

Massachusetts

Granite Links GC	Quincy, MA	Pinehills GC (Nicklaus)	Plymouth, MA
International CC (Oaks)	Bolton, MA	Pinehills GC (Jones)	Plymouth, MA
Red Tail Golf Club	Devens, MA	Shaker Hills CC	Harvard, MA

4¹/₂ Star Courses ✪✪✪✪¹/₂

Connecticut

Fox Hopyard CC	East Haddam, CT
Wintonbury Hills GC	Bloomfield, CT

Maine

Sunday River GC	Bethel, ME

New Hampshire

Mt. Washington GC	Bretton Woods, NH

Massachusetts

Butter Brook GC	Westford, MA
Cranwell Resort	Lenox, MA
Crestview CC	Agawam, MA
Crumpin-Fox Club	Bernardston, MA
Farm Neck Golf Club	Oak Bluffs, MA
Taconic GC	Williamstown, MA
Waverly Oaks GC	Plymouth, MA

Vermont

Green Mountain National	Killington, VT

4 Star Courses ✪✪✪✪

Connecticut

Great River GC	Milford, CT
Richter Park GC	Danbury, CT

Maine

Belgrade Lakes GC	Belgrade Lakes, ME
Dunegrass GC	Old Orchard Beach, ME
Fox Ridge GC	Auburn, ME
The Ledges GC	York, ME
Links at Outlook	South Berwick, ME
Old Marsh CC	Wells, ME
Samoset Resort	Rockport, ME
Sugarloaf GC	Carrabassett Vly, ME

Rhode Island

Meadow Brook	Richmond, RI
Newport National GC	Middletown, RI

Massachusetts

Blackstone National GC	Sutton, MA
Crosswinds GC	Plymouth, MA
Highfields Golf & CC	Grafton, MA
The Ranch GC	Southwick, MA
Shining Rock GC	Northbridge, MA

New Hampshire

Atkinson Resort	Atkinson, NH
Eastman Golf Links	Grantham, NH
Portsmouth CC	Greenland, NH

Vermont

Hermitage GC	Wilmington, VT
Okemo Valley GC	Ludlow, VT
Rutland CC	Rutland, VT
Sugarbush GC	Warren, VT

3½ Star Courses ✪✪✪½

Connecticut

Elmridge GC	Pawcatuck, CT
Lake of Isles GC	N. Stonington, CT
Lyman Orchards CC (Player)	Middlefield, CT
Lyman Orchards CC (Jones)	Middlefield, CT
Oxford Green GC	Oxford, CT
Quarry Ridge GC	Portland, CT
Rockledge CC	West Hartford, CT
Stanley GC	New Britain, CT
Sterling Farms GC	Stamford CT
Topstone GC	South Windsor, CT
Tower Ridge	Simsbury, CT

Maine

Aroostook Valley CC	Fort Fairfield, ME
Boothbay Harbor CC	Boothbay, ME
Brunswick GC	Brunswick, ME
Clinton GC	Clinton, ME
Kebo Valley GC	Bar Harbor, ME
Martindale CC	Auburn, ME
Nonesuch River GC	Scarborough, ME
Northeast Harbor GC	N.E. Harbor, ME
Penobscot Valley CC	Oreno, ME
Point Sebago GC	Casco, ME
Sable Oaks GC	S. Portland, ME
Spring Meadows GC	Gray, ME
Toddy Brook GC	N. Yarmouth, ME
Waterville CC	Oakland, ME
Webhannet GC	Kennebunk, ME

Rhode Island

Cranston CC	Cranston, RI
Montaup CC	Portsmouth, RI

Vermont

Equinox GC	Manchester, VT
Jay Peak Resort GC	Jay, VT
Mt. Anthony CC	Bennington, VT
Stratton Mountain	Stratton Mountain, VT
Woodstock Inn & Resort	Woodstock, VT

Massachusetts

Acushnet River Valley GC	Acushnet, MA
Atlantic CC	Plymouth, MA
Black Swan CC	Georgetown, MA
Blue Rock GC	S. Yarmouth, MA
Captains GC (Port)	Brewster, MA
Captains GC (Starboard)	Brewster, MA
Cold Spring CC	Belchertown, MA
Cranberry Valley GC	Harwich, MA
Cyprian Keyes GC	Boylston, MA
Far Corner GC	West Boxford, MA
Four Oaks CC	Dracut, MA
Foxborough CC	Foxborough, MA
George Wright GC	Hyde Park, MA
Green Hill Municipal GC	Worcester, MA
Juniper Hill GC (Lakeside)	Northborough, MA
Juniper Hill GC (Riverside)	Northborough, MA
Kettle Brook GC	Paxton, MA
New England CC	Bellingham, MA
Pembroke CC	Pembroke, MA
Poquoy Brook GC	Lakeville, MA
Quail Ridge CC	Acton, MA
Southers Marsh GC	Plymouth, MA
Townsend Ridge CC	Townsend, MA
Wachusett CC	West Boylston, MA
Wentworth Hills CC	Plainville, MA

New Hampshire

Balsams Panorama GC	Dixville Notch, NH
Bretwood GC (North)	Keene, NH
Campbell's Scot. Highlds	Salem NH
Crotched Mountain GC	Francestown, NH
Hanover CC	Hanover, NH
Lochmere GC	Tilton, NH
Overlook GC	Hollis, NH
Owl's Nest GC	Campton, NH
Passaconaway CC	Litchfield, NH
Ridgewood CC	Moultonbourough, NH
Rochester CC	Rochester, NH
Stonebridge CC	Goffstown, NH
The Oaks GL	Somersworth, NH

*The *New England GolfGuide* uses a five star rating system when evaluating golf courses. This rating takes into account course layout, condition, variety, challenge, amenities, and professionalism of the staff. A course that has earned a rating of ✪ is average, ✪✪ represents a good course, ✪✪✪ is considered very good. A ✪✪✪✪ course offers an superior experience and a ✪✪✪✪✪ rating is reserved for only the most exceptional courses.

Top 50 Golfing Values in New England 2014

The *New England GolfGuide* Value Rating™ is provided to help our reader's identify the courses that deliver the best value for golfing dollar ($$$). This year we have provided you with the Top 20 (✪✪✪) rated courses with an 18 hole weekend rate of $58 or less and the Top 20 (✪✪✪½) rated courses with an 18 hole weekend rate of $62 or less. We have also provided you with the Top 10 (✪✪✪✪), (✪✪✪✪½) and (✪✪✪✪✪) rated courses with an 18 hole weekend rate of $78 or less.

Of the 663 public golf courses listed in this book, there are only a select group of courses, approximately 8 percent, which are on this list. Our list not only reflects price but includes reader feedback and the reports from our NEGG Course Rater team.

Of course, only you can judge the value of a day on Course A versus Course B. But we've compiled the data on the most objective basis we can and we'll stand by our list. This is just another opportunity for you to send us feedback. Did we miss any great values? Did we rate some course too high or too low? If enough readers tell us something they can move the needle.

Each year, the biggest task of our editorial staff is to update the listed information for all of the courses. As was the case last year, due to the economy, most course have told us that their rates will remain unchanged. As we reviewed the rates we discovered that the average weekend cost of playing 18 holes of golf, with cart, across New England has remained at approximately $64.

In addition to the Top 50 Golfing Values in New England, golfers who like to play into fall or start in early spring can also find a wide variety of wonderful off-season specials. Many of the courses listed in our book have substantial off-season discounts from the standard green fee which can be accessed by going directly to their websites.

Also, don't forget the Fall golf bonus; many courses in the southern areas of New England including Cape Cod provide fine playing conditions and discounts starting in October (and a few stay open year-round). Try **Farm Neck** on Martha's Vineyard in April or October for what might be the best deal of all.

Throughout New England you will find many resort courses that offer stay and play packages. Here are a few which we recommend:

Connecticut

Lake of Isles Golf Club & Resort in Stonington

Maine

Point Sebago Golf Club in Casco
Samoset Resort in Rockport
Sugarloaf Golf Club in Carrabassett Valley
Sunday River Golf Club in Newry

Massachusetts

Blue Rock Golf Course in South Yarmouth
Cranwell Resort in Lenox
Crumpin- Fox Club in Bernardston
Ocean Edge Resort in Brewster

New Hampshire

Atkinson Resort in Atkinson
Crotched Mountain Resort in Francestown
Mt. Washington Golf Club in Bretton Woods

Vermont

Equinox Golf Club in Manchester
Hermitage Golf Club in Wilmington
Lake Morey Resort in Fairlee
Mount Snow Golf Club in Mount Snow
Sugarbush Resort in Warren
Woodstock Inn & Resort in Woodstock

In addition to the top 50 values and recommended resort courses their are many wonderful golf courses throughout New England that can provide you with a fun and enjoyable day. The key is to determine where you want to go and then check out the area for which courses you want to play based on the course information, star rating and player comments.

Top 50 Value Ratings
New England GolfGuide
2014 Season

The *New England GolfGuide* takes the top-rated courses in our listings, and using a formula that balances price, star ratings, reader comments, and rater evaluations. The resulting list below is a ranking of the Top 50 Best Golfing Values in New England for prices as predicted for 2014.

✪✪✪ RATING	COURSE	STATE	GOLF	CART	$ TOTAL
✪✪✪	Lake Kezar	ME	34	12	46
✪✪✪	Laurel View	CT	35	15	50
✪✪✪	Leicester	MA	36	16	52
✪✪✪	Bath	ME	40	13	53
✪✪✪	Bridgton Highlands	ME	36	17	53
✪✪✪	Hunter	CT	39	15	54
✪✪✪	Bar Harbor	ME	40	15	55
✪✪✪	Hickory Ridge	MA	39	16	55
✪✪✪	North Kingstown Municipal	RI	39	16	55
✪✪✪	Richmond	RI	40	15	55
✪✪✪	Laurel Lane	RI	38	18	56
✪✪✪	Poland Spring	ME	40	17	57
✪✪✪	Topstone	CT	44	13	57
✪✪✪	Traditions of Wallingford	CT	57	INC	57
✪✪✪	Triggs Memorial	RI	40	18	58
✪✪✪	Nippo Lake	NH	42	16	58
✪✪✪	River Ridge	CT	42	16	58
✪✪✪	Turner Highlands	ME	42	16	58
✪✪✪	Connecticut National	CT	43	15	58
✪✪✪	Canterbury Woods	NH	58	INC	58

✪✪✪½ RATING	COURSE	STATE	GOLF	CART	$ TOTAL
✪✪✪½	Stanley	CT	33	15	48
✪✪✪½	Crotched Mountain	NH	35	14	49
✪✪✪½	Southers Marsh	MA	37	12	49
✪✪✪½	Rockledge	CT	37	14	51
✪✪✪½	Penobscot Valley	ME	39	15	54
✪✪✪½	Green Hill	MA	40	15	55
✪✪✪½	Toddy Brook	ME	40	15	55
✪✪✪½	Bretwood	NH	42	13	55
✪✪✪½	Nonesuch	ME	40	18	58
✪✪✪½	Rochester	NH	42	16	58

INC = INCLUDED IN WEEKEND GREENS FEES

(Prices reflect anticipated 2014 fees but are subject to change without notice. Please call ahead.)

✪✪½ RATING	COURSE	STATE	GOLF	CART	$ TOTAL
✪✪½	Quarry Ridge	CT	59	INC	59
✪✪½	Spring Meadows	ME	43	16	59
✪✪½	Ridgewood	NH	42	17	59
✪✪½	Wentworth Hills	MA	42	17	59
✪✪½	Sable Oaks	ME	45	15	60
✪✪½	Kettle Brook	MA	60	INC	60
✪✪½	Lochmere	NH	45	16	61
✪✪½	Acushnet	MA	46	16	62
✪✪½	Aroostook	ME	45	17	62
✪✪½	Far Corner	MA	46	16	62

✪✪✪ RATING	COURSE	STATE	GOLF	CART	$ TOTAL
✪✪✪	Highfields	MA	61	INC	61
✪✪✪	Fox Ridge	ME	48	17	65
✪✪✪	Crosswinds	MA	66	INC	66
✪✪✪	Eastman	NH	49	18	67
✪✪✪	Meadow Brook	RI	70	INC	70
✪✪✪	Blackstone	MA	75	INC	75
✪✪✪	Dunegrass	ME	57	18	75
✪✪✪	Links at Outlook	ME	58	17	75
✪✪✪½	Crestview	MA	59	17	76
✪✪✪	Richter Park	CT	78	INC	78

INC = INCLUDED IN WEEKEND GREENS FEES

(Prices reflect anticipated 2014 fees but are subject to change without notice. Please call ahead.)

In addition, there are numerous great courses that offer reduced rates during off-peak times and off-peak months.

The *New England GolfGuide* uses a five star rating system when evaluating golf courses. This rating takes into account both course layout and condition. A course that has earned a rating of ✪ is average, ✪✪ represents a good course, ✪✪✪ is considered very good where as a course that has earned a ✪✪✪✪ is excellent and a ✪✪✪✪✪ rating is reserved for only the most exceptional courses.

Rulewich & Fleury Golf Design

In 1995, The Golf Group, Inc. was formed when the key golf course design and construction staff at the Robert Trent Jones organization decided to continue working together after the Jones office was closed. Under the umbrella of The Golf Group, Inc., Roger Rulewich and David Fleury are now doing business as Rulewich & Fleury Golf Design. Roger joined Jones after graduating from Yale, working on projects worldwide with him for over 30 years. Dave joined the Group in 1999, after studies at the University of Massachusetts and work in golf maintenance, design and construction with Jack Nicklaus and Jerry Pate.

Roger Rulewich (left) and Dave Fleury (right) of Rulewich & Fleury Golf Design.

Rulewich & Fleury Design have worked on both golf course designs and improvements to existing golf facilities, both locally and abroad. Just last fall they completed a complete renovation of Bermuda's Port Royal golf course, home of the PGA's annual Grand Slam event. They are currently overseeing the development of Rei Dom Carlos, a championship golf course at the new Ron d'el Rei Resort in Portugal.

The trademark of Rulewich & Fleury is their complete involvement with a project from start to finish, providing design, hands-on supervision and "shaping" of the finish contouring of each design or redesign with our own staff. Roger's work on Crumpin-Fox in Bernardston, Massachusetts brought the group to its new home, with work for the owner at Fox Hopyard in East Haddam, Connecticut and Fox Hollow in Newport Richie, Florida. Recent new designs in the Northeast include Meadow Brook in Rhode Island, Saratoga National in New York and Ballyowen in New Jersey. Complete renovations of Half Moon in Jamaica and Palmetto Dunes in Hilton Head have broadened their reach.

"No job is too big or too small, and our rewards are the acceptance and satisfaction of each and every client." You can reach Rulewich & Fleury at design@rulewich.com or dave@rulewich.com.

Championship Golf in the Northern Catskills

Thunderhart Golf Course at Sunny Hill is a championship 18-hole golf course located in the Northern Catskills and is part of Sunny Hill Resort. The resort boasts 36 holes of golf which includes 18-holes of resort-style golf at Sunny Hill and 18-holes of championship golf at Thunderhart. For avid golfers, dual memberships are available for both courses.

This championship course, par 72, is set in the Catskill Basin, and offers 11 ponds and 19 sand traps. In addition to breathtaking views, this 6482 yard course is a "must play" with its scenic beauty and challenging design.

The back nine was created in the Parkland style, which has each hole cut through the beautiful forest of the Catskills.

Acquired in 2007 by the Nicholsen family, owners of Sunny Hill Resort & Golf Course, Thunderhart has been transformed into one of the region's premier golf complexes, under the supervision of the golf course superintendent, Erik Nicholsen, and his experienced staff.

Thunderhart offers a fully equipped Pro Shop and is an authorized Nike dealer. With the Clubhouse Grille, Fireside Lounge, and outdoor Pavilion situated next to a scenic pond, Thunderhart is the perfect setting for a group outing or just to sit and discuss the day's round with a group of friends.

Thunderhart at Sunny Hill has everything a golfer could want: scenic beauty, challenging design and layout.

Please see Thunderhart's full color ad at the back of the book.

Indoor Golf Guide

For those of you who don't want to put your clubs away for the winter, here is a list of some indoor golf facilities that have golf simulators that will allow you to fine tune your game while playing a variety of golf courses.

Connecticut

Maggie McFly's Indoor Golf – Brookfield (203) 775-7962
www.maggiemcflys.com
Real clubs, real swings, real PGA courses plus 3Trak technology. Three golf simulator suites each with a flat screen TV, tables and couches for a VIP experience.

Maine

Fore Season Indoor Golf – Cumberland (207) 489-9016
www.fsigolf.com
Recently relocated to the banquet room at Val Halla Golf Course. Seven golf simulators. Men's and ladies leagues. Friday night couple's scramble.

The Links at Outlook – South Berwick (207) 384-4653
www.outlookgolf.com
Just arrived – two new XDream Golf Simulators located in the Outlook Tavern in the Pro Shop building. Off season pub menu available. Bring your own league.

Massachusetts

Big Sticks Golf – Burlington (781) 229-2269
www.bigsticksgolf.com
The place to go for the swing you want with the training and equipment you need. PGA backed aboutGolf simulator. Golf instruction available.

Broken Tee Indoor Golf – Lakeville (508) 923-4653
www.thebrokentee.com
Features the Full Swing Golf simulator with 6 course options. The patented two field tracking system is the industry standard.

Chip Shots Grill & Sports Pub – Littleton (978) 772-0072
www.chipshotspub.com
Two aboutGolf simulators featuring 29 unique courses based on real and fantasy locations. Bring your clubs and your appetite and enjoy a wonderful time.

Massachusetts

Fore! Golf Entertainment - Wilmington (508) 366-3673
www.foregolfentertainment.com
New England's new, premier indoor golf entertainment venue. Eight PGA
Tour widescreen simulators with over 35 courses on each simulator.

Groton Indoor Golf Center – Groton (978) 448-2564
www.grotonpoolandgolf.com
Choose from 28 different virtual golf courses on each of three golf
simulators. Corporate and group leagues are welcome. Private lessons
available.

Milford Sports Center – Milford (508) 473-8300
www.milfordsportscenter.com
New Full Swing golf simulator with 64 world famous courses. The perfect
place to play, improve and enjoy the game of golf. Private lessons available.

Opti Golf Center - Middleton (978) 539-8725
www.optigolfcenters.com
The best indoor golf experience in America. Features a full bar, a large HD
screen TV and eight state of the art golf simulators with real putting. Great
for special events.

Sandbaggers Indoor Golf – Templeton (978) 632-1500
www.sandbaggersindoorgolf.com
Use the driving range, the unique camera system, software and swing
analysis technology to see what your swing really looks like. Two aboutGolf
simulators.

The Tour Golf Bar – Hingham (781) 749-1720
www.thetourgolfbar.com
Located at South Shore Country Club. Choose from nearly 50 PGA
championship golf courses on three aboutGolf simulators on life size
20-foot screens.

Townsend Ridge – Townsend, MA (978) 597-8400
www.townsendridge.com
Two state of the art Full Swing Golf simulators. Great for practice, just
playing a round of golf or joining a winter league. Simulator memberships
available for the winter.

Western MA Family Golf Center – Hadley (413) 586-2311
www.wmassfamilygolf.com
Features a PGA Tour about Golf simulator that's accurate and realistic
with 32 courses to play. Leagues are welcome and there are three PGA Pros
available for lessons.

Indoor Golf Guide

New Hampshire

Atkinson Resort & Country Club – Atkinson (603) 362-8700
www.atkinsonresort.com
Merrill's Tavern has four of the most sophisticated virtual golf simulators
in all of New England. 35 courses to choose from. Tournament play
throughout the winter.

Breakfast Hill Golf Club – Greenland (603) 436-5001
www.breakfasthill.com
Two PGA Tour aboutGolf simulators offer you 30 courses to pick from
around the world. Start your own league or join one of the many available.

Derryfield Country Club – Manchester (603) 669-0235
www.derryfieldgolf.com
State of the art indoor golf facility featuring 2 PGA Tour aboutGolf simulators.
Select from 32 different courses. Leagues and tournaments available.

Pembroke Pines Country Club – Pembroke (603) 210-1365
www.pembrokepinescc.com
Two PGA Tour aboutGolf simulators offering 27 pristine courses around the
world. Leagues welcome. Come play 18 holes or just use the range to practice.

Rhode island

Aquidneck Golf – Portsmouth (401) 864-0496
www.aquidneckgolf.com
Rhode Island's only indoor golf facility with a simulator. Features the
Trugolf simulator with 33 courses to choose from and a swing analyzer.

Vermont

Gonzo's Indoor Golf & Sports Bar – Burlington (802) 881-0660
www.gonzosindoorgolf.com
Vermont's only Indoor Golf Center. A true sports bar with a ping pong table,
2 pool tables and eight Hi-Def golf simulators. Choose from 21 great courses
on each simulator.

New England GolfGuide
What's New in 2014

New Public Golf Courses

Grandview Golf Course – *Leominster, MA*
A scenic, 9-hole course that is friendly yet challenging to all levels of players. Owned and operated by the Vachon family since 1965. Beautiful vistas.

Lebanon Pines Golf Course – *Lebanon, ME*
Great new 9-hole course developed and run by the owner. This course has already received many positive reviews and you can look for steady improvement in 2014.

Rockport Golf Club – *Rockport, MA*
Excellent 9-hole course offering different tees for the 1st and 2nd nines. Easy walking course that provides a good test of golf.

Quail Ridge Country Club – *Acton, MA*
Previously 18 holes. The new redesign offers a championship 9-hole layout that is bound by conservation land and beautiful tree-lined fairways.

Weathervane Golf Club – *Weymouth, MA*
This new 9-hole course provides an enjoyable experience for golfers of all levels built on natural terrain that provides many unique challenges.

Name Changes

Boothbay Harbor Country Club *was previously named Boothbay Country Club in Boothbay, ME.*

Hillside Country Club *was previously named Lombardi's Hillside Country Club in Rehoboth, MA.*

Kelly Greens Golf Course *was previously named Kelly Greens By The Sea in Nahant, MA.*

Rowley Country Club *was previously named Carriage Pines Golf Club in Rowley, MA.*

Featured Courses 2014

Put these on your must-play list.

This section gives you a closer look at some of our region's most highly rated and enjoyed courses. Whenever you visit, tell them you saw them in the *New England GolfGuide* and rate the course at newenglandgolfguide.com.

Private Courses

Allendale, Dartmouth, MA
Cocheco, Dover, NH
CC of Halifax, Halifax, MA
CC of New Bedford, N. Dartmouth, MA
Crestwood, Rehoboth, MA
Elmcrest, East Longmeadow, MA
Farmington Woods, Avon, CT
Harmon Golf & Fitness, Rockland, MA
Marlborough, Marlborough, MA
Ocean Edge, Brewster, MA
Pleasant Valley, Sutton, MA
Reservation, Mattapoisett, MA

Public Courses

CONNECTICUT
Connecticut National, Putnam
Stanley, New Britain

MAINE
Bar Harbor, Trenton
Boothbay Harbor, Boothbay
Dunegrass, Old Orchard Beach
Lake Kezar, Lovell
The Ledges, York
Links at Outlook, South Berwick
Nonesuch River, Scarborough
Spring Meadows, Gray

MASSACHUSETTS
Acushnet River, Acushnet
Brookside, Bourne
Butter Brook, Westford
Crestview, Agawam
Crosswinds, Plymouth
Crumpin-Fox, Bernardston
Dennis Highlands, Dennis
Dennis Pines, Dennis
Far Corner, West Boxford
Foxborough, Foxborough
Glen Ellen, Millis
Granite Links, Quincy
Heather Hill, Plainville
Highfields, Grafton
Hyannis, Hyannis
The International, Bolton
Leicester, Leicester
Maplegate, Bellingham
Olde Barnstable, Marstons Mills
Pembroke, Pembroke
Pinehills, Plymouth
Quail Ridge, Acton
Red Tail, Devens
Shining Rock, Northridge
Southers Marsh, Plymouth
The Ranch, Southwick
Townsend Ridge, Townsend
Wentworth Hills, Plainville

NEW HAMPSHIRE
Atkinson, Atkinson
Breakfast Hill, Greenland
Canterbury Woods, Canterbury
Crotched Mountain, Francestown
Pembroke Pines, Pembroke
Ridgewood, Moultonborough
Windham, Windham

RHODE ISLAND
Cranston, Cranston
Harbor Lights, Warwick

VERMONT
Green Mountain, Killington
Hermitage, Wilmington
Okemo Valley, Ludlow
Tater Hill, North Windham

Allendale Country Club

North Dartmouth, MA

Best Kept Secret in Southeastern MA.

Designed by famed golf course architect Geoffrey Cornish, Allendale Country Club is a private club that offers golfers of all ages and abilities the opportunity to enjoy a fair but challenging layout on a relatively quick course. Stretching to 6,764 yards from the back tees, this beautifully maintained par 72 course is known for its challenging greens and beauty. Allendale Country Club has excellent practice facilities including a driving range, chipping area and putting green.

Allendale Country Club is a perfect spot for golf outings and small groups. The professional staff will ensure you have a great golfing experience. Golf instruction is also available to the general public.

Whether your interests are golf, swimming in an Olympic size pool or social, Allendale Country Club is the place to be. New memberships are currently available. For information on memberships, to schedule a golf outing or a golf lesson please contact Director of Golf, Stephen Brown at (508) 992-8682.

Cochecho Country Club

Dover, NH

Stylish Tradition Since 1923.

Founded in 1923, Cochecho Country Club is a private country club with banquet facilities perfectly suited for weddings, office parties and private events. They have an excellent driving range and practice facility as well as a swimming pool and restaurant for the entire family. The traditional 18 hole, championship golf course, was uniquely built by two different architects from two different eras Described by many players as a "hidden gem", the front nine at Cochecho is an excellent example of a classic golf course designed by architect Wayne Stiles. The back nine, designed by Phil Wogan was added in 1966.

The 6,210, par 70 layout at Cocheco is nestled in its natural environment and known for its subtle challenging greens. Cocheco is a shot makers course that tests a golfers wit as well as his ball striking ability. Each hole on this strategic design has its own character, not only in the look of the hole, but the types of shots required. Higher handicap golfers can enjoy their round just as much as the scratch golfer as the course is forever enjoyable to golfers of all abilities.

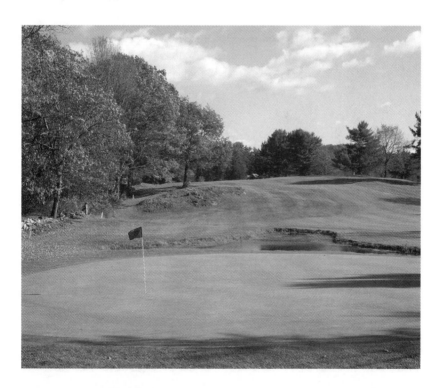

Country Club of Halifax

Halifax, MA

Where the Swingers Go.

Designed by noted golf architect Phil Wogan in 1966, the Country Club of Halifax offers 18 holes of challenging golf playing at 6,738 yards from the tips. This par 72 course is designed for players of all abilities. Whether you are a beginner, a junior player or a low handicap golfer, you are in for a treat on one of the best championship layouts in Massachusetts.

Membership at Halifax offers all of the luxury that you would expect from a private club. Whether you have just finished 18 holes of golf, are keeping in shape in the fitness room or entertaining friends at our fantastic restaurant, you will feel right at home while being attended to by our dedicated staff.

This family friendly club has membership options that can match each individual's needs. All membership categories allow access to the golf practice facilities, fitness room and restaurant.

For both members and non-members the Country Club of Halifax is the perfect venue for your next golf outing, holiday party or private function. Just give us a call and we will make it happen.

Country Club of Halifax · Halifax, MA
www.ccofhalifax.org 781-293-9061

Country Club of New Bedford | North Dartmouth, MA

Tradition at its Best.

Founded in 1902, the Country Club of New Bedford is a club built on tradition and boasts one of the premier golf courses in New England. Designed by Donald Ross, this beautiful and challenging 18 hole, par 70 course plays to slightly over 6400 yards. The traditional clubhouse features a main dining room, a grill room and a main bar and lounge.

The Country Club of New Bedford is an ensemble of many treasures evolving from more than 100 years of tradition, vision and celebration which has led to its current prestigious reputation in the New England area. Located in North Dartmouth, it sets itself apart from other private clubs in the Boston-Providence corridor by offering unpretentious service, championship golf, and warmth and intimacy that is generated and honored in a contemporary setting.

Membership categories include Golf, Social, Junior and Corporate. To learn more about membership opportunities or to schedule a golf tournament, banquet, wedding or other special events, just give us a call at 508-993-3453 or visit us on the web at www.ccnbgolfclub.com.

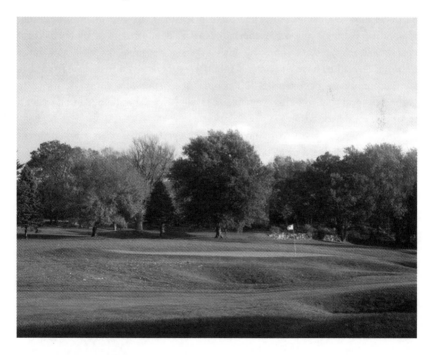

Crestwood Country Club

Rehoboth, MA

Casual – Comfortable – Complete

Crestwood Country Club is a private country club situated on 180 rolling acres in scenic Rehoboth, MA. Located only 10 minutes from providence and 45 minutes from Boston, this 18-hole, 6,600 yard par 71 course is a pleasure and challenge for golfers of all skill levels. Members and guests enjoy outstanding cuisine and service in Crestwood's 39,000 square foot clubhouse. Their new state-of-the-art pool complex provides a wonderful place to spend warm summer days and the full sized practice facility is the finest in the area.

Crestwood Country Club was designed by Geoffrey Cornish and opened in 1959. The course is well laid out with wide and generous, well defined fairways that feature a variety of doglegs and some water hazards; each hole being quite unique. With generous landing areas come well-guarded greens, placing a premium on approach shots. Crestwood is one of the finest groomed layouts in the area, immaculately conditioned and known for its landscape of maples, pines and oaks that provide a picturesque backdrop for every round of golf. Crestwood features an 8-acre driving range where you can hit all of your clubs, two practice greens with a chipping area and bunker area for your short game.

Crestwood Country Club is the ideal place for your golf outing, wedding, graduation party or any other special event. Take advantage of their beautiful space overlooking water and the lush green golf course, as well as a large outdoor deck. They have a variety of function spaces for you to choose from that can accommodate between 25-200 people. They specialize in small, intimate gatherings and their on-site event planner will help you and your family plan a most memorable occasion.

So whether you want to spend a day at the golf course or in the pool, treat yourself to a delightful meal, schedule a golf outing or special event, Crestwood Country Club is the place for you. For information on memberships or to schedule an event please contact (508) 336-8582.

Elmcrest Country Club

East Longmeadow, MA

A Private Club with the Warmth of Home.

Established in 1964, Elmcrest Country Club is a full service community-oriented private club. Offering both golf and social memberships, Elmcrest has strived to provide a venue that emphasizes a family atmosphere. "A family that plays golf together stays together" is their motto and what drives their decision-making. The course is beautifully maintained by a groundskeeping staff that holds themselves accountable to the highest standards. Elmcrest is one of the best venues in Western Massachusetts. The course is 18 holes, Par 70 and at 6,347 yards offers both a challenge and a great deal of fun.

Although Elmcrest is a private club they have an open door policy for the community, having hosted many charitable events over the years for many local organizations including East Longmeadow's Rotary, Chamber of Commerce and Lions Club, and most recently the Ronald McDonald House, to name a few. If membership is not in your immediate plans you can still schedule your golf outing, wedding or any other social event at Elmcrest. Give us a call at 413-525-6641 or visit us at www.golfelmcrestcc.com.

Farmington Woods

Avon, CT

A Very Special Experience.

Farmington Woods is an award-winning, 18 hole championship golf course nestled in the heart of Farmington Valley. Designed by renowned architect Desmond Muirhead in 1970, Farmington Woods is one of central Connecticut's finest full service private clubs. From the moment you step onto the golf course you will be embraced the gentle rolling fairways, undulating greens, well manicured fairways and gently meandering creeks that make the golfing experience at Framington Woods second to none.

The first three are challenging but relatively simple. Holes four through nine are amongst the most challenging in the area and the back nine was designed for a tournament finish. As a result, you will find that a round at Farmington Woods will be challenging, fair and enjoyable.

Whether your interest is golf, tennis or social, Farmington Woods will meet your needs and most certainly exceed your expectations. New memberships are available. For your next golf outing or special event why not plan to call Farmington Woods to receive the service and attention that only a private club can provide.

Harmon Golf & Fitness Club | Rockland, MA

Over the past 10 years, Harmon Golf and Fitness has been in the business of improving golfers, not just in lowering scores, but in the way players approach the game. Harmon Golf has created one of the most unique golf facilities in the World. Every inch of the Harmon Golf campus was designed to improve golfers all over the handicap spectrum from picking up a club for the first time to high ranking PGA Touring Pro's. Every practice area has been designed to simulate every shot you could ever imagine on a golf course. The late Claude Harmon, the patriarch of the Harmon boys and their world famous teaching philosophies and accolades, always believed in practicing with a purpose. In addition to an all grass driving range, Harmon boasts a sensational short game area highlighted by a 9 hole wedge course, and a bunker complex and one acre putting green with severe undulations designed by Brad Faxon and Brad Booth. Harmon also has 16 heated and winterized bays for the inclement New England weather and is proud to serve its members 365 days a year.

Golf fitness training has emerged as a conduit to improving a players overall scoring each and every time they tee up the golf ball. Every golfer at Harmon Golf has access to their 7,000 sq ft gym and flexibility center. Two TPI certified exercise physiologists are on site every day to consult members with any questions and offer group and individual training sessions. Increasing flexibility and strengthening the core are the main objectives.

Harmon Golf is a family friendly golf membership that promises to be the leader in golf value and precious golf time. There are many different membership opportunities available and we would like to offer you a chance to be a "member for a day" by contacting Membership Director Matt Cassaro at (781) 871-7775 or by email at mcassaro@harmongolf.com and scheduling a one day pass. All golfers who try us for a day will be eligible to win a custom fit Titleist Driver. Give Harmon a shot now!

Marlborough Country Club | Marlborough, MA

What's Your Pleasure?

Welcome to Marlborough Country Club, a charming semi-private golf course that is open for public play on Mondays and Tuesdays. Beautifully manicured and challenging for players of all levels, this 18 hole, par 71 layout plays to 6,464 yards from the back tees. The Marlborough Country Club has always been a "golf club" first, providing an excellent, competitive layout for club play, tournaments and outings.

The Marlborough Country Club has enjoyed a rich history having opened in 1922 with an inaugural exhibition match featuring U.S. Open Champion Francis Ouiment and later becoming one of the very first hosts of the PGA Senior Tour. The original course was designed by well known architect Wayne Styles and later expanded in 1970 by New England architect Geoffrey Cornish.

Come and visit our newly renovated club house offering panoramic views of the 10th and 18th holes. Our dining room, players lounge and new function room offer perfect venues for your business meeting, corporate outing, charity event, civic function or special occasion.

The softly lit Marlborough Room is our largest reception facility and can host daytime and evening events. Replete with a large dance floor and a full service bar, this room accommodates 180 people. The Board Room is our small and most intimate room on the second floor and accommodates up to 30 people. Based upon your preference, your event at Marlborough Country Club may be decorated as informally or as elegantly as you choose.

The restaurant, open to the public, embraces patrons with elegant dining that is rich with history and complete with a contemporary menu. It is the oldest established restaurant in Marlborough and was voted #1 banquet facility for 3 consecutive years.

Marlborough Country Club is currently accepting new applications for membership and has several different membership classifications to accommodate people's needs. Our Full Membership, which includes individuals and corporations, provides unlimited golfing and clubhouse privileges. Our Limited membership provides unlimited golfing on weekdays and unlimited golfing on weekends and holidays after 1:30 PM. We also offer Young Executive Memberships for people 23 to 30 years old and Junior Memberships for those 12-22.

Please come visit our facility. Dine with the views of the golf course or play a round of golf on one of the most popular and best conditioned golf courses in Central Massachusetts. It will be a day to remember.

Please see Marlborough's full color ad inside the front of the book.

Ocean Edge | Brewster, Cape Cod, MA

Freedom to Play a Round.

Play Ocean Edge Resort and Golf Club featuring Cape Cod's only Nicklaus Design golf course. The $8.5 million private golf course was completely redesigned in 2008 and is designed for all levels of play. You'll be captivated by the Ocean Edge natural landscape, rolling topography and dramatic elevation changes. Ocean Edge offers memberships for the serious golfer, as well as lessons, women-only clinics and twilight tee times. To encourage the next Tiger Woods, golfers under 10 golf free with an accompanying adult.

Golf aficionados will enjoy spacious accommodations in our 1, 2 and 3-bedroom villas, or in the Guest Wings adjacent to the historic Mansion. Special packages include unlimited golf throughout the year. Relax in one of the resort's 5 restaurants, including the Linx Tavern & Bar in the Golf Clubhouse with indoor or alfresco dining overlooking the 18th hole. You will also find a fully stocked Golf Pro Shop.

Non-golfers can enjoy 2 tennis complexes, a 26-mile bike trail and bike rentals, a Cardio Room and Fitness Center plus 4 outdoor and 2 indoor pools. Resort to freedom at Ocean Edge with golf and so much more.

OCEAN EDGE
RESORT & GOLF CLUB

resort to freedom

BREWSTER, CAPE COD, MA   508.896.9000   OCEANEDGE.COM

Pleasant Valley Country Club | Sutton, MA

A Club Like No Other.

In 1959, Pleasant Valley Country Club was carved out of an expansive three hundred fifty acre apple orchard and in 1961, under the watchful eye of Cosmo "Cuz" Mingolla, the club opened its doors. Today Pleasant Valley Country Club is owned by the Magill Family who once were members, opened the Highfields Golf & Country Club in Grafton and returned to purchase the course they love.

Rich in history and tradition, Pleasant Valley Country Club has built a nationally acclaimed reputation since its debut in 1961. Known as New England's Home of Professional Golf, Pleasant Valley is also considered one of central New England's finest banquet & golf-outing facilities.

Professional golf came to Sutton, Massachusetts beginning with the 1962 LPGA Lady Carling Open. The PGA Tour began its annual retreat to Sutton in 1965 with the Carling World Open, which welcomed international golfers from eleven countries and offered a record purse of $200,000. Since then, Pleasant Valley has hosted forty-seven National Championships on both the LPGA and PGA Tours.

Come experience the history, the comfort and the excitement of Pleasant Valley Country Club, celebrating over 50 years of service to its members and guests.

Here is your opportunity to join a legendary country club at legendary pricing.
For more information contact Bob Recore, membership chair,
at membership@pleasantvalleycc.com or 508-865-4441 ext 307.

Reservation Golf Club

Mattapoisett, MA

Reservation Golf Club has been one of Mattapoisett's best kept secrets for over 100 years. In 1887, Charles King bought a property at the head of the harbor near the mouth of the Mattapoisett River and built a large summer home know as The Reservation, so named as this area at the mouth of the river had been a favorite camping ground for the Wampanoag Indians in years past. Mr. King was an avid golfer and laid out the course that continues to this day.

Reservation Golf Club may not be long (2,788 yards from the back tees playing to Par 35), but it has an abundance of challenging obstacles making it exciting and fun for all levels of golfers. Look out for the Buzzards Bay afternoon breezes, the sneaky water hazards and old stone walls. What you will also notice as you play the course are the beautiful views of the Mattapoisett Harbor, Eel Pond and The Mattapoisett River.

Reservation Golf Club is a private facility with a homey feeling where everyone knows your name. There are golf tournaments all summer long and a variety of other activities throughout the year, including music festivities, movie nights and the annual ski trip in the winter. Weather permitting, the course is open all year round and the public is invited to play from November through April with Pro–Ams every Sunday starting at 8:00 AM. During the summer, public tee times are available from 9:30 AM – 11:00 AM during the week.

If you are looking for a great club to join for golf and comradery, you should check out Reservation Golf Club. Jeff Ferreira, the Membership Chairman, will be more than happy to review the variety of membership options with you. Just give him a call at 508-758-3792.

Please see Reservation Golf Club's full color ad at the back of the book.

NEW ENGLAND GOLFGUIDE®

Why advertise in the *New England GolfGuide*?

1. Repeat Repeat Repeat Exposure

Unlike a magazine or newspaper that people throw away, readers go back to their *GolfGuide* time after time, and many keep them several years!

So your ad gets seen many times more than in any other print medium.

2. You pick your placement.

You can choose the particular regional audience you want to reach, the most likely players for your course or business.

3. The perfect environment.

When someone is going through the *GolfGuide*, they're in a positive mood, and in a golf mindset.

We're where the Golfers are.

You should be here, too.

Connecticut National Golf Club | Putnam, CT

Connecticut National Golf Club is located in the Northeast corner of Connecticut, less than an hour from Providence, RI or Hartford, CT and only 30 minutes from Worcester, MA. *New England Golf Weekly* rates it as one of their Top 25 Public Courses in New England.

Connecticut National is an 18-hole, par 71 course designed by Mark Mangean and can stretch to 6,935 yards from the back tees. It is a visually stunning and enjoyable course with 4 sets of tees to accommodate golfers of all levels of play. There are two practice greens, a driving range and a short game area to help you fine tune and enjoy your round of golf.

Connecticut National is a great choice for golf outings. The professional and well-organized staff will insure that your golf group will have a great day of golf, fun and excellent food.

If it's a wedding or reception that you want, the Overlook Room can accommodate up to 250 guests with its 12 foot ceilings, sparkling chandeliers, plush carpeting and panel accents. Picture windows and French doors open onto expansive decks revealing the property's stunning scenery.

Give us a call (860-928-7748) or check us out at www.ctnationalgolf.com. You won't be disappointed.

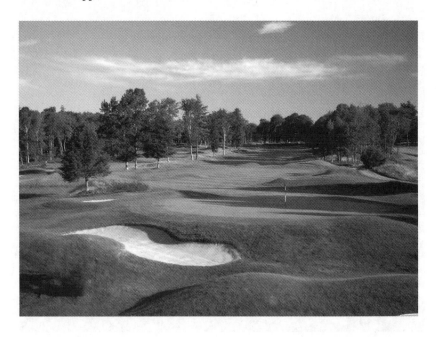

Stanley Golf Course

New Britain, CT

Hartford Area Golf at its Finest.

Stanley Golf Course is one of the most beautiful courses in the Greater Hartford area located just minutes from Hartford, CT and close to all major highways. Since the 1930's, Stanley Golf Course has offered the golfing public a great mix of holes that often seem easy until you play them. With a tremendous variety of holes, some elevated tees and tree lined fairways, Stanley is quite challenging. Many holes feature doglegs where driving accuracy is most important. Others feature downhill drives and uphill approaches making many holes play longer than you expect.

Stanley also offers one of the best practice ranges in the area, with a 19 station driving range, 10 of which are covered, lighted and heated for inclement and winter practice. Upgraded carts feature GPS systems.

The remodeled Whinstone Tavern in the classic stone clubhouse will serve lunch and dinner seven days a week and is available for special events. Stanley Golf Course is a favorite of central Connecticut golfers, offering something for everyone, from beginners to scratch players. A must add to your list of courses to play.

Stanley Golf Course, New Britain, CT   www.stanleygolf.com   860-827-8570

Bar Harbor Golf Course

Trenton, ME

Scenic, Stylish and Challenging.

Bar Harbor Golf Course has quickly become a favorite of golfers who visit or live on the Maine coast. Bar Harbor is a challenging 18 hole course that stretches to 6,680 yards from the back tees and plays to a par of 71. The course plays around and over tidal inlets, wetlands and along the Jordan River. While mostly open so you can feel free to launch your driver, 2nd shots are tough and require precision shot making to large and undulating greens. It's a beautiful spot with scenic, panoramic views of the river and mountains of Acadia National Park. Perhaps the most difficult holes are the 3 par 5's which are all long with hazards crossing each fairway.

Our relaxed atmosphere means you'll never feel pushed by the group behind. Ladies are welcome and club rentals are available in the fully stocked Pro shop. A driving range is less than 5 minutes away. Drinks on the deck after the round will complete your day. You should definitely add Bar Harbor to your list of places to play.

Boothbay Harbor Country Club | Boothbay, ME

Private Conditions in a Beautiful Setting.

Boothbay Harbor Country Club is the perfect Maine golf course, featuring breathtaking vistas, challenging holes and a sea breeze blowing off the ocean. The course is always in pristine condition with excellent, true rolling greens. Located just minutes from the quaint seacoast village of Boothbay Harbor, Boothbay Harbor Country Club's 18 championship holes are truly a "Pure Maine" golfing experience.

Boothbay Harbor Country Club is the perfect place to host your next important Maine golf event. We have PGA professional assistance with all aspects of the event, including announcements, shotgun starts, professional tournament scoring, carts, set up, full oversight with the tournament director for longest drive, closest to the pin, putting and shoot out contests, if required. We pride ourselves in making every possible effort to accommodate the tournament director. To get your planning underway, call (207) 633-3673.

If you noticed Boothbay Harbor Country Club's commitment to excellence in 2013, you will be even more impressed with what's yet to come. Improvements to the golf course are under way with the guidance of Bruce Hepner, who spent years working with famed architect Tom Doak. These improvements, combined with the new driving range and practice facilities, are being made with the goal of creating a premier golf destination. Construction of a new clubhouse will begin in the Fall.

For the traveling golfer, stay and play packages are available at many local hotels and inns, which can provide you with the same playing privileges as club members. For vacationers, 2 week memberships, 1 week memberships and weekend memberships are available. Boothbay Harbor Country Club is a semi-private facility open to the public after 1 PM 7 days a week.

Please see Boothbay Harbor's full color ad inside the front of the book.

Dunegrass Golf Club
Old Orchard Beach, ME

Nonesuch River Golf Club
Scarborough, ME

Designed by internationally renowned golf architect Dan Maples, **Dunegrass Golf Club** has gained the reputation as one of Portland's premier public golf courses. The signature first hole is recognized as one of the prettiest in New England and sets the pace for a challenging round of golf. Natural features including streams, hillsides, undulations and rock croppings have been preserved to produce a visual feast.

Fairways guarded by strategically placed bunkers, ample water throughout and large greens make Dunegrass a "target style" course. However, the landing areas are large and few forced carries exist, to ensure an enjoyable golf experience for players of all levels.

Join us for appetizers, cocktails, lunch or dinner at the Dunes Bar & Grill after your round of golf. The gracious dining room is complimented by the Dunes patio, which overlooks the 18th hole.

Just a bit south of Portland, Maine, sits Scarborough, a charming town with a four season appeal and home of **Nonesuch River Golf Club** and its full practice facility. This 18-hole par 70 course attracts players of all levels from across New England and points beyond. Known for its outstanding customer service and course conditions, Nonesuch River Golf Club provides an affordable and memorable golfing experience to all.

As a rule, the greens putt true, and medium fast. Rolling hills and visual interest help guide well-hit shots further down the fairway. Nonesuch River Golf Club provides you with a quality golf experience with bent grass fairways and greens with loads of variety. The practice facility, open to the public, is perhaps the most extensive in Greater Portland, and includes grass tees on the range, a practice bunker and two putting greens, and a full golf academy for individual and group lessons for all levels.

With great golf, wonderful scenery, inviting clubhouses and courteous staff, picking Nonesuch River Golf Club or Dunegrass Golf Club for your next golfing experience is an easy decision.

Please see Dunegrass and Nonesuch's full color ad inside the front of the book.

www.dunegrass.com | 207-934-4513   www.nonesuchgolf.com | 207-883-0007

Lake Kezar Country Club | Lovell, ME

The Best Kept Secret in Western Maine.

Nestled in the foothills of the White Mountains, Lake Kezar Country Club is a par 72 gem that combines a 1924 Donald Ross design, with a spectacular and breathtaking back nine opened in 1998. The challenge and beauty of the brooks, ponds, stonewalls, and majestic Eastern white pines are never ending. Lake Kezar Country Club offers four sets of tees on every hole to accommodate any level of golfer.

With superior public accessibility and discounted group rates, Lake Kezar Country Club has become the destination for many corporate, group and family outings. We don't have houses, condos, tennis courts, or swimming pools, we just have Cadillac conditions at Volkswagen prices. If you plan to golf in Northern New England, Lake Kezar Country Club is a must visit.

Lake Kezar Country Club has been rated the Number One Golfing Value in New England for 2014 by the New England GolfGuide.

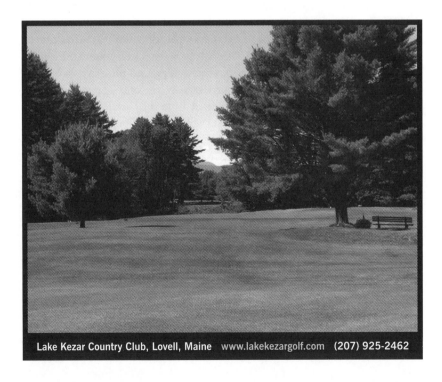

Lake Kezar Country Club, Lovell, Maine   www.lakekezargolf.com   (207) 925-2462

Links at Outlook

South Berwick, ME

18 Holes, Two Experiences.

If you're seeking a different golf experience, consider the Links at Outlook. You can play two styles of courses, but all in one scenic setting. It's just 45 minutes from Portland or 75 minutes from Boston.

The Links at Outlook start you off with a links-style nine, but without the ocean. The front nine (a former farm) is mostly treeless, with high grasses and gentle mounding defining the fairways. Here you'll find challenging, undulating greens, where you can run a ball up along the ground (a seemingly forgotten art). Open land usually means breezes, and often there are plenty enough to keep you alert on this lovely track.

The back nine has a distinctly different character. Fir trees line the fairways as the course climbs over and around a hill that eventually places you nearly 200 feet over the flatter front nine. From several spots up here, you can see the front nine holes, as well as some of the mountains many miles distant.

It's the front-to-back difference that makes for the appeal of the Links at Outlook. On the front nine, you can hit lots of drivers and play the big game. On the back, you have to play more strategically through the narrower fairways.

To really have a different look at the course, play different tees on successive visits. There's a difference of about 1000 yards between the blacks and the whites, and the former makes for a very tough course. Says head pro Dave Paskowski, PGA, "We hosted the Seacoast Amateur last year, the area's most prestigious event, and they found it all they could handle from the back. Many had played a scramble here from the blues earlier in the year, and thought they knew the course. Well, only about 20 players even broke 80. It was definitely a surprise for them." Most players will have a fine time from the whites or blues, he says.

Paskowski says the staff is happy to host outings, tournaments, weddings, and personal and business meetings of all kinds. The restaurant stays open and even offers Sunday brunch through the winter. Make the trip.

Please see Links at Outlook's full color ad at the back of the book.

Spring Meadows | Gray, ME

Green Fees? Affordable. Fun? Priceless.

Spring Meadows Golf Club can be played from a range of tees that can challenge golfer's from all skill levels. The course yardage ranges from the Ladies' tee at 4706 to the Black tee at 6656.

As you prepare to hit your first tee shot, you are blown away by the different colors showcased by the trees lining the left side of the fairway. As you approach your ball in the fairway, you notice that the fairway is like a living room carpet and your ball is sitting up like nothing you have ever experienced before in golf. A crisp 7 iron and 2 putt for par later, you begin thinking to yourself that this is going to be the dream round. This is golf at Spring Meadows Golf Club.

It doesn't end with the first hole, the elevated 7th tee gives the golfer a view over much of the front 9 and a challenge as well. Although only measuring 320 yards, the seventh hole challenges the golfers with a pond that has a history of collecting miscalculated wedge shots.

You will enjoy the entire experience at Spring Meadows. The course condition, the scenery, the staff, and of course the Player's Lounge, serving all your favorite beverages. Call us and reserve your tee time today to enjoy Maine golf at its best.

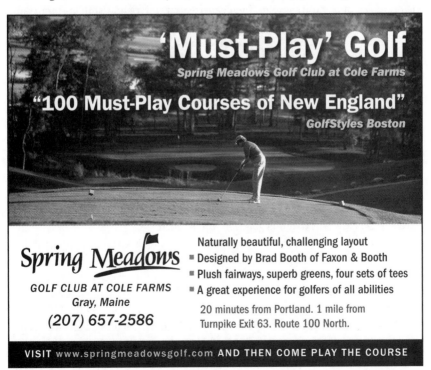

Acushnet River | Acushnet, MA

Acushnet, Where Silva Created Gold.

Acushnet River Valley Golf Course, in Acushnet, MA, designed by nationally renowned golf course architect Brian Silva, opened for play in 1998. He created a premiere golfing experience with four sets of tees measuring 5,099 yards to 6,807 yards allowing golfers of all skill levels to enjoy their rounds of golf. While the course plays to a par of 72, the tees can be set up to offer a superb championship course with a par of 70.

Acushnet River Valley offers two diverse layouts in one 18 hole beautiful and challenging layout. On the front nine, you stroll through tall pines, each hole its own cathedral. The back nine are sculpted over a Scottish links layout, with mounding and grasses reminiscent of the original traditions of course design and layout. The two sides complement one another in perfect balance.

You'll need to play Acushnet only once to realize the reason why people thoroughly enjoy their experience. But the more you return, perhaps the more you'll unravel the secrets of scoring well against this proud layout. It's the kind of place that definitely grows on you.

Acushnet River Valley is an excellent setting for your next golf outing, whether it's a small group or full shotgun. Their experienced and friendly staff are prepared to service all of your needs from initial setup to finish including the preparation of a special menu for those interested in dining in their outdoor facility.

Acushnet River Valley is an upscale public golf facility with bent grass greens that provide smooth and fast putting surfaces. Their full service practice facility includes a 12 station driving range and 12,000 square foot putting green. They are dedicated to the growth of the game and provide lessons, golf clinics, golf schools and a variety of junior programs throughout the summer to assist you in improving all aspects of your game. Whether it's a quick tune up that's needed or a series of lessons, they have the right program for you.

Travel & Leisure - Golf Boston ranks Acushnet River Valley "in the Top 10 Best Values in the State of Massachusetts" and according to the *Fall River Herald,* "a course well worth checking out. It's worth the money and certainly worth the drive to get a taste of Carolina golf right up the road."

Acushnet River Valley has developed the most unique season pass program in the golf market. It offers golf in quantities of 20, 40 or 60 rounds, walking or riding. The season passes are available at the Pro Shop every month and they are good for one year from the date of purchase! Season Passes are transferable and offer the best value to golf at Acushnet River Valley. Forty rounds of golf for $1500.00 equates to $37.50 per round of golf with a cart! Limited quantities are available. Call today to make your purchase (508-998-7777).

The Brookside Club

Bourne, MA

Featured Courses - MA

Just over the Bourne Bridge, you'll find a classic public golf course with a private club feel. The Brookside Club was originally designed by Michael Hurdzan in 1986, and later refined by John Sanford in 1996. This par 70, 6300 yard golf course starts out with panoramic ocean views with 3 sets of tees for all skill levels, rolling hills and very true and quick greens.

The practice facility features a driving range with matts and grass, a short game area in which you can work on your chipping & putting. After your round of golf there's an expansive old New England clubhouse that's home to the Sunset Grille, the perfect 19th hole.

Enjoy a classic Cape Cod golf experience here at The Brookside Club. The 1st golf course on Cape Cod just over the Bourne Bridge.

Butter Brook Golf Club

Westford, MA

Massachusetts' Hidden Gem.

Butter Brook Golf Club, located in the Boston suburb of Westford, is the masterful creation of world renowned golf course architect Mark Mungeam. He has beautifully transformed a farm into a hidden gem of a layout set upon 210 acres of sandy soil, rolling hills, mature trees, and expansive wetlands. The course's name is derived from the Butter Brook, which gently meanders through the property.

Having opened for play in 2007, the championship course satisfies all skill levels by having four sets of tees which range from 4,900 to just over 6,700 yards. Featuring bent grass greens and fairways, the A4 and L93 varieties provide for an exceptionally smooth and true putting experience. The club is also equipped with a practice facility (mats and grass tee capabilities), putting and chipping areas, and a grille room to host your next corporate golf outing.

Seeking the best golfing value in a serene setting conveniently located less than 25 miles from downtown Boston? Look no further than the unforgettable Butter Brook Golf Club. Please visit www.butterbrookgc.com online or call us at (978) 692-6560 to book your next tee time!

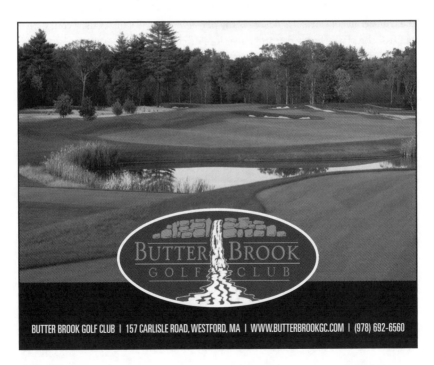

BUTTER BROOK GOLF CLUB | 157 CARLISLE ROAD, WESTFORD, MA | WWW.BUTTERBROOKGC.COM | (978) 692-6560

Crestview Country Club

Agawam, MA

The Gem of Western Massachussetts.

Crestview Country Club, while continuing to offer an exclusive membership, is now open to the public for the first time since its founding in 1958. Golf course architects have long considered Crestview "the gem" of the region. In April 2012, the club was purchased by a family operated partnership headed by golf course architect David Fleury of Rulewich & Fleury Golf Design.

Located only 10 minutes from Bradley International Airport, Crestview Country Club boasts breathtaking vistas of the Connecticut River Valley. With three of Crestview's holes actually crossing state boundaries, and playing into Suffield, CT, the property in easily accessed from Western MA and Northern CT, making Crestview the perfect home away from home.

With 400 acres of gentle rolling New England farmland, Geoffrey Cornish created an American classic with Crestview. Immersed in nature, Crestview is a true "walk in the park" experience. The conditioning at Crestview has always been known as "tournament ready", and the strength of the course has made it a perennial favorite to host numerous events, including U.S. amateur qualifiers and the LPGA tour event, The Friendly's Classic. While it has been a challenging tournament venue, the true genius of Cornish's design is the playability for all skill levels, a course that can truly be played every day and never lose its charm.

Crestview is a high-quality property, and in keeping with the new owner's vision, has something for everyone and can be enjoyed by all at a great value. The property is affectionately known by its members as their "stay-cation." While the heart of the property is the championship golf course, that's really just the beginning at Crestview, the expansive facilities include six Har-Tru tennis courts, an Olympic size salt water pool and separate kiddy pool, playground, fitness facility, and one of the largest practice and golf teaching academies in the region.

The clubhouse at Crestview enjoys panoramic vistas with commanding views, a perfect setting for weddings, corporate outings, and charity functions, with seating in the main banquet rooms for up to 280 guests and additional capacity for up to 500 guests. The facility also hosts a full service dining experience at "The View" restaurant that is now open to the public year-round. Crestview is home to some of the premier charity golf outings in the region, and is a natural selection for anyone planning a golf event, or corporate function.

For more information about Crestview's public play rates, membership options, event planning, restaurant reservations, or upcoming entertainment events, please visit the club's website at www.crestviewcc.com, or call at (413) 786-2593.

Please see Crestview's full color ad inside the front of the book.

Crosswinds Golf Club

Plymouth, MA

Designed by the award winning team of Hurdzan/Fry, Crosswinds is one of the newest Championship daily fee courses in Plymouth, MA. Featuring 27 holes, Crosswinds offers a unique blend of rolling fairways and large gently undulating greens. The course offers five tee options measuring over 7,000 yards from the black championship markers and invites golfers of all abilities for a memorable golfing experience. Challenging yet fun, this course takes advantage of the natural topography, offering dramatic elevation changes, panoramic views, and comfortable spacing between holes for a resort-style atmosphere. The practice area features a multi-level driving range, a chipping green, and 2 separate putting greens.

Crosswinds Golf Club welcomes a brand new clubhouse that offers the perfect atmosphere for any event. The banquet facility is available for both private and corporate use and can hold up to 200 people, with a beautiful view of the course. The new kitchen has everything to offer from grill food to catered entrees of your choice for your outing. The clubhouse also hosts a beautiful full service bar, which is the perfect spot after your round to relax, have a cold one, and watch the game on the flat-screen TV's.

Crosswinds Golf Club offers several league options for all levels of golfers. These options include men's, women's, and mixed leagues running all week long. Whether you have a foursome, twosome, or single, these leagues are a great way to meet new people, have fun, and most important, enjoy golf! Crosswinds Golf Club also offers many different opportunities to save on golf during the season. For a limited time offer, Crosswinds offers a 10 Round Golf Card for weekdays and weekends. The cards can be bought in the online store or right in the Pro Shop.

For more information on leagues, functions or events, please call our clubhouse at 508-830-1199 or visit our website at golfcrosswinds.com.

Please see Crosswinds Golf Club's full color ad inside the front of the book.

Crumpin-Fox Club

Bernardston, MA

Minutes Away – World's Apart.

Crumpin-Fox Club was conceived in 1969 as the "Field of Dreams" of David Berelson, who engaged the services of Roger Rulewich of Robert Trent Jones, Inc. to locate a site that would accommodate a Pine Valley type golf course. The Bernardston site was chosen, but the project stalled until 1977 when Andy St. Hillaire bought the project, completed what are now the back nine holes and built the present clubhouse.

In 1987, Crumpin-Fox was sold to William A. Sandri, who hired Roger Rulewich to complete the front nine holes and oversee extensive renovations to the existing back nine holes, the driving range and irrigation system. Bent grass fairways were planted and the new course opened in June of 1990.

According to Michael Zaranek, Director of Golf, "our continuing goal is to provide an enjoyable and challenging experience and promote the values of the game of golf." Crumpin-Fox has been recognized by *Golf Week* magazine as one of the top 100 courses to play in America.

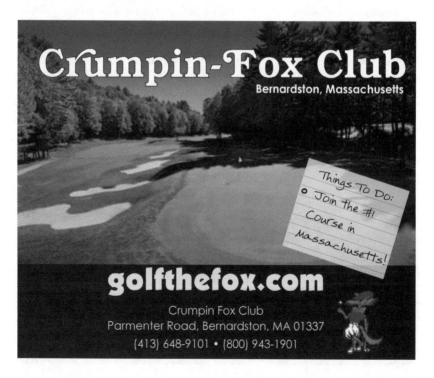

Dennis Highlands
Dennis Pines

Dennis, MA

Dennis is the "place to go" to enjoy the best of what Cape Cod has to offer. Boasting world class beaches, theater, dining and two of the finest golf courses on The Cape, why would you go anywhere else?

Dennis Highlands is the perfect start to your golf vacation. The Highlands tends to be more forgiving off the tee, but don't get too comfortable around the greens as the large rolling terrain requires all of your focus and concentration. The staff at the Highlands takes great pride in providing all guests with a championship golf course that is always immaculately maintained and customer service that rivals any private facility.

Dennis Pines will flat out test your skill. The Pines has four sets of tees that can accommodate any golfer, but the Championship tees at 7,029 yards will provide the most accomplished player a true test of golf. The 10th, 11th & 12th holes are the Cape's version of "Amen Corner", making or breaking a great round. Since 1965, Dennis Pines has, and will continue to be a favorite stop of golfers of all abilities.

Whether you choose to play Dennis Highlands or Dennis Pines, you are in for a delightful day on the links.

Far Corner | West Boxford, MA

For the Peace, and For the Challenge.

If you want a course that offers peace and quiet with your challenge, consider Far Corner in West Boxford, MA. It's 27 holes spread over 250 acres with the beauty of old growth trees, several ponds, and dramatic elevation changes. Players are able to play any one, two or three of the 9 hole venues, The Heron, The Fox or The Hawk, depending on the day and time they tee off.

Far Corner, designed by the venerable Geoffrey Cornish in 1967 is run by one of the region's most respected families, the Flynns, who manage several other courses. At a Flynn course you can expect at least three things: a friendly staff, lovingly attended greens, and a casual, relaxed atmosphere, where the most important thing on anyone's mind is golf.

Far Corner is an excellent tournament setting. From long, wide open fairways, to an "inland" island green, to blind shots that must curve over a mountain top, to snap-your-neck doglegs, you'll use every club and probably hit shots you've never tried before. There is possibly more variety hole-by-hole at Far Corner than anywhere else in the state.

Come try Far Corner. It's really not that far.

THE HAWK
AT FAR CORNER

THE HERON
AT FAR CORNER

THE FOX
AT FAR CORNER

27 Holes of Classic New England Golf

www.farcornergolf.com

(978) 352-8300 • West Boxford, MA

Foxborough Country Club | Foxborough, MA

Foxborough Country Club (FCC) is the premier semi-private country club in Southeastern Massachusetts. Its pristine 18 hole course was designed in 1955 by legendary golf course architect Geoffrey Cornish. The 6,849 yard classic Cornish design is a tree lined layout with 4 sets of tees, 37 bunkers, and a few water hazards for every skill level. A player must move the ball in both directions and read the tricky fast greens to score well.

Public play is normally Tuesday & Thursdays; 10am to closing, Wednesday; 7am to 4pm, Friday: 7am to 10:30am, Saturday, Sundays & Holidays after 1pm. No tee times are given. First come — first on the tee. Call the Golf Shop (508-543-4661 ext. 4) for current availabilities.

Second to its great golf course is FCC's membership. "Super friendly", "easy to get a game" are just some of the many attributes of FCC.

Lunches and Friday night dining are engineered specifically for member and guest satisfaction. To include affordability! A special "On The Turn" menu is available in the clubhouse in order to expedite the turn. Recent renovations to the Clubhouse allow for function and Monday golf outings up to 140 people.

FCC's location is within a mile of I-95, I-495 and Route 1 and within minutes of Gillette Stadium and Patriot Place.

Foxborough Country Club

- 2014 Memberships Available (Full, Limited, Intermediate & Trial)
- Superb Practice Facilities
- Individual + Group Instructions Given By Lou Rivers, PGA
- Full Service Restaurant + Bar

www.foxboroughcc.com • (508) 543-4661

Granite Links Golf Club | Quincy, MA

A Superior Experience in a Spectacular Setting.

When first opened, Granite Links was voted "Top Ten Best New Upscale Golf Course in the Country" by *Golf Digest* and more recently was named to this publication's prestigious list of "100 Greatest Golf Courses in America!" where the public can play. Granite Links is a private membership club that also provides a limited level of non-member access. The course is conveniently located just 7 miles south of Boston.

27 challenging holes of links style golf offer the most scenic vistas anywhere, including breathtaking views of Boston's skyline to the North, the Harbor Islands to the South and East, and the densely forested backdrop of the Blue Hills Reservation to the West.

As the name indicates, this is a links style course, situated atop what were once actively mined quarries. Remnants of the quarries will be revealed on the course in the form of granite outcroppings and some rather impressive water hazards — some of which run 40 to 400 feet deep!

Granite Links offers one of the few lighted driving ranges in the region for nighttime practice and enjoyment. Adjacent to the Driving Range is the newly expanded Crossing Nines Turn Shack. It's the perfect spot to refresh when at the range or making the turn. Starting at 7AM, golfers can enjoy muffins, bagels, freshly made hot breakfast sandwiches, fruit cups and hot brewed coffee. Later in the day there's hot off the grill burgers and dogs, flat bread pizzas and made-to-order sandwiches, plus full bar service.

Our shingled Nantucket Style clubhouse sits 300 feet above sea level with outdoor balconies perched above a water-filled quarry overlooking the 18th green. The Members Only Grille and locker rooms are located here along with the very popular Tavern Restaurant, which is open to non-members.

The elegant clubhouse Ballroom and tented Pavilion each provide spectacular and much sought after settings for weddings, corporate events and social events.

Please see Granite Links's full color ad at the back of the book.

Heather Hill Country Club
Wentworth Hills
Country Club | Plainville, MA

Heather Hill Country Club was purchased by John and Connie Poholek in 1982, two very successful businessmen, with the goal of making Heather Hill the best it can be by improving the operation and focusing on customer service. In 2013 Connie Poholek, his sister Karen Finocchi and brother-in-law Elmo Finocchi purchased Wentworth Hills. With both courses now secured, their goal is to put Plainville golf on the map.

Heather Hill Country Club is Southern New England's only 27 hole golf course. The 18 hole, Par 70 Middle/South course measures 6005 yards and the 9 Hole, Par 36 North Course measures 3,368 yards. Comfortable yardages but both challenging and enjoyable with all new tees. Their newly renovated club house is a great place to relax after a round of golf. The redecorated bar and grill offers a new menu that that has never been better. Their affordable rates make Heather Hill a great place to visit and play.

Wentworth Hills Country Club is an 18 hole masterpiece that is affordable, challenging and delightful for golfers of all abilities. The 18 hole, Par 71 course measures 6202 yards and is a particularly pleasant walking course offering beautiful views and premium course conditions. The rolling landscape includes tree-lined fairways, dramatic elevation changes, open meadows, well placed bunkers and demanding water features. Once played, you will certainly agree that Wentworth Hills may be a public course but certainly has a private club feel.

Heather Hill Country Club | (508) 695-0309
Wentworth Hills Country Club | (508) 316-0240

Highfields | Grafton, MA

The first thought after a round at Highfields is "Now that was a challenge!"

This strategic Mark Mungeam design demands your full attention the entire round. Pars are meant to be earned, and the rewards for a well-played hole are well worth the effort.

From the back tees of 7021, the slope is 140. For those with stronger feelings of self-preservation, the middle tees at 6024 still offer a 131 slope and plenty of course to maneuver around.

Every occasion shines at Highfield's Golf & Country Club. The club provides a beautiful backdrop for Wedding receptions, rehearsal dinners, corporate socials, business meetings, golf outings, luncheons and a host of other special occasions. Customized event planning and impeccable service make any event at Highfields truly a special occasion. Our dedication and attention to detail will allow everyone to relax and enjoy the event.

Our beautifully decorated Clubhouse surrounds you with warmth and casual elegance. Our spacious Claddagh Room can seat up to 225 guests and boasts magnificent views of our perfectly manicured golf course and the Worcester Hills, with a private patio overlooking the 18th green.

For occasions where the guest list is smaller and the moments more intimate, Highfield's Golf & Country Club offer smaller private dining rooms.

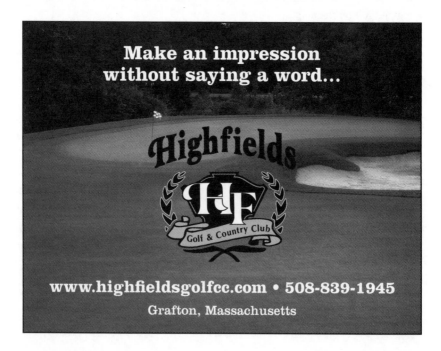

The International

Bolton, MA

A World Class Golf & Special Event Destination.

- Less than an hour from Boston, MA and Providence, RI
- Welcoming the public with open arms
- Our Tom Fazio designed golf course, The Oaks, welcomes public play six days a week
- Our Fireplace Room restaurant also welcomes the public six days a week, featuring both casual and fine dining
- We throw the best parties and special events on the planet
- Our facilities are perfect for your wedding, corporate event, or golf tournament
- 50 rooms of boutique lodging just steps from the first tee
- A variety of options for business meetings or conferences of any size..... in case you need an excuse
- 100 years of golf history on 500 acres of natural beauty
- You can now book tee times, hotel rooms, or make dinner reservations all online at: www.theinternational.com
- Or call us at (978) 779-6911

Please see The International's full color ad at the back of the book.

Hyannis Golf Course

Hyannis, MA

Situated at the center of Cape Cod, just minutes from a wide variety of local attractions, Hyannis Golf Club offers convenience and a friendly atmosphere that is conducive to families, beginners, juniors and seniors.

The course is a short drive from Barnstable Airport and the Mid-Cape Highway, while the ferries departing to Martha's Vineyard and Nantucket are also within easy reach. The area's popular beaches and the bustling Hyannis Main Street, where shopping, dining and live music are summertime staples, beckon once your round of golf is over.

But it might be difficult to leave quickly. The club's grille room and outdoor deck provide a relaxing spot to add up your score. With a large banquet room, Hyannis is a popular choice for golf outings. It also annually plays host to the Cape Cod Open, the area's premier professional tournament.

Since being purchased by the town of Barnstable in 2007, the club has worked to attract golfers of all abilities by moving up tees, widening fairways and setting up a course that promotes speedy play and low scoring. Scratch golfers who choose to play the championship tees will still find it plenty challenging, but those in search of a more casual experience will enjoy the numerous improvements. Playing from the white tees (or red ladies tees), they will hit to generous fairways from elevated tees, with expansive, receptive greens that are considered among the finest on the Cape.

At approximately 6,000 yards from the white tees and 6600 from the Blues, the par-71 course is not long, and golfers won't be required to hit driver off every tee. Unlike many newer, tricked-up designs, good shots are rewarded.

The course includes a large practice area and two putting greens, offering ample opportunity to sharpen your game. With a wooded, hilly natural setting, Hyannis Golf is a pleasant course where beginners, juniors, seniors and families are welcomed and where they will find a layout that is intriguing and fair.

Olde Barnstable Fairgrounds Golf Course
Marston Mills, MA

The Olde Barnstable Fairgrounds Golf Course, which borders the Cape Cod's largest sand plain conservation area, opened in 1992. The Mark Mungeon design has 18 holes of golf that are as challenging as they are scenic. This par 71 course is owned and operated by the Town of Barnstable.

Olde Barnstable Fairgrounds is located in Marstons Mills, less than 1 mile off from Exit 5 off of Route 6. This area of Cape Cod is a combination of wooded conservation area and a quiet residential area. Next door there is a grass air field that has gliders and sky divers that can be seen from the course.

The Course has four sets of tees for players of all abilities with yardages ranging from 6479 yards from the tips and 5072 yards from the forward tees. It is one of the best walkable courses on Cape Cod and has large undulating greens and an attractive layout, which is nicely maintained with professional and courteous staff.

The Golf Shop is fully stocked with name brand products and the restaurant has a fully menu of pub food. The practice area has 23 hitting stations with a chipping area, sand bunker and putting green.

Olde Barnstable Fairgrounds Golf Course has played host to several USGA qualifiers, WGAM, NEPGA events as well as the home of the Cape Cod Open. This is an municipal course with the Private Course feel, it should be on your "Must Play" list on Cape Cod.

Leicester Country Club

Leicester, MA

Sporty, Fun and Challenging.

Leicester Country Club, located just minutes from downtown Worcester, MA, is an immaculate 18-hole golf course that players call "fast playing", "really challenging" and "really surprising". Players love the diversity of the golf course. The par fours range from 309 yards to 437 yards, each with its own character. There are 3 par fives and 5 par threes which results in a picturesque and enjoyable Par 70. Leicester Country Club is well known for its excellent greens and is considered to be the best public course and one of the best golf values in the Worcester area.

Leicester Country Club has focused on making positive changes every year. Recent changes that have enhanced the golfing experience include the development of several new holes, new ladies tees and improved drainage.

Leicester Country Club's beautiful setting is the ideal spot for your next golf outing, fundraiser, wedding or special event. Their function facility has rooms for 30 or 300 guests and their experienced staff will focus on making your special day one to remember for a lifetime.

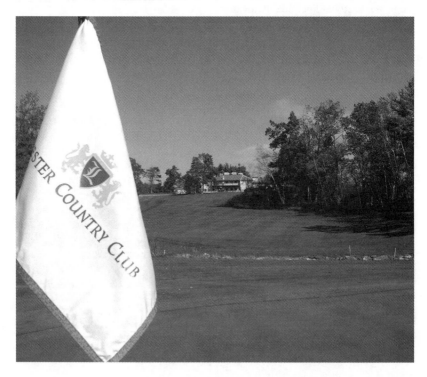

Maplegate Country Club

Bellingham, MA

Spectacular Golf in Peaceful Surroundings.

Maplegate Country Club is located just off Interstate 495 in Bellingham and Franklin. Established in 1990, Maplegate is a beautiful golf course set on 150 acres of rolling hills nestled amongst large pine, maple, oak and beech trees with many holes bordered by picturesque old stone walls. Exceptional detail went into all aspects of building the course and its facilities, resulting in a championship golf course that provides interesting, challenging and relaxing rounds of golf for everyone. Known for its great landing areas, you can take out your driver on every Par 4 and Par 5 on the course. From the championship tees Maplegate's par 72 course stretches to over 6,800 yards.

The Golf School at Maplegate is the perfect place to learn how to play or to improve your golf game. The teaching staff, led by PGA professional Greg Dowdell, are dedicated to the advancement of your game in an atmosphere that is both professional and enjoyable. The key to their success, and yours, is the ability to customize a program to each person's need.

Pembroke Country Club

Pembroke, MA

More Ways to Play.

Pembroke Country Club is a championship par 71 course measuring 6,677 from the blue tees with a slope of 132 and a 73.3 rating. The course layout designed by Philip A. Wogan has long been recognized as one of the best layouts on the South Shore requiring use of almost all the clubs in your bag. Facilities include an all grass full size driving range, full service restaurant, pro-shop and banquet facilities. Pembroke Country Club is a public golf course with limited memberships available.

Opened in 1973, Pembroke Country Club is located a short 25 minute drive from Boston nestled among the tall pines of the South Shore. Five par fours are over 420 yards providing a challenge for golfers of all abilities. In 2009 the course was purchased by former NHL all-star Jeremy Roenick who grew up playing at PCC and loving the course. Over the past several years, under the direction of Golf Course Architect and Superintendent Patrick Sullivan, much work has been done to clear out and open the course to enhance playability. Also course conditions, tee boxes, fairways and greens have been upgraded to provide an excellent golfing experience.

In addition to course improvements the pro shop, grille room, and function halls have been upgraded. The view from the grille room patio overlooking the course is spectacular. PCC's two function halls can accommodate functions from 50 to 500 occupants for weddings, fundraisers, parties, meetings and special events.

At Pembroke Country Club we are continually striving to enhance our customers golfing experience by focusing our efforts on course playing conditions, customer service and providing a value to the golfing public.

Please see Pembroke Country Club's full color ad inside the front of the book.

Pembroke Country Club
94 West Elm Street, Pembroke MA
781-829-2273 WWW.PEMBROKEGOLF.COM

Featured Courses - MA

Pinehills Jones & Nicklaus | Plymouth, MA

Five Star Choices. Times Two.

At Pinehills, it's all about the golf. From the attended bag drop to the extensive practice facilities, Pinehills leaves no doubt about its purpose.

Two 18-hole designs await your pleasure: Jones and Nicklaus. The Rees Jones, as the website says, "is characterized by his signature style, challenging to play, enjoyable for both experts and novices alike, and respectful of the land, with built-in subtleties that offer a new playing experience every time."

Of the two, the Jones course requires more precise tee shots and approaches, and rewards you with easier putts. From the first tee, you're off to work, negotiating an uphill dogleg left to a well-guarded green. The ninth is an eye-opening par 5 that requires a carry over a hillside, a medium-length second shot, and an approach to a thin but wide green, fronted by a pond. The par 5 15th hole requires a carry over an abyss of brush to a rising fairway and a distant elevated green.

The Nicklaus 18, designed by Jack Nicklaus II, has a different character, with much of the same appeal. Also cut around and through the kettles (carved by glaciers), the Nicklaus design offers somewhat broader landing areas, but more challenging putts once you reach the green. Favorites include the daunting third hole, a long par 3 that requires a carry over a fronting trap, and the wonderful eighteenth, which requires a semi-blind tee shot that must find the fairway rather than the long-stretching pond which guards the green.

There is great variety, beauty, and challenge all around. The marvelous practice facilities and cart are included in your fee. Arrive early enough to take advantage. After your round, enjoy the inviting grill and lounge.

Pinehills is one of only six five-star rated courses in the *New England GolfGuide* 2014 Edition. Come play once and you'll return again and again.

Please see Pinehills' full color ad on the inside back cover.

Quail Ridge Country Club | Acton, MA

Whether you're looking for a summer membership for the family, a venue for your corporate outing, or just a casual round of golf, look no further than Quail Ridge Country Club. The recently redesigned 9-hole golf course is perfect if you've only got time for nine, but if you're looking to play 18 holes, several holes play to different pars and even to different greens based on which 9 you're playing. The course also hosts leagues and corporate outings, as well as serving as the home to the State Champions Quail Ridge Junior Golf team (8-13 year olds).

In addition to the golf course, Quail Ridge boasts four regulation tennis courts, which are perfect for casual play, or instruction. The tennis team at Quail holds private lessons, as well as several junior clinics and camps throughout the summer.

The pool at Quail Ridge is surrounded by a spacious deck and lounge area, and has full time food service whether you're looking for a snack, or a full meal.

Finally, the Fitness Center at Quail Ridge is fully equipped with state of the art equipment. The weight and cardio room is stocked with free weights, weight machines, bikes, ellipticals, and treadmills. Across the hall is a spacious aerobic and yoga room.

Whether you're looking to play golf or tennis, swim, or get in shape, Quail Ridge is the perfect place for you and you're family this summer. Call 978-264-0399 or stop by for more information.

- New 9-Hole Championship Golf Course
- Supervised Multi-Faceted Pool
- All Sports Youth Programs
- Four Har-Tru Tennis Courts
- State of the Art Fitness Center
- Golf Leagues & Swim Team

FREE GOLF
with purchase of golf cart
Monday-Friday
Expires April 2014. Cannot be combined with any other offers.

Quail Ridge Country Club
354 Great Rd., Rt. 2A, Acton, MA
978-264-0399
www.quailridgeacton.com

Membership Discount
Up to
$200 OFF
Call for Details

Red Tail Golf Club

Devens, MA

One of the Best.

Nestled within a natural environment interspersed through the former U.S. Army base that was Fort Devens, the 18-hole march at Red Tail Golf Club can be tantamount to a war of attrition over one of Massachusetts' top public golf courses. And whether it is the guard tower seemingly randomly situated overlooking the 18th tee box, or the hidden old munitions bunker laying aside the 17th green, reminders abound at Red Tail of the property's military history.

Commissioned for play in 2002, Brian Silva of New England's top design firm of Cornish, Silva and Mungeam, devised a 7,000 yard masterpiece composed upon a varied and visually stunning landscape. Although brute force and power are certainly assets in engaging Red Tail, pinpoint target acquisition is equally rewarded in the golfer's battle to strategically evade the variety of minefields and other hidden ambush opportunities lying in wait at Red Tail.

Red Tail is a study in variety. While some holes such as the par three 11th and the par four 17th are defined by sandy waste bunkers reminiscent of the Sandhills of North Carolina, other holes like the par four 4th and 14th, as well as the classic risk-reward par five finishing 18th, incorporate dramatic elevation drops evoking comparisons to the spectacular mountain golf of northern New England. And with the blind approach or tee shots required on the par four 14th and 16th, respectively, you can even detect subtleties perhaps inspired by the great links courses of Scotland and Ireland.

Perhaps Red Tail's most unique and memorable design feature is the manner in which many of its greens are camouflaged naturally into the surrounding terrain. Whether it be the plateau greens of the 2nd and 9th, the semi-punchbowl surfaces of the 4th and 14th or the greens emanating out of the hillsides on the 7th and 8th, the somewhat refreshing absence of wetlands, bunkers and other beachhead obstacles fronting many of Red Tail's green complexes encourage frontal assaults characterized by run-up approach shots played low.

Located 35 miles northwest of Boston in Devens, Massachusetts, Red Tail boasts New England's first Audubon International Signature Sanctuary designation. In melding varied and strategic shot values into this natural splendor — USGA command deemed Red Tail fit to serve as host to the 2009 U.S. Women's Amateur Public Links Championship — Red Tail Golf Club understandably and appropriately captures its lofty perch among the best golf courses in New England.

Please see Red Tail's full color ad inside the front of the book.

Shining Rock Golf Club | Northbridge, MA

One of America's Best New Courses.

Carved through over 165 acres, and with an elevation change of over 400 feet, the golf course at Shining Rock provides members and daily guests with a true test of golf in an idyllic setting. Opened for the first time in 2010, and already a multiple award recipient, Shining Rock is the Boston area's newest 18 hole championship golf course. Elevated tees, large multi-tiered greens and dramatic views of the Blackstone Valley are among the highlights that golfers will speak of in the coming years.

Going into only its 4th year, Shining Rock was named the 5th best public course in the state by *Golf Magazine*. The course also entered great company when it was named to *Golfweek's* list of 40 best new courses in America, joining only one other club in New England to achieve this prestigious honor.

With a multi-club membership available to its members, members get to call Shining Rock home. It is a par 72 course, which measures out at over 6875 yards from the tips. It features a great blend of holes that force you to use every club in your bag. In 2011, Shining Rock announced the opening of their new golfhouse, restaurant, and bar.

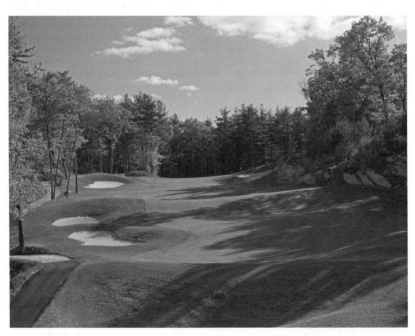

Southers Marsh | Plymouth, MA

What's Red and Green and Fun All Over?

New England GolfGuide calls Southers Marsh in Plymouth "The best golf value in Massachusetts. It has 18 wonderful holes, and the nicest, most sincere group of owner managers you'll find anywhere, the Stearns family. They care about their golfers, and they care about their course."

Maybe they're always in such a good mood because of their surroundings. The course was designed around and through a working cranberry bog. That means from the clubhouse, or anywhere around the course itself, there is a visual feast of pink and lime, or red and green, for much of the year.

Southers Marsh is a par 31-30-61 with seven par 4s and eleven par 3s. Total yardage from the back tees is 4111, perfect for a quicker-than-usual 18, but stop right there if you're thinking "pitch-and-putt." No way. There are carries a-plenty over the bogs, strategically placed bunkers, and long grasses designed to force certain shots. And contoured greens to keep par a challenge. The shortest hole on the course, the 12th, a mere 97 yards, is actually one of the toughest because it's an island green which looks like a sliver from the tee. There's no bailout either— it's hit-the-green or surrender to the bog.

That's followed by the 13th, a dogleg right par 4 of 304 yards that plays like 395 because it's all uphill, with a well-defended green. The finishing holes of 4-3-3-4 can crunch many a good scorecard.

Even the most accomplished golfers will be challenged, but four sets of tees ensure that golfers of all abilities will be able to enjoy themselves. The club has a 300-yard driving range and a full service restaurant with a beautiful mahogany deck overlooking the course. The restaurant is well known locally for the good food and good cheer well after the last golfer has come in and the Stearns are happy to host a party or wedding in a most inviting setting.

Please see Southers Marsh on the front cover of the book.

The Best Golf Value in Massachusetts
10 Consecutive Years, 2005-2014

Plymouth, Massachusetts
www.southersmarsh.com • 508-830-3535

The Ranch Golf Club

Southwick, MA

Golf Digest's "Best Public Golf Course in MA".

The golf experience you dreamed about awaits you in Western Massachusetts at the Foothills of the Berkshires. Blue sky, emerald grass greens and 18 of the most beautiful holes you have ever played. Each hole is a stunning new picture, a new challenge of risk and reward. Which route to take, which club to use, the choice is yours. The Ranch Golf Club was voted in the Top 50 of all Public Golf Courses in *GolfWorld's* Readers' Choice Awards. It is considered to be the best upscale affordable golf experience in New England. The Ranch is a well-conditioned course with a great layout and superior guest services that will appeal to all ability levels. At The Ranch your passion for golf will truly be satisfied.

After your round, enjoy lunch or dinner in the rustic charm of The Ranch Tavern, a turn-of-the-century barn. The patio overlooks the first fairway and is the perfect setting for an outdoor get-together. The menu includes appetizers and salads, as well as hearty sandwiches and complete dinners.

Whether you are simply playing golf or have scheduled an outing, wedding or meeting, The Ranch Golf Club provides a comfortable environment with great service.

Townsend Ridge

Townsend, MA

Central Massachusetts'
Most Enjoyable Golfing Experience!

Built in 1996, Townsend Ridge Country Club is one of New England's most enjoyable golf courses. Townsend Ridge Country Club is a daily fee course with a private club atmosphere. This 18 hole par 70 championship course is just minutes from Routes 2, 3, and 495. Townsend Ridge's magnificent 18 holes are spread over 140 acres that wind through the countryside offering breathtaking views. With three sets of tees ranging from 4709 yards to 6215 yards, the course will challenge all golfers of any age and skill level.

The front nine typically plays a little easier than the back nine, though the front side boasts one of the most formidable holes in New England with the fourth hole. This narrow uphill par four requires a strong accurate drive followed by an uphill second shot to a deep green bunkered on the left and the back. Both nines offer a wonderful mix of holes that will be sure to test all ability levels. Set back off the hustle and bustle, and nestled amongst the vast array of hemlock, pine and birch trees you will feel like you are on a little mini vacation in the New England country side during your round.

The recently renovated golf shop includes two, new state of the art, Full Swing golf simulators. These simulators boast world championship golf courses such as Pebble Beach, St. Andrews, Pinehurst #2 & Bay Hill, just to name a few. Interactive practice situations allow golfers to stay sharp even when the outside elements don't allow it. Other amazing features include real time ball flight, multiple hitting surfaces, high definition projection and infrared tracking systems. Whether you like practicing, playing a round with friends, or joining our nightly leagues, Townsend Ridge is open all winter long.

Rounding out Townsend Ridge's club amenities is our newest addition, Bistro on the Green. This upscale pub and restaurant boasts a sophisticated menu and an extensive cocktail selection, as well as two flat screen high definition televisions, a gas fire place and Keno. It is the perfect place to spend some time following your round of golf or to visit for your next dining experience.

With a Picturesque Ballroom overlooking the 9th and 18th greens, it is the perfect spot to host your next function. Townsend Ridge specializes in corporate & charity outings as well so be sure to inquire about hosting your event here. Affordable memberships are also available and with seven membership types you will be sure to find the perfect one for your golfing needs.

Please see Townsend Ridge's full color ad inside the front of the book.

Atkinson Resort & Country Club | Atkinson, NH

Atkinson Resort & Country Club is a public country club with a distinguished reputation for golf and the amenities that draw players on and off the course. Conveniently located in scenic Atkinson, New Hampshire, just over the Massachusetts line near Plaistow and Salem, the resort is dedicated to the education and advancement of golfers of all skill levels and abilities and to welcoming all guests with warm, inviting hospitality.

The resort's 18-hole championship golf course, rated four stars by *New England GolfGuide*, rolls across 420 acres of New Hampshire field and forest. The 9-hole Par 3 course, which has earned "PGA Family Course" designation, is a favorite for casual games, family events and beginners.

Skill growth is a commitment at the course, especially at the Willowcreek Golf Academy where state-of-the-art analysis tools give the resort's PGA professionals a customized approach to the lessons, clinics and outfitting they provide to golfers seeking to improve their games. This facility is unequalled anywhere else in New England, with 12 heated hitting bays for year-round live flight practice and three coaching studios that feature the Trackman radar-based, club-fitting system and V1 Pro Golf video swing analysis.

A highly-coveted wedding spot, the Atkinson Resort & Country Club maintains a sterling reputation for guest service and attention to detail, core to delivering an exceptional experience. With over 15,000 square feet of meeting space, superior culinary creativity, and expert planning services, Atkinson Resort & Country Club will exceed your expectations. The resort boasts two restaurants, the Stagecoach Grille and Merrill's Tavern, each with chef-inspired selections to suit all tastes. Overnight guests can take full advantage of the services and amenities in the resort's well-appointed, oversized Fieldstone Suites. From top-notch golf to elegant weddings, superb dining and overnight accommodations, come and experience everything Atkinson Resort & Country Club has to offer.

Please see Atkinson's full color ad inside the front of the book.

Breakfast Hill Golf Club | Greenland, NH

Try It Just Once and You'll Be Back.

Quaintly nestled under trademark soaring pines sits Breakfast Hill Golf Course, an upscale public golf course amongst the areas best layouts. Featuring rolling fairways, contoured greens and picturesque woodlands, the championship par 71 layout has consistently been ranked amongst New Hampshire's very best by multiple golf publications. The state-of-the-art clubhouse is spectacular and the expansive golf shop carries only the best lines in golf equipment and apparel.

The practice facility is one of the most all inclusive in the area. Every aspect of one's precision can be tested and enhanced. The driving range includes four target greens and vary-ing distances. A practice bunker sits on a hilltop with a sprawling view of the practice facility and the club's closing holes. The 10,000 square foot putting green can be the perfect boost to one's short game improvement.

Breakfast Hill is located only minutes from I-95 and only an hour from Boston and Portland. Come judge for yourself what Breakfast Hill has to offer. You'll be back.

Crotched Mountain Golf Club | Francestown, NH

The Crotched Mountain Golf Club (CMGC) is nestled in the beautiful Monadnock Region of Southern New Hampshire in a spectacular setting of mountain vistas, lush fairways and plush greens and is located just 45 minutes from Manchester, Concord, Nashua, and Keene. CMGC offers tremendous playing conditions combined with very affordable greens fees and cart rates. This countryside gem is quickly becoming recognized as the top daily fee golfing value in the state and is well worth the drive. Visit CMGC's website at www.crotchedmountaingolfclub.com to check out daily greens fees, hole by hole videos, course photos and great golf specials.

In CMGC's 200 year old "main building", along with a fully stocked golf shop, golfers will also find the Toll Booth Restaurant & Tavern. The "Tavern" as it is known to locals, offers outside deck seating looking up at the eighteenth tee, a full service restaurant plus a colonial style tavern all offering a diverse menu and twelve ice cold draft beer selections. The Tavern provides a perfect ending to a perfect golf day. During the winter, golfers can also enjoy year round action on CMGC's state of the art "HD Golf" indoor simulator which is open daily from November through March.

The front nine holes at CMGC were designed by world famous golf course architect Donald Ross in 1920. The back nine followed in the early 1970's and was designed true to the inspiration Donald Ross had for this spectacular location. CMGC features a number of "signature" holes that simply need to be seen to be appreciated. On the front, the short par three third hole looks down at the ski area and is affectionately known to the members as "the shortest par 5 in NH"! The back nine is highlighted by the par 4 fourteenth with awesome views encountered by golfers as they hit their second shot to a green that appears to drop off the edge of a mountain.

Regarding the course overall, don't be fooled by the relatively short yardage of 6,100 feet from the blue tees as it is very unusual for a visiting player to play to their handicap at CMGC. Although not heavily bunkered, CMGC greens are on the small side and well protected. CMGC is truly the perfect course for players of all abilities. New for the 2014 season, CMGC is adding a set of forward "green" tees to better accommodate players of all abilities: young, old, low handicapper or high handicapper alike.

Finally, new in 2013, CMGC introduced "The Gibson Room", a state of the art function facility that is perfect for golf outings and is becoming New Hampshire's premier wedding venue.

Canterbury Woods

Canterbury, NH

Canterbury Woods Country Club, located just 10 miles north of Concord, NH, opened in 2003. It is the special design of Ross Forbes who has "uncovered" 18 unique holes that utilize the existing terrain in a manner that will provide enjoyment for both beginners and experienced golfers. Wide fairway corridors with generous landing areas set up multiple strategic options for playing each hole. Subtle undulations on the greens and a variety of greenside chipping areas will test your short game skills. Four sets of tees allow the course to play from 4,800 yards to over 6,600 yards.

Canterbury Woods practice facilities feature grass teeing areas and a 300 yard long driving range that includes four target greens that lend a realistic feel to your practice sessions. The excellent PGA staff is available for instruction and club fitting.

Canterbury Woods is also an excellent venue for weddings, business meetings and outings. Two scenic ceremony sites and a beautiful reception area feature breathtaking views and can accommodate up to 125 people in a smoke free environment with two outside porches.

With a mission to provide friendly, affordable public golf, you need to put Canterbury Woods on your list of places to play.

Pembroke Pines Country Club | Pembroke, NH

Pembroke Pines Country Club is nestled in the valley at the bottom of Whittemore Road just minutes from Manchester and Concord. In addition to the picturesque 18 hole, par 72 "walker friendly" golf course, the club also features a new clubhouse, a large, fully stocked Pro Shop and new carts. The practice area includes a driving range, putting green and practice bunker area. Pembroke Pines is quite unique as it offers the golfer two very different experiences on one course. The front 9 is wide open with plenty of room to recover whereas the back 9 has tight fairways and is a shot makers paradise.

Pembroke Pines is under new management dedicated to making the improvements necessary to make this course the place to play. Bunker renovations are under way and a new and increased irrigation system has been installed. There is a new bar and fireplace and a large, elegant banquet facility to accommodate outings and special events.

There are a variety of membership categories that can accommodate each individual or family need. To learn more about membership opportunities or to schedule a golf tournament, banquet, wedding or other special events, just give us a call at (603) 210-1365 or visit us on the web at www.pembrokecc.net.

Ridgewood Country Club | Moultonborough, NH

You will find Ridgewood Country Club an enjoyable challenge for players of all skill levels. The front nine offers lush holes carved out of dense forest and marsh, requiring accurate shot making and excellent feel on the beautiful undulating greens. The back nine is a links-style layout unique to New Hampshire with generous fairways that lay over rolling hills and banked mounds providing fun and exciting shot making opportunities.

Sharpen your game at Ridgewood's Aqua Driving Range complete with targets and an island green, the closest you can get to the famous island green at Sawgrass without leaving New Hampshire! Practice facilities include 2 putting greens and a separate short game practice area. Everything you need to fine tune your skills.

The Pro Shop is fully stocked with the latest equipment and attire to help inspire confidence in your game. Pricing is competitive and customized orders are never a problem. The professional staff are fully versed in club repair and can regrip, repair and restore equipment that may need special attention.

The Overlook Restaurant is newly renovated, has a sophisticated design and lively atmosphere. With its locally inspired bistro menu, six different beers on tap and stunning panoramic views of the Belknap and Ossipee Mountains, The Overlook is a perfect place to share a meal with family and friends.

Windham Country Club | Windham, NH

A Club That Scores and Cares.

Windham Country Club looks like a mighty challenge from many tees. And it is. But if you play smart (maybe the toughest challenge in golf!), you can make pars. Elevated tees and greens, some water here and there, and a few massive boulders make this a memorable course to play.

Local knowledge is a wonderful thing, so repeat visits are highly encouraged to learn the dos and don'ts of where to aim at Windham.

Opened in 1995, this delightful daily fee layout places a real emphasis on golf outings. From the great clubhouse to the attentive pro staff, Windham takes care of a group's whole day.

The club also has another specialty: its affiliation with Northeast Passage. Northeast Passage is a nationally recognized leader in the provision of innovative therapeutic recreation services. Northeast Passage delivers disability-related health promotion and adapted sports programs throughout New England, and is a program of the University of New Hampshire's College of Health and Human Services and is an affiliate of Disabled Sports USA.

Windham, in conjunction with Northeast Passage, runs an adaptive golf program to introduce individuals with disabilities to the game through instruction and on-course play.

"We provide specialized clubs, grip aids, as well as solo rider adaptive golf carts," says Head Golf Professional Joanne Flynn, "to make accessing the course easier for wheelchair users and others with mobility impairments." The program helps individuals learn the best way to get back on the course after an injury or experience golf for the first time in a safe and supportive atmosphere. The course provides carts free to those who require them.

Come visit Windham soon.

(603) 434-2093 | windhamcc.com

Cranston Country Club

Cranston, RI

One of Rhode Island's Most Outstanding Values.

Located in scenic western Cranston, 15 minutes south of Providence and 7 miles from T.F. Green airport in Warwick, Cranston Country Club is an 18 hole championship course laid out over 170 acres of rolling terrain.

Cranston Country Club offers wide landing areas and large greens that make for a great day for all skill levels. The signature hole # 8 is a true island green with yardages ranging from 100 yards to 160 yards form the tips. It is a conversation piece for all after your round.

Playing to 6914 yards from the Championship tees and a slope of 130, the course requires both power and sound course management to go low on this course. Golfers looking for a good test without the stress of a 7,000 yard challenge can play from the blue tees at 6,493 yards, slope 125, or the white tees at 6,109, slope 122. The golf course is meticulously maintained and has a reputation for its conditions from tee to green.

Cranston Country Club has a great practice facility offering golfers the opportunity to practice on a natural grass tee. The range is perfect for golfers looking to warm up before a round or the player looking to improve his game without hitting off of mats.

Cranston
Country Club

Cranston Country Club
69 Burlingame Road
Cranston, RI 02921
Phone: 401-826-1683
www.cranstoncc.com

Green Mountain National

Killington, VT

Green Mountain: Accessible & Exceptional.

While Vermont has some of the finest golf courses in Northeast, the beauty and design of Green Mountain National Golf Course ranks among the entire region's finest. *New England GolfGuide* has given Green Mountain a four-star rating, and considers it one of the best courses in Vermont.

With an exceptionally varied, and some might say robust, layout, the course exudes a championship feel, from the pro shop to the lounge, from the mountain setting to the last putt on 18.

It's a great experience for golfers of all ability levels. Multiple tees allow you to take on the course at the appropriate level for your game. In fact, it's not a bad idea at all to play your first round from the middle tees before hiking to the back tees. A little local knowledge might save a few balls and a few surprises, and give you more confidence for the second round.

Located in the heart of Central Vermont, just off Route 100, the Vermont Golf Trail, just minutes away from the Killington Resort, there are many exceptional lodging choices available within minutes of the course and multiple activities for you and your family to enjoy during your visit.

Green Mountain National is also perfect for outings or tournaments. The course specializes in golf instruction as well as activities designed specifically for women golfers.

What separates this course from others is its unique and challenging design features. Generously carved out of the Green Mountains, the course offers solitude and a private golf experience that delights players and changes from hole to hole.

Although you'll know you're in the mountains, you needn't be a Sherpa to play. Gently sloping fairways that feature generous landing areas, distinctive changes in elevation, and undulating greens provide natural beauty. View the centuries-old rock formations carved by the glaciers, and be sure to stop a moment on the #16 Tee, as you enjoy the panoramic views in a spectacular setting.

Take a moment to explore the website gmngc.com and see what Green Mountain National Golf Course has to offer.

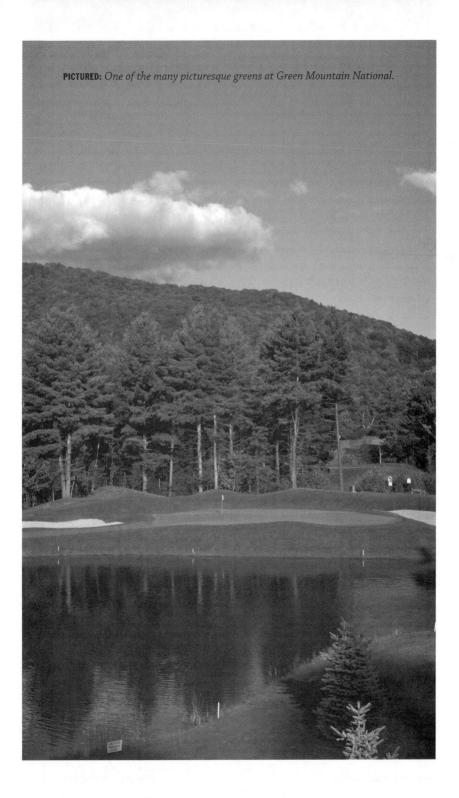

PICTURED: *One of the many picturesque greens at Green Mountain National.*

Hermitage | Wilmington, VT

At the southern end of Vermont lies a wonderful Desmond Muirhead design: Hermitage Golf Club in Wilmington. Though the course has undergone many changes since Muirhead's original work in 1972, most are in the area of conditioning, new grasses, and refinement.

Today a first-time player is struck by the beauty of the course, as it wraps around the hillsides and ridges of this ski-region landscape. Such placement means elevated tees and greens, and occasional sidehill lies if one isn't driving right down the middle. Several greens have sizeable breaks, influenced by the surrounding hillsides, one of the quirks of mountain golf, and one of the delights of a little local knowledge. Though hilly, many find it eminently walkable.

For those who love drivers, come on down. Several generous fairways await the "big dog," including the spectacular par 5 eleventh hole, which features a 250-foot drop-off from the tee. Whale away and you might have just a short iron to the green. From there, you face long and short, up and down holes that will delight just about any player. Hermitage stretches to 6549 yards from the blues and plays at 6164 yards from the whites presenting an opportunity to score well or card a few double bogeys — that part is up to you.

The clubhouse sports a fine grill and bar overlooking the course, the 19th Hole Lounge, complete with a billiards table if you still have that urge to sink a few.

Hermitage has new and exciting ownership news, as it is now owned by The Hermitage. Adjacent to Haystack Mountain, The Hermitage is an elegant four-star country inn, complete with its own covered bridge, fine dining restaurant, upscale pub, art collection and nationally renowned wine cellar. For onsite offerings, this unique property also provides a 9-mile hiking and cross-country ski trail, mountain biking, and fly-fishing. With the spectacular views outside and breathtaking décor inside, guests find themselves completely surrounded by the utmost in Vermont beauty and serenity. The Hermitage's establishment as a charming, all-encompassing property combined with its commitment for service and luxury make it a perfect base lodge for the Hermitage community.

- Hermitage is now offering affordable club memberships for unlimited golf, skiing and countless other activities and amenities.
- Only 4-Star golf course in Southern Vermont, and continues to receive accolades from the golf media.
- What was once considered a diamond in the rough is getting closer to being that "perfect stone".
- The Hermitage is a highly recognized wedding destination in New England.
- Special stay & play packages are available. Stay for two nights or two months, but all packages include golf daily with cart.

Please see Hermitage's full color inside the front of the book.

Okemo Valley | Ludlow, VT
Tater Hill | North Windham, VT

Two Magnificently Designed Courses To Explore.

A longtime winter destination for skiers and winter sports enthusiasts, Okemo Mountain Resort is quickly becoming just as popular with golfers and summer visitors.

Two 18-hole championship courses, **Okemo Valley Golf Club** and **Tater Hill Golf Club**, offer challenging play with spectacular mountain scenery on distinctly different courses.

Okemo Valley Golf Club is Vermont's premier heathland-style course. Designed to honor the traditions of the game and the Green Mountain valley terrain, the par-70, 18-hole championship layout features wide, emerald fairways framed with rolling fields of golden fescue. Moderate elevation changes, strategically placed hazards and undulating greens are the hallmarks of this scenic course. Four sets of tee boxes ensure that players of all ability levels can enjoy the course, while providing a challenge for the accomplished golfer. Although truly punishing features are few, risk-reward is an element that grows with course knowledge.

Golf is a family game at Okemo Valley Golf Club. The Family Fore Course is a four-hole layout offering beginners and future players all the Okemo Valley attributes with none of the pressures of championship-course play on Friday, Saturday and Sunday afternoons throughout the season.

Off the course, golfers can enjoy lunch or a cold beer at Willie Dunn's Grille or work on their game with a putting green, driving range and even an indoor training center with swing stations, a nine-hole putting green and a full-swing golf simulator. Clinics and private lessons are also available. At day's end, the resort offers comfortable accommodations at the Jackson Gore Inn or in a mountainside condominium. The village of Ludlow offers a variety of dining options, but the convenience and caliber of the cuisine at Jackson Gore's Coleman Brook Tavern makes it a locals' favorite. Call (802) 228-1396.

Tater Hill Golf Club is nestled in a pastoral setting 22 miles away from Okemo Valley Golf Club. This par-71, 18-hole championship course measures 6,400 yards. Although it offers plenty of challenge for low handicaps, golfers of all ability levels can enjoy the layout that features undulating fairways, spectacular views, cottage-style flower gardens and the casual ambience of an old Vermont hill-farm. Call (802) 875-2517.

Please see Okemo Valley's full color ad inside the front of the book.

Allendale Country Club, Dartmouth, MA	1	Farmington Woods GC, Avon, CT	7
Cochecho Country Club, Dover, NH	2	Harmon Golf & Fitness, Rockland, MA	8
Country Club of Halifax, Halifax, MA	3	Marlborough CC, Marlborough, MA	9
CC of New Bedford, N. Dartmouth, MA	4	Ocean Edge, Brewster, MA	10
Crestwood CC, Rehoboth, MA	5	Pleasant Valley CC, Sutton, MA	11
Elmcrest CC, East Longmeadow, MA	6	Reservation GC, Mattapoisett, MA	12

Allendale Country Club

1

1047 Allen Street
Dartmouth, MA (508) 992-8682
www.allendalecc.net

Club Pro: Stephen Brown, PGA
Payment: All Types
Tee Times: Private Club

Tees	Holes	Yards	Par	USGA	Slope
BACK	18	6764	72	73.4	133
MIDDLE	18	6410	72	71.8	128
FRONT	18	5540	73	72.4	127

Fee 9 Holes: Weekday: **Weekend:**
Fee 18 Holes: Weekday: **Weekend:**
Twilight Rates: **Discounts:**
Cart Rental: **Driving Range:** Yes
Lessons: Yes (open to public) **Schools:** No   **Junior Golf:** Yes
Membership: Yes   **Architect/Yr Open:** Geoffrey Cornish/1956
Other: Restaurant / Clubhouse / Lockers / Showers / Bar-Lounge

COUPON

A fair but challenging course for the beginner as well as the advanced player. Membership includes the full use of the practice facilities, lockers and swimming pool.

	1	2	3	4	5	6	7	8	9
PAR	4	4	3	4	3	5	4	4	5
YARDS	387	406	170	386	153	466	394	429	485
	10	11	12	13	14	15	16	17	18
PAR	4	5	3	4	3	5	4	4	4
YARDS	356	486	162	352	156	524	353	344	401

Directions: Route 24 South to Exit 12 (Route 140). Take 140 South to Route 6 and take an immediate right onto Tucker Road. Go 1.5 miles and turn left on Allen Street. Course is on the left.

Cochecho Country Club

2

145 Gulf Road
Dover, NH (603) 742-8580
www.cochechocc.com

Club Pro: Tim Loch, PGA
Payment: Visa, MC, Disc, Cash
Tee Times: Private Club

Tees	Holes	Yards	Par	USGA	Slope
BACK	18	6210	70	70.0	123
MIDDLE	18	5959	70	68.6	121
FRONT	18	5432	74	72.4	129

Fee 9 Holes: Weekday: **Weekend:**
Fee 18 Holes: Weekday: **Weekend:**
Twilight Rates: **Discounts:**
Cart Rental: **Driving Range:** Yes
Lessons: Yes (open to public) **Schools:** Yes   **Junior Golf:** Yes
Membership: Yes   **Architect/Yr Open:** Wayne Stiles, Phil Hogan/1923
Other: Restaurant / Clubhouse / Lockers / Showers / Bar-Lounge

A shot makers golf course that will test your strategy as well as your ball striking ability. Known for its subtle challenging greens. Challenging but enjoyable for golfers of all skill levels.

	1	2	3	4	5	6	7	8	9
PAR	4	4	3	4	4	4	4	5	3
YARDS	308	423	128	275	371	343	360	450	185
	10	11	12	13	14	15	16	17	18
PAR	4	4	3	4	4	3	5	4	4
YARDS	349	426	154	365	385	155	486	371	425

Directions: I-95 to Exit 4 to Route 4 North to Exit 7 towards Dover/Durham. Turn right on Route 9, right on Portland Avenue (Route 4), right on Atlantic which becomes Gulf Road. Course on right.

Country Club of Halifax

100 Country Club Drive
Halifax, MA (781) 293-9063
www.halifaxcc.com

Club Pro: Bob Giusti, PGA
Payment: All Types
Tee Times: Private Club

Tees	Holes	Yards	Par	USGA	Slope
BACK	18	6708	72	73.1	130
MIDDLE	18	6482	72	72.0	127
FRONT	18	5465	73	73.2	128

Fee 9 Holes: Weekday: **Weekend:**
Fee 18 Holes: Weekday: **Weekend:**
Twilight Rates: **Discounts:**
Cart Rental: **Driving Range:** Yes
Lessons: Yes (open to public) **Schools:** Yes   **Junior Golf:** Yes
Membership: Yes   **Architect/Yr Open:** Phil Wogan/1966
Other: Restaurant / Clubhouse / Lockers / Showers / Bar-Lounge / Lodging Partner

Gently rolling terrain, easy walking course. From the middle tees playing 6482 yards, you might think "oh pretty easy course." Not so fast—this course will give you all you can handle. You will use almost every club in your bag, and the greens—the best you'll ever play on.

	1	2	3	4	5	6	7	8	9
PAR	4	5	3	4	4	4	4	3	5
YARDS	347	486	151	377	406	379	392	180	463
	10	11	12	13	14	15	16	17	18
PAR	4	5	3	4	4	5	3	4	4
YARDS	323	473	197	422	392	503	165	404	422

Directions: I-95 (Route 128) to Route 24 South to Exit 16. Follow Route 106 East 15 minutes through Bridgewater and through the center of Halifax. Course is on the right.

Country Club of New Bedford

585 Slocum Road
N. Dartmouth, MA (508) 992-9339
www.ccnbgolfclub.com

Club Pro: Scott Trethewey, PGA
Payment: Visa, MC, Amex, Cash
Tee Times: Private Club

Tees	Holes	Yards	Par	USGA	Slope
BACK	18	6417	70	71.4	127
MIDDLE	18	6116	70	69.9	124
FRONT	18	5634	72	73.4	129

Fee 9 Holes: Weekday: **Weekend:**
Fee 18 Holes: Weekday: **Weekend:**
Twilight Rates: **Discounts:**
Cart Rental: **Driving Range:** No
Lessons: Yes (open to public) **Schools:** Yes   **Junior Golf:** Yes
Membership: Yes   **Architect/Yr:** Donald Ross/1902
Other: Restaurant / Clubhouse / Lockers / Showers / Bar-Lounge

A traditional country club that boasts one of the premier golf courses in New England. Home of the region's Women's Invitational Fourball Tournament.

	1	2	3	4	5	6	7	8	9
PAR	4	4	4	5	4	4	3	4	4
YARDS	324	359	362	498	450	345	154	371	410
	10	11	12	13	14	15	16	17	18
PAR	4	4	4	4	4	3	4	3	4
YARDS	387	394	367	318	387	122	310	154	404

Directions: Route 24 South to Exit 12 (Route 140). Take Route 140 South to Route 6 and turn right on Route 6. Follow 6/10 mile to Slocum Road. Turn right and the course is 1/10 mile on left.

Crestwood Country Club 5

90 Wheeler Street
Rehoboth, MA (508) 336-8582
www.crestwoodcc.com

Tees	Holes	Yards	Par	USGA	Slope
BACK	18	6599	71	72.2	130
MIDDLE	18	6342	71	71.4	127
FRONT	18	5656	74	72.9	126

Club Pro: Greg Rounds
Payment: All Types
Tee Times: Private Club
Fee 9 Holes: Weekday: **Weekend:**
Fee 18 Holes: Weekday: **Weekend:**
Twilight Rates: **Discounts:**
Cart Rental: **Driving Range:** Yes
Lessons: Yes (open to public) **Schools:** Yes **Junior Golf:** Yes
Membership: Yes   **Architect/Yr Open:** Geoffrey Cornish/1959
Other: Restaurant / Clubhouse / Lockers / Showers / Bar-Lounge

Challenging 18-hole championship course situated on 180 rolling acres in scenic Rehoboth, Massachusetts. Located only 10 minutes from Providence and 45 minutes from Boston. Great course for players of any skill level; known for its superb, fast and slippery greens.

	1	2	3	4	5	6	7	8	9
PAR	4	4	3	4	3	4	4	5	4
YARDS	346	435	158	325	170	375	351	517	423
	10	11	12	13	14	15	16	17	18
PAR	4	4	5	4	4	3	4	3	5
YARDS	407	354	491	410	372	174	381	139	514

Directions: Take I-95 South to 195 to exit 1 in MA. Follow Route 114A North. Take a right at the first light which is County Street. Follow County Street for 2.7 miles, take a left onto Reed Street. Follow Reed Street to Wheeler Street, take a right on Wheeler the club will be on the left hand side.

Elmcrest Country Club 6

105 Somersville Road
East Longmeadow, MA
(413) 525-8444
www.golfelmcrestcc.com

Tees	Holes	Yards	Par	USGA	Slope
BACK	18	6347	70	70.2	120
MIDDLE	18	5904	70	68.1	115
FRONT	18	5363	72	73.9	119

Club Pro: Dan Lapierre
Payment: All Types
Tee Times: Private Club
Fee 9 Holes: Weekday: **Weekend:**
Fee 18 Holes: Weekday: $65 inc. cart (subject to availabilty)
Discounts: Seniors $55 inc. cart (subject to availabilty)
Cart Rental: **Driving Range:** Yes
Lessons: Yes (open to public) **Schools:** Yes **Junior Golf:** Yes
Membership: Yes   **Architect/Yr Open:** Geoffrey Cornish/1964
Other: Restaurant / Clubhouse / Lockers / Showers / Bar-Lounge

A course dedicated to its members, the local community and the game of golf. One of the best venues in Western Massachusetts offering free golf clinics for juniors.

	1	2	3	4	5	6	7	8	9
PAR	4	4	4	3	5	4	3	4	4
YARDS	331	366	328	184	445	341	142	295	344
	10	11	12	13	14	15	16	17	18
PAR	4	3	4	4	4	4	5	3	4
YARDS	322	180	368	387	379	413	489	156	424

Directions: I-90 (Mass Pike) to Exit 6 (I-91 South) to Exit 4 (Route 83 South). Stay on Route 83 South and go through the center of East Longmeadow and through the rotary for 3 miles to Somersville Road on your right.

Farmington Woods Golf Club

43 Heritage Drive
Avon, CT (860) 673-0062
www.farmingtonwoods.com

Tees	Holes	Yards	Par	USGA	Slope
BACK	18	6577	72	72.6	134
MIDDLE	18	6119	72	70.6	128
FRONT	18	5523	72	71.8	120

Club Pro: George DeVita, PGA
Payment: Visa, MC, Check, Cash
Tee Times: Private Club
Fee 9 Holes: Weekday: **Weekend:**
Fee 18 Holes: Weekday: **Weekend:**
Twilight Rates: **Discounts:**
Cart Rental: **Driving Range:** Yes
Lessons: Yes (open to public)   **Schools:** Yes   **Junior Golf:** Yes
Membership: Yes   **Architect/Yr Open:** Desmond Muirhead/1970
Other: Restaurant / Clubhouse / Lockers / Showers / Bar-Lounge

Award-winning, 18 hole championship golf course nestled in the heart of Farmington Valley. One of Central Connecticut's finest full-service private clubs.

	1	2	3	4	5	6	7	8	9
PAR	4	4	5	3	4	5	4	3	4
YARDS	335	390	450	182	282	464	353	145	402
	10	11	12	13	14	15	16	17	18
PAR	4	4	5	3	4	4	4	3	5
YARDS	351	387	512	142	366	371	372	139	479

Directions: I-84 to Exit 39 (Route 4 - Farmington). Take Route 4 for 5½ miles and turn right on Route 167 (West Avon Road). The course is ½ mile on left.

Harmon Golf & Fitness Club

161 Concord Street
Rockland, MA (781) 871-7775
www.harmongolf.com

Tees	Holes	Yards	Par	USGA	Slope
BACK	9	3008	70	70.6	127
MIDDLE	9	2738	70	69.2	125
FRONT	9	2376	70	68.8	124

Club Pro: Tom Cavicchi, Dir. of Golf
Payment: All Credit Cards, Check, Cash
Tee Times: Private Club
Fee 9 Holes: Weekday: **Weekend:**
Fee 18 Holes: Weekday: **Weekend:**
Twilight Rates: **Discounts:**
Cart Rental: **Driving Range:** Yes
Lessons: Yes (open to public)   **Schools:** Yes   **Junior Golf:** Yes
Membership: Yes   **Architect/Yr Open:** Brian Silva/2002
Other: Restaurant / Clubhouse / Lockers / Showers / Bar-Lounge / Fitness Center

Championship 9-hole course, 9-hole wedge course and superb practice facilities. The focus is on a golf specific workout program so that your body and swing are in tune with each other.

	1	2	3	4	5	6	7	8	9
PAR	4	4	3	4	5	4	3	4	4
YARDS	320	390	150	317	465	285	120	294	397
PAR									
YARDS									

Directions: Route 3 to Exit 14 (Route 228). Keep right off the ramp and travel 2 miles to Route 123 which becomes Route 139/Route 123; at which point take your 1st right onto Concord Street. Course is on the left.

Marlborough Country Club

200 Concord Road
Marlborough, MA (508) 481-5340
www.marlboroughcc.com

Club Pro: Greg Farland, PGA
Payment: All Types
Tee Times: Private Club

Tees	Holes	Yards	Par	USGA	Slope
BACK	18	6476	71	72.0	131
MIDDLE	18	6155	71	70.2	129
FRONT	18	5624	72	73.7	130

COUPON

Fee 9 Holes: Weekday: **Weekend:**
Fee 18 Holes: Weekday: $65 inc. cart (M-T subject to availabilty)
Discounts: Seniors $55 inc. cart (M-T subject to availabilty)
Cart Rental: **Driving Range:** Yes
Lessons: Yes (open to public) **Schools:** Yes   **Junior Golf:** Yes
Membership: Yes   **Architect/Yr Open:** Wayne Stiles/1922
Other:

Beautiful and challenging with many elevated tees and greens. Open to the public on Mondays and Tuesdays. Subject to availability.

	1	2	3	4	5	6	7	8	9
PAR	4	4	4	4	3	4	3	5	4
YARDS	330	410	358	316	218	357	155	485	466
	10	11	12	13	14	15	16	17	18
PAR	4	5	3	5	4	3	4	4	3
YARDS	312	539	162	435	398	365	405	368	176

Directions: I-95 to Exit 26, Route 20 towards Weston. Travel 14.1 miles, right on Concord Road, course in .4 miles on the left.

Ocean Edge Resort & Golf Club

2907 Main Street
Brewster, MA (774) 323-6200
www.oceanedge.com

Club Pro: Michael Madieros, PGA
Payment: All Types
Tee Times: Private Club

Tees	Holes	Yards	Par	USGA	Slope
BACK	18	7011	72	73.1	133
MIDDLE	18	6404	72	70.7	130
FRONT	18	4886	72	78.5	130

Fee 9 Holes: Weekday: **Weekend:**
Fee 18 Holes: Weekday: **Weekend:**
Twilight Rates: **Discounts:**
Cart Rental: **Driving Range:** Yes
Lessons: Yes (members/resort guests)
Schools: Yes   **Junior Golf:** Yes
Membership: Yes   **Architect/Yr Open:** Nicklaus Design/2008
Other: Restaurant / Clubhouse / Lockers / Showers / Bar-Lounge

Originally opened in 1985 but completely renovated in 2008. Challenging but strategically appropriate for all levels of play.

	1	2	3	4	5	6	7	8	9
PAR	4	4	3	5	4	4	4	3	5
YARDS	332	376	163	496	357	300	409	171	544
	10	11	12	13	14	15	16	17	18
PAR	4	4	4	4	4	4	3	5	4
YARDS	386	418	327	381	316	340	185	559	347

Directions: Tak Exit 10 on Route 6 (Mid-Cape Highway). Follow Route 124 North to Route 6A. Turn right. Entrance is 1.5 miles on the right.

Pleasant Valley Country Club

11 ▶

95 Armsby Road
Sutton, MA (508) 865-5244
www.pleasantvalleycc.com

Tees	Holes	Yards	Par	USGA	Slope
BACK	18	6864	72	73.3	135
MIDDLE	18	6313	72	71.0	133
FRONT	18	5385	73	70.9	125

Club Pro: Paul Parajeckas, PGA
Payment: Visa, MC, Amex, Disc, Cash
Tee Times: Private Club
Fee 9 Holes: Weekday: **Weekend:**
Fee 18 Holes: Weekday: **Weekend:**
Twilight Rates: **Discounts:**
Cart Rental: **Driving Range:** Yes
Lessons: Yes (members only)   **Schools:** Yes   **Junior Golf:** Yes
Membership: Yes   **Architect/Yr Open:** Don Hoening/1962
Other: Restaurant / Clubhouse / Lockers / Showers / Bar-Lounge

Known as New England's Home of Professional Golf. Considered one of central New England's finest banquet and golf outing facilities.

	1	2	3	4	5	6	7	8	9
PAR	4	5	3	4	4	5	5	4	3
YARDS	438	455	162	375	330	495	548	384	137
	10	11	12	13	14	15	16	17	18
PAR	4	4	4	4	3	4	3	4	5
YARDS	394	354	322	346	190	317	187	368	511

Directions: I-90 (Mass Pike) to Exit 10A. Exit onto Route 146 South (Providence). Travel 4 miles to Exit 7. Turn right onto Armsby Road at the Pleasant Valley sign.

Reservation Golf Club

12 ▶

10 Reservation Road
Mattapoisett, MA (508) 758-3792
www.reservationgolfclub.com

Tees	Holes	Yards	Par	USGA	Slope
BACK	9	2788	35	67.1	122
MIDDLE	9	2669	34	67.1	122
FRONT	9	2475	34	70.3	125

Club Pro: Jim Rogers, Pro Shop Manager
Payment: Member Account, Cash, Check, All Credit Card
Tee Times: Private Club
Fee 9 Holes: Weekday: **Weekend:**
Fee 18 Holes: Weekday: **Weekend:**
Twilight Rates: **Discounts:**
Cart Rental: **Driving Range:** Yes
Lessons: No   **Schools:** No   **Junior Golf:** Yes
Membership: Yes   **Architect/Yr Open:** Charles King/1895
Other: Restaurant / Snack Bar / Lockers / Showers / Bar-Lounge / Private Beach

Located at the mouth of the Mattapoisett River providing amazing views of Mattapoisett Harbor, Eel Pond and the Mattapoisett River.

	1	2	3	4	5	6	7	8	9
PAR	4	5	4	3	3	4	3	4	4
YARDS	281	455	350	149	137	410	174	398	315
PAR									
YARDS									

Directions: Route 24 South to Exit 14A (I-495 South). Merge onto I-195 West at Exit 1 towards Wareham/New Bedford. Take Exit 19A toward Mattapoisett. Turn right onto Route 6 West. Go 1 mile and turn left onto Reservation Road.

Ponkapoag GC (#1)	60
Ponkapoag GC (#2)	61
Presidents Golf Course	62
Quail Ridge Country Club	63
Reedy Meadow GC	64
Ridder Golf Club	65
River Bend CC	66
Robert T. Lynch GC	67
Rockland Country Club	68
Rockport GC	69
Rolling Green GC	70
Rowley CC	71
Sagamore Spring GC	72
Sandy Burr CC	73
Sassamon Trace Golf Course	74
Scituate Country Club	75
Shining Rock Golf Club	76
South Shore CC	77
Southers Marsh Golf Club	78
Squirrel Run GC	79
Stoneham Oaks	80
Stony Brook Golf Course	81
Stow Acres CC (North)	82
Stow Acres CC (South)	83
Strawberry Valley GC	84
Swanson Meadows	85
Tewksbury CC	86
Trull Brook Golf Course	87
Unicorn Golf Course	88
Village Links	89
Waverly Oaks–Challenger 9	90
Waverly Oaks Golf Club	91
Wayland Country Club	92
Weathervane GC	93
Wenham Country Club	94
White Pines Golf Course	95
Widow's Walk Golf Course	96
William J. Devine GC	97
Willowdale Golf Course	98
Woburn Country Club	99

Amesbury Golf & CC	1	Glen Ellen CC	30	
Atlantic Country Club	2	Granite Links Golf Club	31	
Beverly Golf & Tennis	3	Green Harbor Golf Club	32	
Black Swan CC	4	Hickory Hill GC	33	
Bradford Country Club	5	Hillview Golf Course	34	
Braintree Muni. GC	6	Kelley Greens GC	35	
Brookmeadow CC	7	Lakeview Golf Club	36	
Bungay Brook Golf Club	8	Leo J. Martin GC	37	
Butter Brook Golf Club	9	Lost Brook Golf Club	38	
Butternut Farm GC	10	Maplegate Country Club	39	
Candlewood Golf Club	11	Maynard Golf Club	40	
Cape Ann Golf Club	12	Meadow at Peabody, The	41	
Cedar Glen Golf Club	13	Merrimack Valley GC	42	
Cedar Hill Golf Club	14	Middleton Golf Course	43	
Chelmsford Country Club	15	Millwood Golf Course	44	
Country Club of Billerica	16	Mt. Hood Golf Course	45	
Crosswinds Golf Club	17	New England CC	46	
Crystal Lake GC	18	New Meadows GC	47	
D.W. Fields Golf Course	19	Newton Commonwealth GC	48	
Easton Country Club	20	North Hill GC	49	
Evergreen Valley GC	21	Norwood Country Club	50	
Far Corner Golf Course	22	Olde Salem Greens	51	
Fore Kicks GC &		Olde Scotland Links	52	
Sports Complex	23	Ould Newbury GC	53	
Foxborough Country Club	24	Pembroke Country Club	54	
Four Oaks Country Club	25	Pinecrest Golf Club	55	
Fresh Pond Golf Club	26	Pinehills Golf Club (Jones)	56	
Gannon Golf Course	27	Pinehills Golf Club (Nicklaus)	57	
Garrison Golf Center	28	Pine Meadows GC	58	
George Wright GC	29	Pine Oaks GC	59	

Amesbury Golf & Country Club ✪✪ 1

Monroe Street
Amesbury, MA (978) 388-5153
www.amesburygolf.com

Club Pro: Butch Mellon
Payment: Cash, Personal Checks, Visa, MC
Tee Times: 5 days adv.

Tees	Holes	Yards	Par	USGA	Slope
BACK					
MIDDLE	9	3048	35	70.5	125
FRONT	9	2691	35	71.9	126

Fee 9 Holes: Weekday: $20   **Weekend:** $21
Fee 18 Holes: Weekday: $30   **Weekend:** $32
Twilight Rates: No   **Discounts:** None
Cart Rental: $15pp/18, $7.50pp/9   **Driving Range:** No
Lessons: No **Schools:** No   **Junior Golf:** Yes
Membership: Yes   **Architect/Yr Open:** Wayne Stiles/1923
Other: Clubhouse / Lockers / Showers / Snack Bar / Bar-Lounge

Great 1st tee panorama. Featured in *Yankee Magazine*. Beaches nearby. Fairways are better!
"Scenic views, friendly players and staff, good mix of holes." –GM

	1	2	3	4	5	6	7	8	9
PAR	4	3	4	4	5	4	4	3	4
YARDS	381	170	349	309	524	299	365	162	380
PAR									
YARDS									

Directions: Take I-95 North to Route 110 West; then take right at lights near Burger King; take right onto Monroe Street. Course is ⅓ mile on left.

Atlantic Country Club ✪✪✪½ 2

450 Little Sandy Pond Road
Plymouth, MA (508) 759-6644
www.atlanticcountryclub.com

Club Pro: Don Daley, PGA
Payment: Cash, Visa, MC
Tee Times: 7 days adv.

Tees	Holes	Yards	Par	USGA	Slope
BACK	18	6262	72	70.8	127
MIDDLE	18	5840	72	69.0	119
FRONT	18	4918	72	68.3	116

Fee 9 Holes: Weekday: $28 M-Th   **Weekend:** $33 F/S/S/H
Fee 18 Holes: Weekday: $48 M-Th   **Weekend:** $58 F/S/S/H
Twilight Rates: After 3pm   **Discounts:** None
Cart Rental: $18pp/18, $9pp/9   **Driving Range:** Yes
Lessons: $30/half hour **Schools:** No **Junior Golf:** No
Membership: Yes   **Architect/Yr:** Cornish, Silva, & Mungeam/1994
Other: Soft Drinks / Snack Bar / Banquet Facilities

COUPON

Mon-Thurs 12:30 - 2:30pm special. Player Comments: "Great track at a reasonable price. Many fine holes with challenging tee box selection. Compares with the best in state." "Great putting greens."–FP

	1	2	3	4	5	6	7	8	9
PAR	4	3	4	5	4	5	3	4	4
YARDS	302	144	410	475	343	467	134	387	345
	10	11	12	13	14	15	16	17	18
PAR	4	3	4	4	5	4	5	3	4
YARDS	336	156	310	281	460	330	491	105	364

Directions: Route 3 to Exit 2. Take left at bottom of exit ramp. Take first right onto Herring Pond Road. Right onto Long Pond Road. Left onto Carter's Bridge Road. Right onto Upland Road to Little Sandy Pond Road. Course is 1 mile on left.

Beverly Golf & Tennis ✪✪✪

134 McKay Street
Beverly, MA (978) 922-9072
www.beverlygolfandtennisclub.net

Club Pro: David Dionne, PGA
Payment: All Major
Tee Times: public 5 days adv.

Tees	Holes	Yards	Par	USGA	Slope
BACK	18	6276	70	70.8	126
MIDDLE	18	5862	70	68.8	122
FRONT	18	5241	70	70.8	116

Fee 9 Hole: Weekday: $25   **Weekend:** $28
Fee 18 Holes: Weekday: $42   **Weekend:** $47
Twilight Rates: None   **Discounts:** Senior & Junior
Cart Rental: $16pp/18, $8pp/9 per cart   **Driving Range:** Yes
Lessons: Yes **Schools:** Yes   **Junior Golf:** Yes
Membership: Yes   **Architect/Yr Open:** 1910
Other: Clubhouse / Lockers / Showers / Snack Bar / Restaurant / Bar-Lounge

COUPON

Signature hole is #15, the postage stamp. Classic short, downhill par three!

	1	2	3	4	5	6	7	8	9
PAR	4	4	3	4	4	3	4	5	4
YARDS	445	420	160	395	295	194	397	580	320
	10	**11**	**12**	**13**	**14**	**15**	**16**	**17**	**18**
PAR	4	3	3	5	4	3	4	5	4
YARDS	300	245	195	476	357	163	392	570	393

Directions: I-95/Route 128 to Exit 20B, right off ramp. Go through fork keeping Henry's Market on your right. Next fork go left, ½ mile on right.

Black Swan Country Club ✪✪✪½

258 Andover Street
Georgetown, MA (978) 352-7926
www.blackswancountryclub.com

Club Pro: Matt Cunningham, PGA
Payment: All
Tee Times: 6 days adv.

Tees	Holes	Yards	Par	USGA	Slope
BACK	18	6803	72	72.9	129
MIDDLE	18	6425	72	71.3	124
FRONT	18	5379	72	71.7	124

Fee 9 Holes: Weekday: $22   **Weekend:** $48
Fee 18 Holes: Weekday: $41   **Weekend:** $58
Twilight Rates: After 2:30pm   **Discounts:** Senior & Junior
Cart Rental: $17pp/18, $9pp/9   **Driving Range:** Yes
Lessons: Yes **Schools:** No   **Junior Golf:** Yes
Membership: Yes   **Architect/Yr Open:** Phillp Wogan/1990
Other: Restaurant / Clubhouse / Lockers / Showers / Bar-Lounge / Function Room / Pro Shop
GPS: Yes

Beautiful setting. Numerous water hazards and white sand. Bunkers challenge the best of players, while gentle slopes and wide fairways accommodate the casual golfer.

	1	2	3	4	5	6	7	8	9
PAR	4	5	3	5	4	3	4	4	4
YARDS	375	456	190	515	374	164	385	435	416
	10	**11**	**12**	**13**	**14**	**15**	**16**	**17**	**18**
PAR	4	4	3	5	4	4	4	3	5
YARDS	385	300	153	520	355	392	368	138	504

Directions: I-95 North to Exit 54B to Route 97 Georgetown. Follow to Route 133 West. Andover Street is 1.2 miles on the left.

Bradford Country Club ✪✪✪

5

201 Chadwick Road
Bradford, MA (978) 372-8587
www.bradfordcc.com

Club Pro: Kevin Murphy
Payment: Visa, MC
Tee Times: 5 days adv.

Tees	Holes	Yards	Par	USGA	Slope
BACK	18	6077	70	70.8	130
MIDDLE	18	5495	70	68.2	127
FRONT	18	4367	70	66.5	120

Fee 9 Holes: Weekday: $19   **Weekend:** $22
Fee 18 Holes: Weekday: $37   **Weekend:** $42
Twilight Rates: After 4pm   **Discounts:** Senior/Junior
Cart Rental: $18pp/18, $10pp/9   **Driving Range:** No
Lessons: Yes **Schools:** No   **Junior Golf:** Yes
Membership: Yes   **Architect/Yr Open:** Cornish & Silva/1989
Other: Clubhouse / Bar-Lounge / Restaurant / Lockers / Outings / Leagues
GPS: No

COUPON

New ownership and management. Open March - November.

	1	**2**	**3**	**4**	**5**	**6**	**7**	**8**	**9**
PAR	4	4	3	4	4	3	4	5	4
YARDS	368	346	156	375	382	146	353	491	479
	10	**11**	**12**	**13**	**14**	**15**	**16**	**17**	**18**
PAR	4	3	5	4	4	4	4	3	4
YARDS	427	195	510	413	418	401	410	171	428

Directions: I-495 to Exit 48. North on Route 125 to Salem Street. Turn right onto Boxford Road (1st street after Bradford House Restaurant). Take first right on Chadwick Road to Clubhouse.

Braintree Municipal Golf Course ✪✪✪

6

101 Jefferson Street
Braintree, MA (781) 843-6513
www.braintreegolf.com

Club Pro: Bob Beach, PGA
Payment: Cash, Visa, MC
Tee Times: 5 days adv.

Tees	Holes	Yards	Par	USGA	Slope
BACK	18	6554	72	71.6	129
MIDDLE	18	6212	72	70.5	127
FRONT	18	5386	72	71.0	117

Fee 9 Holes: Weekday: **Weekend:**
Fee 18 Holes: Weekday: $39   **Weekend:** $47
Twilight Rates: After 4pm   **Discounts:** Residents, Seniors, Juniors
Cart Rental: $18pp   **Driving Range:** Yes
Lessons: $50/half hour **Schools:** **Junior Golf:** Yes
Membership: $1950/year   **Architect/Yr Open:** Styles & Van Kleek
Other: Restaurant / Clubhouse / Snack Bar   **GPS:**

Braintree Municipal now has their own mobile app (free). "An overlooked gem. Generous fairways combine with great sloping greens and excellent conditions. Best value in Greater Boston." –JD

	1	**2**	**3**	**4**	**5**	**6**	**7**	**8**	**9**
PAR	4	4	3	4	3	5	4	5	4
YARDS	335	335	171	302	165	494	383	500	364
	10	**11**	**12**	**13**	**14**	**15**	**16**	**17**	**18**
PAR	5	4	3	5	4	4	3	4	4
YARDS	481	408	172	465	411	391	174	347	314

Directions: I-93 to Route 3 South to Exit 6. Take Route 37 South for 2 miles. Right on Jefferson Street. Club is on the right.

Brookmeadow Country Club ✪✪✪

100 Everendon Road
Canton, MA (781) 828-4444
www.brookmeadowgolf.com

Tees	Holes	Yards	Par	USGA	Slope
BACK	18	6585	36	71.7	123
MIDDLE	18	6239	36	70.1	118
FRONT	18	5156	36	71.2	114

Club Pro: Ryan MacDonald
Payment: Cash, Visa, MC, Amex, Disc
Tee Times: 14 days adv.
Fee 9 Holes: Weekday: $25   **Weekend:** $25
Fee 18 Holes: Weekday: $40   **Weekend:** $56
Twilight Rates: After 6pm   **Discounts:** Senior & Junior
Cart Rental: $16pp/18, $9pp/9   **Driving Range:** Yes
Lessons: Call for rates **Schools:** No   **Junior Golf:** Yes
Membership: Yes   **Architect/Yr Open:** Frank Simoni/1966
Other: Clubhouse / Lockers / Showers / Snack Bar / Bar-Lounge / Function Room

Brookmeadow is easy to walk and offers an interesting and challenging golf experience to all skill levels. You won't find a better value on the South Shore.

	1	2	3	4	5	6	7	8	9
PAR	4	4	4	3	4	3	4	5	5
YARDS	376	387	308	163	346	151	385	484	522
	10	11	12	13	14	15	16	17	18
PAR	4	3	5	4	4	3	5	4	4
YARDS	348	179	464	351	358	192	530	351	404

Directions: I-95 to Exit 11A (Neponset Street in Canton). Go 1 mile and take a right before the viaduct (stone bridge) onto Walpole Street. Club is 1 mile on right.

Bungay Brook Golf Club ✪✪½

30 Locust Street
Bellingham, MA (508) 883-1600
www.bungaybrook.com

Tees	Holes	Yards	Par	USGA	Slope
BACK	9	3136	36	70.2	120
MIDDLE	9	2885	36	69.2	113
FRONT	9	2314	36	66.8	110

Club Pro: Jim Cook, PGA, Teaching Pro
Payment: Visa, MC, Amex
Tee Times: 2 weeks adv.
Fee 9 Holes: Weekday: $21 before noon/$27 after noon
         Weekend: $28 F/S/S
Fee 18 Holes: Weekday: $42 before noon/$46 after noon
         Weekend: $52 F/S/S

COUPON

Twilight Rates: No   **Discounts:** Senior & Junior
Cart Rental: $6pp/9   **Driving Range:** Yes
Lessons: Yes **Schools:**   **Junior Golf:**
Membership: No   **Architect/Yr Open:** Howard Maurer/2002
Other: Restaurant / Bar-Lounge   **GPS:**

Fine conditions, fast greens, fast pace. All-grass driving range. Worth a visit.

	1	2	3	4	5	6	7	8	9
PAR	4	3	4	5	3	4	5	4	4
YARDS	278	153	313	450	107	421	434	393	336
PAR									
YARDS									

Directions: I-495 to Exit 16. 4 miles to Bellingham town line. Take first left on Locust Street; ½ mile to course.

Butter Brook Golf Club   ✪✪✪✪¹/₂   ▶9

157 Carlisle Road
Westford, MA (978) 692-6560
www.butterbrookgc.com

Tees	Holes	Yards	Par	USGA	Slope
BACK	18	6702	72	72.6	133
MIDDLE	18	6174	72	70.4	128
FRONT	18	4849	72	69.4	120

Club Pro: Peter Maki, PGA
Payment: Visa, MC, Amex, Personal Checks
Tee Times: 7 days adv.
Fee 9 Holes: Weekday: $35   **Weekend:** After 3pm
Fee 18 Holes: Weekday: $50   **Weekend:** $80 w/cart
Twilight Rates: Weekends after 3pm - $45pp/9, $65pp/18
Discounts: Senior & Junior - $5 off weekdays
Cart Rental: $18pp/18, $9pp/9
Lessons: Yes **Schools:** Yes   **Driving Range:** Yes
Membership: Yes   **Junior Golf:** Yes
Other: Bar-Lounge   **Architect/Yr Open:** Mark Mungeam/2002
GPS:

"Family-owned and operated with great pride. Challenging track with wonderful variety." –JD
180 acres of serene rolling hills, tall pine trees, beautiful ponds, and a babbling brook. 18 holes.
Voted one of the 100 Must Play Courses in New England.

	1	2	3	4	5	6	7	8	9
PAR	5	4	3	4	3	4	5	3	5
YARDS	507	293	123	396	132	401	492	157	551
	10	11	12	13	14	15	16	17	18
PAR	4	3	5	4	3	4	5	4	4
YARDS	374	195	501	309	175	377	475	394	322

Directions: I-495 Exit 32 Boston Road toward Route 225/Westford. Proceed toward Route 110
(.3 miles). Cross over Route 110. Follow for 1.2 miles to end of road. Left onto Route 225 East for
1.2 miles. Entrance on right.

Butternut Farm Golf Club   ✪✪✪   ▶10

115 Wheeler Road
Stow, MA (978) 897-3400
www.butternutfarm.com

Tees	Holes	Yards	Par	USGA	Slope
BACK	18	6302	70	71.2	130
MIDDLE	18	5755	70	69.3	126
FRONT	18	4778	70	67.6	117

Club Pro: Trevor Page
Payment: Most Major
Tee Times: 7 days adv.
Fee 9 Holes: Weekday: $27   **Weekend:**
Fee 18 Holes: Weekday: $39   **Weekend:** $50
Twilight Rates: $40 after 1pm, $30 after 2pm   **Discounts:** Senior
Cart Rental: $18pp/18, $11pp/9   **Driving Range:** No
Lessons: No **Schools:** No   **Junior Golf:** No
Membership: Yes   **Architect/Yr Open:** Robert Page III/1993
Other: Clubhouse / Restaurant / Bar-Lounge / Snack Bar / Lockers / Function Rooms

Brand new clubhouse. Carolina-type fairways, real tight, bent grass on fairways and tees, tall trees. "Great
shape. Greens are lush. Challenging, fair—but choose the right tees—or else." Four function rooms.

	1	2	3	4	5	6	7	8	9
PAR	4	3	4	3	4	4	5	4	5
YARDS	314	155	375	150	403	383	434	268	452
	10	11	12	13	14	15	16	17	18
PAR	5	3	4	3	4	4	3	4	4
YARDS	600	128	351	190	364	325	173	340	350

Directions: I-495 to Exit 27. Take Route 117 East for approximately 4 miles. Take right onto Wheeler
Road. Or, Route 2 West to Route 62 West. Follow through Stow center to 1st set of lights. Take left.
2nd right is Wheeler Road.

Candlewood Golf Course ✪ 11 ▶

75 Essex Road (Route 133)
Ipswich, MA (978) 356-5377
www.candlewoodgolf.net

Tees	Holes	Yards	Par	USGA	Slope
BACK					
MIDDLE	9	2108	32		
FRONT					

Club Pro:
Payment: Cash Only
Tee Times: No
Fee 9 Holes: Weekday: $14
Fee 18 Holes: Weekday: $19
Twilight Rates: $11 after 5pm
Cart Rental: $20pp/18, $12pp/9
Lessons: Schools: No
Membership: Yes
Other: Snack Bar

Weekend: $15
Weekend: $20
Discounts: Senior
Driving Range: No
Junior Golf: No
Architect/Yr Open:
GPS:

Course is easy to walk and good for senior citizens and beginners. Monday-Friday Senior Citizens play for $10. "Short but fun" –FP

	1	2	3	4	5	6	7	8	9
PAR	4	4	3	3	3	4	4	4	3
YARDS	350	350	120	140	135	253	290	280	190
PAR									
YARDS									

Directions: I-95/Route 128 to Route 1A to Route 133 in Ipswich. Turn right at hospital on Route 133.

Cape Ann Golf Club ✪✪ 12 ▶

99 John Wilse Avenue (Route 133)
Essex, MA (978) 768-7544
www.capeanngolf.com

Tees	Holes	Yards	Par	USGA	Slope
BACK	9	3036	35	68.3	119
MIDDLE	9	2826	34	68.3	119
FRONT	9	2212	34	65.2	113

Club Pro:
Payment: Cash or Credit
Tee Times: Yes
Fee 9 Holes: Weekday: $24
Fee 18 Holes: Weekday: $37
Twilight Rates: After 4pm
Cart Rental: $15pp/18, $10pp/9
Lessons: No **Schools:** No
Membership:
Other: Bar-Lounge / Snack Bar

Weekend: $24
Weekend: $37
Discounts:
Driving Range: No
Junior Golf: No
Architect/Yr Open: Donald Ross/1931
GPS:

Recent improvements include irrigation, putting green and new tee boxes. "Great views of the Crane's Beach area." –FP

	1	2	3	4	5	6	7	8	9
PAR	4	4	3	4	4	4	3	4	4
YARDS	342	364	169	414	336	278	197	385	341
PAR									
YARDS									

Directions: I-95/Route 128 to Exit 15 (School Street); follow signs toward Essex. Go north on Route 133. Course is 2 miles up on the right.

Cedar Glen Golf Club

$\star \frac{1}{2}$ 13

60 Water Street
Saugus, MA (781) 233-3609
www.cedarglengolf.com

Tees	Holes	Yards	Par	USGA	Slope
BACK	9	2809	35	67.0	107
MIDDLE	9	2731	35	67.0	107
FRONT	9	2185	35	71.7	114

Club Pro:
Payment: Cash Only (ATM on premises)
Tee Times: No
Fee 9 Holes: Weekday: $20   **Weekend:** $22
Fee 18 Holes: Weekday: $33   **Weekend:** $35
Twilight Rates: No   **Discounts:** Sr. & Jr - $16 wkdays
Cart Rental: $8pp/9   **Driving Range:** No
Lessons: No **Schools:** Yes   **Junior Golf:** No
Membership: No   **Architect/Yr Open:**
Other: Clubhouse / Snack Bar   **GPS:**

COUPON

New watering system. New tees. Friendly fun course; lots of regulars.

	1	2	3	4	5	6	7	8	9
PAR	4	5	3	4	4	3	4	4	4
YARDS	331	453	226	300	350	130	280	322	339
PAR									
YARDS									

Directions: Take I-95 to Walnut Street. Follow Walnut Street east to Water Street. Take right, course is on left.

Cedar Hill Golf Club

NR 14

1137 Park Street
Stoughton, MA (781) 344-8913
www.stoughton.org

Tees	Holes	Yards	Par	USGA	Slope
BACK					
MIDDLE	9	2208	33	61.2	105
FRONT	9	2155	33	61.2	105

Club Pro:
Payment: Cash, Visa, MC, Discover
Tee Times: No
Fee 9 Holes: Weekday: $18   **Weekend:** $21
Fee 18 Holes: Weekday: $23   **Weekend:** $26
Twilight Rates: No   **Discounts:** Senior & Junior
Cart Rental: $25pp/18, $15pp/9, $3/pull **Driving Range:** No
Lessons: Yes **Schools:** No   **Junior Golf:** Yes
Membership: Yes   **Architect/Yr Open:**
Other: Snack Bar / Bar-Lounge / Clubhouse **GPS:**

COUPON

A place to come play a quick enjoyable round especially for ladies and seniors. Get a frequent player card, play 9 rounds and get the 10th free.

	1	2	3	4	5	6	7	8	9
PAR	4	4	4	4	3	4	3	3	4
YARDS	258	302	286	268	120	324	140	176	281
PAR									
YARDS									

Directions: Route 24, Exit 18B, turn onto Route 27. Course is on left.

Chelmsford Country Club   ✪¹/₂   15 ▶

GB RTE 495

66 Park Road
Chelmsford, MA (978) 256-1818
www.sterlinggolf.com

Tees	Holes	Yards	Par	USGA	Slope
BACK	9	2467	33	64.2	103
MIDDLE	9	2368	33	64.2	108
FRONT	9	2202	34	66.1	107

Club Pro: Gary Burke
Payment: Visa, MC, Amex, Discover, Cash
Tee Times: 4 days adv.
Fee 9 Holes: Weekday: $19   **Weekend:** $22
Fee 18 Holes: Weekday: $26   **Weekend:** $30
Twilight Rates: Weekends only   **Discounts:** Senior & Junior
Cart Rental: $16pp/18, $9pp/9   **Driving Range:** Yes
Lessons: Yes **Schools:** Yes   **Junior Golf:** Yes
Membership: Yes   **Architect/Yr Open:** 1954; C. Fitzgerald/1962
Other: Snack Bar / Bar-Lounge / Function Hall   **GPS:**

COUPON

First tee redesigned. A fun golf course for all playing levels. Overall enhanced conditions. Managed by Sterling Golf Management, Inc. Beginner-friendly course. Bar and lounge. "Helpful hints on the stone markers." –FP

	1	2	3	4	5	6	7	8	9
PAR	4	3	3	5	4	3	4	4	3
YARDS	237	196	140	453	352	120	318	415	196

PAR									
YARDS									

Directions: I-495 to Route 110 to Chelmsford Center. Then take Route 27 South. Take left onto Park Road. Course is 200 yards on left.

Country Club of Billerica   ✪✪   16 ▶

51 Baldwin Road
Billerica, MA
(978) 667-9121 ext. 22
www.countryclubofbillerica.com

Tees	Holes	Yards	Par	USGA	Slope
BACK	18	5847	69	67.9	123
MIDDLE	18	5598	69	66.4	119
FRONT	18	4791	69	66.5	115

Club Pro: Steve Miller
Payment: Cash, Visa, MC, Discover
Tee Times: 3 days adv.
Fee 9 Holes: Weekday: $21   **Weekend:** $23
Fee 18 Holes: Weekday: $33   **Weekend:** $38
Twilight Rates: After 6pm   **Discounts:** None
Cart Rental: $16.50/18, $10.50/9 per cart   **Driving Range:** $8 lg., $6 sm.
Lessons: $45/half hour **Schools:** Yes   **Junior Golf:** Yes
Membership: Yes   **Architect/Yr Open:** Phil Wogan/1971
Other: Restaurant / Bar-Lounge / Clubhouse   **GPS:**

COUPON

Challenging and affordable for all. Picturesque layout between tall trees. Easy walk. Great 19th hole.

	1	2	3	4	5	6	7	8	9
PAR	5	3	4	5	3	4	3	3	4
YARDS	465	160	371	490	115	376	147	138	392
	10	**11**	**12**	**13**	**14**	**15**	**16**	**17**	**18**
PAR	4	4	4	3	4	4	3	5	4
YARDS	296	360	234	153	396	294	190	552	382

Directions: I-95/Route 128 to Route 3A North. Take Route 3A North into Billerica Center. Take right before Friendly's restaurant and at the end of the road, take a right and then the third left onto Baldwin Street. Course is on right.

Crosswinds Golf Club ✪✪✪✪

17

424 Long Pond Road
Plymouth, MA (508) 830-1199
www.golfcrosswinds.com

Club Pro: Dan Neary, PGA
Payment: Visa, MC, Amex
Tee Times: 7 days adv.

Tees	Holes	Yards	Par	USGA	Slope
BACK	27/18	6528	72	72.1	133
MIDDLE	27/18	6036	72	70.2	129
FRONT	27/18	5371	72	71.7	126

Fee 9 Holes: Weekday: $30 M-Th
Fee 18 Holes: Weekday: $50 M-Th
Twilight Rates: No
Cart Rental: Included
Lessons: Yes **Schools:** Yes
Membership: Yes

Weekend: $33 F/S/S/H
Weekend: $69 F/S/S/H
Discounts:
Driving Range: $9 large, $3 small
Junior Golf: Yes
Architect/Yr Open: Hurdzan/Fry/2002

COUPON

Other: Full Service Clubhouse / All Turf Range / Short Game Practice Area / Bar-Lounge

New clubhouse on site with full banquet facilities. Excellent for corporate outings.
Player comments: "Maturing nicely. New superintendent has brought quality way up. "Definitely an upgrade from its first seasons." –JD

	1	2	3	4	5	6	7	8	9
PAR	5	4	4	4	5	3	4	3	4
YARDS	490	355	317	326	491	141	340	162	360
	10	11	12	13	14	15	16	17	18
PAR	4	3	4	5	5	4	4	3	4
YARDS	370	138	376	475	471	398	296	164	366

Directions: Route 3 to Exit 5. Right off exit onto Long Pond Road. Follow Long Pond Road 4 miles. Crosswinds Golf Club entrance on left.

Crystal Lake Golf Club ✪✪½

18

940 North Broadway
Haverhill, MA (978) 374-9621
www.golfcrystallake.com

Club Pro: Peter Vlahos, PGA
Payment: Visa, MC, Disc, Cash
Tee Times: Weekends 7 days adv.

Tees	Holes	Yards	Par	USGA	Slope
BACK	18	6504	72	72.4	129
MIDDLE	18	6280	72	71.0	126
FRONT	18	5399	73	70.9	120

Fee 9 Holes: Weekday: $20
Fee 18 Holes: Weekday: $34
Twilight Rates: After 4:30pm
Cart Rental: $18pp/18, $10pp/9
Lessons: Yes **Schools:** No
Membership: Yes

Weekend: $20
Weekend: $34
Discounts: Junior/Senior
Driving Range: No
Junior Golf: Yes
Architect/Yr Open: Geoffrey Cornish/1961

COUPON

Other: Snack Bar / Restaurant / Bar-Lounge
GPS:

Under new ownership in 2010. Total improvements in tees, fairways and condition of course. Redesigned hole #5, #13. New bunkers, new carts and new clubhouse in 2012.

	1	2	3	4	5	6	7	8	9
PAR	4	3	4	4	5	3	4	5	4
YARDS	377	228	385	380	498	224	361	495	429
	10	11	12	13	14	15	16	17	18
PAR	4	5	4	3	4	4	3	4	5
YARDS	410	500	372	182	350	321	135	442	455

Directions: I-495 to Exit 50 (Route 97). At end of ramp, go across Route 97 to monument, and turn left at the blinking red light. Course is 2.5 miles on left. From the north: take Exit 50 (Route 97), left at end of ramp, left at lights.

D.W. Field Golf Course

331 Oak Street
Brockton, MA (508) 580-7855
www.brockton.ma.us

Club Pro: Brian Mattos, PGA
Payment: Visa, MC
Tee Times: 7 days adv.
Fee 9 Holes: Weekday: None
Fee 18 Holes: Weekday: $27 (M-Th)
Twilight Rates: After 4pm
Cart Rental: $16pp
Lessons: $30/30 min. **Schools:** No
Membership: Yes
Other: Snack Bar / Clubhouse

Tees	Holes	Yards	Par	USGA	Slope
BACK	18	5972	70	68.4	120
MIDDLE	18	5630	70	66.9	116
FRONT	18	5370	70	70.1	111

Weekend: None
Weekend: $32
Discounts: Senior
Driving Range: No
Junior Golf: Yes
Architect/Yr Open: Stiles & Van Kleek/1927

COUPON

Considered an easy walker. Open year round. Rates could change. New dress code.

	1	2	3	4	5	6	7	8	9
PAR	4	5	5	4	3	4	4	3	4
YARDS	305	485	485	300	165	340	335	135	355
	10	**11**	**12**	**13**	**14**	**15**	**16**	**17**	**18**
PAR	4	4	4	4	3	4	4	3	4
YARDS	315	340	360	405	125	300	345	175	360

Directions: Route 24 to Exit 18B, 3 sets of lights and take a right onto Oak Street. Course is 1.5 miles on the left.

Easton Country Club

✪✪½ 20 ▶

265 Purchase Street
South Easton, MA (508) 238-2500
www.eastoncountryclub.com

Club Pro: Rob Citrano
Payment: Visa, MC, Amex, Disc
Tee Times: 6 days adv. online
Fee 9 Holes: Weekday: $28 after 12
Fee 18 Holes: Weekday: $38 (M-Th)
Twilight Rates: After 3:30pm
Cart Rental: $15pp/18, $11pp/9
Lessons: $45/45 min. **Schools:** Yes
Membership: Full, Weekday, Junior
Other: Restaurant / Clubhouse / Lockers / Showers / Snack Bar / Bar-Lounge / Function Room

Tees	Holes	Yards	Par	USGA	Slope
BACK	18	6513	71	71.6	124
MIDDLE	18	6216	71	69.8	121
FRONT	18	5042	71	68.8	115

Weekend: No
Weekend: $45
Discounts: Senior & Junior M-Th
Driving Range: Yes - $5/bucket
Junior Golf: Yes
Architect/Yr Open: Sam Mitchell/1961

COUPON

New champion tees challenges the better golfers. New Senior/Junior tees offers playability for all levels. "Friendly staff and pro, well run inner club." –FP

	1	2	3	4	5	6	7	8	9
PAR	4	5	4	3	4	3	4	4	5
YARDS	436	483	281	155	387	164	418	315	491
	10	**11**	**12**	**13**	**14**	**15**	**16**	**17**	**18**
PAR	4	4	4	5	3	4	3	4	4
YARDS	338	358	345	525	164	365	165	422	423

Directions: Take Route 24 South to Exit 17B. Take Route 123 West to Route 138 South to Purchase Street on right (approx. 2 miles). Take a right onto Purchase Street; course is 7/10 mile on left.

Evergreen Valley Golf Course ✪ 21

18 Boyd Drive
Newburyport, MA (978) 463-8600
www.evergreenvalleygolf.com

Tees	Holes	Yards	Par	USGA	Slope
BACK	9	2997	35	67.4	108
MIDDLE	9	2902	35	67.4	108
FRONT	9	2631	35	67.4	108

Club Pro: Donna Koen
Payment: Cash, Check
Tee Times: No
Fee 9 Holes: Weekday: $12
Fee 18 Holes: Weekday: $24
Twilight Rates: No
Cart Rental: $25/18, $14/9 per cart, $3/pull
Lessons: Yes **Schools:** No
Membership: Yes
Other: Snack Bar and Deck

Weekend: $10-$14
Weekend: $20-$25
Discounts: Call ahead for info
Driving Range: No
Junior Golf: No
Architect/Yr Open: Francis Vitale Sr.
GPS:

Located in historic Newburyport, MA. 9 holes, 2 sets of tees. Open April - November. Drainage improvements. "Nice layout and affordable." —GM

	1	2	3	4	5	6	7	8	9
PAR	4	4	4	5	3	4	4	3	4
YARDS	370	300	420	460	155	390	305	165	215
PAR									
YARDS									

Directions: I-95 to Exit 57. Go east. Take left on Noble Road (across from Papa Gino's), then left at stop sign. Entrance to club is 300 feet on left.

Far Corner Golf Course ✪✪✪½ 22

5 Barker Road
West Boxford, MA (978) 352-8300
www.farcornergolf.com

Tees	Holes	Yards	Par	USGA	Slope
BACK	27/18	6719	72	72.9	130
MIDDLE	27/18	6189	72	70.9	126
FRONT	27/18	5655	73	71.4	115

Club Pro: John O'Connor, PGA
   Bob Flynn, PGA, Dir. of Golf
Payment: Cash, MC, Visa
Tee Times: 7 days adv.
Fee 9 Holes: Weekday: $21.50
Fee 18 Holes: Weekday: $41
Twilight Rates: After 4pm weekends
Cart Rental: $16pp/18, $8pp/9
Lessons: $50/half hour, $270/6 lessons
Membership: No **Schools:** Yes
Other: Snack Bar / Restaurant / Bar-Lounge / Clubhouse / Showers

Weekend: $24
Weekend: $46
Discounts: Senior & Junior
Driving Range: All grass
Junior Golf: Yes
Architect/Yr Open: Geoffrey Cornish/1967

A classic on the North Shore. Terrific, friendly staff. 27 holes - 3rd nine: Yardage: 3092, Championship Par: 36, Slope: 131. Enlarged driving range. Open year round.

	1	2	3	4	5	6	7	8	9
PAR	5	4	4	3	4	4	3	4	5
YARDS	510	350	310	190	460	330	170	390	450
	10	**11**	**12**	**13**	**14**	**15**	**16**	**17**	**18**
PAR	4	5	4	5	4	3	4	3	4
YARDS	270	470	360	530	380	170	320	135	390

Directions: I-95 North, to Exit 53B to Route 97 Georgetown. Follow to Route 133 West, to West Boxford Village. Go right onto Main Street. Course is 2 miles on left.

Fore Kicks GC & Sports Complex   NR   23 ▶

GB
RTE
495

10 Pine Street
Norfolk, MA (508) 384-4433
www.forekicks.com

Tees	Holes	Yards	Par	USGA	Slope
BACK					
MIDDLE	9	1003	27		
FRONT					

Club Pro: C. Estes, J. Marston
Payment: Cash, Credit
Tee Times: Yes
Fee 9 Holes: Weekday: $12/day, $15/night   **Weekend:** $15 S/S
Fee 18 Holes: Weekday: $17/day, $20/night   **Weekend:** $20 S/S
Twilight Rates: No   **Discounts:** Senior & Junior
Cart Rental: $3pp/pull   **Driving Range:** Indoors
Lessons: Yes **Schools:** Yes   **Junior Golf:** Yes
Membership: Yes   **Architect/Yr Open:** Brian Silva/2002
Other: Lounge / Indoor Soccer / Basketball Courts / Pro Shop / Putting Course /
         Fully Lighted Golf Course to 10pm

COUPON

Links-style. Lighted for night play. Features an indoor air-conditioned driving range. "Impressive multi-sport complex." –AP

	1	2	3	4	5	6	7	8	9
PAR	3	3	3	3	3	3	3	3	3
YARDS	115	112	81	78	118	93	122	127	157
PAR									
YARDS									

Directions: I-495 to Route 1 North to Pine Street Exit in Foxboro. Right-hand turn after exiting Route 1 onto Pine Street. Course is 2 miles down on left.

Four Oaks Country Club   ✪✪✪½   24 ▶

1 Clubhouse Lane
Dracut, MA (978) 455-0054
www.fouroakscountryclub.com

Tees	Holes	Yards	Par	USGA	Slope
BACK	18	6268	70	71.4	136
MIDDLE	18	5789	70	68.8	129
FRONT	18	4348	70	65.5	118

Club Pro: Anthony Martinho, PGA
Payment: Cash, Visa, MC, Amex, Disc
Tee Times: 6 days adv.
Fee 9 Holes: Weekday: $22   **Weekend:** $26
Fee 18 Holes: Weekday: $40   **Weekend:** $50
Twilight Rates: After 2:00pm   **Discounts:** Senior & Junior
Cart Rental: $19pp/18, $10pp/9   **Driving Range:** No
Lessons: $60/40 min. **Schools:** No **Junior Golf:** Yes
Membership: Yes   **Architect/Yr Open:** Jeffrey Brem/2006
Other: Restaurant / Showers / Snack Bar / Bar-Lounge / Function Room
GPS: Yes

"Consistently challenging hole-by-hole. Several huge greens with lots of undulation make approach shots critical. Front 9 is wide open, back 9 gets tighter. A great day of golf for any level of player." –JD

	1	2	3	4	5	6	7	8	9
PAR	4	5	4	3	5	4	4	4	3
YARDS	327	478	335	132	468	357	360	364	160
	10	**11**	**12**	**13**	**14**	**15**	**16**	**17**	**18**
PAR	4	4	3	4	4	3	4	4	4
YARDS	400	356	182	305	374	139	320	342	390

Directions: I-93 to Route 113 West. Go 5 miles to Meadow Creek Drive.

Foxborough Country Club ✪✪✪½ 25

33 Walnut Street
Foxborough, MA (508) 543-4661
www.foxboroughcc.com

Tees	Holes	Yards	Par	USGA	Slope
BACK	18	6849	72	73.9	134
MIDDLE	18	6607	72	72.7	130
FRONT	18	5627	73	73.6	127

Club Pro: Louis Rivers, PGA
Payment: Visa, MC, Amex, Disc
Tee Times: Call ahead for availability
Fee 9 Holes: Weekday: **Weekend:**
Fee 18 Holes: Weekday: $69 M-Th **Weekend:** $69 F/S/S/H
Twilight Rates: After 4pm **Discounts:** Jr. (up to 18yrs) $15pp/18
Cart Rental: $16pp/18, $10pp/9 **Driving Range:** Yes
Lessons: $50/half hour **Schools:** No **Junior Golf:** Yes
Membership: Yes **Architect/Yr Open:** Geoffrey Cornish/1955
Other: Restaurant / Bar- Lounge / Clubhouse / Showers
GPS:

COUPON

Player Comments: "Excellent golf course, tough but fair. Great greens." Be sure to call for tee times. Improved drainage systems. Dress code. Semi-private.

	1	2	3	4	5	6	7	8	9
PAR	4	4	3	5	4	3	4	4	5
YARDS	396	397	199	507	330	186	334	437	529
	10	11	12	13	14	15	16	17	18
PAR	4	5	3	4	4	4	4	3	5
YARDS	405	555	169	326	330	409	429	157	502

Directions: I-95 to Exit 7B (140 North) towards Foxborough. Take first left onto Walnut Street. Club will be on left after stop sign.

Fresh Pond Golf Club ✪✪½ 26

691 Huron Avenue
Cambridge, MA (617) 349-6282
www.freshpondgolf.com

Tees	Holes	Yards	Par	USGA	Slope
BACK	9	2931	35	70.0	120
MIDDLE	9	2732	35	66.9	111
FRONT	9	2306	35	66.5	114

Club Pro: Bob Carey, Dir. of Golf
Payment: Cash, Check, Visa, MC
Tee Times: Weekends only
Fee 9 Holes: Weekday: $22 **Weekend:** $26
Fee 18 Holes: Weekday: $32 **Weekend:** $38
Twilight Rates: No **Discounts:** Sr, Jr $14 (residents only)
Cart Rental: $14pp/18, $9pp/9 **Driving Range:** No
Lessons: $50/half hour **Schools:** No **Junior Golf:** Yes
Membership: Yes **Architect/Yr Open:** Donald Ross
Other: Snack Bar / Vending Machines **GPS:**

COUPON

Great course for all levels. Season tickets available. Off-season rates. Conditions better than ever. Great pro shop. Open Apr. - Dec.

	1	2	3	4	5	6	7	8	9
PAR	4	4	3	4	5	3	4	3	5
YARDS	417	312	169	401	476	221	370	147	465
PAR									
YARDS									

Directions: I-95 to Route 2 East to Cambridge. Go west on Huron Avenue to course.

Gannon Golf Course

✪✪½ 27 ▶

60 Great Woods Road
Lynn, MA (781) 595-5674
www.gannongolfclub.com

Tees	Holes	Yards	Par	USGA	Slope
BACK	18	6106	70	69.9	118
MIDDLE	18	6036	70	67.9	113
FRONT	18	5215	71	68.8	115

Club Pro: Mike Foster, PGA
Payment: Visa, MC, Disc
Tee Times: 2 days adv.
Fee 9 Holes: Weekday: $19
Fee 18 Holes: Weekday: $34
Twilight Rates: After 3:30pm
Cart Rental: $15pp/18, $7.50pp/9
Lessons: No **Schools:** No
Membership: Yes
Weekend: $21 after 3:30pm
Weekend: $42 Spring/Fall only
Discounts: Junior
Driving Range: No
Junior Golf: Yes
Architect/Yr Open: Wayne Stiles/1931

Other: Snack Bar / Clubhouse / Lockers / Restaruant / Showers / Bar Lounge
GPS:

Golf Course features the rolling terrain which Stiles was famous for. Wonderful views of Boston as well as Lynn Woods Reservation. Challenging 18 holes in magnificent condition.

	1	2	3	4	5	6	7	8	9
PAR	4	4	4	4	4	3	4	4	3
YARDS	346	309	357	404	333	187	318	414	216
	10	11	12	13	14	15	16	17	18
PAR	4	4	4	4	3	5	3	4	5
YARDS	309	335	401	383	158	486	228	319	588

Directions: I-95 North to Exit 44B. Rotary to 129 East - Lynn/Swampscott. 1.9 miles on right (Lynn Woods). I-95 South to Route 1 South. Left onto 129 East, to rotary. Follow 129 East - Lynn/Swampscott. 1.9 miles on right (Lynn Woods).

Garrison Golf Center

NR 28 ▶

654 Hilldale Avenue
Haverhill, MA (978) 374-9380
www.garrisongolf.com

Tees	Holes	Yards	Par	USGA	Slope
BACK					
MIDDLE	9	1005	27		
FRONT					

Club Pro: Ted Murphy, Kevin Murphy
Payment: Cash, Visa, MC
Tee Times: No
Fee 9 Holes: Weekday: $10
Fee 18 Holes: Weekday: $19
Twilight Rates: No
Cart Rental: $2/pull
Lessons: $50/session **Schools:** Yes
Membership: No
Other:
Weekend: $11
Weekend: $20
Discounts: $9 Senior & Junior
Driving Range: $7 one size bucket
Junior Golf: Yes
Architect/Yr Open: Manuel Francis/1969
GPS:

COUPON

A short testing 9-hole par 3 with beautiful Vesper Velvet greens. Designed in 1966 by legendary Manuel Francis. Great course for women and juniors. 12 play tickets $90 (seniors $80).

	1	2	3	4	5	6	7	8	9
PAR	3	3	3	3	3	3	3	3	3
YARDS	105	100	130	75	100	130	130	135	100
PAR									
YARDS									

Directions: I-495N to Exit 50 straight for one mile, left at 2nd stop sign for ¼ mile.

George Wright Golf Club ✪✪✪½ 29

420 West Street
Hyde Park, MA (617) 364-2300
www.georgewrightgolfcourse.com

Club Pro: Scott Allen, PGA
Payment: Visa, MC
Tee Times: 2 days adv. S/S
Fee 9 Holes: Weekday: $22.50 M-F
Fee 18 Holes: Weekday: $37 M-F
Twilight Rates: No
Cart Rental: $20pp/18, $11pp/9
Lessons: $40/half hour **Schools:** No
Membership: Yes
Other: Snack Bar / Bar-Lounge

Tees	Holes	Yards	Par	USGA	Slope
BACK	18	6367	70	69.5	126
MIDDLE	18	6166	70	68.6	123
FRONT	18	5054	70	70.3	115

Weekend: $26 S/S/H
Weekend: $44 S/S/H
Discounts: Senior & Junior
Driving Range: No
Junior Golf: Yes
Architect/Yr Open: Donald Ross/1938
GPS:

Rated #14 in *Golfweek's* 2009 rating of the top municipal golf courses in the United States. Boston resident rates available. After 2 easy holes to get you warmed up, it kicks into gear and keeps you working hard the rest of the way. "A must-play if you have not visited this hidden gem recently." –SD

	1	2	3	4	5	6	7	8	9
PAR	4	4	5	3	4	4	4	3	4
YARDS	367	313	480	150	400	380	387	162	440
	10	11	12	13	14	15	16	17	18
PAR	4	4	4	4	3	5	4	3	4
YARDS	449	347	399	369	182	493	318	158	372

Directions: I-95/Route 128 to Route 1 North to Washington Street (left) in Hyde Park. Take a right onto Beach Street. Follow signs to course.

Glen Ellen Country Club ✪✪✪ 30

84 Orchard Street, Route 115
Millis, MA (508) 376-2775
www.theglencc.com

Club Pro: David Hodgdon, Golf Operations
Payment: Visa, MC, Amex, Disc, Cash, Check
Tee Times: 7 days adv.
Fee 9 Holes: Weekday: $27
Fee 18 Holes: Weekday: $41
Twilight Rates: After 3pm weekdays
                    After 5pm weekends
Cart Rental: $20pp/18, $10pp/9
Lessons: Yes **Schools:** Yes
Membership: Yes
Other: Snack Bar / Showers / Bar-Lounge

Tees	Holes	Yards	Par	USGA	Slope
BACK	18	6634	72	72.0	125
MIDDLE	18	6237	72	70.1	123
FRONT	18	5148	72	69.4	122

Weekend:
Weekend: $56
Discounts: Senior & Junior

Driving Range: Yes
Junior Golf: Yes
Architect/Yr Open: Ron Pritchard/1963
GPS:

COUPON

A well manicured course that is challenging enough for the skilled player yet playable for the average player. Welcoming to women and juniors. Host facility for 2012 Public Links Championship. Home of U.S. Kids Golf Boston Director Andy Ingham.

	1	2	3	4	5	6	7	8	9
PAR	4	3	4	4	4	5	4	3	5
YARDS	431	153	376	316	381	508	325	130	475
	10	11	12	13	14	15	16	17	18
PAR	5	4	3	4	4	4	4	5	3
YARDS	503	410	168	475	353	333	375	385	145

Directions: I-495 to Exit 18, take right at end. Straight for 4 miles. Take left onto Holliston Street. Follow 2 miles and take right onto Goulding Street. Course is on left.

Granite Links Golf Club ✪✪✪✪✪ 31 ▶

100 Quarry Hills Drive
Quincy, MA (617) 689-1900
www.granitelinksgolfclub.com

Tees	Holes	Yards	Par	USGA	Slope
BACK	27/18	6818	72	73.4	141
MIDDLE	27/18	6300	72	71.6	134
FRONT	27/18	5001	72	70.6	124

Club Pro: Stephen Clancy, PGA
Payment: Visa, MC, Amex, Disc
Tee Times: 4 days adv.
Fee 9 Holes: Weekday: $70 w/cart M-W **Weekend:** $70 w/cart Th/F/S/S after 1pm
Fee 18 Holes: Weekday: $125 w/cart M-W **Weekend:** $125 w/cart Th/F/S/S
Twilight Rates: After 4pm
Discounts: Seniors Tues. & Wed., Milton/Quincy residents
Cart Rental: Included   **Driving Range:** $10/bucket
Lessons: $50/half hour, $95/hour, 5 lessons/$225 **Junior Golf:** Yes
Membership: Yes   **Architect/Yr Open:** John Sanford/2003
Other: Restaurant / Clubhouse / Lockers (Members Only) / Showers / Bar-Lounge
GPS: Yes

Golf Digest Top 100 golf courses. 27-hole course with exceptional views and conditions.

Granite/Milton

	1	2	3	4	5	6	7	8	9
PAR	5	4	4	3	4	4	3	5	4
YARDS	488	375	399	154	353	331	187	499	298
	10	11	12	13	14	15	16	17	18
PAR	4	3	4	5	4	3	4	4	5
YARDS	454	171	411	486	364	188	323	335	484

Directions: I-93 to Exit 8 and follow signs to Quarry Hills. Turn right onto Riccuti Drive and follow for 1 mile to club entrance.

Green Harbor Golf Club ✪✪¹⁄₂ 32 ▶

624 Webster Street
Marshfield, MA (781) 834-7303
www.greenharborgolfclub.com

Tees	Holes	Yards	Par	USGA	Slope
BACK	18	6245	71	69.6	122
MIDDLE	18	5757	71	67,8	115
FRONT	18	4967	71	68.5	114

Club Pro: Charles Lanzetta, Dir. of Golf
Payment: Cash, Visa, MC, Personal Checks
Tee Times: 7 days adv.
Fee 9 Holes: Weekday: $23   **Weekend:** $25
Fee 18 Holes: Weekday: $38   **Weekend:** $47
Twilight Rates: After 5pm   **Discounts:** Srs. Tues 6am-12pm
Cart Rental: No   **Driving Range:** No
Lessons: Yes **Schools:** Yes   **Junior Golf:** Yes
Membership: Yes   **Architect/Yr Open:** Manuel Francis/1971
Other: Clubhouse / Snack Bar / Lounge **GPS:**

Flat, open course. Water on 5 holes. Features velvet bent grass. Open March 15 - December 15.

	1	2	3	4	5	6	7	8	9
PAR	4	4	4	4	3	4	5	3	4
YARDS	406	353	347	300	155	310	507	155	318
	10	11	12	13	14	15	16	17	18
PAR	4	5	5	4	4	3	4	3	4
YARDS	349	505	462	345	280	185	364	158	316

Directions: I-93 to Route 3 South to Exit 12 (Route 139). 139 East 4.5 miles. Right on Webster Street, 1 mile on left.

Hickory Hill Golf Course   ✪✪½   ▶ 33

200 North Lowell Street
Methuen, MA (978) 686-0822
www.golfhickoryhill.com

Club Pro:
Payment: Visa, MC, Cash
Tee Times: 7 days adv.

Tees	Holes	Yards	Par	USGA	Slope
BACK	18	6287	71	70.8	123
MIDDLE	18	6017	71	69.6	119
FRONT	18	5367	71	70.7	121

Fee 9 Holes: Weekday: $23 M-F   **Weekend:** $28
Fee 18 Holes: Weekday: $40 M-Th, $45 F   **Weekend:** $50
Twilight Rates: After 3pm wknd; 6pm wkdy   **Discounts:** Senior & Junior (Senior T-Th am)
Cart Rental: $17pp/18, $12pp/9   **Driving Range:** Yes
Lessons: **Schools:** No   **Junior Golf:** No
Membership: No   **Architect/Yr Open:** Manuel Francis/1968
Other: Clubhouse / Showers / Bar-Lounge   **GPS:**

Course offers a senior discount Tuesday, Wednesday and Thursday 7am-12pm, $35/walk, $45/ride.
Good variety of holes, tougher back nine. Great conditions, very friendly staff.

	1	2	3	4	5	6	7	8	9
PAR	4	3	5	4	4	5	4	3	4
YARDS	349	173	511	382	379	513	367	155	348
	10	11	12	13	14	15	16	17	18
PAR	5	4	4	3	4	4	4	3	4
YARDS	489	390	340	141	326	357	304	114	379

Directions: I-93 to Exit 46. Take Route 113 West, follow 1.5 miles, course is on left.

Hillview Golf Course   ✪✪   ▶ 34

149 North Street
North Reading, MA (978) 664-4435
www.hillviewgc.com

Club Pro: Chris Carter, PGA
Payment: Visa, MC, Amex, Disc
Tee Times: Yes

Tees	Holes	Yards	Par	USGA	Slope
BACK	18	5802	69	67.4	120
MIDDLE	18	5251	69	65.2	118
FRONT	18	4500	69	66.0	110

Fee 9 Holes: Weekday: $21   **Weekend:** $24
Fee 18 Holes: Weekday: $39   **Weekend:** $42
Twilight Rates: No   **Discounts:** Sr. & Jr. (M-Th) $16 before 1pm
Cart Rental: $16pp/18, $8pp/9   **Driving Range:** Yes
Lessons: Yes **Schools:** No   **Junior Golf:** Yes
Membership: No   **Architect/Yr Open:** 1950s
Other: Snack Bar / Restaurant / Bar-Lounge / Clubhouse

A popular course in a good location. Interesting layout. New green and fairway improvements.
A player-friendly course.

	1	2	3	4	5	6	7	8	9
PAR	5	3	4	4	4	4	4	5	3
YARDS	484	170	410	325	357	323	394	539	191
	10	11	12	13	14	15	16	17	18
PAR	4	4	4	4	3	4	3	4	3
YARDS	372	310	346	355	180	324	236	239	173

Directions: I-93 to Exit 40 and follow Route 62 East 1½ miles. Turn left on North Street. Course is ½ mile up on left.

Kelley Greens Golf Course ✪✪ 35 ▶

1 Willow Road
Nahant, MA
(781) 581-0840 ext. 101
www.kelleygreens.com

Tees	Holes	Yards	Par	USGA	Slope
BACK	9	1940	30	30.0	103
MIDDLE	9	1865	30	28.5	87
FRONT	9	1671	30	30.0	103

Club Pro:
Payment: Visa, MC, Amex, Disc
Tee Times: Call (781) 581-0840
Fee 9 Holes: Weekday: $17   **Weekend:** $20
Fee 18 Holes: Weekday: $28   **Weekend:** $31
Twilight Rates: No   **Discounts:** Senior/Junior memberships
Cart Rental: $20/18, $12/9 per cart   **Driving Range:** No
Lessons: No **Schools:** Yes   **Junior Golf:** Yes
Membership: Yes   **Architect/Yr Open:**
Other: Ask about our Golf & Lunch special   **GPS:**

Full service bar and lottery. Serving lunch and dinner. Functions and outings for up to 200 guests. Open year round.

	1	2	3	4	5	6	7	8	9
PAR	3	3	3	3	3	4	4	4	3
YARDS	139	177	174	140	187	319	282	251	172
PAR									
YARDS									

Directions: Take 1A to rotary, follow Nahant Causeway 2.6 miles. Right after the end of Ocean Avenue. Follow Willow Road to the end. Kelley Greens is on the right. Follow signs to course.

Lakeview Golf Course ✪1/2 36 ▶

Route 1A
Wenham, MA (978) 468-9584
www.lakeviewgc.com

Tees	Holes	Yards	Par	USGA	Slope
BACK	9	2001	31		
MIDDLE	9	1836	31	59.3	91
FRONT	9	1550	31		

Club Pro: Tom Gillis, PGA
Payment: Cash, MC, Visa
Tee Times: Yes
Fee 9 Holes: Weekday: $18   **Weekend:** $20
Fee 18 Holes: Weekday: $27   **Weekend:** $29
Twilight Rates: After 6pm   **Discounts:** Senior & Junior $14
Cart Rental: $14pp/18, $7pp/9   **Driving Range:** No
Lessons: Private and group **Schools:** No   **Junior Golf:** Yes
Membership: Yes   **Architect/Yr Open:** 1918
Other: Snack Bar   **GPS:**

COUPON

Executive-style golf course. Senior rate: $14 for 9 holes, M-W before noon. Junior rate: $14 for 9 holes.

	1	2	3	4	5	6	7	8	9
PAR	4	3	3	4	3	4	3	3	4
YARDS	325	215	165	320	125	255	150	160	325
PAR									
YARDS									

Directions: I-95/Route 128 to Exit 20 North (Route 1A). The course is 2 miles on the right.

Leo J. Martin Golf Club ✪½ 37

85 Park Road
Weston, MA (781) 891-1119

Club Pro: Mike Wortis, PGA
Payment: Visa, MC
Tee Times: Weekends
Fee 9 Holes: Weekday: $19 M-Th
Fee 18 Holes: Weekday: $27 M-Th
Twilight Rates: After 5pm
Cart Rental: $30/18, $16/9 per cart
Lessons: $45/half hour **Schools:** Junior
Membership: No
Other: Snack Bar

Tees	Holes	Yards	Par	USGA	Slope
BACK	18	6320	72	70.7	126
MIDDLE	18	6140	72	67.6	118
FRONT	18	6140	75	70.9	116

Weekend: $19 F/S/S/H
Weekend: $30 F/S/S/H
Discounts: Sr. & Jr. weekdays M-Th
Driving Range: $12/lg, $7/sm
Junior Golf: Yes
Architect/Yr Open: Donald Ross
GPS:

Considered an easy walker. Seniors seem to enjoy it. Tee times first come, first serve M-F.
Friendly beginners course.

	1	2	3	4	5	6	7	8	9
PAR	4	5	3	5	3	4	4	4	4
YARDS	315	500	155	525	140	360	325	355	265
	10	11	12	13	14	15	16	17	18
PAR	3	4	3	4	4	4	5	4	5
YARDS	140	290	240	400	420	360	530	260	560

Directions: Where I-95/Route 128 meets I-90 (Mass Pike). From Mass Pike Weston exit (Route 30), take first left onto Park Road to course on left.

Lost Brook Golf Club ✪✪✪ 38

750 University Avenue
Norwood, MA (781) 769-2550
www.lostbrookgolfclub.com

Club Pro: Chris Hawley
Payment: Cash, Credit Cards
Tee Times: Weekends
Fee 9 Holes: Weekday: $16
Fee 18 Holes: Weekday: $25
Twilight Rates: Yes
Cart Rental: $3/pull
Lessons: Yes **Schools:** No
Membership: No
Other: Clubhouse / Snack Bar

Tees	Holes	Yards	Par	USGA	Slope
BACK					
MIDDLE	18	3002	54		
FRONT	18	2468	58		

Weekend: $18
Weekend: $27
Discounts: Senior & Junior
Driving Range: No
Junior Golf: No
Architect/Yr Open: Sam Mitchell/1967
GPS:

Expertly maintained par 3 golf course. Tree-lined fairways surround the elevated greens.
"Excellent conditions, challenging and enjoyable for all levels." —GM

	1	2	3	4	5	6	7	8	9
PAR	3	3	3	3	3	3	3	3	3
YARDS	93	198	212	202	141	158	176	190	111
	10	11	12	13	14	15	16	17	18
PAR	3	3	3	3	3	3	3	3	3
YARDS	170	171	168	162	126	148	202	190	185

Directions: I-95/Route 128 to Exit 13. Follow University Avenue approximately 1.5 miles to course located at Meditech. Course is on the left.

Maplegate Country Club   ✪✪✪½   ▶39

160 Maple Street
Bellingham, MA (508) 966-4040
www.maplegate.com

Club Pro: Greg Dowdell
Payment: Visa, MC, Amex, Disc
Tee Times: 7 days adv.

Tees	Holes	Yards	Par	USGA	Slope
BACK	18	6815	72	74.2	133
MIDDLE	18	5837	72	69.5	122
FRONT	18	4852	72	70.2	124

Fee 9 Holes: Weekday: $27 walk, $35 w/cart
Fee 18 Holes: Weekday: $59 ride
Twilight Rates: After 1pm
Cart Rental: $20pp/18
Lessons: Yes **Schools:** Jr. & Sr.
Membership: Yes
Other: Snack Bar

Weekend: $35 w/cart
Weekend: $69 w/cart before noon
Discounts: Senior
Driving Range: Yes
Junior Golf: Yes
Architect/Yr: Leonard French & Phil Wogan/1990
GPS:

COUPON

Must be straight shooter, but interesting layout for all abilities. Carts required weekends and holidays before noon. "Nice greens. Friendly staff." –FP

	1	2	3	4	5	6	7	8	9
PAR	5	4	3	5	4	4	4	3	4
YARDS	515	335	173	522	431	435	417	145	434
	10	11	12	13	14	15	16	17	18
PAR	4	4	3	4	5	3	5	4	4
YARDS	376	382	191	388	510	227	530	357	447

Directions: I-495 to Exit 18 bear right. Take 126 North. Right at first light to Maple Street. Course is 1 mile on left.

Maynard Golf Course   NR   ▶40

50 Brown Street
Maynard, MA (978) 637-2268
www.sterlinggolf.com

Club Pro: Dennis Maxfield
Payment: Visa, MC, Amex, Disc
Tee Times: 7 days adv.

Tees	Holes	Yards	Par	USGA	Slope
BACK	9	3013	35	68.2	123
MIDDLE	9	2853	35	68.2	123
FRONT	9	2601	35	71.5	124

Fee 9 Holes: Weekday: $21
Fee 18 Holes: Weekday: $32
Twilight Rates: After 4pm
Cart Rental: $16pp/18; $10pp/9
Lessons: Yes **Schools:** Yes
Membership: Yes
Other: Restaurant / Showers / Snack Bar / Bar-Lounge / Function Room

Weekend: $25
Weekend: $34
Discounts: Senior, Junior
Driving Range: No
Junior Golf: Yes
Architect/Yr: Wayne Stiles/1921

Formerly Maynard Country Club, a member-owned, semi-private club. Professionally maintained to provide an outstanding golf experience.

	1	2	3	4	5	6	7	8	9
PAR	4	5	3	4	4	3	4	4	4
YARDS	375	487	148	345	355	165	342	338	298
PAR									
YARDS									

Directions: I-95 to Route 20 West to Route 27 North. Travel 4 miles and take a left on Waltham Street. Bear right onto Acton Street. Brown Street is ¼ mile on right.

Meadow at Peabody, The ✪✪✪ 41

80 Granite Street
Peabody, MA (978) 532-9390
www.peabodymeadowgolf.com

Club Pro: Peter Cronan
Payment: Visa, MC, Amex
Tee Times: 3 days adv.

Tees	Holes	Yards	Par	USGA	Slope
BACK	18	6708	71	72.4	128
MIDDLE	18	5869	71	69.4	121
FRONT	18	5136	71	70.8	123

Fee 9 Holes: Weekday: $21 ($19/resident) **Weekend:** $24 ($21/resident)
Fee 18 Holes: Weekday: $40 ($35/resident) **Weekend:** $44 ($38/resident)
Twilight Rates: No **Discounts:** Sr. & Jr. before noon M-F
Cart Rental: $16pp/18, $9pp/9 **Driving Range:** No
Lessons: $40/45 min. **Schools:** No **Junior Golf:** Yes
Membership: No **Architect/Yr Open:** Silva & Cornish/2001
Other: Restaurant / Showers **GPS:**

Player Comments: "A real workout for the first visit, a ton of fun your next few times around."
"Fun layout, hilly, but fair course." "Careful—several blind shots." "Great greens" –FP
Dress code. Lodging available at nearby Marriott.

	1	2	3	4	5	6	7	8	9
PAR	5	4	4	4	4	3	5	3	4
YARDS	526	343	312	324	388	110	437	146	372
	10	11	12	13	14	15	16	17	18
PAR	4	5	3	4	4	4	3	4	4
YARDS	360	457	153	389	319	329	143	341	420

Directions: I-95/Route 128 to Exit 28 (Forest Street/Centennial Drive). Bear right at end of ramp.
Go through lights at bottom of hill to Summit. Left onto Lynnfield Street, Left onto Washington Street.
Immediate right onto Granite Street. Street dead-ends to course.

Merrimack Valley Golf Course ✪✪✪ 42

210 Howe Street
Methuen, MA (978) 683-7771
www.merrimackvalleygolfclub.com

Club Pro: Bill Pappas
Payment: Cash, Visa, MC
Tee Times: 7 days adv.

Tees	Holes	Yards	Par	USGA	Slope
BACK	18	6012	70	70.4	130
MIDDLE	18	5730	70	69.2	126
FRONT	18	5226	70	67.6	117

Fee 9 Holes: Weekday: $18 **Weekend:** $25
Fee 18 Holes: Weekday: $30 **Weekend:** $40
Twilight Rates: $20 after 3pm wknds/holidays **Discounts:** None
Cart Rental: $18pp/18, $9pp/9 **Driving Range:** No
Lessons: Yes **Schools:** No **Junior Golf:** Yes
Membership: Yes **Architect/Yr Open:** Donald Ross/1906
Other: Restaurant / Bar-Lounge **GPS:**

Improvements include better drainage. Noted for plush greens. All new tees, all new irrigation, fairways,
greens, drainage. One of the best values in New England. Redesigned by Geo Sargent in 2009.

	1	2	3	4	5	6	7	8	9
PAR	5	4	5	4	3	3	4	5	3
YARDS	485	371	487	305	133	194	383	507	141
	10	11	12	13	14	15	16	17	18
PAR	4	3	5	3	4	3	4	3	5
YARDS	378	174	461	149	327	178	366	152	539

Directions: I-495 to Exit 47, Route 213. Take Exit 3 off Route 213. At lights at end of exit ramp,
go left. Club is ¾ mile on left.

Middleton Golf Course ✪✪✪

105 South Main Street
Middleton, MA (978) 774-4075
www.middletongolf.com

Tees	Holes	Yards	Par	USGA	Slope
BACK	18	3215	54	57.0	83
MIDDLE	18	3000	54	53.9	75
FRONT	18	2280	54	52.1	71

Club Pro: Chris Costa, PGA
Payment: Major Credit Cards, Checks, Cash
Tee Times: See website
Fee 9 Holes: Weekday: $23   **Weekend:** $23
Fee 18 Holes: Weekday: $36   **Weekend:** $36
Twilight Rates: After 3:30pm, F/S/S only   **Discounts:** Senior & Junior
Cart Rental: $12pp/18, $8pp/9   **Driving Range:** Lessons only
Lessons: Yes **Schools:** Yes   **Junior Golf:** Yes
Membership: No   **Architect/Yr Open:** Geoffrey Cornish/1966
Other: Clubhouse / Bar (Beer & Wine Only) / Greenside Cafe / Club Fitting Center

COUPON

Beautifully maintained, one of the nation's top par 3 courses. Open year round.

	1	2	3	4	5	6	7	8	9
PAR	3	3	3	3	3	3	3	3	3
YARDS	170	160	185	170	150	170	145	215	190
	10	11	12	13	14	15	16	17	18
PAR	3	3	3	3	3	3	3	3	3
YARDS	135	110	195	160	155	240	215	225	225

Directions: I-95 to Route 114 West about 2.5 miles. Parking lot entrance on the left.

Millwood Golf Course ✪

175 Millwood Street
Framingham, MA (508) 877-1221
www.millwoodgolfcourse.com

Tees	Holes	Yards	Par	USGA	Slope
BACK	14	4057	53	64.5	108
MIDDLE	14	3816	53	63.3	106
FRONT	14	3361	53	64.7	102

Club Pro:
Payment: Visa, MC
Tee Times: 7 days adv.
Fee 9 Holes: Weekday: $27   **Weekend:** $30
Fee 18 Holes: Weekday: **Weekend:**
Twilight Rates: After 5pm   **Discounts:** Senior ($21 M-F)
Cart Rental: $10pp   **Driving Range:** No
Lessons: No **Schools:** No   **Junior Golf:** No
Membership: No   **Architect/Yr Open:** William Drake/1967
Other: Snack Bar   **GPS:**

A friendly family-owned course, with 14 holes. Added traps on 7th hole. New tee on 9th. Open April - November.

	1	2	3	4	5	6	7	8	9
PAR	4	3	4	4	4	3	4	4	5
YARDS	338	112	306	230	363	156	281	312	438
	10	11	12	13	14	15	16	17	18
PAR	4	3	4	3	4				
YARDS	362	160	295	138	307				

Directions: Route 9 to Edgell Road. At light, make right onto Edgell Road for 1 mile. Turn left onto Belknap Road, then third right onto Millwood Street.

Mt. Hood Golf Course ✪✪

100 Slayton Road
Melrose, MA (781) 665-6656
www.playgolfne.com

Tees	Holes	Yards	Par	USGA	Slope
BACK	18	5633	69	67.1	117
MIDDLE	18	5312	69	65.4	115
FRONT	18	4462	74	66.5	112

Club Pro: Mike Farrell, PGA
Payment: Visa, MC, Amex, Disc
Tee Times: Weekends, 6 days adv. (members 5 days adv.)
Fee 9 Holes: Weekday: $24   **Weekend:** $28
Fee 18 Holes: Weekday: $41   **Weekend:** $47
Twilight Rates: Yes   **Discounts:** Senior & Junior
Cart Rental: $17pp/18, $9pp/9   **Driving Range:** No
Lessons: $30/half hour **Schools:**   **Junior Golf:** Yes
Membership: Yes   **Architect/Yr Open:**
Other: Clubhouse / Showers / Snack Bar / Restaurant / Bar-Lounge

Hole #12 redone, overlooks Boston skyline. Now under Friel Management. Come visit an old town course with a nice, friendly staff. –FP

	1	2	3	4	5	6	7	8	9
PAR	5	4	3	5	4	4	3	4	3
YARDS	477	340	202	532	303	338	215	362	180
	10	11	12	13	14	15	16	17	18
PAR	3	4	4	4	5	3	4	4	3
YARDS	140	282	386	332	450	210	321	304	166

Directions: From Route 1 – take left onto Essex Street then left onto Waverly Avenue. Take left onto Slayton Road.

New England Country Club ✪✪✪½

180 Paine Street
Bellingham, MA (508) 883-2300
www.newenglandcountryclub.com

Tees	Holes	Yards	Par	USGA	Slope
BACK	18	6483	71	70.9	135
MIDDLE	18	5867	71	68.2	125
FRONT	18	4927	71	68.9	122

Club Pro: Mark Copithorne
Payment: Visa, MC
Tee Times: 5 days adv.
Fee 9 Holes: Weekday: $39 w/cart M-Th   **Weekend:** $44 w/cart F/S/S
Fee 18 Holes: Weekday: $59 w/cart M-Th   **Weekend:** $69 w/cart F/S/S
Twilight Rates: After 1pm   **Discounts:** Early Bird, Senior
Cart Rental: Included   **Driving Range:** All grass
Lessons: $45/45 min. **Schools:** Clinics   **Junior Golf:** No
Membership: Yes, full and partial   **Architect/Yr Open:** Hale Irwin/1990
Other: Clubhouse / Restaurant / Pub / Outdoor Deck / Tent / GPS Carts
GPS: Yes

COUPON

It only looks short on the card; great course from the whites—absolute killer from the blues. Great variety of holes. GPS in carts and multiple sets of tees. Spectacular, well-groomed Hale Irwin championship golf course.

	1	2	3	4	5	6	7	8	9
PAR	5	4	4	3	5	3	4	4	4
YARDS	497	357	314	145	490	122	386	320	352
	10	11	12	13	14	15	16	17	18
PAR	4	5	3	4	4	4	3	4	4
YARDS	355	501	145	382	327	297	140	340	397

Directions: I-495 North to Exit 16 (King Street). Continue west on King Street for 6 miles. At light make a left onto Wrentham Street. Bear right at the fire station onto Paine Street. Course is .25 miles up hill on left.

New Meadows Golf Club ✪¹/₂ 47 ▶

32 Wildes Road
Topsfield, MA (978) 887-9307
www.newmeadowsgolf.com

Club Pro: Jerry Peckerman, Manager
Payment: Cash, Check
Tee Times: Call ahead
Fee 9 Holes: Weekday: $17
Fee 18 Holes: Weekday: $32
Twilight Rates: No
Cart Rental: $24pp/18, $12pp/9
Lessons: No **Schools:** No
Membership: No
Other: Clubhouse / Snack Bar

Tees	Holes	Yards	Par	USGA	Slope
BACK					
MIDDLE	9	2883	35	64.8	117
FRONT					

Weekend: $19
Weekend: $36
Discounts: None
Driving Range: No
Junior Golf: No
Architect/Yr Open: Phil Wogan/1964
GPS:

New Meadows offers a relaxed atmosphere for golfers of all ages and handicap ranges. It is especially enjoyable for seniors, women, juniors, and mid- to high- handicap golfers. Please call for tee times. New irrigation and cart paths.

	1	2	3	4	5	6	7	8	9
PAR	4	4	3	4	4	4	5	3	4
YARDS	352	365	160	348	345	368	459	128	358
PAR									
YARDS									

Directions: New Meadows is 1.9 miles north of the US Route 1 and Route 97 intersection, and 3.2 miles south of the US Route 1 and Route 133 intersection.

Newton Commonwealth GC ✪✪ 48 ▶

212 Kenrick Street
Newton, MA (617) 630-1971
www.sterlinggolf.com

Club Pro: Mike Albrecht, PGA
Payment: Cash, Most Credit Cards
Tee Times: 2 days adv.
Fee 9 Holes: Weekday: $24 M-Th
Fee 18 Holes: Weekday: $30 M-Th
Twilight Rates: After 5pm
Discounts: Sr./$18, Jr./$14 M-Th before 8am
Cart Rental: $16pp/18, $10pp/9
Lessons: $55/half hour **Schools:** No
Membership: Yes
Other: Snack Bar

Tees	Holes	Yards	Par	USGA	Slope
BACK	18	5354	70	65.8	122
MIDDLE	18	4992	70	64.5	117
FRONT	18	4329	70	65.8	118

Weekend:
Weekend: $37 F-Sun

Driving Range: No
Junior Golf: No
Architect/Yr Open: Donald Ross/1897

New routing makes this a "new course" for anyone who hasn't been here recently. Resident discounts. Well-stocked pro shop. Friendly staff. Open year round. Donald Ross greens make par a challenge. New irrigation relieves formerly wet holes. Redesigned 7th tee and cart path. Redesigned 18th hole.

	1	2	3	4	5	6	7	8	9
PAR	4	5	3	3	5	4	3	5	3
YARDS	252	476	179	110	435	255	162	473	180
	10	11	12	13	14	15	16	17	18
PAR	4	4	3	4	4	5	3	4	4
YARDS	259	295	148	263	231	422	130	376	355

Directions: I-95/Route 128 to Route 30 East exit. Follow 4.8 miles to Grant Avenue. Go left and follow the golfer logo signs.

GB
RTE
495

COUPON

COUPON

North Hill Country Club   ✪✪   49

29 Merry Avenue
Duxbury, MA (781) 934-3249
www.northhillgolf.com

Tees	Holes	Yards	Par	USGA	Slope
BACK	9	3456	36	74.6	131
MIDDLE	9	3324	36	71.2	121
FRONT	9	2887	736	68.2	117

Club Pro: Bill Allen, PGA
Payment: Most Major Credit Cards
Tee Times: 7 days adv.
Fee 9 Holes: Weekday: $18   **Weekend:** $20
Fee 18 Holes: Weekday: $30   **Weekend:** $33
Twilight Rates: No   **Discounts:**
Cart Rental: $15pp/18, $8pp/9   **Driving Range:** Limited
Lessons: Private and Group **Schools:** No   **Junior Golf:** Yes
Membership: Yes   **Architect/Yr Open:** William Mitchell/1962
Other: Snack Bar / Bar-Lounge / Clubhouse   **GPS:**

"Nice layout. Fun track." From the tips, a real challenging course.

	1	2	3	4	5	6	7	8	9
PAR	5	4	4	3	4	5	4	3	4
YARDS	555	438	426	205	350	488	374	190	430
PAR									
YARDS									

Directions: Route 3 to Exit 11, get on Route 14 East, course is approximately 2 miles on right (Merry Avenue).

Norwood Country Club   ✪½   50

400 Providence Highway
Norwood, MA (781) 769-5880
www.norwoodcc.com

Tees	Holes	Yards	Par	USGA	Slope
BACK	18	5630	71	67.1	112
MIDDLE	18	5383	71	65.9	108
FRONT	18	4676	71	68.7	108

Club Pro: John Resnick
Payment: Most Major Credit Cards
Tee Times: 1 week adv.
Fee 9 Holes: Weekday: $19   **Weekend:** $22 after 12pm
Fee 18 Holes: Weekday: $28   **Weekend:** $34 ($28 after 1pm)
Twilight Rates: Yes   **Discounts:** Sr, Jr, military, college
Cart Rental: $16pp/18, $10pp/9   **Driving Range:** Yes
Lessons: $60/hour **Schools:** No   **Junior Golf:** Yes
Membership: Junior   **Architect/Yr Open:** Sam Mitchell/1975
Other: Clubhouse / LockeShowers / Bar-Lounge / Lighted Driving Range

COUPON

A straightaway track. Excellent course for seniors and beginners. Easy to walk. New cart paths in 2012. Rates subject to change. "Good practice facilities." –FP

	1	2	3	4	5	6	7	8	9
PAR	4	4	4	4	5	4	3	3	5
YARDS	344	209	332	365	397	387	144	125	420
	10	**11**	**12**	**13**	**14**	**15**	**16**	**17**	**18**
PAR	4	4	5	3	4	3	4	4	4
YARDS	298	298	477	131	332	115	402	326	342

Directions: I-95/Route 128 to Route 1 South to Norwood. Note: course is on the northbound side of Route 1. To change direction, go to Norwood exit and then go around rotary and head north.

Olde Salem Greens

⚫½ **51** ▶

75 Wilson Street
Salem, MA (978) 744-2149
www.oldesalemgreens.com

Club Pro:
Payment: Cash, Visa, MC, Amex
Tee Times: 6 days adv.

Tees	Holes	Yards	Par	USGA	Slope
BACK	9	3646	35	68.4	116
MIDDLE	9	3028	35	68.5	116
FRONT	9	2483	35	68.4	112

Fee 9 Holes: Weekday: $20 ($17 resident)
Fee 18 Holes: Weekday: $35 ($30 resident)
Twilight Rates: After 5pm
Cart Rental: $15/18, $7.50/9 per person
Lessons: No **Schools:** No
Membership: Passes (please call)
Other: Snack Bar / Bar-Lounge

Weekend: $20 ($18 resident)
Weekend: $36 ($32 resident)
Discounts: Sr. & Jr. (with restrictions)
Driving Range: No
Junior Golf: Yes
Architect/Yr Open: Stiles and Van Kleek/1933
GPS:

COUPON

Residents' rate. New putting green.

	1	2	3	4	5	6	7	8	9
PAR	4	3	4	5	4	4	4	3	4
YARDS	374	253	367	545	345	398	291	153	304
PAR									
YARDS									

Directions: I-95/Route 128 to Route 114 toward Salem. Take Essex Street to Highland Avenue. Take a left on Wilson Street to course.

Olde Scotland Links

⚫⚫⚫ **52** ▶

695 Pine Street
Bridgewater, MA (508) 279-3344
www.oldescotlandlinks.com

Club Pro: Chris Anthony
Payment: Visa, MC, Amex, Disc
Tee Times: 7 days adv., 10 days online

Tees	Holes	Yards	Par	USGA	Slope
BACK	18	6790	72	72.6	126
MIDDLE	18	6306	72	70.3	124
FRONT	18	5396	72	70.9	117

Fee 9 Holes: Weekday: $25
Fee 18 Holes: Weekday: $44
Twilight Rates: Yes
Cart Rental: $16pp/18, $9pp/9
Lessons: Yes **Schools:** Yes
Membership: Weekday Season Pass
Other: Clubhouse

Weekend: $28
Weekend: $53
Discounts: Senior & Junior
Driving Range: Yes
Junior Golf: Yes
Architect/Yr: Cornish, Silva, Mungeam/1997
GPS:

COUPON

Player Comments: "Nice layout." "Beautiful design, affordable." Walkable and enjoyable for all abilities. Open year-round. New clubhouse and function area.

	1	2	3	4	5	6	7	8	9
PAR	4	4	3	4	4	5	4	3	5
YARDS	400	372	154	302	372	519	359	189	456
	10	11	12	13	14	15	16	17	18
PAR	4	4	5	3	4	4	3	4	5
YARDS	435	359	520	205	357	362	130	321	494

Directions: I-95 to Route 24 South to Exit 15. Follow Route 104 East for about ½ mile to first set of lights. Take right onto Old Pleasant Street and follow for 2 miles. Course is on the right.

Ould Newbury Golf Course ○○ ▸ 53

319 Newburyport Turnpike (Route 1)
Newbury, MA (978) 465-9888
www.ouldnewbury.com

Tees	Holes	Yards	Par	USGA	Slope
BACK	9	3115	35	71.8	129
MIDDLE	9	2943	35	69.4	120
FRONT	9	2723	38	71.3	126

Club Pro: James Hilton
Payment: Cash, Disc, MC, Visa
Tee Times: No
Fee 9 Holes: Weekday: $25   **Weekend:**
Fee 18 Holes: Weekday: $38   **Weekend:**
Twilight Rates: No   **Discounts:** None
Cart Rental: $24/18, $15/9 per cart **Driving Range:** No
Lessons: $60/45 min. **Schools:** No **Junior Golf:** No
Membership: Yes   **Architect/Yr Open:** 1916
Other: Clubhouse / Lockers / Showers / Snack Bar

Sig. Hole: #9 is a 207-yard uphill par 3 that requires a shot over a 50-foot hickory tree. Closed to public on weekends.

	1	2	3	4	5	6	7	8	9
PAR	4	5	4	4	4	3	4	4	3
YARDS	394	453	359	401	298	143	373	318	204
PAR									
YARDS									

Directions: I-95 to Exit 55 (Central Street/Byfield-Newbury). Turn East and follow signs to Governor Dummer Academy. At the intersection of Route 1, turn left. Club entrance is 600 yards on the right.

Pembroke Country Club ○○○½ ▸ 54

94 West Elm Street
Pembroke, MA (781) 829-2273
www.pembrokegolf.com

Tees	Holes	Yards	Par	USGA	Slope
BACK	18	6677	71	73.3	132
MIDDLE	18	6329	71	71.8	125
FRONT	18	5343	72	72.2	124

Club Pro: Bill Allen, PGA, Dir. of Instruction
Payment: Visa, MC, Amex, Disc, Cash, Check
Tee Times: 7 days adv.
Fee 9 Holes: Weekday: $35 with cart   **Weekend:** $39 with cart
Fee 18 Holes: Weekday: $57 with cart   **Weekend:** $67 with cart
Twilight Rates: Weekends after 1pm   **Discounts:** Sr. 60+, Jr. -18
Cart Rental: Included   **Driving Range:** Yes
Lessons: Yes **Schools:** Yes   **Junior Golf:** Yes
Membership: Yes   **Architect/Yr Open:** Phil Wogan/1972
Other: Clubhouse / Restaurant / Bar-Lounge

Pembroke Country Club is a championship 18 hole golf course. The secluded par 71 is nestled amongst the tall pines of the South Shore. With narrow fairways and five par fours over 420 yards, it provides challenge for all golfers. "Recent ownership change, greatly improved conditions, outing friendly venue." –SD

	1	2	3	4	5	6	7	8	9
PAR	5	4	3	4	4	4	3	4	4
YARDS	504	323	181	434	402	346	143	420	341
	10	11	12	13	14	15	16	17	18
PAR	4	3	4	5	4	4	4	3	5
YARDS	385	159	428	547	343	371	347	182	473

Directions: Route 3 South. Exit 13 turn right (3.2 miles) on Broadway. Stay left at both forks; course is located 2 miles on right-hand side.

Pinecrest Golf Club

GB
RTE
495

212 Prentice Street
Holliston, MA (508) 429-9871
www.pinecrestgolfclub.org

Club Pro: Andy Froude
Payment: Cash or Credit
Tee Times: Sat, Sun

Tees	Holes	Yards	Par	USGA	Slope
BACK					
MIDDLE	18	4906	66	63.2	103
FRONT	18	4260	66	63.2	103

Fee 9 Holes: Weekday: $17   **Weekend:** $21
Fee 18 Holes: Weekday: $28   **Weekend:** $32
Twilight Rates: After 5pm wkdys, 4pm wknds **Discounts:** Senior & Junior
Cart Rental: $14pp/18, $8pp/9   **Driving Range:** Yes, grass
Lessons: Yes **Schools:** Yes   **Junior Golf:** Yes
Membership: Yes   **Architect/Yr Open:** 1955
Other: Clubhouse / Snack Bar / Bar-Lounge / Restaurant

COUPON

The course is relatively level and easy to walk. Very tight greens that are a true test of one's iron shot accuracy. The par 3s are fairly long. Most golfers are able to play 18 holes in under 4 hours.

	1	2	3	4	5	6	7	8	9
PAR	4	3	4	3	4	3	4	4	4
YARDS	398	165	275	153	325	190	317	305	295
	10	11	12	13	14	15	16	17	18
PAR	3	4	3	5	4	4	4	3	3
YARDS	165	264	205	472	245	405	305	200	222

Directions: I-495 to Route 85 Exit 20 toward Holliston. Follow 3 miles to first flashing yellow light. Take right onto Chestnut Street, look for signs.

Pinehills Golf Club (Jones) ✪✪✪✪✪ 56

54 Clubhouse Drive
Plymouth, MA (508) 209-3000
www.pinehillsgolf.com

Tees	Holes	Yards	Par	USGA	Slope
BACK	18	7175	72	73.8	135
MIDDLE	18	6762	72	72.4	131
FRONT	18	6201	72	69.6	125

Club Pro: John Tuffin, PGA
Payment: Visa, MC, Amex, Checks
Tee Times: 7 days adv.
Fee 18 Holes: Weekday: $100 cart/range balls M-Th
          Weekend: $110 cart/range balls F/S/S/H
Twilight Rates: $60 after 3pm M-Th, $70 after 2pm F/S/S
Discounts: None
Cart Rental: Included   **Driving Range:** Natural Grass
Lessons: Yes **Schools:** Yes   **Junior Golf:** Yes
Membership: Yes   **Architect/Yr Open:** Rees Jones/2001
Other: Clubhouse / Grill / Bar / Banquet Facilities / Lockers / Showers / Restaurant

COUPON

"Excellent layout. Challenging but fair for men or women. Friendliest staff, best service ever encountered." –AP
"Greens slightly easier than Nicklaus, but tougher to get to them. Many dramatic holes." –JD

	1	2	3	4	5	6	7	8	9
PAR	4	4	5	3	4	4	3	4	5
YARDS	348	404	501	177	403	431	165	397	552
	10	11	12	13	14	15	16	17	18
PAR	4	5	4	4	3	5	4	3	4
YARDS	360	548	420	370	219	495	401	169	402

Directions: Route 3 South, Exit 3. Turn left and follow signs.

Pinehills GC (Nicklaus)   ✪✪✪✪✪   57

54 Clubhouse Drive
Plymouth, MA (508) 209-3000
www.pinehillsgolf.com

Tees	Holes	Yards	Par	USGA	Slope
BACK	18	6640	72	71.7	131
MIDDLE	18	6129	72	69.3	125
FRONT	18	5185	72	69.4	123

Club Pro: John Tuffin, PGA
Payment: Visa, MC, Amex, Checks
Tee Times: 7 days adv. (866) 855-4653
Fee 9 Holes: Weekday: **Weekend:**
Fee 18 Holes: Weekday: $100 cart/range balls M-Th
                Weekend: $110 cart/range balls F/S/S/H
Twilight Rates: After 3:30pm   **Discounts:** None
Cart Rental: Included   **Driving Range:** Natural grass/mats
Lessons: Yes **Schools:** Yes   **Junior Golf:** Yes
Membership: No   **Architect/Yr Open:** Jack Nicklaus II/2002
Other: Clubhouse / Grill / Bar / Banquet Facilites / Lockers / Showers / Restaurant / Caddy Program

Player Comments: "Broader fairways than Jones, trickier greens." Great and beautiful design, fine clubhouse, top-flight service. *New England GolfGuide's* first-ever 5-star course.

	1	2	3	4	5	6	7	8	9
PAR	4	5	3	4	4	5	3	4	4
YARDS	357	500	199	365	357	491	145	343	326
	10	11	12	13	14	15	16	17	18
PAR	4	5	4	3	4	3	5	4	4
YARDS	365	486	403	165	280	144	486	344	373

Directions: Route 3 South, Exit 3. Turn left and follow signs.

Pine Meadows Golf Club   ✪✪   58

255 Cedar Street
Lexington, MA (781) 862-5516
www.pinemeadowsgolfclub.com

Tees	Holes	Yards	Par	USGA	Slope
BACK					
MIDDLE	9	2759	35	64.5	110
FRONT	9	2405	35	69.2	117

Club Pro: Joe McKinney
Payment: Cash, Visa, MC
Tee Times: 7 days adv.
Fee 9 Holes: Weekday: $21   **Weekend:** $23
Fee 18 Holes: Weekday: $31   **Weekend:** $33
Twilight Rates: No   **Discounts:** Srs, Jrs., Residents
Cart Rental: $8pp/9   **Driving Range:**
Lessons: Yes **Schools:** No   **Junior Golf:** No
Membership: No   **Architect/Yr Open:**
Other: Snack Bar   **GPS:**

The course has open fairways and is excellent for beginners and intermediate players.

	1	2	3	4	5	6	7	8	9
PAR	5	5	4	3	4	3	4	4	3
YARDS	484	481	241	225	336	201	324	301	166
PAR									
YARDS									

Directions: I-95/Route 128 to Exit 31A. Go through 2 lights, take right onto Hill Street, take right onto Cedar Street.

Pine Oaks Golf Course ✪✪½ 59 ►

68 Prospect Street
S. Easton, MA (508) 238-2320
www.pineoaks.com

Tees	Holes	Yards	Par	USGA	Slope
BACK	9	2973	34	67.0	115
MIDDLE	9	2912	34	67.0	111
FRONT	9	2500	34	67.0	111

Club Pro: Leigh Bader, PGA
Payment: Visa, MC, Amex, Disc
Tee Times: No
Fee 9 Holes: Weekday: $23   **Weekend:** $25
Fee 18 Holes: Weekday: $30   **Weekend:** $36
Twilight Rates: After 4pm   **Discounts:** Senior & Junior M-F
Cart Rental: $13pp/18, $7.50pp/9   **Driving Range:** No
Lessons: Yes **Schools:** Yes   **Junior Golf:** Yes
Membership: Yes   **Architect/Yr Open:** Geoffrey Cornish/1964
Other: Clubhouse / Lockers / Snack Bar / Bar-Lounge / Discount Golf Shop

COUPON

New short game practice area. Plenty of water for a 9-hole course. New bunkers with 5 new tee areas. *Golf Shop Operations* "Top 100 Pro Shop" for the last 10 years. A number of Pros on staff for equipment sales or lessons.

	1	2	3	4	5	6	7	8	9
PAR	4	5	4	3	4	3	3	4	4
YARDS	326	558	407	175	378	245	149	302	372
PAR									
YARDS									

Directions: Route 24 to Exit 16B, straight for 3.5 miles, right on Prospect Street.

Ponkapoag Golf Club (#1) ✪½ 60 ►

2167 Washington Street
Canton, MA (781) 828-4242
www.ponkapoaggolf.com

Tees	Holes	Yards	Par	USGA	Slope
BACK	18	6545	72	72.0	126
MIDDLE	18	6010	72	69.8	120
FRONT	18	5316	74	70.8	115

Club Pro: Michael Fleming, PGA
Payment: Visa, MC, Cash
Tee Times:
Fee 9 Holes: Weekday: $19 M-Th   **Weekend:** $19 F/S/S
Fee 18 Holes: Weekday: $27 M-Th   **Weekend:** $30 F/S/S
Twilight Rates: No   **Discounts:** Sr. & Jr. weekdays
Cart Rental: $17pp/18, $8pp/9   **Driving Range:** $7/bucket
Lessons: Yes **Schools:** Junior   **Junior Golf:** Yes
Membership: Limited, Juniors   **Architect/Yr Open:** Donald Ross
Other: Restaurant / Clubhouse / Beer & Wine / Showers

A great design by Donald Ross suffering from neglect. "Rustic." April -December.

	1	2	3	4	5	6	7	8	9
PAR	4	3	5	4	4	4	4	3	5
YARDS	370	135	490	304	375	412	380	170	425
	10	**11**	**12**	**13**	**14**	**15**	**16**	**17**	**18**
PAR	4	5	3	5	4	4	3	4	4
YARDS	335	440	162	440	344	382	206	345	295

Directions: I-93 to Exit 2A. Go South on Route 138 (Washington Street) into Canton. Clubhouse is on left at first light.

Ponkapoag Golf Club (#2)

✪½ 61

2167 Washington Street
Canton, MA (781) 828-4242
www.ponkapoaggolf.com

Club Pro: Michael Fleming, PGA
Payment: Visa, MC, Cash
Tee Times:
Fee 9 Holes: Weekday: $19 M-Th
Fee 18 Holes: Weekday: $27 M-Th
Twilight Rates: No
Cart Rental: $17pp/18, $8pp/9
Lessons: Yes **Schools:** Junior
Membership: Limited, Juniors
Other: Restaurant / Clubhouse / Beer & Wine / Showers

Tees	Holes	Yards	Par	USGA	Slope
BACK	18	6195	71	70.3	116
MIDDLE	18	5712	71	67.5	112
FRONT	18	5028	72	68.5	113

Weekend: $19 F/S/S
Weekend: $30 F/S/S
Discounts: Senior & Junior
Driving Range: $7/bucket
Junior Golf: Yes
Architect/Yr Open: Donald Ross

A great design suffering from neglect. "Playing here is 'roughing it.' Don't bring new clubs." –RM
Designed by Donald Ross.

	1	2	3	4	5	6	7	8	9
PAR	4	4	3	5	4	4	4	3	4
YARDS	364	407	188	456	249	389	312	150	377
	10	11	12	13	14	15	16	17	18
PAR	5	3	4	5	4	3	4	4	4
YARDS	450	125	315	448	320	160	340	300	362

Directions: I-93 South to Exit 2A. Go South on Route 138 (Washington Street) into Canton. Clubhouse is on left at first light.

Presidents Golf Course

✪✪½ 62

357 West Squantum Street
Quincy, MA (617) 328-3444
www.presidentsgc.com

Club Pro: Dana Smith, PGA
Payment: Visa, MC
Tee Times: 2 days adv. Fri/Sat/Sun
Fee 9 Holes: Weekday:
Fee 18 Holes: Weekday: $38 M-Th
Twilight Rates: After 4pm
Cart Rental: $16pp/18, $16 per cart/9
Lessons: $40/half hour **Schools:** No
Membership: Yes
Other: Clubhouse / Lockers / Showers / Snack Bar / Restaurant / Putting Green / Bar-Lounge

Tees	Holes	Yards	Par	USGA	Slope
BACK	18	5750	70	68.1	125
MIDDLE	18	5260	70	66.2	118
FRONT	18	4425	71	66.8	113

Weekend:
Weekend: $47
Discounts: Senior & Junior (M-Th)
Driving Range: No
Junior Golf: Yes
Architect/Yr Open: Tom & George Fazio/1977

Player Comments: "Home of Norfolk County Classic. Championship tees are true test of your short game. Greens are sloping and fast. You have to have the short stick working well." Incredible views of the Boston skyline, Neponset River and Blue Hill Reservation.

	1	2	3	4	5	6	7	8	9
PAR	4	3	4	3	5	4	3	4	4
YARDS	345	90	270	150	440	415	120	350	330
	10	11	12	13	14	15	16	17	18
PAR	3	4	5	3	4	5	5	4	3
YARDS	150	260	465	165	365	460	480	300	105

Directions: I-93 to Exit 11A (Granite Avenue). Take left at first light (approx. 1 mile). Take left at next light. From I-93 North, take Exit 9 (Adams Street). Go straight approx. 1 mile. Right 1 mile at lights. Left at next light.

Quail Ridge Country Club ✪✪✪½ 63 ▶

354 Great Road
Acton, MA (978) 264-0399
www.quailridgeacton.com

Club Pro: Mark Laviano, PGA
Payment: Visa, MC
Tee Times: 7 days adv.
Fee 9 Holes: Weekday: $25
Fee 18 Holes: Weekday: $34
Twilight Rates: After 4pm
Cart Rental: $15pp/18, $10pp/9
Lessons: Yes **Schools:** No
Membership: Yes
Other: Restaurant / Clubhouse / Showers / Bar-Lounge

Tees	Holes	Yards	Par	USGA	Slope
BACK	9	3068	35		
MIDDLE	9	2882	35		
FRONT	9	2740	35		

Weekend: $25
Weekend: $34
Discounts: Sr & Jr (M-Th anytime)
Driving Range: No
Junior Golf: Yes
Architect/Yr Open: Mark Mungeam/2003

Members play golf on a modern, yet classically designed course. Situated in a forested valley in the town of Acton, Massachusetts, just 30 miles from Boston's hub. The course is bound by conservation land and tree lined fairways. New 9-hole Championship layout. "Excellent challenge—give it a try." –FP

	1	2	3	4	5	6	7	8	9
PAR	4	4	4	3	4	4	5	4	3
YARDS	345	352	380	173	349	320	470	325	178
	10	11	12	13	14	15	16	17	18
PAR	5	4	4	3	4	4	4	4	3
YARDS	541	316	415	154	324	316	308	337	168

Directions: 495 North or South to Route 2 East, Exit 29A. Then take Exit 42, go left onto Route 27, follow to intersection of 2A and 119. Left at light. Quail Ridge is 100 yards on left.

Reedy Meadow GC at Lynnfield ✪ 64 ▶

195 Summer Street
Lynnfield, MA (781) 334-9877
www.town.lynnfield.ma.us/golf

Club Pro: Don Lyons, PGA
Payment:
Tee Times: No
Fee 9 Holes: Weekday: $20
Fee 18 Holes: Weekday: $30
Twilight Rates: $10 after 6pm
Cart Rental: $13pp/18, $8pp/9
Lessons: Yes **Schools:** Yes
Membership: $850/5-day; $950/7-day
Other: Clubhouse / Bar-Lounge / Snack Bar

Tees	Holes	Yards	Par	USGA	Slope
BACK	9	2560	34	63.8	
MIDDLE	9	2485	34	63.0	102
FRONT	9	2240	68	64.8	94

Weekend: $21
Weekend: $31
Discounts: Senior (M-F) & Junior
Driving Range: No
Junior Golf: Yes
Architect/Yr Open:
GPS:

Many cosmetic changes to this course. Great greens. Family and junior friendly.

	1	2	3	4	5	6	7	8	9
PAR	4	4	3	4	5	3	4	4	3
YARDS	350	355	225	260	476	139	270	340	145
PAR									
YARDS									

Directions: I-95/Route 128 to Exit 41; follow to Main Street in Lynnfield Center.

Ridder Golf Club

65 ❂❂

Route 14, Oak Street
Whitman, MA (781) 447-9003
www.ridderfarm.com

Club Pro: Tim Kilcoyne
Payment: Visa, MC
Tee Times: 7 days adv.
Fee 9 Holes: Weekday: $20
Fee 18 Holes: Weekday: $37.50
Twilight Rates: No
Cart Rental: $12.50pp/18, $6.25pp/9
Lessons: $45/half hour **Schools:** Jr.
Membership: Yes, annual fee
Other: Restaurant / Snack Bar / Bar-Lounge

Tees	Holes	Yards	Par	USGA	Slope
BACK	18	5909	70	68.1	113
MIDDLE	18	5857	70	66.3	110
FRONT	18	4981	70	67.1	107

Weekend: $25
Weekend: $47.50
Discounts: Junior
Driving Range: Yes
Junior Golf: Yes
Architect/Yr Open: Hohman & Cornish/1961
GPS:

Junior summer program. New 6th tee. Open March - December. Great walking course. Roomy fairways on front, tighter back 9.

	1	2	3	4	5	6	7	8	9
PAR	4	4	3	4	4	4	4	3	4
YARDS	334	368	154	289	384	299	257	197	387
	10	11	12	13	14	15	16	17	18
PAR	4	5	4	3	4	3	4	5	4
YARDS	312	468	370	166	427	225	385	476	359

Directions: Route 3 to Route 18 South for 9-10 miles. Then Route 14 East for 2.2 miles.

River Bend Country Club

66 ❂❂❂

250 East Center Street
West Bridgewater, MA
(508) 580-3673
www.riverbendcc.com

Club Pro: Lyman J. Doane II, PGA
Payment: Most Major Cards, No Checks
Tee Times: 7 days adv.
Fee 9 Holes: Weekday: $20
Fee 18 Holes: Weekday: $37
Twilight Rates: After 5pm
Cart Rental: $15pp/18, $10pp/9
Lessons: No **Schools:**
Membership: Yes, Inner Club
Other: Bar-Lounge / Snack Bar

Tees	Holes	Yards	Par	USGA	Slope
BACK	18	6312	71	69.9	125
MIDDLE	18	5773	71	67.6	124
FRONT	18	4915	71	67.7	120

Weekend: $24 after 2pm F/S/S
Weekend: $44 F, $48 S/S
Discounts: Sr. & Jr., M-F
Driving Range: No
Junior Golf: No
Architect/Yr Open: Phil Wogan/1997
GPS:

Sig. Hole: #17, 162-yard par 3. "...manicured magnificently, very fair greens." –RW "Great conditions. The greens hold and putt wonderfully." –KR "Key to scoring here is smart course management. Use the driver less." –AG

	1	2	3	4	5	6	7	8	9
PAR	4	5	4	3	4	4	4	3	4
YARDS	330	436	286	113	333	345	337	166	361
	10	11	12	13	14	15	16	17	18
PAR	4	4	4	4	3	4	5	3	5
YARDS	358	326	363	317	171	340	501	162	516

Directions: I-95/Route 128 to Route 24 South. Take Exit 16A onto Route 106 East for 2.5 miles. Course is on the right.

Robert T. Lynch Municipal GC ✪✪½ 67 ▶

1281 West Roxbury Parkway
Brookline, MA (617) 730-2078
www.brooklinegolf.com

Club Pro: Tom Ellis, PGA
Payment: Visa, MC, Amex, Cash
Tee Times: 6 days adv. online
Fee 9 Holes: Weekday: $26
Fee 18 Holes: Weekday: $39
Twilight Rates: After 4pm
Cart Rental: $19pp/18, $14pp/9
Lessons: $45/half hour **Schools:** Junior
Membership: No
Other: Restaurant / Clubhouse / Bar-Lounge

Tees	Holes	Yards	Par	USGA	Slope
BACK	18	6317	71	70.4	124
MIDDLE	18	5958	71	68.4	117
FRONT	18	5615	72	72.5	119

Weekend: $28
Weekend: $41
Discounts: Juniors (25/50 play punch cards)
Driving Range: No
Junior Golf: Yes
Architect/Yr Open: Stiles & Van Kleek/1931
GPS:

Improvements: Tight fairways, elevated greens, low terrain, small hills, and lots of brooks.
Dress code: collared shirts.

	1	2	3	4	5	6	7	8	9
PAR	5	4	3	4	3	5	4	4	4
YARDS	460	335	148	317	177	506	340	390	365
	10	11	12	13	14	15	16	17	18
PAR	4	4	3	4	4	5	4	3	4
YARDS	330	290	119	380	400	520	330	160	391

Directions: I-95 to Route 9 East, 4 miles to Chestnut Hill Mall on left. Exit onto Hammond Street.
Go to rotary; 4th right to Newton Street. 100 yards on left. From Boston: Route 9 to Hammond Street.
Turn left. 1 mile to rotary — 4th right to Newton Street. 100 yards on left.

Rockland Golf Course NR 68 ▶

276 Plain Street
Rockland, MA (781) 878-5836
www.rocklandgolfcourse.com

Club Pro: Charles Lanzetta, Dir. of Golf
Payment: Visa, MC, Disc, Amex
Tee Times: 3 days adv.
Fee 9 Holes: Weekday: $15
Fee 18 Holes: Weekday: $25
Twilight Rates: After 6pm
Cart Rental: $13.65pp/18, $8.50pp/9
Lessons: $40/half hour **Schools:** Yes
Membership: Yes
Other: Clubhouse / Snack Bar / Restaurant / Bar-Lounge

Tees	Holes	Yards	Par	USGA	Slope
BACK	18	3300	54	56.0	78
MIDDLE	18	3014	54	58.0	87
FRONT	18	2100	60	N/A	N/A

Weekend: $15
Weekend: $28; $20 after 2pm
Discounts: Senior/Junior/Military
Driving Range: No
Junior Golf: Yes
Architect/Yr Open: Skip & Phil Wogan/1964

Longest par 3 course in the nation. Tees and greens are in fine shape, but rough areas can balloon your
scores. "Nice course, easy to play, easy to walk."

	1	2	3	4	5	6	7	8	9
PAR	3	3	3	3	3	3	3	3	3
YARDS	212	136	202	137	146	152	171	95	207
	10	11	12	13	14	15	16	17	18
PAR	3	3	3	3	3	3	3	3	3
YARDS	227	202	137	145	162	228	152	132	171

Directions: Route 3 to Exit 16B. Left onto Route 139 for 3 to 4 miles. Course is on right.

Rockport Golf Club

★★★ 69

36 Country Club Road
Rockport, MA (978) 546-3340
www.rockportgolfclub.net

Club Pro: Stephen Clayton, PGA
Payment: Visa, MC, Personal Checks
Tee Times: 1 day adv.
Fee 9 Holes: Weekday: $25
Fee 18 Holes: Weekday: $37
Twilight Rates: No
Cart Rental: $22pp/18, $13pp/9
Lessons: $50/half hour **Schools:** No
Membership: Yes
Other: Pro Shop

Weekend: $25
Weekend: $37
Discounts: No
Driving Range: No
Junior Golf: No
Architect/Yr Open: 1914

Tees	Holes	Yards	Par	USGA	Slope
BACK					
MIDDLE	9	3077	35	69.8	125
FRONT	9	2795	37	72.5	125

Excellent 9-hole course using different tees for 1st and 2nd nines. Easy walking course that provides a good test of golf. Open to the public on weekends after 3:30pm. "Worth the ride to Rockport." –FP

	1	2	3	4	5	6	7	8	9
PAR	3	4	4	5	4	4	3	4	4
YARDS	165	349	353	528	348	430	136	402	368
PAR									
YARDS									

Directions: 128 North to Gloucester, MA. At intersection of Route 127 – turn left towards Rockport. At the 5 corner interesection proceed onto Broadway and turn right at end. Travel ¾ mile to Country Club Road on right.

Rolling Green Golf Course

NR 70

911 Lowell Street
Andover, MA (978) 475-4066
www.rollinggreengolf.biz

Club Pro: Bernie Melanson, Dir. of Golf
Payment: Visa, MC
Tee Times: No
Fee 9 Holes: Weekday: $16
Fee 18 Holes: Weekday: $23
Twilight Rates: No
Cart Rental: $3/9, $6/18 pull cart
Lessons: Yes **Schools:** No
Membership: No
Other: Snack Bar

Weekend: $17
Weekend: $24
Discounts: Senior & Junior
Driving Range: $6/sm, $8/lg bucket
Junior Golf: No
Architect/Yr Open:
GPS:

Tees	Holes	Yards	Par	USGA	Slope
BACK	9	1523	27		
MIDDLE	9	1511	27		
FRONT	9	1339	27		

Now an executive 9-hole course. Brand-new 12-stall driving range. Excellent Junior programs.

	1	2	3	4	5	6	7	8	9
PAR	3	3	3	3	3	3	3	3	3
YARDS	180	195	105	170	240	120	175	170	145
PAR									
YARDS									

Directions: I-93 to Exit 43. Right onto Route 133 East. Take your first left.

Rowley Country Club ✪✪ 71 ▶

235 Dodge Road
Rowley, MA (978) 948-2731
www.rowleycountryclub.com

Tees	Holes	Yards	Par	USGA	Slope
BACK	9	3325	36	71.3	125
MIDDLE	9	3115	36	71.3	125
FRONT	9	2492	36	68.5	122

Club Pro: Paul Nimblett, Tammy White
Payment: Visa, MC, Amex, Disc
Tee Times: 1 week adv.
Fee 9 Holes: Weekday: $19   **Weekend:** $22
Fee 18 Holes: Weekday: $32   **Weekend:** $35
Twilight Rates: No   **Discounts:** Senior & Junior
Cart Rental: $16pp/18, $8pp/9   **Driving Range:** $10/lg, $6/med, $4/sm
Lessons: Yes **Schools:** Yes   **Junior Golf:** Yes
Membership: Yes   **Architect/Yr Open:**
Other: Clubhouse / Restaurant / Bar-Lounge / Short Game School / Parent-Child Lessons

COUPON

Formerly Carriage Pines Golf Club. "Voted best 9-hole course on the North Shore." –JF (PGA)
Nike golf camps. Condition is best ever. Come try us. Yardage below from back tees.

	1	2	3	4	5	6	7	8	9
PAR	4	3	4	5	4	4	3	5	4
YARDS	365	194	353	458	345	336	204	473	346
PAR									
YARDS									

Directions: I-95 to Exit 54A (Rowley/Georgetown). 2 miles to Rowley Country Club sign and make left. Follow for 1 mile, club is on right.

Sagamore Spring Golf Club ✪✪ 72 ▶

1287 Main Street
Lynnfield, MA (781) 334-3151
www.sagamoregolf.com

Tees	Holes	Yards	Par	USGA	Slope
BACK	18	5936	70	68.9	124
MIDDLE	18	5505	70	66.8	118
FRONT	18	4784	70	67.7	115

Club Pro: Steven Vaughn, PGA
Payment: Cash, Credit Cards
Tee Times: 4 days adv.
Fee 9 Holes: Weekday: $24, $34w/cart   **Weekend:** $26, $36 w/cart
Fee 18 Holes: Weekday: $42, $58w/cart   **Weekend:** $48, $64 w/cart
Twilight Rates: After 3pm weekends   **Discounts:** Sr., Jrs. play your age
Cart Rental: $16pp/18, $10pp/9   **Driving Range:** $8/xl, $5/lg bucket
Lessons: $50/half hour **Schools:** No   **Junior Golf:** Yes - pay their age
Membership: No   **Architect/Yr Open:** Richard Luff/1929
Other: Clubhouse / Showers / Bar-Lounge

COUPON

150 acre picturesque 18-hole facility 20 minutes from Boston with the feel of Maine or New Hampshire. Signature hole #9, 210 yard, par 3 over water.

	1	2	3	4	5	6	7	8	9
PAR	5	4	5	4	4	3	4	3	3
YARDS	465	344	473	364	276	146	336	179	198
	10	**11**	**12**	**13**	**14**	**15**	**16**	**17**	**18**
PAR	4	5	5	4	3	4	4	3	3
YARDS	247	499	431	398	137	330	317	185	180

Directions: Exit 41 off I-95/Route 128. Bear right off exit, 3 miles on Main Street. Clubhouse on right.

Sandy Burr Country Club ✪✪½ 73

103 Cochituate Road
Wayland, MA (508) 358-7211
www.sandyburr.com

Club Pro: Brian Golden
Payment: Most Major Credit Cards
Tee Times: 5 days adv. (members 7 days adv.)
Fee 9 Holes: Weekday: $30
Fee 18 Holes: Weekday: $50
Twilight Rates: After 2pm
Cart Rental: $20pp/18, $11pp/9
Lessons: $50/half hour **Schools:** No
Membership: Yes
Other: Clubhouse / Restaurant / Bar-Lounge

Tees	Holes	Yards	Par	USGA	Slope
BACK	18	6427	72	71.9	126
MIDDLE	18	6042	72	68.9	122
FRONT	18	4578	69	66.9	110

Weekend: $35
Weekend: $60
Discounts: Sr. & Jr. (+60, -16) $30, $45 w/cart
Driving Range: No
Junior Golf: No
Architect/Yr Open: Donald Ross/1922

Player Comments: "A great Donald Ross course with a good mix of holes. Good to very good shape—depending on the month." Early bird and midday 9-hole rate. Twilight rates.

	1	2	3	4	5	6	7	8	9
PAR	5	5	3	4	3	4	4	4	4
YARDS	462	497	125	423	193	399	323	354	272
	10	11	12	13	14	15	16	17	18
PAR	3	5	4	3	4	4	4	5	4
YARDS	131	437	319	161	340	345	335	513	363

Directions: I-95/Route 128 to Route 20 West exit, at Wayland Center take left onto Route 27 South. Course is ¼ mile on right.

Sassamon Trace Golf Course ✪✪½ 74

233 South Main Street
Natick, MA (508) 655-1330
www.sassamontrace.com

Club Pro: Pete Meagher, PGA
Payment: Visa, MC, Amex, Cash
Tee Times: 7 days adv.
Fee 9 Holes: Weekday: $20
Fee 18 Holes: Weekday: $32
Twilight Rates: Yes
Cart Rental: $16pp/18, $8pp/9
Lessons: No **Schools:** No
Membership: Yes
Other: Restaurant / Clubhouse

Tees	Holes	Yards	Par	USGA	Slope
BACK	9	2383	32	31.7	111
MIDDLE	9	2167	32	30.9	107
FRONT	9	1744	32	29.8	96

Weekend: $22
Weekend: $36
Discounts: Sr. & Jr. (weekdays)
Driving Range: No
Junior Golf: Yes
Architect/Yr: Cornish, Silva, and Mungeam/2001
GPS:

COUPON

MetroWest's most unique 9-hole layout. Expansive greens place a premium on putting. A blend of links and traditonal styles.

	1	2	3	4	5	6	7	8	9
PAR	3	4	3	5	3	4	3	3	4
YARDS	158	326	180	529	162	341	177	143	367
PAR									
YARDS									

Directions: I-95/Route 128, to Exit 20 (Route 9 West) and follow for 6.5 miles to Route 27 South. Course is 3 miles south on Route 27 on right.

Scituate Country Club ✪✪✪ 75 ►

91 Driftway
Scituate, MA (781) 545-9768
www.scituatecc.com

Tees	Holes	Yards	Par	USGA	Slope
BACK	9	3077	35		
MIDDLE	9	2974	35	70.0	128
FRONT	9	2564	36	71.2	125

Club Pro: Jim Dee, PGA
Payment: Cash, Credit Cards
Tee Times: 1 week adv.
Fee 9 Holes: Weekday: $28 after 11am Mon **Weekend:** No public play
Fee 18 Holes: Weekday: $38 after 11am Mon **Weekend:** No public play
Twilight Rates: No   **Discounts:** None
Cart Rental: $16pp/18, $10pp/9   **Driving Range:** No
Lessons: $30/half hour **Schools:** No   **Junior Golf:** Yes (members only)
Membership: Yes   **Architect/Yr Open:** Wayne Stiles/1919
Other: Restaurant / Clubhouse / Bar-Lounge / Showers / Lockers / Snack Bar

Open to the public on Mondays only after 11am. Beautifully maintained seaside golf links with rolling terrain. Great shape. Open April - November.

	1	2	3	4	5	6	7	8	9
PAR	4	3	5	4	4	4	4	3	4
YARDS	407	156	504	373	308	359	357	124	386
PAR									
YARDS									

Directions: Route 3 South to Exit 13. Go left off exit. Go to first set of lights, take right onto Route 123. 4 miles to roundabout, go towards Scituate Harbor. Go 1 mile, turn right on Driftway. Club on right.

Shining Rock Golf Club ✪✪✪✪ 76 ►

94 Clubhouse Lane
Northbridge, MA (508) 234-0400
www.shiningrock.com

Tees	Holes	Yards	Par	USGA	Slope
BACK	18	6683	72	72.9	135
MIDDLE	18	6486	72	71.7	133
FRONT	18	5599	72	70.2	126

Club Pro: Lee Danielian
Payment: Visa, MC, Amex
Tee Times: 7 days adv.
Fee 9 Holes: Weekday: $35   **Weekend:** $41
Fee 18 Holes: Weekday: $53   **Weekend:** $64
Twilight Rates: No   **Discounts:** Senior & Junior
Cart Rental: $17pp/18, $11pp/9   **Driving Range:** No
Lessons: Yes **Schools:** No   **Junior Golf:** No
Membership: Yes   **Architect/Yr Open:** 2010
Other: Restaurant

A challenging picturesque course with views of Blackstone Valley. Hole #4 will challenge golfers—referred to as "The Rock"—it has a 200 yard carry over a ravine. "Great new course. Fun, fat, and challenging greens." –FP

	1	2	3	4	5	6	7	8	9
PAR	4	4	5	4	3	4	4	3	5
YARDS	411	396	508	328	239	300	315	200	495
	10	11	12	13	14	15	16	17	18
PAR	4	4	3	5	4	3	5	4	4
YARDS	370	372	213	502	335	190	620	302	390

Directions: Take Exit 21B off of Route 495. Follow for 4 miles to set of lights in Upton Center. Take a right onto Route 140 and an immediate left onto Hartford Street. Golf course is 1 mile up on the right.

South Shore Country Club

274 South Street
Hingham, MA (781) 749-8479
www.southshorecc.com

Club Pro: Joe Keefe, PGA
Payment: Visa, MC, Cash, Check
Tee Times: 7 days adv.

Tees	Holes	Yards	Par	USGA	Slope
BACK	18	6444	72	71.0	128
MIDDLE	18	6197	72	69.9	124
FRONT	18	5064	72	69.3	116

Fee 9 Holes: Weekday: $30 M-Th $36 F
Fee 18 Holes: Weekday: $42 M-Th $47 F
Twilight Rates: After 5pm
Cart Rental: $16pp/18, $9pp/9
Lessons: Call for details **Schools:** Yes, Jr.
Membership: Currently a waiting list
Other: Snack Bar / Restaurant / Bar-Lounge / Clubhouse / Lockers / Showers

Weekend:
Weekend: $47 after 11am
Discounts: Sr. & Jr. weekdays
Driving Range: Yes
Junior Golf: Yes
Architect/Yr Open: Stiles & Van Kleek/1922

Gets more enjoyable with every replay. Classic design. Course in excellent condition.

	1	2	3	4	5	6	7	8	9
PAR	4	3	5	4	4	4	4	3	5
YARDS	277	156	521	319	371	410	360	197	502
	10	11	12	13	14	15	16	17	18
PAR	4	3	4	4	4	5	4	3	5
YARDS	295	179	372	401	327	530	380	148	452

Directions: Route 3 to Exit 14 onto Route 228 North. At 4-mile mark, exit Route 228 and continue straight onto Central Street. At 2nd 4-way stop, turn left onto South Street. Go ½ mile, club is on left.

Southers Marsh Golf Club

30 Southers Marsh Lane
Plymouth, MA (508) 830-3535
www.southersmarsh.com

Club Pro: Jocko Tavares
Payment: Visa, MC, Amex, Disc, No Checks
Tee Times: 7 days adv.

Tees	Holes	Yards	Par	USGA	Slope
BACK	18	4111	61.0	61.8	112
MIDDLE	18	3694	61	60.4	109
FRONT	18	2907	61	58.2	93

Fee 9 Holes: Weekday:
Fee 18 Holes: Weekday: $30 M-Th
Twilight Rates: After 3pm
Cart Rental: $12pp/18
Lessons: $30/half hour **Schools:** No
Membership: Yes
Other: Clubhouse / Bar-Lounge

Weekend:
Weekend: $37 F/S/S
Discounts: Sr. (M-Th) & Jr. (7 days)
Driving Range: Yes
Junior Golf:
Architect/Yr Open: Dahn Tibbett/2001
GPS:

COUPON

The golf, course conditions, and service of a resort course without the corporate feel, time commitment or expense.

	1	2	3	4	5	6	7	8	9
PAR	4	3	3	4	3	4	3	4	3
YARDS	300	139	175	353	138	285	129	263	158
	10	11	12	13	14	15	16	17	18
PAR	3	3	3	4	3	4	3	3	4
YARDS	123	121	97	304	121	314	157	165	352

Directions: Route 3 to Exit 6B (or 6 and turn left at bottom of ramp from the South) toward Carver. At second light, turn left onto Pilgrim Hill Road. Turn right at light onto Federal Furnace Road. After 4 miles, SMGC on left. Also minutes from Exit 2 off Route 495.

Squirrel Run Golf Course ✪✪ 79 ▶

32 Elderberry Drive
Plymouth, MA (508) 746-5001
www.golfatsquirrelrun.com

Club Pro: David Moore, PGA
Payment: Visa, MC
Tee Times: 7 days adv.
Fee 9 Holes: Weekday: $15
Fee 18 Holes: Weekday: $27
Twilight Rates: After 4pm
Cart Rental: $22/18 per cart
Lessons: Yes **Schools:** No
Membership: Yes
Other: Restaurant / Clubhouse / Bar-Lounge / Snack Bar

Tees	Holes	Yards	Par	USGA	Slope
BACK	18	2859	57	55.4	85
MIDDLE	18	2338	57	53.7	82
FRONT	18	1990	57	56.0	83

Weekend: No
Weekend: $30
Discounts: Senior & Junior
Driving Range: No
Junior Golf: Yes
Architect/Yr Open: Ray Richard/1991

COUPON

Player Comments: "A challenge to anyone's short game." "Immaculate greens and tees." Sister course: Village Links. Winner of the 2006 Plymouth Golden Sprinkler Award for Service & Condition.

	1	2	3	4	5	6	7	8	9
PAR	4	3	3	3	4	3	3	3	4
YARDS	286	105	125	90	263	98	131	123	206
	10	11	12	13	14	15	16	17	18
PAR	3	3	3	3	3	3	3	3	3
YARDS	99	78	102	102	140	100	116	74	100

Directions: Route 3 to Exit 6. Go approximately 2 miles to course on left. Look for Squirrel Run sign.

Stoneham Oaks NR 80 ▶

101 R Montvale Avenue
Stoneham, MA (781) 438-7888
www.stoneham-ma.gov

Club Pro: Kent Pratt, PGA
Payment: Cash Only
Tee Times: No
Fee 9 Holes: Weekday: $10 after 2pm
Fee 18 Holes: Weekday: $20 after 2pm
Twilight Rates: No
Cart Rental: $13/9 per cart, $2/pull
Lessons: $40/half hour **Schools:** No
Membership: No
Other:

Tees	Holes	Yards	Par	USGA	Slope
BACK					
MIDDLE	9	1125	27	N/A	N/A
FRONT					

Weekend: $16
Weekend: $27
Discounts: Senior & Junior
Driving Range: No
Junior Golf: No
Architect/Yr Open:
GPS:

Very hilly, many trees. Very scenic. Various reduced weekday rates between 7am and 2pm.

	1	2	3	4	5	6	7	8	9
PAR	3	3	3	3	3	3	3	3	3
YARDS	89	147	179	128	95	113	153	139	82
PAR									
YARDS									

Directions: I-93 to Exit 36, Stoneham, Montvale Avenue, 1 block. Course is at rear of the Stoneham Ice Rink.

Stony Brook Golf Course

NR   81 ▶

70 Valley Road
Southboro, MA (508) 485-3151
www.stonybrookgolfcourse.com

Club Pro:
Payment: Visa, MC
Tee Times: Yes
Fee 9 Holes: Weekday: $14
Fee 18 Holes: Weekday: $18
Twilight Rates: After 5pm
Cart Rental: $3/pull
Lessons: No **Schools:** No
Membership: Yes
Other: Snack Bar / Accessories / Kids' Camps

Tees	Holes	Yards	Par	USGA	Slope
BACK					
MIDDLE	9	1342	27		
FRONT					

Weekend: $14
Weekend:
Discounts: $12 Senior & Junior
Driving Range: No
Junior Golf: No
Architect/Yr Open: Ernest Kallender/1970
GPS:

COUPON

Player Comments: "No-frills course, but always improving. Plays fair. Greens are beautiful, honest but must be read right. Need accurate iron play." Good for beginners and experienced golfers.

	1	2	3	4	5	6	7	8	9
PAR	3	3	3	3	3	3	3	3	3
YARDS	145	138	210	125	132	165	169	107	151
PAR									
YARDS									

Directions: Accessible from Routes I-90, I-495, and Route 9. Located in Southboro off Route 30 on Valley Road.

Stow Acres CC (North)

✪✪½   82 ▶

58 Randall Road
Stow, MA (978) 568-1100
www.stowacres.com

Club Pro: Dave Carlson, PGA
Payment: Visa, MC, Amex, Discover, Cash
Tee Times: 10 days adv.
Fee 9 Holes: Weekday: $30 M-Th
Fee 18 Holes: Weekday: $50 M-Th
Twilight Rates: After 6pm
Cart Rental: $18.25pp/18, $9pp/9
Lessons: Yes **Schools:** Yes
Membership: Gold Card membership
Other: Clubhouse / Showers-Men Only / Snack Bar / Bar-Lounge

Tees	Holes	Yards	Par	USGA	Slope
BACK	18	6939	72	72.8	130
MIDDLE	18	6310	72	70.5	127
FRONT	18	6011	72	72.5	130

Weekend: $40 F/S/S
Weekend: $66 F/S/S
Discounts: Senior & Junior weekdays
Driving Range: $9/lg, $7/med, $5/sm bucket
Junior Golf: Yes
Architect/Yr Open: Geoffrey Cornish/1972

Player Comments: "Sensational greens." PGA Tour Qualifier site. Championship layout. Black tees added. Open mid-March to mid-December. Season passes and family passes.

	1	2	3	4	5	6	7	8	9
PAR	5	4	4	4	5	3	4	3	4
YARDS	503	374	354	387	472	180	318	165	426
	10	**11**	**12**	**13**	**14**	**15**	**16**	**17**	**18**
PAR	4	4	5	3	4	4	3	4	5
YARDS	359	392	424	169	340	369	166	376	536

Directions: I-95/Route 128 to Route 20/117 Exit. Go west on Route 117 approximately 15 miles; left in Stow Center onto Route 62 West, follow signs from Route 62 to course.

Stow Acres CC (South) ✪✪½ 83 ▶

58 Randall Road
Stow, MA (978) 568-1100
www.stowacres.com

Club Pro: Dave Carlson, PGA
Payment: Visa, MC, Amex, Discover, Cash
Tee Times: 10 days adv.
Fee 9 Holes: Weekday: $28
Fee 18 Holes: Weekday: $40
Twilight Rates: After 6pm
Cart Rental: $18.25pp/18, $9pp/9
Lessons: $80/hour **Schools:** Yes
Membership: Yes
Other: Clubhouse / Snack Bar / Bar-Lounge

Tees	Holes	Yards	Par	USGA	Slope
BACK	18	6520	72	71.8	120
MIDDLE	18	6105	72	70.5	118
FRONT	18	5642	72	72.5	120

Weekend: $35
Weekend: $55
Discounts: Senior & Junior weekdays
Driving Range: $9/lg, $7/med, $5/sm bucket
Junior Golf: Yes
Architect/Yr Open: Geoffrey Cornish/1965
GPS:

Player Comments: "Sensational greens." Variety of instructional packages. Variety of inner clubs. New cart paths. Course conditions improved. Prices subject to change. Season passes and family passes.

	1	2	3	4	5	6	7	8	9
PAR	4	4	3	4	5	5	3	4	4
YARDS	375	416	123	301	476	487	212	346	368
	10	11	12	13	14	15	16	17	18
PAR	5	3	4	4	5	3	4	3	5
YARDS	543	127	366	292	441	151	407	167	507

Directions: Route I-95/128 to Route 20/117 Exit. Go west on Route 117 approximately 15 miles; left in Stow Center onto Route 62 West, follow signs from Route 62 to course.

Strawberry Valley Golf Course NR 84 ▶

164 Washington Street
Abington, MA (781) 347-4877
www.calmgolf.com

Club Pro: Tony Morosco
Payment: Visa, MC, Amex, Disc
Tee Times: 7 days adv.
Fee 9 Holes: Weekday: $17
Fee 18 Holes: Weekday: $28
Twilight Rates: $14 after 6pm weekdays
$14 after 4pm weekends
Cart Rental: $12.50pp/18, $8.50pp/9
Lessons: Yes **Schools:** Yes
Membership: Yes
Other: Snack Bar

Tees	Holes	Yards	Par	USGA	Slope
BACK	9	2578	35		
MIDDLE	9	2280	34	66.9	99
FRONT	9	2217	34		

Weekend: $17
Weekend: $30
Discounts: Senior $15, Junior $14

Driving Range: No
Junior Golf: Yes
Architect/Yr Open:
GPS:

Player-friendly. Features senior, junior and beginner play. New management. Open year round. New irrigation systems.

	1	2	3	4	5	6	7	8	9
PAR	4	4	4/5	4	4	3	3	4	4
YARDS	228	357	475	234	240	119	148	295	306
PAR									
YARDS									

Directions: Route 3 to Route 18 South. Course is approximately 7 miles on right.

Swanson Meadows

★★ ▶ 85

216 Rangeway Road
North Billerica, MA (978) 670-7777
www.swansonmeadows.com

Club Pro: Angelo Scippa, Manager
Payment: All Major Credit Cards
Tee Times: 7 days adv.
Fee 9 Holes: Weekday: $19
Fee 18 Holes: Weekday: $38
Twilight Rates: After 5pm
Cart Rental: $14/9 per cart
Lessons: Schools: No
Membership: Yes, Season Passes
Other: Restaurant / Lounge

Tees	Holes	Yards	Par	USGA	Slope
BACK					
MIDDLE	9	2180	32		
FRONT	9	1829	32		

Weekend: $23
Weekend: $46
Discounts: Senior
Driving Range: No
Junior Golf:
Architect/Yr: Cornish, Silva, Mungeam/2001
GPS:

Player Comments: "Quick hike after work." "Layout squeezed onto a moderate space." –RW
New clubhouse, restaurant, and lounge.

	1	2	3	4	5	6	7	8	9
PAR	4	4	4	3	3	4	3	3	4
YARDS	360	286	345	163	119	296	121	146	344
PAR									
YARDS									

Directions: Route 3 to Exit 29. Take Route 129 East. Off ramp, go 1 mile, take right on to Rangeway Road. Course is 1 mile on left.

Tewksbury Country Club

★★ ▶ 86

1880 Main Street
Tewksbury, MA (978) 640-0033
www.tewksburycc.com

Club Pro: Mike Rogers, PGA
Payment: Visa, MC, Amex, Disc, Checks
Tee Times: F/S/S (978-640-0033 x14)
Fee 9 Holes: Weekday: $21
Fee 18 Holes: Weekday: $36
Twilight Rates: After 3pm S/S
Cart Rental: $16pp/18, $10pp/9
Lessons: Yes **Schools:** Junior
Membership: Yes
Other: Clubhouse / Restaurant

Tees	Holes	Yards	Par	USGA	Slope
BACK	9	2632	33	32.8	116
MIDDLE	9	2393	33	31.8	110
FRONT	9	1937	33	31.0	110

Weekend: $24
Weekend: $40
Discounts: Senior & Junior
Driving Range: No
Junior Golf: Yes
Architect/Yr Open: Frank Stasio/1998
GPS:

Impeccably manicured golf course. A challenge for all ability levels. Beautiful stone walls and fountains. Post and beam clubhouse.

	1	2	3	4	5	6	7	8	9
PAR	4	3	3	4	4	5	4	3	3
YARDS	369	182	165	402	377	477	334	178	150
PAR									
YARDS									

Directions: I-93 to Exit 42 (Dascomb Road) toward Tewksbury. Turn left onto Shawsheen Street. Follow Shawsheen to Route 38. Turn right onto Livingston Street. From Route 128, take Route 38 North to Livingston Street.

Trull Brook Golf Course ✪✪✪

170 River Road
Tewksbury, MA (978) 851-6731
www.trullbrook.com

Tees	Holes	Yards	Par	USGA	Slope
BACK	18	6345	72	69.8	123
MIDDLE	18	6006	72	68.8	122
FRONT	18	5193	72	69.6	118

Club Pro: Sheldon Alman, Manager
Payment: Visa, MC, Amex, Disc
Tee Times: 1 week adv.
Fee 9 Holes: Weekday: $22.50 M-F pm   **Weekend:** $25
Fee 18 Holes: Weekday: $42 M-Th   **Weekend:** $50
Twilight Rates: After 5pm
Discounts: Sr. & Jr. (M-Th); Clergy: $16.50; Junior under 17 accompanied with adult: $31.50/18
Cart Rental: $15/18, $7.75/9 per cart   **Driving Range:** No
Lessons: Yes **Schools:** No   **Junior Golf:** Yes
Membership: No   **Architect/Yr Open:** Geoffrey Cornish/1962
Other: Clubhouse / Lockers / Showers / Snack Bar / Bar-Lounge / Winter Tennis Center

Player Comments: "Very well kept. Nice greens." "Challenging course. Scenic." Geoffrey Cornish design. Dress code. Open dawn to dusk.

	1	2	3	4	5	6	7	8	9
PAR	4	5	4	3	4	3	5	4	4
YARDS	338	498	383	123	368	138	470	353	384
	10	**11**	**12**	**13**	**14**	**15**	**16**	**17**	**18**
PAR	4	3	5	4	4	3	4	5	4
YARDS	323	168	463	323	343	178	373	458	323

Directions: From I-495 or I-93, take Route 133 exit, follow West toward Lowell. At Mobil station, sharp right onto River Road. Course is ⅓ mile on left.

Unicorn Golf Course ✪✪

460 William Street
Stoneham, MA (781) 438-9732
www.stoneham-ma.gov

Tees	Holes	Yards	Par	USGA	Slope
BACK	9	3234	35	70.8	126
MIDDLE	9	3185	35	69.6	121
FRONT	9	2902	37	73.0	124

Club Pro: Carl Marchio
Payment: Cash Only
Tee Times: No
Fee 9 Holes: Weekday: $19   **Weekend:** $20
Fee 18 Holes: Weekday: No   **Weekend:** No
Twilight Rates: No   **Discounts:** Senior & Junior (M-F), Resident
Cart Rental: $13/9 per cart   **Driving Range:** No
Lessons: Yes **Schools:** No   **Junior Golf:** No
Membership: No   **Architect/Yr Open:** Stiles & Van Kleek/1928
Other: Snack Bar   **GPS:**

Stoneham resident rates. The course is relatively level; easy walk. Nice par 3s, and #7 and #9 are great holes.

	1	2	3	4	5	6	7	8	9
PAR	4	4	4	3	4	5	4	3	4
YARDS	389	326	335	168	395	499	448	178	447
PAR									
YARDS									

Directions: I-93 to Montvale Avenue. Follow to end. Take left onto Route 28, then left at next set of lights (Williams Street). Course is ¼ mile on left.

Village Links

●● 89 ▶

265 South Meadow Road
Plymouth, MA (508) 830-4653
www.golfatvillagelinks.com

Club Pro: David L. Moore, PGA
Payment: Visa, MC
Tee Times: 7 days adv.
Fee 9 Holes: Weekday:
Fee 18 Holes: Weekday: $25
Twilight Rates: Yes
Cart Rental: $16pp/18
Lessons: $40/half hour **Schools:** Yes
Membership:
Other: Restaurant / Clubhouse / Bar-Lounge

Tees	Holes	Yards	Par	USGA	Slope
BACK					
MIDDLE	18	2407	54		
FRONT	18	1986	54	52.8	78

Weekend:
Weekend: $27
Discounts: Senior & Junior
Driving Range:
Junior Golf: Yes
Architect/Yr Open: Ray Richard/2000
GPS:

COUPON

18-hole par 3, executive-style. Associated with Pinehurst Village. Sister course to Squirrel Run. "Excellent holes include #4, 5, 8, 11, 15, 17." –AP

	1	2	3	4	5	6	7	8	9
PAR	3	3	3	3	3	3	3	3	3
YARDS	134	141	159	57	114	124	113	60	76
	10	11	12	13	14	15	16	17	18
PAR	3	3	3	3	3	3	3	3	3
YARDS	133	112	130	84	79	96	136	74	164

Directions: Route 3 to Exit 6 West (Route 44). Turn left at the 3rd set of lights onto Seven Hills Road. Turn right at the 1st set of lights onto South Meadow Road. Village Links is 2.5 miles on the right.

Waverly Oaks - Challenger 9

●● 90 ▶

444 Long Pond Road
Plymouth, MA (508) 224-6016
www.waverlyoaksgc.com

Club Pro: John Sheehan
Payment: Most Major Credit Cards
Tee Times: Not needed
Fee 9 Holes: Weekday: $25 w/cart
Fee 18 Holes: Weekday:
Twilight Rates: No
Cart Rental: Included
Lessons: Yes **Schools:** Yes
Membership: No
Other:

Tees	Holes	Yards	Par	USGA	Slope
BACK	9	2268	33		
MIDDLE	9	2005	33		
FRONT	9	1659	33		

Weekend: $32.50 w/cart F/S/S
Weekend:
Discounts: Junior
Driving Range: $5/bucket
Junior Golf: Yes
Architect/Yr Open: Brian Silva/1998
GPS:

Player Comments: "Pure fun! A great opening hole. Several par 4s reachable from tee." 3 sets of tees. First come, first serve. Executive course layout for golfers of all levels. Play Pass packs available.

	1	2	3	4	5	6	7	8	9
PAR	4	4	4	3	4	4	4	3	3
YARDS	298	298	199	103	334	259	255	159	94
PAR									
YARDS									

Directions: Take Route 3 to Exit 3, follow signs.

Waverly Oaks Golf Club ✪✪✪✪½ 91 ▶

444 Long Pond Road
Plymouth, MA (508) 224-6700
www.waverlyoaksgc.com

Tees	Holes	Yards	Par	USGA	Slope
BACK	18	7114	72	68.5	118
MIDDLE	18	6682	72	65.9	113
FRONT	18	5587	72	63.6	108

Club Pro: John Sheehan
Payment: Visa, MC, Amex, Disc
Tee Times: 7 days adv.
Fee 9 Holes: Weekday: $40 w/cart
Fee 18 Holes: Weekday: $75 w/cart
Twilight Rates: Weekend $60 after 2pm
Cart Rental: Included
Lessons: $35/half hour **Schools:** No
Membership: Season Pass

Weekend: $50 w/cart (F/S/S)
Weekend: $95 w/cart (F/S/S)
Discounts: Jr/Sr weekday only
Driving Range: $5/bucket
Junior Golf: Yes
Architect/Yr Open: Brian Silva/1998

 COUPON

Other: Full Restaurant / Clubhouse / Bar-Lounge / Showers / Corporate Outings / Small Group Outings / All Rates Include Range Balls

Player Comments: "Best course all round I've played. Not a blemish. Money well worth it." "A gem." –RW
Improvements at 17th hole. Tee times can be made online at www.waverlyoaksgolfclub.com.

	1	2	3	4	5	6	7	8	9
PAR	4	4	3	5	5	4	4	3	4
YARDS	325	394	191	502	515	432	410	184	353
	10	11	12	13	14	15	16	17	18
PAR	4	4	4	5	3	4	5	3	4
YARDS	386	372	311	512	163	449	606	221	356

Directions: Route 3 to Exit 3. Right off ramp. Right at first stop sign. Entrance is 2 miles on right.

Wayland Country Club ✪✪ 92 ▶

121 Old Sudbury Road
Wayland, MA (508) 358-4775
www.waylandcc.com

Tees	Holes	Yards	Par	USGA	Slope
BACK	18	5974	70	67.9	114
MIDDLE	18	5836	70	68.2	112
FRONT	18	4875	71	68.2	111

Club Pro: John Gordon, PGA
Payment: Credit Cards, Cash
Tee Times: Call Monday for weekends
Fee 9 Holes: Weekday: $25
Fee 18 Holes: Weekday: $37
Twilight Rates: After 6pm
Cart Rental: $16pp/18, $10pp/9
Lessons: $40-$80/hour **Schools:** Yes
Membership: Yes

Weekend: $28
Weekend: $47 ($28 after 2pm)
Discounts: Senior & Junior
Driving Range: No
Junior Golf: Yes
Architect/Yr Open: Mitchell/1920s

Other: Restaurant / Clubhouse / Snack Bar / Bar-Lounge
GPS: No

Course is fairly flat with small greens and alternating wide and narrow fairways. Easy to walk. Great staff.

	1	2	3	4	5	6	7	8	9
PAR	5	4	4	3	4	3	4	3	4
YARDS	443	412	384	139	353	188	260	153	405
	10	11	12	13	14	15	16	17	18
PAR	4	4	5	4	3	4	4	3	5
YARDS	320	326	500	346	174	378	400	198	457

Directions: I-95/Route 128 to Route 20 West; right onto Route 27 North; approximately 1 mile on right.

Weathervane Golf Club

New ▶ **93**

14 Sandtrap Circle
Weymouth, MA (781) 335-1500
www.weathervanegolf.com

Tees	Holes	Yards	Par	USGA	Slope
BACK	9	3117	36	69.4	125
MIDDLE	9	2830	36	65.8	121
FRONT	9	2525	36	63.4	117

Club Pro: Richard O'Brian, Dir. of Golf
Payment: Visa, MC, Disc, Personal Checks
Tee Times: 7 days adv.
Fee 9 Holes: Weekday: $25   **Weekend:** $30
Fee 18 Holes: Weekday: $40   **Weekend:** $50
Twilight Rates: No   **Discounts:** Junior
Cart Rental: $15pp/18, $10pp/9   **Driving Range:** Yes
Lessons: Yes **Schools:** Yes   **Junior Golf:** Yes
Membership: Yes   **Architect/Yr Open:** Cornish, Silva, Mungeam/2010
Other:

Weathervane provides an enjoyable experience for golfers at all levels. The natural terrain provides many unique challenges. The sand traps are filled with pristine white sand and the island green on the finishing hole can make or break your round.

	1	2	3	4	5	6	7	8	9
PAR	4	3	4	3	5	4	4	5	4
YARDS	260	130	320	160	480	320	390	510	260
	10	11	12	13	14	15	16	17	18
PAR	4	4	4	5	3	4	5	3	4
YARDS	386	372	311	512	163	449	606	221	356

Directions: South on Route 93 to Route 3 South to Exit 16 B (Route 18). Travel 1 mile to South Shore Hospital and take a left at the lights to Columbian Square. Go straight through the intersection to Union Street. Weathvane Drive is 1 mile on left. Take a right on Sandtrap Circle.

Wenham Country Club

✪✪½ ▶ **94**

94 Main Street
Wenham, MA (978) 468-4714
www.wenhamcountryclub.com

Tees	Holes	Yards	Par	USGA	Slope
BACK					
MIDDLE	18	4554	65	63.3	118
FRONT	18	4321	67	65.3	111

Club Pro: Darin Chin-Aleong, PGA
Payment: Cash, Visa, MC
Tee Times: Take out 1 day advance (wknds)
Fee 9 Holes: Weekday: $23   **Weekend:** $27 (after 12pm)
Fee 18 Holes: Weekday: $36   **Weekend:** $40 (after 12pm)   *COUPON*
Twilight Rates: 3 hours before sundown   **Discounts:** None
Cart Rental: $15pp/18, $9pp/9   **Driving Range:** No
Lessons: Yes **Schools:** No   **Junior Golf:** Yes
Membership: Yes   **Architect/Yr Open:** 1899
Other: Clubhouse   **GPS:**

Tee boxes are renovated. This par 65 course offers a challenge for golfers of all abilities; as you play this lovely layout, you'll find opportunities to test each club in your bag.

	1	2	3	4	5	6	7	8	9
PAR	4	3	3	4	3	4	3	4	3
YARDS	347	115	187	279	208	309	153	278	170
	10	11	12	13	14	15	16	17	18
PAR	3	5	3	3	4	4	4	4	4
YARDS	216	413	186	136	357	246	382	300	272

Directions: Take Route 128 North to Exit 20A. Go right at the end of the ramp. Follow Route 1A for 3 miles and the course is on the right.

White Pines Golf Course

549 Copeland Street
Brockton, MA (508) 586-3260
www.whitepinesbrockton.com

Tees	Holes	Yards	Par	USGA	Slope
BACK					
MIDDLE	9	2687	36		
FRONT					

Club Pro:
Payment: Cash Only
Tee Times:
Fee 9 Holes: Weekday: $17
Fee 18 Holes: Weekday: $24
Twilight Rates: No
Cart Rental: $12pp/18, $8pp/9
Lessons: Schools: No
Membership: No
Other:

Weekend: $18
Weekend: $25
Discounts: Senior & Junior
Driving Range: None
Junior Golf:
Architect/Yr Open: 1926
GPS:

Rolling terrain, friendly staff. "Fun little 9-hole course." —FP

	1	2	3	4	5	6	7	8	9
PAR	4	4	5	4	4	4	3	4	4
YARDS	235	389	467	267	246	334	127	282	340
PAR									
YARDS									

Directions: Route 24 to Exit 16A (Route 106). Take left onto Crescent Street. After 1.5 miles, go left onto North Elm. Club is 1.5 miles on left.

Widow's Walk Golf Course

✪✪✪ 96 ▶

250 The Driftway
Scituate, MA (781) 544-0032
www.widowswalkgolf.com

Tees	Holes	Yards	Par	USGA	Slope
BACK	18	6403	72	71.2	129
MIDDLE	18	6062	72	69.6	127
FRONT	18	4562	72	66.2	113

Club Pro: Bob Sanderson, PGA
Payment: Visa, MC, Amex, Disc
Tee Times: 4 days adv.
Fee 9 Holes: Weekday: $23 M-Th
Fee 18 Holes: Weekday: $39 M-Th
Twilight Rates: Yes
Cart Rental: $16pp/18, $9pp/9
Lessons: $60/45 min. **Schools:** No
Membership: Yes
Other: Restaurant / Bar

Weekend: $26 F/S/S
Weekend: $47 F/S/S
Discounts: Senior & Junior M-Th
Driving Range: $4/bucket
Junior Golf: Yes
Architect/Yr Open: Michael Hurdzan/1997
GPS:

COUPON

Challenging course, very well groomed, great ocean views. Some of the best public greens anywhere.

	1	2	3	4	5	6	7	8	9
PAR	5	3	4	4	4	5	3	4	5
YARDS	504	126	350	351	302	486	167	313	481
	10	11	12	13	14	15	16	17	18
PAR	4	3	4	4	3	5	4	3	5
YARDS	425	140	313	412	183	486	312	191	520

Directions: Route 3 to Exit 13, Route 53 North to Route 123 East. 6 miles on Route 123 East to rotary. Second right on rotary. Course is 7/10 mile on left.

William J. Devine Golf Course ✪✪½ ▶ 97

1 Circuit Drive
Dorchester, MA (617) 265-4084
www.cityofbostongolf.com

Tees	Holes	Yards	Par	USGA	Slope
BACK	18	5966	70	69.8	127
MIDDLE	18	5622	70	68.1	121
FRONT	18	5031	7270	64.7	115

Club Pro: Kevin Frawley
Payment: Visa, MC, Cash
Tee Times: Weekends & Holidays
Fee 9 Holes: Weekday: $18
Fee 18 Holes: Weekday: $31
Twilight Rates: No
Cart Rental: $20pp/18, $11pp/9
Lessons: $50/half hour **Schools:** No
Membership: Yes, waiting list
Other: Clubhouse / Snack Bar / Lockers / Function Facility

Weekend: $20
Weekend: $35
Discounts: Senior & Junior
Driving Range: No
Junior Golf: Yes
Architect/Yr Open: Donald Ross/1896

Second oldest public course in the U.S., a Donald Ross design. Across from Franklin Park Zoo. Great summer programs for juniors. "Some terrific holes with a great Boston skyline." –FP

	1	2	3	4	5	6	7	8	9
PAR	4	4	4	3	4	4	4	3	4
YARDS	378	302	404	163	344	334	370	149	331
	10	11	12	13	14	15	16	17	18
PAR	4	5	4	3	4	3	4	4	5
YARDS	299	502	382	118	338	152	327	267	462

Directions: Follow signs to Franklin Park Zoo. Take 93 North/South. Take Columbia Road exit. Follow Columbia Road to Franklin Park.

Willowdale Golf Course ✪½ ▶ 98

54 Willow Street
Mansfield, MA (508) 339-3197

Tees	Holes	Yards	Par	USGA	Slope
BACK					
MIDDLE	9	1935	30		
FRONT					

Club Pro:
Payment: Cash Only
Tee Times: No
Fee 9 Holes: Weekday: $15
Fee 18 Holes: Weekday: $18
Twilight Rates: No
Cart Rental: $2/pull
Lessons: No **Schools:** No
Membership: No
Other: Snack Bar / Bar-Lounge / Clubhouse

Weekend: $17
Weekend: $20
Discounts: Senior M-F $1 off
Driving Range: No
Junior Golf: Yes
Architect/Yr Open:
GPS:

Executive-style course, considered an easy walker. Open April 1 - December 1. "Fun for all levels of golfers." –FP

	1	2	3	4	5	6	7	8	9
PAR	4	3	3	4	4	3	3	3	3
YARDS	265	180	190	320	285	180	100	210	205
PAR									
YARDS									

Directions: I-95 to Mansfield exit. Route 140 to Mansfield Center, School Street exit. First right on Willow Street.

Woburn Country Club

★½ 99 ▶

**GB
RTE
495**

5 Country Club Road
Woburn, MA (781) 933-9880
www.thewoburncountryclub.com

Tees	Holes	Yards	Par	USGA	Slope
BACK					
MIDDLE	9	2996	34	68.9	121
FRONT	9	2565	35	68.0	104

Club Pro: Paul Barkhouse, PGA
Payment: Visa, MC
Tee Times: 2 days adv. (weekends only)
Fee 9 Holes: Weekday: $20   **Weekend:** $21
Fee 18 Holes: Weekday: $29   **Weekend:** $34
Twilight Rates: No   **Discounts:** Senior & Junior (weekdays only)
Cart Rental: $28/18, $16/9 per cart   **Driving Range:** No
Lessons: $40/half hour **Schools:** No   **Junior Golf:** Yes
Membership: Residents only   **Architect/Yr Open:**
Other: Restaurant / Snack Bar / Function Hall   **GPS:**

Small greens. Need a good short game to score well, every lie in the book. Dress code required. Resident rates available.

	1	2	3	4	5	6	7	8	9
PAR	4	4	4	4	4	4	3	4	3
YARDS	373	363	359	371	410	326	190	389	215
PAR									
YARDS									

Directions: I-93 to I-95/Route 128 South, Exit 33A (Winchester), straight through Woburn Four Corners, take left at first set of lights onto Country Club Road

Barrie Bruce Golf Schools
"a pair of sneakers and a good attitude"

Barrie Bruce Golf Schools

• Group lessons for adults new to the game
• Private lessons for all levels
• Junior Golf Clinics
• Learn to golf in a fun and relaxing setting

Country Club of Billerica
51 Baldwin Road, Billerica, MA

Wentworth Hills Country Club
27 Bow Road, Plainville, MA

www.barriebrucegolfschools.com   **(978) 337-2448**

Map at right shows actual
position of these two areas.

★ Norton

★ Plymouth

Brewster ★

Bourne ★

Falmouth ★

Hyannis

Chatham

Martha's Vineyard

Nantucket

Acushnet River Valley GC	1
Back Nine Club	2
Ballymeade CC	3
Bass River Golf Course	4
Bay Pointe CC	5
Bayberry Hills GC	6
Blue Rock Golf Club	7
Brookside Club, The	8
Cape Cod CC	9
Captains GC, Port Course	10
Captains GC, Starboard	11
Chatham Seaside Links	12
Chemawa Golf Course	13
Chequessett GC	14
Cotuit-Highground GC	15
Cranberry Valley GC	16
Dennis Highlands	17
Dennis Pines GC	18
Falmouth Country Club	19
Farm Neck Golf Club	20
Fire Fly Country Club	21
Harwich Port Golf Club	22
Heather Hill CC	23
Hidden Hollow CC	24
Highland Links	25
Hillside CC	26
Holly Ridge Golf Club	27
Hyannis Golf Club	28
John F. Parker Municipal GC	29
Lakeville Country Club	30
Little Harbor CC	31
Locust Valley GC	32

Marion Golf Course	33	Rochester Golf Club	45
MGA Links at Mamantapett	34	Sandwich Hollows GC	46
Miacomet Golf Club	35	Siasconset Golf Course	47
Middlebrook CC	36	Stone-E-Lea Golf Course	48
Mink Meadows GC	37	Sun Valley CC	49
Norton Country Club	38	Swansea Country Club	50
Olde Barnstable GC	39	Swansea CC Exec. Par 3	51
Paul Harney GC	40	Touisset Country Club	52
Pine Valley CC	41	Twin Brooks GC	53
Poquoy Brook GC	42	Wampanoag Golf Club	54
Quashnet Valley CC	43	Wentworth Hills CC	55
Rehoboth Country Club	44	Whaling City GC	56

KEY TO THE STAR RATINGS:
5✪ = Outstanding   4✪ = Excellent   3✪ = Very Good   2✪ = Good   1✪ = Average   **NR** = Not Rated

Acushnet River Valley GC ✪✪✪½

SE MA/ CAPE

685 Main Street
Acushnet, MA (508) 998-7777
www.golfacushnet.com

Tees	Holes	Yards	Par	USGA	Slope
BACK	18	6302	72	70.0	122
MIDDLE	18	5735	72	66.9	116
FRONT	18	5099	72	68.4	115

Club Pro: Gary Cardoza, Jr., PGA
Payment: All Types
Tee Times: 7 days adv.
Fee 9 Holes: Weekday: $20
Fee 18 Holes: Weekday: $39
Twilight Rates: After 12pm
Cart Rental: $16pp/18, $8pp/9
Lessons: $40/half hour **Schools:** Yes
Membership: Season Passes
Other: Snack Bar / Clubhouse / Bar-Lounge

Weekend: $27
Weekend: $46
Discounts: Junior
Driving Range: $6/lg, $4/sm bucket
Junior Golf: Yes
Architect/Yr Open: Brian Silva/1998
GPS: Yes

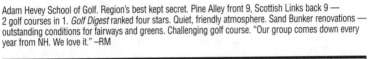

Adam Hevey School of Golf. Region's best kept secret. Pine Alley front 9, Scottish Links back 9 — 2 golf courses in 1. *Golf Digest* ranked four stars. Quiet, friendly atmosphere. Sand Bunker renovations — outstanding conditions for fairways and greens. Challenging golf course. "Our group comes down every year from NH. We love it." –RM

	1	2	3	4	5	6	7	8	9
PAR	4	4	4	5	4	3	4	3	5
YARDS	375	289	275	436	336	119	382	141	501
	10	11	12	13	14	15	16	17	18
PAR	4	3	5	4	5	4	4	3	4
YARDS	315	113	470	388	529	257	328	145	336

Directions: I-95/Route 128 to Route 24 South to Route 140 South. Take Exit 6 to Route 18 South. Stay on Route 18 South for 2 miles. At lights, turn left onto Tarkiln Hill Road, which becomes Main Street in Acushnet. Course will be on left about 2 miles after Acushnet Town Hall.

Back Nine Club, The ✪✪½ 2

17 Heritage Hill Drive
Lakeville, MA (508) 947-9991
www.thebacknineclub.com

Tees	Holes	Yards	Par	USGA	Slope
BACK	18	3012	54	54.7	84
MIDDLE	18	2575	54	54.7	84
FRONT	18	2155	54	54.7	84

Club Pro: Dave Marchand, Manager
Payment: Visa, MC, Amex, Disc, Cash
Tee Times: 7 days adv.
Fee 9 Holes: Weekday: $15
Fee 18 Holes: Weekday: $25
Twilight Rates: $20 after 5pm
Cart Rental: $10p/18, $7pp/9
Lessons: Yes **Schools:** Yes
Membership: Yes
Other: Restaurant / Bar-Lounge / Leagues / Outings / Function Hall

Weekend: $15
Weekend: $25
Discounts: Junior
Driving Range: No
Junior Golf: Yes
Architect/Yr Open: Geoffrey Cornish/1974

Completely renovated clubhouse now with full restaurant and bar. Renovated pro shop and new outside deck. Course renovations are ongoing. Sig. Hole: #16, 145-yard par 3. Beginner-friendly certified by NGCOA. Open all year round. Challenging and beautiful, excellent Par-3 Course.

	1	2	3	4	5	6	7	8	9
PAR	3	3	3	3	3	3	3	3	3
YARDS	155	190	160	140	145	155	115	170	145
	10	11	12	13	14	15	16	17	18
PAR	3	3	3	3	3	3	3	3	3
YARDS	140	130	125	110	145	120	145	160	125

Directions: Take I-495 to Exit 5. Go south on Route 18. Go through intersection of Route 18 and Route 105 and take first right after mini-mart onto Highland Road. Take first right onto Heritage Hill Drive and course is ¼ mile down road.

Ballymeade Country Club ✪

125 Falmouth Woods Road
North Falmouth, MA (508) 540-4005
www.ballymeade.com

Club Pro: Craig Garris, PGA
Payment: Cash, Credit Cards
Tee Times: 1 week adv.
Fee 9 Holes: Weekday: **Weekend:**
Fee 18 Holes: Weekday: $71/am, $56/12pm, $37/3pm (includes cart)
         Weekend: $81/am, $66/12pm, $40/3pm (includes cart)
Twilight Rates: After 3pm   **Discounts:** None
Cart Rental: Included   **Driving Range:** $8/lg bucket
Lessons: $50/half hour; $75/hr **Schools:** No **Junior Golf:** Yes
Membership: Yes   **Architect/Yr Open:** Jim Fazio/1988
Other: Restaurant / Clubhouse / Bar-Lounge / Lockers / Snack Bar / Showers
GPS: Yes

Tees	Holes	Yards	Par	USGA	Slope
BACK	18	6928	72	74.3	139
MIDDLE	18	6358	72	71.7	134
FRONT	18	5001	72	69.9	119

Player Comments: "Challenging. Scenic." Hole 11: Highest point on Cape; can see the Bay, New Bedford, over Marion to Fairhaven, all the boats in between. Off-season rates. Open year-round.

	1	2	3	4	5	6	7	8	9
PAR	4	3	5	4	3	4	4	5	4
YARDS	355	183	464	333	164	419	367	464	390
	10	11	12	13	14	15	16	17	18
PAR	5	3	4	4	3	4	4	4	5
YARDS	500	164	403	415	380	331	156	367	503

Directions: Over Bourne Bridge to Route 28 South. Exit at North Falmouth Route 151, 9 miles from the bridge. Turn right off the exit ramp. Course is less than 1 mile on the right.

Bass River Golf Course ✪✪½ 4

62 Highbank Road
South Yarmouth, MA
(508) 398-9079
www.golfyarmouthcapecod.com

Club Pro: Ron Hewins
Payment: Visa, MC, Disc, Amex
Tee Times: 7 days adv. (508) 398-4112
Fee 9 Holes: Weekday: $35   **Weekend:** $35
Fee 18 Holes: Weekday: $58   **Weekend:** $58
Twilight Rates: After 4pm   **Discounts:** Junior
Cart Rental: $20pp/18, $12pp/9   **Driving Range:** No
Lessons: Yes **Schools:** No   **Junior Golf:** Yes
Membership: Yes   **Architect/Yr Open:** Donald Ross/1900
Other: Clubhouse / Restaurant / Bar-Lounge **GPS:**

Tees	Holes	Yards	Par	USGA	Slope
BACK	18	6138	72	69.7	127
MIDDLE	18	5716	72	67.3	121
FRONT	18	4974	69.9	70.5	122

Regulation seaside layout with wide fairways and smaller greens. Signature Hole #19 borders Bass River.

	1	2	3	4	5	6	7	8	9
PAR	3	4	4	4	4	4	3	5	3
YARDS	165	282	391	329	348	282	105	464	155
	10	11	12	13	14	15	16	17	18
PAR	4	4	5	5	3	4	5	4	4
YARDS	247	386	450	500	140	333	474	319	339

Directions: Route 6 to Exit 8. Take right off ramp; then take 1st left after high school and go through one intersection to course.

Bay Pointe Country Club ✪✪½ 5

19 Bay Pointe Drive
Onset, MA (508) 759-8802
www.baypointeclub.com

Club Pro: Tom Tobey, PGA
Payment: Cash, Visa, MC, Amex
Tee Times: 3 weeks adv.

Tees	Holes	Yards	Par	USGA	Slope
BACK	18	6201	70	71.6	125
MIDDLE	18	5720	70	69.6	125
FRONT	18	5380	72	71.3	125

Fee 9 Holes: Weekday: $15
Fee 18 Holes: Weekday: $30
Twilight Rates: After 1:30pm
Cart Rental: $18pp/18, $9pp/9
Lessons: $50/45 min. **Schools:** No
Membership: Yes
Other: Clubhouse / Lockers / Showers / Snack Bar / Restaurant / Bar-Lounge / Pool / Tennis

Weekend: $20
Weekend: $42
Discounts: Yes
Driving Range: Irons only
Junior Golf: No
Architect/Yr Open: Geoffrey Cornish/1963

COUPON

SE MA/ CAPE

Lots of improvements made, under new ownership. Great staff. Located at western mouth of Cape, 5 minutes from Bourne Bridge. Typical Cape course, superbly manicured, excellent greens and fairways. Juniors and senior discounts. Open year round.

	1	2	3	4	5	6	7	8	9
PAR	5	4	4	3	4	4	3	3	5
YARDS	481	465	384	189	452	283	101	227	517
	10	11	12	13	14	15	16	17	18
PAR	3	4	3	4	3	5	4	5	4
YARDS	195	391	203	360	208	526	337	492	390

Directions: I-495 turns into Route 25. Take Exit 2 from Route 25. At 7th light go right, course is ⅔ mile on right. From Route 3 South take Route 6 at Sagamore Rotary toward Buzzard's Bay. Cross bridge into Wareham and go left at first light (Onset Avenue). Course ⅔ mile on right.

Bayberry Hills Golf Course ✪✪✪ 6

631 West Yarmouth Road
South Yarmouth, MA
(508) 394-5597
www.golfyarmouthcapecod.com

Club Pro: Jim Armentrout, Dir. of Golf
Payment: Visa, MC, Disc
Tee Times: 7 days adv. (508) 398-4112

Tees	Holes	Yards	Par	USGA	Slope
BACK	27/18	6523	72	72.0	128
MIDDLE	27/18	6087	72	69.6	124
FRONT	27/18	5323	72	70.5	122

Fee 9 Holes: Weekday: $33 cart included
Fee 18 Holes: Weekday: $85 cart included
Twilight Rates: After 4pm
Cart Rental: $20pp/18, $12pp/9
Lessons: Yes; $8/res.; $12/non-res. **Schools:** No
Membership: Yes, non-resident/resident rates
Other: Clubhouse / Bar-Lounge / Restaurant

Weekend: $33 cart included
Weekend: $85 cart included
Discounts: Junior
Driving Range: $10/lg, $7/md, $4/sm
Junior Golf: Yes
Architect/Yr Open: Cornish/Silva/1988
GPS:

COUPON

Immaculate condition. 27 holes, with a 9-hole links style course.

	1	2	3	4	5	6	7	8	9
PAR	4	5	3	4	4	4	5	3	4
YARDS	395	485	140	336	335	350	505	146	350
	10	11	12	13	14	15	16	17	18
PAR	4	4	3	4	4	5	4	3	5
YARDS	372	384	130	320	352	503	349	160	475

Directions: Take Exit 8 off Route 6 East. Turn South onto Station Avenue. Take right at second traffic light onto Old Townhouse Road. Entrance to course at end of street.

Blue Rock Golf Course ✪✪✪½ ▶7

48 Todd Road
South Yarmouth, MA (508) 398-9295
www.bluerockgolfcourse.com

Tees	Holes	Yards	Par	USGA	Slope
BACK	18	2890	54	56.4	83
MIDDLE	18	2563	54	56.4	83
FRONT	18	2170	54	55.8	80

Club Pro: Patrick Fannon, PGA
Payment: Visa, MC, Cash, Check
Tee Times: 7 days adv.
Fee 9 Holes: Weekday: Call   **Weekend:** Call
Fee 18 Holes: Weekday: Call   **Weekend:** Call
Twilight Rates: Call for rates
Discounts: Senior (before 8:30am) & Junior (17 and under)
Cart Rental: $15/single; $28/double   **Driving Range:** Members only
Lessons: Yes **Schools:** Yes   **Junior Golf:** Yes
Membership: Yes   **Architect/Yr Open:** Geoffrey Cornish/1962
Other: Clubhouse / Snack Bar / Restaurant / Bar-Lounge / Hotel / Tennis / Pool / Golf School / Golf Clinic

"A great test for your short game; lots of wonderful carries and challenges. A better challenge than some regulation courses." –JD

	1	2	3	4	5	6	7	8	9
PAR	3	3	3	3	3	3	3	3	3
YARDS	103	127	118	125	247	145	170	165	165
	10	11	12	13	14	15	16	17	18
PAR	3	3	3	3	3	3	3	3	3
YARDS	150	117	190	147	185	185	144	129	173

Directions: Take Mid-Cape Highway East to Exit 8. Turn right off the ramp. Take first left on White's Path, right to intersection, turn left on Great Western Road. Course is ¼ mile on right.

Brookside Club, The ✪✪✪ ▶8

11 Brigadoon Road (Route 28)
Bourne, MA (508) 743-4653
www.thebrooksideclub.com

Tees	Holes	Yards	Par	USGA	Slope
BACK	18	6317	70	71.1	126
MIDDLE	18	5826	70	68.1	124
FRONT	18	5169	70	69.6	118

Club Pro: Chad Schofield, PGA
Payment: Visa, MC, Amex, Disc, Checks, Cash
Tee Times: 7 days adv.
Fee 9 Holes: Weekday: $27 w/cart   **Weekend:** $37 w/cart
Fee 18 Holes: Weekday: $64 w/cart   **Weekend:** $74 w/cart
Twilight Rates: After 2pm M-T; After 4pm F/S/S
Discounts: Senior & Junior M-Th
Cart Rental: $17pp/18, $8.50pp/9   **Driving Range:** $7/lg., $4/sm.
Lessons: $45/half hour **Schools:** No   **Junior Golf:** Yes
Membership: Yes   **Architect/Yr Open:** Michael Hurdzan, 1986
Other: Bar / Restaurant / Clubhouse   **GPS:**

Hole #1 offers you a breathtaking view of Onset Beach and Cape Cod Canal. The course also features lush fairways, rolling hills and fast greens.

	1	2	3	4	5	6	7	8	9
PAR	4	3	4	4	5	3	4	4	4
YARDS	379	156	359	365	503	96	361	421	332
	10	11	12	13	14	15	16	17	18
PAR	5	4	4	3	4	4	4	3	4
YARDS	576	336	330	128	354	351	313	130	342

Directions: Routes I-495/25 over Bourne Bridge to Route 28 South. Course is 2 miles on right.

Cape Cod Country Club ✪✪✪ 9

48 Theater Drive
East Falmouth, MA (508) 563-9842
www.capecodcountryclub.com

Tees	Holes	Yards	Par	USGA	Slope
BACK	18	6404	71	71.7	129
MIDDLE	18	6018	71	69.6	125
FRONT	18	5348	72	71.0	120

Club Pro: C. Holmes, Golf Dir., J. Munroe, PGA
Payment: Cash, MC, Visa
Tee Times: 7 days adv.
Fee 9 Holes: Weekday: $27 after 2pm M-Th **Weekend:** $32 after 2pm
Fee 18 Holes: Weekday: $42 M-Th **Weekend:** $56 F/S/S
Twilight Rates: After 2pm **Discounts:** Tues/Ladies, Wed/Sr.
Cart Rental: $16pp/18 **Driving Range:** No
Lessons: Call for details **Schools:** No **Junior Golf:** No
Membership: No **Architect/Yr Open:** Emmet & Tull/1928
Other: Clubhouse / Snack Bar / Bar-Lounge **GPS:**

Sig. Hole: #14, The Volcano, is the most talked-about hole. Course plays longer than the scorecard statistics. The impeccable fairways are lined with pine trees.

	1	2	3	4	5	6	7	8	9
PAR	4	3	5	4	4	5	4	4	3
YARDS	307	175	460	419	360	509	300	407	156
	10	11	12	13	14	15	16	17	18
PAR	4	5	3	5	4	3	3	4	4
YARDS	405	515	220	461	351	180	183	300	310

Directions: Take Route 28 South of Bourne Bridge, take right onto Route 151. Course is approximately 3 miles on right.

Captains Golf Course (Port) ✪✪✪½ 10

1000 Freeman's Way
Brewster, MA (508) 896-1716
www.captainsgolfcourse.com

Tees	Holes	Yards	Par	USGA	Slope
BACK	18	6724	72	73.5	130
MIDDLE	18	6164	72	70.7	128
FRONT	18	5345	72	71.1.	119

Club Pro: Mark O'Brien, Director of Ops.
Payment: Visa, MC, Amex, Discover
Tee Times: Up to 1 year adv.
Fee 9 Holes: Weekday: $35 after 12pm **Weekend:** $35 after 12pm
Fee 18 Holes: Weekday: $76 summer **Weekend:** $76 summer
Twilight Rates: After 4pm **Discounts:** Junior, $5 after 5pm
Cart Rental: $20pp/18, $12pp/9 **Driving Range:** $8/lg, $5/sm bucket
Lessons: Yes **Schools:** Yes **Junior Golf:** Yes
Membership: Yes **Architect/Yr Open:** Brian Silva/1985
Other: Bar / Restaurant / Banquet Facility **GPS:**

COUPON

Outings are our specialty. Player Comments: "Holes 12 through 16 are a spectacular sequence." Reservations available online. New irrigation system. Lower Cape's best 2 layouts.

	1	2	3	4	5	6	7	8	9
PAR	4	4	3	4	3	5	4	5	4
YARDS	321	374	160	361	141	508	427	529	337
	10	11	12	13	14	15	16	17	18
PAR	4	3	5	5	4	3	4	3	5
YARDS	357	177	515	408	353	153	336	197	510

Directions: Route 6 to Exit 11. Right off exit ramp and travel 1.5 miles to Freeman's Way on right. Turn onto Freeman's and course is 1.5 miles on right.

Captains GC (Starboard)

✪✪✪½

 11

1000 Freeman's Way
Brewster, MA (508) 896-1716
www.captainsgolfcourse.com

Club Pro: Mark T. O'Brien, Director of Ops.
Payment: Visa, MC, Amex, Discover
Tee Times: Up to 1 year in adv.

Tees	Holes	Yards	Par	USGA	Slope
BACK	18	6776	72	72.6	130
MIDDLE	18	6198	72	69.4	123
FRONT	18	5359	72	71.2	116

Fee 9 Holes: Weekday: $35 after 12pm
Fee 18 Holes: Weekday: $76 summer
Twilight Rates: After 4pm
Cart Rental: $20pp/18, $12pp/9
Lessons: Yes **Schools:** Yes
Membership: Yes
Other: Bar / Restaurant / Banquet Facility

Weekend: $35 after 12pm
Weekend: $76 summer
Discounts: Junior, $5 after 5pm
Driving Range: $8/lg, $5/sm bucket
Junior Golf: Yes
Architect/Yr Open: Brian Silva/1985
GPS:

COUPON

Outings are our specialty. Player Comments: "Excellent layout. Best-conditioned course I've played."
Reservations avaliable online. New irrigation system. Come play both sides.

	1	2	3	4	5	6	7	8	9
PAR	4	3	5	4	3	4	5	4	4
YARDS	352	131	491	401	178	287	507	370	322
	10	11	12	13	14	15	16	17	18
PAR	4	3	4	5	4	4	4	3	5
YARDS	344	182	326	481	378	361	427	156	504

Directions: Route 6 to Exit 11. Right off exit ramp and travel 1.5 miles to Freeman's Way on right.
Turn onto Freeman's and course is 1.5 miles on right.

Chatham Seaside Links

NR 12

209 Seaview Street
Chatham, MA (508) 945-4774
www.mychatham.com/chathamgolf.html

Club Pro: Dennis Donohoe
Payment: Cash, MC, Visa
Tee Times: No

Tees	Holes	Yards	Par	USGA	Slope
BACK					
MIDDLE	9	2465	34	65.6	107
FRONT	9	2400	34	65.6	109

Fee 9 Holes: Weekday: $19
Fee 18 Holes: Weekday: $30
Twilight Rates: No
Cart Rental: $12pp/18, $7.50pp/9
Lessons: Schools: No
Membership: Yes
Other: Snacks

Weekend: $19
Weekend: $30
Discounts: Senior & Junior
Driving Range: No
Junior Golf: No
Architect/Yr Open: 1895
GPS:

Links-style golf course with ocean views. Course irrigated. Open April 1 to October 31.

	1	2	3	4	5	6	7	8	9
PAR	4	4	3	3	4	4	4	4	4
YARDS	295	285	150	140	350	305	325	295	320
PAR									
YARDS									

Directions: Route 6 to Exit 11 (Route 137). Go left to Route 28 and left again to Main Street
Chatham. Take Seaview off Main Street to course.

Chemawa Golf Course ✪✪✪

350 Cushman Road
North Attleboro, MA
(508) 399-7330

Tees	Holes	Yards	Par	USGA	Slope
BACK	18	5267	68	65.1	113
MIDDLE	18	4884	68	63.5	110
FRONT	18	4351	69	64.6	109

Club Pro:
Payment: Most Major Credit Cards
Tee Times: Weekend and holiday
Fee 9 Holes: Weekday: $21
Fee 18 Holes: Weekday: $30
Twilight Rates: No
Cart Rental: $26pp/18, $13pp/9
Lessons: No **Schools:** No
Membership: No
Other: Snack Bar / Bar-Lounge / Enlarged Putting Green

Weekend: $23
Weekend: $36
Discounts: Senior, $27pp/18, $20pp/9
Driving Range: No
Junior Golf: No
Architect/Yr Open: Steve Espisito/1956

Player Comments: "Parkland layout presents water and wetlands in play on 11 holes with generous driving zones. Early version of the island green on 16th." "Challenging, difficult."

	1	2	3	4	5	6	7	8	9
PAR	4	4	4	4	4	4	5	4	3
YARDS	334	286	324	321	312	236	427	265	136
	10	11	12	13	14	15	16	17	18
PAR	4	3	4	3	3	4	3	4	4
YARDS	348	126	309	146	198	332	109	265	410

Directions: I-95 South to I-295 toward Woonsocket, Route 1 South. Take right onto May Street, then take a right onto Cushman Road.

Chequessett Golf, Tennis & Sailing ✪✪

680 Chequesset Neck Road
Wellfleet, MA (508) 349-3704
www.cycc.net

Tees	Holes	Yards	Par	USGA	Slope
BACK					
MIDDLE	9	2621	35	66.1	107
FRONT	9	2387	35	67.9	110

Club Pro: Chris Hicks, PGA
Payment: Visa, MC
Tee Times: Unlimited w/CC
Fee 9 Holes: Weekday: $35
Fee 18 Holes: Weekday: $50
Twilight Rates: After 4pm
Cart Rental: $16pp/18, $10pp/9
Lessons: Yes **Schools:** No
Membership: Yes
Other: Snack Bar (Seasonal) / Tennis / Sailing

Weekend: $35
Weekend: $50
Discounts: Juniors
Driving Range: No
Junior Golf: Yes
Architect/Yr Open: 1929
GPS:

COUPON

Nice scenic holes with two sets of tees for 18 holes of play. Small, tough greens. Good for family play.

	1	2	3	4	5	6	7	8	9
PAR	4	3	4	5	3	4	4	4	4
YARDS	234	127	368	435	109	314	373	380	281
PAR									
YARDS									

Directions: From Orleans rotary take Route 6 to Wellfleet. At Wellfleet Center light, go left at light onto Main Street. Take left on Commercial Street toward harbor. Go 1.5 miles past the harbor to the course on the right.

Cotuit-Highground Golf Course   NR   15

31 Crockers Neck Road
Cotuit, MA (508) 428-9863

Tees	Holes	Yards	Par	USGA	Slope
BACK					
MIDDLE	9	1290	28		
FRONT	9	1059	28		

Club Pro: Steve Heher, PGA
Payment: Cash Only
Tee Times: No
Fee 9 Holes: Weekday: $15   **Weekend:** $15
Fee 18 Holes: Weekday: $20   **Weekend:** $20
Twilight Rates: After 4pm   **Discounts:** Senior & Junior
Cart Rental: Some available   **Driving Range:** No
Lessons: Yes **Schools:** No   **Junior Golf:** Yes
Membership: Yes   **Architect/Yr Open:** 1927
Other: Bar-Lounge / Snack Bar   **GPS:**

Player comments: "Good value." Family fun. Links-style course, very tight greens. Accuracy is very important. Open year-round.

	1	2	3	4	5	6	7	8	9
PAR	3	3	4	3	3	3	3	3	3
YARDS	115	180	290	130	140	110	100	180	115
PAR									
YARDS									

Directions: Take Route 6 to Exit 2 (Route 130 South), left onto Route 28, right onto Main Street in Cotuit Center. Take right onto School Street then second left onto Crocker Neck Road.

Cranberry Valley Golf Course ✪✪✪½   16

183 Oak Street
Harwich, MA (508) 430-5234
www.cranberrygolfcourse.com

Tees	Holes	Yards	Par	USGA	Slope
BACK	18	6745	72	71.9	129
MIDDLE	18	6296	72	70.4	125
FRONT	18	5518	72	71.5	115

Club Pro: Dennis Hoye, PGA
Payment: Cash, Visa, MC
Tee Times: Up to 10 days adv.
Fee 9 Holes: Weekday: **Weekend:**
Fee 18 Holes: Weekday: $62   **Weekend:** $62
Twilight Rates: After 2:30pm   **Discounts:** None
Cart Rental: $18pp/18, $9pp/9   **Driving Range:** $5/sm, $8/lg bucket
Lessons: $45/half hour **Schools:** Jr.   **Junior Golf:** Yes
Membership: Yes, resident & non-resident   **Architect/Yr Open:** Cornish & Robinson/1974
Other: Restaurant/Bar   **GPS:**

Player Comments: "Very fine play, great condition." Large teeing areas and 53 sand bunkers. Open March - Dec. Seasonal rates. Hosted 2006 Mass Women's State Open. All traps recently renovated. New range expanded.

	1	2	3	4	5	6	7	8	9
PAR	4	5	4	3	4	4	3	5	4
YARDS	365	505	390	197	435	340	176	510	383
	10	11	12	13	14	15	16	17	18
PAR	4	4	4	3	5	4	4	3	5
YARDS	361	352	372	174	445	308	443	205	521

Directions: Take Exit 10 off Route 6 East. Take a right off the ramp and take first left at 4-way stop onto Queen Anne Road. Take third right (Oak Street). Course is ½ mile on left.

Dennis Highlands Golf Course ✪✪✪

825 Old Bass River Road
Dennis, MA (508) 385-8347
www.dennisgolf.com

Tees	Holes	Yards	Par	USGA	Slope
BACK	18	6464	71	70.9	120
MIDDLE	18	6076	71	68.5	117
FRONT	18	4927	71	67.8	112

Club Pro: Tony Day, PGA
Payment: MC, Visa, Discover, Cash
Tee Times: 4 days adv.; up to 7 for non-members
Fee 9 Holes: Weekday: $41, 5:30am-7am and after 1pm
Fee 18 Holes: Weekday: $66   **Weekend:** $66
Twilight Rates: $41 after 1pm; $29 after 4pm   **Discounts:** Senior/Junior
Cart Rental: $18pp/18, $13pp/9   **Driving Range:** $8/lg., $5/sm.
Lessons: Call for appt.   **Schools:** Yes   **Junior Golf:** Yes
Membership: Available
Architect/Yr Open: Jack Kidwell/Michael Hurdzan/1983
Other: Clubhouse / Restaurant / Bar-Lounge

COUPON

Putting is key to good round. Added green tee markers. Seasonal rates. Enlarged some tees and rebuilt 7th green. Open year round. Family-friendly venue. Home of the Dennis Fourball.

	1	2	3	4	5	6	7	8	9
PAR	4	5	3	4	4	4	3	5	3
YARDS	309	494	151	331	347	409	160	472	141
	10	11	12	13	14	15	16	17	18
PAR	4	3	4	4	4	5	3	4	5
YARDS	371	151	365	392	383	529	170	377	519

Directions: Take Route 6 to Exit 9B, follow ½ mile. Take left onto Bob Crowell Road. At end take right onto Old Bass River Road, course is 2.4 miles up on left.

Dennis Pines Golf Course   ✪✪✪

50 Golf Course Road
East Dennis, MA (508) 385-8347
www.dennisgolf.com

Tees	Holes	Yards	Par	USGA	Slope
BACK	18	7029	72	74.2	133
MIDDLE	18	6525	72	72.1	131
FRONT	18	5845	72	73.6	126

Club Pro: Tony Day, PGA
Payment: Visa, MC, Disc, Cash
Tee Times: Up to 7 days adv.
Fee 9 Holes: Weekday: $41, 5:30am-7am and after 1pm
Fee 18 Holes: Weekday: $66   **Weekend:** $66
Twilight Rates: $41 after 1pm, $29 after 4pm   **Discounts:** None
Cart Rental: $18 pp/18, $13 pp/9   **Driving Range:** $8/lg., $5/sm.
Lessons: Yes   **Schools:** Yes   **Junior Golf:** Yes
Membership: Available   **Architect/Yr Open:** Henry Mitchell/1964
Other: Snack Bar / Restaurant / Bar-Lounge   **GPS:**

COUPON

One of Cape's busiest courses. Wonderful layout with dramatic holes set among tall pines. Call for early morning and twilight rates.

	1	2	3	4	5	6	7	8	9
PAR	4	4	5	3	5	4	3	4	4
YARDS	373	369	471	188	476	423	187	442	389
	10	11	12	13	14	15	16	17	18
PAR	4	4	5	3	4	5	4	3	4
YARDS	351	357	518	172	405	472	344	183	405

Directions: Take Exit 9B off of Route 6, proceed north on Route 134, take a right approximately 2.5 miles to Golf Course Road, Dennis Pines Golf Course is located at the end of Golf Course Road.

Falmouth Country Club

✪✪½ ▶ **19**

630 Carriage Shop Road
Falmouth, MA (508) 548-3211
www.falmouthcountryclub.com

Club Pro: Matthew Burgess, PGA
Payment: Visa, MC
Tee Times: 14 days adv.

Tees	Holes	Yards	Par	USGA	Slope
BACK	18	6665	72	72.2	133
MIDDLE	18	6234	72	71.2	128
FRONT	18	5551	72	72.6	132

Fee 9 Holes: Weekday: $27/walk; $35/ride **Weekend:** $27/walk, $35/ride
Fee 18 Holes: Weekday: $49/non-res, $35/res **Weekend:** $64/non-res, $52/res
Twilight Rates: After 2pm **Discounts:** None
Cart Rental: $15pp/18, $8pp/9 **Driving Range:** Yes - $6/bucket
Lessons: Yes **Schools:** Yes **Junior Golf:** Yes
Membership: Yes **Architect/Yr Open:** Vinnie Bartlett/1969
Other: Clubhouse / Snack Bar / Bar-Lounge **GPS:**

COUPON

27 holes—an 18-hole course and a 9-hole, now managed by Billy Casper Golf Management.
"Nice wide open layout. Easy to walk. Great for bird watchers." –FP

	1	2	3	4	5	6	7	8	9
PAR	4	3	4	4	4	3	4	5	4
YARDS	400	175	370	384	403	174	318	531	426
	10	11	12	13	14	15	16	17	18
PAR	5	4	3	4	5	5	4	3	4
YARDS	516	385	151	427	545	500	380	190	390

Directions: Take Route 28 South into Falmouth. Take right onto Route 151 East, follow 3.5 miles to Sandwich Road on right. Look for signs, left onto Carriage Shop Road.

Farm Neck Golf Club

✪✪✪✪½ ▶ **20**

1 Farm Neck Way
Oak Bluffs, MA (508) 693-3057
www.farmneck.net

Club Pro: Mike Zoll, PGA
Payment: Visa, MC, Amex, Cash
Tee Times: 3 days adv. (in season)

Tees	Holes	Yards	Par	USGA	Slope
BACK	18	6815	72	72.8	135
MIDDLE	18	6301	72	70.5	133
FRONT	18	4987	72	64.3	118

Fee 9 Holes: Weekday: $90 after 4pm **Weekend:** $90 after 4pm
Fee 18 Holes: Weekday: $160 (in season) **Weekend:** $160 (in season)
Twilight Rates: After 4pm **Discounts:** None
Cart Rental: $18pp/18, $9pp/9 **Driving Range:** $10/lg, $7/med, $5/sm bucket
Lessons: $65/half hour **Schools:** No **Junior Golf:** Yes
Membership: Waiting list **Architect/Yr Open:** Cornish/1979; Robinson/1996
Other: Restaurant / Bar-Lounge / Snack Bar / Lockers / Showers

New Greens Holes #4 and # 12. Scenic, splendid, and challenging with ocean breezes and views, meadows and interior woodlands.
"A treasure." "Pure golf experience." –JD Off-season rates a great value: call ahead.

	1	2	3	4	5	6	7	8	9
PAR	4	5	4	3	4	3	4	5	3
YARDS	378	490	340	157	325	189	371	486	175
	10	11	12	13	14	15	16	17	18
PAR	4	5	4	4	4	3	4	4	5
YARDS	376	519	379	343	331	163	388	368	523

Directions: Follow Country Road in Oak Bluffs, Martha's Vineyard. Farm Neck Way is off of Country Road.

Fire Fly Country Club

320 Fall River Avenue
Seekonk, MA (508) 336-6622

Club Pro: Keith Allcock, PGA
Payment: Visa, MC
Tee Times: Weekends only
Fee 9 Holes: Weekday: $16
Fee 18 Holes: Weekday: $20
Twilight Rates: After 7pm
Cart Rental: $13pp/18, $7.50pp/9, $10/Senior
Lessons: $40/half hour; $25/Jr. **Schools:** No
Membership: Yes
Other: Snack Bar / Restaurant / Bar-Lounge

Tees	Holes	Yards	Par	USGA	Slope
BACK	18	3644	59	58.0	87
MIDDLE	18	3083	59	55.4	81
FRONT	18	2786	59	58.0	86

Weekend: $17
Weekend: $23
Discounts: Sr & Jr (M-F) $17/18
Driving Range: $6/bucket
Junior Golf: Yes
Architect/Yr: Joanne Carner & Don Hoenig/1962

COUPON

Executive course, great for beginners and seasoned golfers who like to practice their short game. Junior clinics available at the Golf Learning Center.

	1	2	3	4	5	6	7	8	9
PAR	3	3	3	3	4	3	4	4	3
YARDS	145	150	148	147	441	122	286	251	123
	10	11	12	13	14	15	16	17	18
PAR	4	3	3	3	3	3	3	4	3
YARDS	240	146	126	87	139	155	182	240	134

Directions: From Providence I-95 to I-195 East to Exit 1 MA (Seekonk/Barrington). (From Fall River take 195 West to Exit 1 MA.) Go north on Route 114. At fork, bear left. Take right at Fire Fly.

Harwich Port Golf Club

South Street
Harwich Port, MA (508) 432-0250
www.harwichport.com

Club Pro:
Payment: Cash Only
Tee Times: No
Fee 9 Holes: Weekday: $20
Fee 18 Holes: Weekday: $30
Twilight Rates: No
Cart Rental: $3/pull
Lessons: No **Schools:** No
Membership: Yes
Other: Snack Bar

Tees	Holes	Yards	Par	USGA	Slope
BACK					
MIDDLE	9	2538	34		
FRONT					

Weekend: $20
Weekend: $30
Discounts: None
Driving Range: Members only
Junior Golf: No
Architect/Yr Open: Don Blakely/1920
GPS:

The course is considered an easy walker. Recommended for beginners and senior citizens. Members only after 5:30pm. New state-of-the-art irrigation system.

	1	2	3	4	5	6	7	8	9
PAR	4	3	4	4	4	4	3	4	4
YARDS	358	170	340	330	325	255	155	295	310
PAR									
YARDS									

Directions: Take Route 6 to Exit 9 or 10. Take Route 28 to South Street. Course is 200 yards on right.

SE
MA/
CAPE

Heather Hill Country Club

✪✪½

149 West Bacon Street
Plainville, MA (508) 695-0309
www.heatherhillcountryclub.com

Club Pro: Mike Cosentino, Golf Instruction
Payment: Cash, Check
Tee Times: 1 week adv.
Fee 9 Holes: Weekday: $17
Fee 18 Holes: Weekday: $25
Twilight Rates: No
Cart Rental: $28/18, $14/9 per cart
Lessons: $25/half hour **Schools:** No
Membership: No
Other: Clubhouse / Snack Bar / Bar-Lounge

Tees	Holes	Yards	Par	USGA	Slope
BACK	27/18	6335	72	67.8	117
MIDDLE	27/18	6034	72	66.5	115
FRONT	27/18	4986	70	67.1	111

COUPON

Weekend: $21
Weekend: $34
Discounts: None
Driving Range: No
Junior Golf: No
Architect/Yr Open: 1955
GPS:

27-hole course: Middle and South courses play for 18. North course is 9 holes, 3368 yards. Open year round.

	1	2	3	4	5	6	7	8	9
PAR	4	4	5	4	4	4	3	3	4
YARDS	340	397	489	373	274	419	197	173	339
	10	11	12	13	14	15	16	17	18
PAR	4	3	5	4	4	4	3	4	4
YARDS	388	169	518	334	317	367	183	413	315

Directions: Take I-495 to Exit 15, follow Route 1A South to Route 106; take right on West Bacon Street in Plainville Center. Course is on right.

Hidden Hollow Country Club

NR

30 Pierce Lane
Rehoboth, MA (508) 252-9392

Club Pro:
Payment: Cash Only
Tee Times: No
Fee 9 Holes: Weekday:
Fee 18 Holes: Weekday: $18
Twilight Rates: No
Cart Rental: $20pp/18,
Lessons: No **Schools:** No
Membership: No
Other: Snack Bar / Bar-Lounge / Clubhouse

Tees	Holes	Yards	Par	USGA	Slope
BACK					
MIDDLE	9	2905	35		
FRONT					

Weekend:
Weekend: $22
Discounts: None
Driving Range: No
Junior Golf: No
Architect/Yr Open: William B. Clark/1962
GPS:

Small, Old-style, picturesque short course. Popular preference of female golfers.

	1	2	3	4	5	6	7	8	9
PAR	4	4	3	4	4	5	4	3	4
YARDS	341	307	187	382	400	481	313	233	261
PAR									
YARDS									

Directions: I-195 to MA Exit 2. North off exit to Davis Street. Left on Pleasant. Course is 1 mile on left.

Highland Links

⭐⭐ **25** ▶

Highland Road
North Truro, MA (508) 487-9201
www.trurolinks.com

Club Pro: Jim Knowles, PGA
Payment: Visa, MC
Tee Times: Yes
Fee 9 Holes: Weekday: $35
Fee 18 Holes: Weekday: $60
Twilight Rates: No
Cart Rental: $18pp/18, $9pp/9
Lessons: $45/half hour **Schools:** No
Membership: Yes, $575
Other: Clubhouse / Snack Bar

Tees	Holes	Yards	Par	USGA	Slope
BACK					
MIDDLE	9	2720	35	67.0	114
FRONT	9	2294	36	67.8	117

Weekend: $35
Weekend: $60
Discounts: None
Driving Range: No
Junior Golf: Yes
Architect/Yr Open: Isiah M. Small/1892
GPS:

SE MA/ CAPE

Off-season rates available. The oldest links in New England. Wind, water, and a layout tucked into a natural site. See golf the way it was played in the old days. "Every golfer should make a journey here. Don't expect anything fancy, but it is a treat to play." –JD Improved irrigation and rebuilt #9 tee.

	1	2	3	4	5	6	7	8	9
PAR	4	5	3	4	4	5	3	4	3
YARDS	250	460	160	346	380	464	171	353	136
PAR									
YARDS									

Directions: Take Route 6 to Truro. Course is just past the Truro elementary school. (Look for signs on Route 6.)

Hillside Country Club

⭐⭐½ **26** ▶

82 Hillside Avenue
Rehoboth, MA (508) 252-9761
www.hillsidecountryclub.com

Club Pro:
Payment: Visa, MC, Disc, Cash
Tee Times:
Fee 9 Holes: Weekday: $18
Fee 18 Holes: Weekday: $25
Twilight Rates: No
Cart Rental: $18pp/18, $12pp/9
Lessons: No **Schools:** No
Membership: Yes
Other: Restaurant / Tiki Bar / Day Spa / Salt Water Pool / Fire Pits / Bocce / Tennis Courts / Volleyball Courts / Functions

Tees	Holes	Yards	Par	USGA	Slope
BACK					
MIDDLE	9	5912	72	68.4	126
FRONT	9	5686	70	67.5	119

Weekend: $22
Weekend: $28
Discounts: None
Driving Range: No
Junior Golf: Yes
Architect/Yr Open: George Cardono/1975

COUPON

New ownership, new management, major renovations and improvements. Play Blue tees on the front, White on the back. Two sets of tees mean change of par on the second 9. "Friendly staff. Good value." –FP

	1	2	3	4	5	6	7	8	9
PAR	4	3	5	3	4	4	5	4	4
YARDS	426	171	463	182	292	315	433	316	358
	10	11	12	13	14	15	16	17	18
PAR	4	3	5	3	4	4	4	4	4
YARDS	415	164	488	183	316	336	420	355	360

Directions: Take Route 24 South to Route 44 West - Taunton. Right onto River Street, first right onto Hillside Avenue.

Holly Ridge Golf Club

★★½

121 Country Club Road
Sandwich, MA (508) 428-5577
www.hollyridgegolf.com

Tees	Holes	Yards	Par	USGA	Slope
BACK	18	2952	54	55.4	74
MIDDLE	18	2715	54	54.1	N/A
FRONT	18	2194	54	54.8	N/A

Club Pro: Jean Enright
Payment: Visa, MC, Amex, Disc, Checks
Tee Times: 7 days adv.
Fee 9 Holes: Weekday: $21   **Weekend:** $21
Fee 18 Holes: Weekday: $34   **Weekend:** $34
Twilight Rates: After 3pm   **Discounts:** Senior & Junior
Cart Rental: $10pp/18, $6pp/9
Driving Range: $10/lg, $7/med, $4/sm
Lessons: $55/half hour **Schools:** Yes
Membership: No   **Junior Golf:** Yes
Other: Restaurant / Bar-Lounge / Clubhouse   **Architect/Yr Open:** Geoffrey Cornish/1967
GPS:

With a variety of par 3 holes nestled among the hollies and pines, the course appeals to golfers of all levels and is friendly to couples and families. Fun, friendly and affordable.

	1	2	3	4	5	6	7	8	9
PAR	3	3	3	3	3	3	3	3	3
YARDS	163	183	142	158	120	184	187	130	202
	10	11	12	13	14	15	16	17	18
PAR	3	3	3	3	3	3	3	3	3
YARDS	124	167	183	128	189	188	211	138	155

Directions: Take Route 3 South over Sagamore Bridge onto Route 6/Mid-Cape Highway. Take Exit 2 south on Route 130 for 1.6 miles, then left onto Cotuit Road for 1.4 miles and left onto Farmersville Road for 1.6 miles. Follow signs for Holly Ridge.

Hyannis Golf Club

★★★ 28

1840 Route 132
Hyannis, MA (508) 362-2606
www.barnstablegolf.com

Tees	Holes	Yards	Par	USGA	Slope
BACK	18	6621	71	71.1	133
MIDDLE	18	6002	71	70.6	129
FRONT	18	5149	72	71.9	127

Club Pro: Bruce McIntyre, Dir. of Golf
Payment: Cash, Check, Visa, MC, Amex
Tee Times: 10 days adv.
Fee 9 Holes: Weekday: $30   **Weekend:** $30
Fee 18 Holes: Weekday: $50   **Weekend:** $61
Twilight Rates: After 4pm   **Discounts:** Junior, after 12pm
Cart Rental: $19pp/18, $10pp/9   **Driving Range:** Yes
Lessons: $40/half hour; $80/hour   **Schools:** Jr. & Sr.
Junior Golf: Yes
Membership: Yes   **Architect/Yr Open:** Cornish and Robinson/1965
Other: Restaurant / Bar-Lounge / Lodging Partner

Home of Cape Cod's Open and Senior Open. Some of the Cape's most memorable holes. Lots of elevation changes from tees to fairways and back up to greens. Four sets of tees now available.

	1	2	3	4	5	6	7	8	9
PAR	4	4	4	4	5	4	3	3	4
YARDS	342	388	326	392	528	332	144	195	406
	10	11	12	13	14	15	16	17	18
PAR	5	3	4	4	5	3	4	4	4
YARDS	455	125	367	315	515	138	308	338	388

Directions: Take Route 6 (Mid-Cape Highway) to Exit 6 (Route 132). Go south on Route 132 for ¼ mile and golf course is on left.

John F. Parker Municipal GC ⚙⚙

29

17 Fisher Street
Taunton, MA (508) 822-1797
www.johnfparkergc.com

Club Pro: Hank Wojtkunski, PGA
Payment: Cash Only
Tee Times: No
Fee 9 Holes: Weekday: $18
Fee 18 Holes: Weekday: $21
Twilight Rates: No
Cart Rental: $8pp/9
Lessons: Yes **Schools:** Yes
Membership: Yes
Other: Snack Bar / Bar-Lounge

Tees	Holes	Yards	Par	USGA	Slope
BACK					
MIDDLE	9	3068	35	69.8	117
FRONT					

Weekend: $21
Weekend: $24
Discounts: Senior
Driving Range: $4/lg bucket
Junior Golf: Yes
Architect/Yr Open: 1938
GPS:

SE MA/ CAPE

Fun course to play and great, friendly staff. "Small, true greens with good fairways mowed with false fronts. Good for all levels of play." –GG

	1	2	3	4	5	6	7	8	9
PAR	4	4	4	5	4	3	4	4	3
YARDS	360	412	350	478	345	168	330	390	235
PAR									
YARDS									

Directions: Route 24 to Route 140. Go west on Route 140 to center of Taunton. Pick up Route 44 West out of city. Go to 2nd set of traffic lights at Highland Street. Go right on Highland Street. Turn left onto Fisher Street.

Lakeville Country Club ⚙⚙

30

Clear Pond Road
Lakeville, MA (508) 947-6630
www.lakevillecountryclub.com

Club Pro:
Payment: Visa, MC
Tee Times: 1 week adv.
Fee 9 Holes: Weekday: $26 M-Th $41/cart **Weekend:** $27 F/S/S $42/cart
Fee 18 Holes: Weekday: $40 M-Th $55/cart **Weekend:** $45 F/S/S $60/cart
Twilight Rates: After 1pm
Cart Rental: $15pp/18, $10pp/9
Lessons: No **Schools:** No
Membership: No
Other: Restaurant / Clubhouse / Snack Bar / Bar-Lounge

Tees	Holes	Yards	Par	USGA	Slope
BACK	18	6335	72	70.6	125
MIDDLE	18	5890	72	68.6	123
FRONT	18	4863	72	67.4	111

Discounts: Senior
Driving Range: No
Junior Golf: No
Architect/Yr Open: Roger Beach/1970

Early-bird special before 8:30am. Enthusiastic, friendly staff. Course is in good shape. Public course with private conditions.

	1	2	3	4	5	6	7	8	9
PAR	4	3	4	4	5	5	3	5	3
YARDS	334	216	351	432	533	538	216	521	166
	10	**11**	**12**	**13**	**14**	**15**	**16**	**17**	**18**
PAR	4	4	5	4	5	4	3	3	4
YARDS	339	380	500	324	463	335	139	178	370

Directions: I-495 to Exit 5. Go south on Route 18. Take left at first light to Route 79, then first right onto Clear Pond Road. Entrance is ½ mile on right.

Little Harbor Country Club

NR 31 ▶

1 Little Harbor Road
Wareham, MA (508) 295-2617
www.littleharborcountryclub.com

Tees	Holes	Yards	Par	USGA	Slope
BACK					
MIDDLE	18	3038	56	54.4	79
FRONT	18	2692	56	51.9	72

Club Pro: Shawn Lapworth
Payment: Visa, MC, Amex, Cash
Tee Times: 3 days adv.
Fee 9 Holes: Weekday: $18
Fee 18 Holes: Weekday: $28
Twilight Rates: After 3pm
Cart Rental: $11pp/18, $6pp/9
Lessons: $70 **Schools:** No
Membership: Associate
Other: Clubhouse / Snack Bar

Weekend: $20
Weekend: $31
Discounts: Senior & Junior
Driving Range: No
Junior Golf: Yes
Architect/Yr Open: Richard Bowler/1963
GPS:

COUPON

Holes range from 110 yards to 315 yards. Course and greens are in great condition. Open year round.

	1	2	3	4	5	6	7	8	9
PAR	3	3	3	3	3	4	4	3	3
YARDS	100	135	142	138	225	291	275	162	189
	10	11	12	13	14	15	16	17	18
PAR	3	3	3	3	3	3	3	3	3
YARDS	205	125	140	132	183	100	156	132	208

Directions: Take Route 6 to Depot Street. Follow Great Neck Road 2.5 miles. Go right on Stockton Shortcut Street. Take the 2nd right onto Little Harbor Road.

Locust Valley Golf Course

✪✪ 32 ▶

106 Locust Street
Attleboro, MA (508) 222-1500
www.locustvalleygolfcourse.com

Tees	Holes	Yards	Par	USGA	Slope
BACK					
MIDDLE	9	3065	36	69.8	124
FRONT	9	2615	36	NA	NA

Club Pro:
Payment: Visa, MC
Tee Times: No
Fee 9 Holes: Weekday:
Fee 18 Holes: Weekday: $11 unlimited
Twilight Rates: No
Cart Rental: $14pp/18
Lessons: No **Schools:** No
Membership: Yes
Other: Snack Bar / Bar-Lounge

Weekend:
Weekend: $15 unlimited
Discounts: Senior & Junior (M-F)
Driving Range: No
Junior Golf: No
Architect/Yr Open: 1939
GPS:

Special weekday fee $7.50 - Monday, Juniors; Thursday, Ladies. Wide open and an easy walker. Saturday and Sunday $10 after 2pm. "Great greens." –GG

	1	2	3	4	5	6	7	8	9
PAR	5	5	4	4	4	3	4	3	4
YARDS	465	485	360	335	375	150	373	160	362
PAR									
YARDS									

Directions: I-95 to Exit 3A to Route 123. Proceed on Route 123, at second light continue straight for 1 mile and follow to the end of road. Take a right onto Route 152 and an immediate left onto Tyler Street. Road ends at course.

Marion Golf Course

10 South Drive
Marion, MA (508) 748-0199
www.mariongolf.com

Club Pro:
Payment: Cash Only
Tee Times: No
Fee 9 Holes: Weekday: $14.50
Fee 18 Holes: Weekday: $22
Twilight Rates:
Cart Rental: $10pp/9, $20pp/18
Lessons: No **Schools:** No
Membership: Yes
Other: Club Rentals

Tees	Holes	Yards	Par	USGA	Slope
BACK	9	2695	34	67.1	121
MIDDLE	9	2695	34	67.1	121
FRONT	9	2089	35	66.0	117

Weekend: $17
Weekend: $24.50
Discounts: Sr./Jr. $2 off for 18 holes
Driving Range: No
Junior Golf: Yes
Architect/Yr Open: George Thomas/1904
GPS:

COUPON

European-style links. Open year round. "Several greens are defended by stone walls and cross bunkers. A wonderful 9 for the golf purist." –AP

	1	2	3	4	5	6	7	8	9
PAR	4	4	3	5	4	4	4	3	3
YARDS	315	290	175	460	365	430	365	180	115

PAR									
YARDS									

Directions: I-495 to I-195 East. Go to Exit 20. Bear right off exit onto Route 105. Follow to lights, bear left onto Route 6. Follow to next set of lights, bear right onto Point Road. Follow approximately 1.5 miles. Course on right.

MGA Links at Mamantapett

300 West Main Street (Route 123)
Norton, MA (508) 222-0555
www.mgalinks.org

Club Pro: Pete Walsh, PGA
Payment: Cash, Credit Cards, Checks
Tee Times: No
Fee 9 Holes: Weekday: $15
Fee 18 Holes: Weekday: $20
Twilight Rates: No
Cart Rental: $3/18, $2/9 pull carts only
Lessons: No **Schools:** No
Membership: Yes
Other: Lounge

Tees	Holes	Yards	Par	USGA	Slope
BACK					
MIDDLE	18	2421	54		
FRONT	18	2321	56		

Weekend: $15
Weekend: $20
Discounts: Junior $7pp/9, $10pp/18
Driving Range: No
Junior Golf: Yes
Architect/Yr Open: 1972
GPS:

Good course for women, seniors, short game and irons practice. First Tee and MGA ForeKids Program Monday through Thursday. Available for adult public play daily. Open year round.

	1	2	3	4	5	6	7	8	9
PAR	3	3	3	3	3	3	3	3	3
YARDS	117	135	82	140	93	91	115	136	108
	10	**11**	**12**	**13**	**14**	**15**	**16**	**17**	**18**
PAR	3	3	3	3	3	3	3	3	3
YARDS	131	138	125	203	141	113	147	233	173

Directions: Take I-495 to Exit 10 (Route 123 West). Go approximately 4 miles. Course is on left.

Miacomet Golf Club ✪✪

12 West Miacomet Road
Nantucket, MA (508) 325-0333
www.miacometgolf.com

Tees	Holes	Yards	Par	USGA	Slope
BACK	18	6890	72	73.6	128
MIDDLE	18	6393	72	71.5	125
FRONT	18	5145	72	70.6	121

Club Pro: Phillip Truono
Payment: Visa, MC, Amex, Disc
Tee Times: 4 days adv.
Fee 9 Holes: Weekday: $75   **Weekend:** $75
Fee 18 Holes: Weekday: $119   **Weekend:** $119
Twilight Rates: $50 after 4pm   **Discounts:** Senior
Cart Rental: $21pp/18, $12pp/9 **Driving Range:** $10/lg, $5/sm bucket
Lessons: $125/hour **Schools:** Yes **Junior Golf:** Yes
Membership: Waitlist   **Architect/Yr Open:** H. Maurer/1970
Other: Restaurant / Clubhouse / Snack Bar / Bar-Lounge / Lodging Partner

One of the best conditioned courses in New England. A course for all golfers. Difficult par 3's from the Tips.

	1	2	3	4	5	6	7	8	9
PAR	4	4	3	5	5	4	4	3	4
YARDS	380	328	191	464	473	350	389	210	357
	10	11	12	13	14	15	16	17	18
PAR	4	4	3	4	5	3	4	4	5
YARDS	398	331	167	377	450	122	374	393	439

Directions: Nantucket is an island 25 miles off the coast of Cape Cod. Airport and ferry boat dock are in Hyannis.

Middlebrook Country Club ✪✪

149 Pleasant Street
Rehoboth, MA (508) 252-9395

Tees	Holes	Yards	Par	USGA	Slope
BACK					
MIDDLE	9	2784	35	67.0	122
FRONT	9	2509	35	N/A	108

Club Pro:
Payment: Visa, MC
Tee Times: Weekends
Fee 9 Holes: Weekday: $17   **Weekend:** $20
Fee 18 Holes: Weekday: $22   **Weekend:** $25
Twilight Rates: After 2:00pm   **Discounts:** Senior
Cart Rental: $24/18, $14/9 per cart **Driving Range:** No
Lessons: No **Schools:** No   **Junior Golf:** No
Membership: Currently full   **Architect/Yr Open:** 1950
Other: Snack Bar / Bar-Lounge / Clubhouse **GPS:**

Open April 1 - November 30.
"Fun layout with hands-on husband and wife owners. Well-kept. Give it a try." –FP

	1	2	3	4	5	6	7	8	9
PAR	4	4	4	4	5	3	3	4	4
YARDS	340	360	301	350	500	213	130	300	290
PAR									
YARDS									

Directions: Take I-195 to MA Exit 2. North off exit to Davis Street. Right on Davis to Pleasant Street. Left on Pleasant. Course is one mile on right.

Mink Meadows Golf Course ✪✪ 37 ▶

320 Golf Club Road
Vineyard Haven, MA (508) 693-0600
www.minkmeadowsgc.com

Club Pro: Chet Nowak
Payment: Visa, MC, Amex, Disc, Check
Tee Times: 2 days adv.
Fee 9 Holes: Weekday: $60
Fee 18 Holes: Weekday: $88
Twilight Rates: After 4:30pm
Cart Rental: $18pp/18, $11pp/9
Lessons: Yes **Schools:** No
Membership: Yes
Other: Snack Bar

Tees	Holes	Yards	Par	USGA	Slope
BACK					
MIDDLE	9	3078	35	69.9	126
FRONT	9	2729	35	71.7	123

Weekend: $60
Weekend: $88
Discounts: Jr. membership
Driving Range: $8/lg, $4/sm bucket
Junior Golf: Yes
Architect/Yr Open: Wayne Stiles/1939
GPS:

Easy to walk, beautiful, challenging course. Off-season rates.

	1	2	3	4	5	6	7	8	9
PAR	4	4	4	4	3	4	3	5	4
YARDS	349	328	355	424	186	394	166	500	376
PAR									
YARDS									

Directions: From ferry, proceed to Main Street in Vineyard Haven. Take 2nd left and proceed to 2nd right (Franklin Street). Go 1.25 miles down Franklin Street to club entrance on left.

Norton Country Club ✪✪✪ 38 ▶

188 Oak Street
Norton, MA (508) 285-2400
www.nortoncountryclub.com

Club Pro: Jeff Martin
Payment: Most Major Credit Cards
Tee Times: 7 days adv.
Fee 9 Holes: Weekday: $25 M-Th
Fee 18 Holes: Weekday: $40 M-Th
Twilight Rates: $30 after 4pm
Cart Rental: $16pp/18, $10pp/9
Lessons: Yes **Schools:** No
Membership: Yes
Other: Clubhouse / Lockers / Showers / Snack Bar / Bar-Lounge

Tees	Holes	Yards	Par	USGA	Slope
BACK	18	6545	71	72.2	137
MIDDLE	18	6201	71	69.9	132
FRONT	18	5040	71	71.0	124

Weekend: $30 F/S/S
Weekend: $66 including cart F/S/S
Discounts: Lunch specials M-Th
Driving Range: No
Junior Golf: No
Architect/Yr Open: Cornish & Silva/1989

COUPON

Course is for serious golfers. "Beautiful course, great condition." "Not too long but tough. Course management a must, especially for first 6 holes."

	1	2	3	4	5	6	7	8	9
PAR	4	4	3	5	5	4	3	4	4
YARDS	346	426	143	500	492	419	105	383	313
	10	11	12	13	14	15	16	17	18
PAR	4	4	3	4	5	4	3	4	4
YARDS	328	344	138	298	489	414	120	358	389

Directions: Take Route 123 (Exit 10) off I-495. Take 123 West toward Norton Center to Oak Street. Club is 1 mile on the left.

Olde Barnstable Fairgrounds GC ✪✪✪

39 ▶

1460 Route 149
Marstons Mills, MA (508) 420-1141
www.obfgolf.com

Tees	Holes	Yards	Par	USGA	Slope
BACK	18	6479	71	71.4	128
MIDDLE	18	6113	71	69.7	124
FRONT	18	5072	71	69.1	119

Club Pro: Merry Holway, PGA
Payment: Cash, MC, Visa, Checks
Tee Times: 10 days adv.
Fee 9 Holes: Weekday:
Fee 18 Holes: Weekday: $66
Twilight Rates: After 4pm
Cart Rental: $19pp/18, $10pp/9
Lessons: Yes **Schools:** No
Membership: Yes
Other: Restaurant / Lodging Partner / Bar-Lounge

Weekend:
Weekend: $66
Discounts: Junior after 12pm
Driving Range: Yes
Junior Golf: Yes
Architect/Yr: Mark Mungeam/1992

COUPON

Player Comments: "From 1st tee to 18th green, a great test of golf. Great Cape Cod conditions."
Rates subject to change. Home to the 2007 Cape Cod Open. Four sets of tees now available.

	1	2	3	4	5	6	7	8	9
PAR	5	3	5	3	4	4	4	4	4
YARDS	485	140	503	158	365	351	430	317	385
	10	11	12	13	14	15	16	17	18
PAR	5	4	3	4	4	3	4	3	5
YARDS	510	335	157	340	380	172	395	155	535

Directions: Sagamore Bridge to Route 6, Exit 5, take right off ramp. Bear right on Route 149.
Course is ½ mile on left.

Paul Harney Golf Club ✪✪✪½

40 ▶

74 Club Valley Drive
East Falmouth, MA (508) 563-3454
www.paulharneygolf.com

Tees	Holes	Yards	Par	USGA	Slope
BACK	18	3570	59	58.9	91
MIDDLE	18	3315	59	56.7	89
FRONT	18	3200	61	61.0	89

Club Pro: Mike Harney
Payment: Cash, Visa, MC
Tee Times: No
Fee 9 Holes: Weekday: $30 M-Th
Fee 18 Holes: Weekday: $30 M-Th
Twilight Rates: After 2pm, $25
Cart Rental: $15 pp/18, $7.50 pp/9
Lessons: $40/half hour, $75/hour **Schools:** Yes
Membership: No
Other: Bar-Lounge / Snack Bar

Weekend: $30 F/S/S
Weekend: $30 F/S/S
Discounts: None
Driving Range: No
Junior Golf: Yes
Architect/Yr Open: Paul Harney/1968
GPS:

COUPON

A true test for all golfers. Executive-style course. Paul Harney inducted into PGA Hall of Fame in 2005.
Family-friendly and fun for all levels and abilities.

	1	2	3	4	5	6	7	8	9
PAR	4	3	3	3	3	3	4	3	3
YARDS	345	155	160	235	155	180	260	160	170
	10	11	12	13	14	15	16	17	18
PAR	3	3	3	3	4	4	3	3	4
YARDS	185	225	150	90	250	270	165	175	255

Directions: From Bourne Bridge take Route 28 East. Then take Route 151 toward Mashpee. Go 3-4
miles and take a left onto Fordham Road. Take left onto Club Valley Road to clubhouse.

Pine Valley Country Club ✪✪½

136 Providence Street
Rehoboth, MA (508) 336-9815

Tees	Holes	Yards	Par	USGA	Slope
BACK					
MIDDLE	9	3015	35		118
FRONT	9	2375	35		113

Club Pro:
Payment: Visa, MC
Tee Times: No
Fee 9 Holes: Weekday: | **Weekend:** $32 w/cart
Fee 18 Holes: Weekday: $16/sr.; $20/reg. | **Weekend:** $22
Twilight Rates: Yes | **Discounts:**
Cart Rental: $10pp/18, $5pp/9 | **Driving Range:** No
Lessons: No **Schools:** No | **Junior Golf:** No
Membership: No | **Architect/Yr Open:** 1945
Other: Snack Bar / Bar-Lounge | **GPS:**

Player Comments: Interesting layout, friendly staff, affordable prices.

	1	2	3	4	5	6	7	8	9
PAR	4	3	4	5	4	3	4	4	44
YARDS	387	172	397	568	306	218	383	301	283
PAR									
YARDS									

Directions: I-95 to I-195 East; take Exit 2 Route 136 North. Left onto Davis; turn right at end of road.

Poquoy Brook Golf Course ✪✪✪½

20 Leonard Street
Lakeville, MA (508) 947-5261
www.poquoybrook.com

Tees	Holes	Yards	Par	USGA	Slope
BACK	18	6817	72	72.4	128
MIDDLE	18	6291	72	69.9	125
FRONT	18	5415	73	71.0	114

Club Pro: Nora Berard, Dir. of Golf
Payment: Cash, All Major Credit Cards
Tee Times: M-F, 7 days adv.; S/S, 5 days adv.
Fee 9 Holes: Weekday: $24 | **Weekend:** $27
Fee 18 Holes: Weekday: $40 | **Weekend:** $49
Twilight Rates: After 5pm | **Discounts:** Junior under 18
Cart Rental: $16pp/18, $11pp/9 | **Driving Range:** $5/lg, $3/sm
Lessons: Yes **Schools:** Yes | **Junior Golf:** Yes
Membership: Yes | **Architect/Yr Open:** Geoffrey Cornish/1962
Other: Clubhouse / Lockers / Showers / Snack Bar / Restaurant / Bar-Lounge

COUPON

Player Comments: "Good conditions, good staff, nice clubhouse." "Interesting layout with great holes."
Open year round. Grows on you with each replay. 2 new tees completed and a great new website.

	1	2	3	4	5	6	7	8	9
PAR	4	4	3	4	5	4	4	3	5
YARDS	351	390	176	307	518	326	381	180	485
	10	11	12	13	14	15	16	17	18
PAR	4	4	3	4	5	3	4	4	5
YARDS	372	336	185	366	436	173	426	428	455

Directions: I-495 South: take Exit 5, Route 18 South. Bear right off exit. Take first right (Taunton
Street) and then first left onto Leonard Street. Course is on right.

Quashnet Valley Country Club ★★½ ▶43

309 Old Barnstable Road
Mashpee, MA (508) 477-4412
www.quashnetvalley.com

Tees	Holes	Yards	Par	USGA	Slope
BACK	18	6601	72	71.7	132
MIDDLE	18	6093	72	69.1	121
FRONT	18	5094	72	70.3	119

Club Pro: Bob Chase, PGA
Payment: Visa, MC, Disc
Tee Times: 1 week, prepay 6 months
Fee 9 Holes: Weekday: $24   **Weekend:** $29
Fee 18 Holes: Weekday: $47   **Weekend:** $57
Twilight Rates: After 2pm   **Discounts:** None
Cart Rental: $18pp/18, $9pp/9   **Driving Range:** Yes
Lessons: $60 **Schools:** Yes   **Junior Golf:** Yes
Membership: Yes   **Architect/Yr Open:** Cornish & Robinson/1973
Other: Clubhouse / Showers / Snack Bar / Bar-Lounge / Banquet Facilities

Golf Digest's 4 Star Rating. Host of 2010 MGA Public Links. The experience begins and ends with challenging par 5s. Very natural setting with only one set parallel fairways on the course. No visible homes until the 10th hole. Ponds and streams abound. Player Comments: "Excellent layout. Great shape. Must play when on Cape. Friendly staff. Beautiful setting through old cranberry bogs."

	1	2	3	4	5	6	7	8	9
PAR	5	3	4	4	3	4	5	3	4
YARDS	505	135	328	310	153	420	488	173	349
	10	11	12	13	14	15	16	17	18
PAR	4	4	4	5	4	4	4	3	5
YARDS	302	390	322	530	354	360	339	155	480

Directions: Take Route 6 East to Exit 2. Take right onto Route 130 South, follow 7.2 miles then take a right onto Great Neck Road. Follow 1.6 miles, take right onto Old Barnstable Road. Course is on left at the end.

Rehoboth Country Club ★½ ▶44

155 Perryville Road
Rehoboth, MA (508) 252-6259
www.rehobothcountryclub.com

Tees	Holes	Yards	Par	USGA	Slope
BACK	18	6760	72	71.4	124
MIDDLE	18	6340	72	69.3	121
FRONT	18	5490	72	70.6	114

Club Pro:
Payment: Visa, MC,
Tee Times: 7 days adv.
Fee 9 Holes: Weekday: $20   **Weekend:** $26
Fee 18 Holes: Weekday: $30   **Weekend:** $36
Twilight Rates: After 12pm   **Discounts:** Senior & Junior
Cart Rental: $16pp/18, $8pp/9   **Driving Range:** No
Lessons: No **Schools:** No   **Junior Golf:** No
Membership: Yes   **Architect/Yr Open:** Geoffrey Cornish/1966
Other: Snack Bar / Clubhouse / Restaurant / Bar-Lounge
GPS: Yes

Improved greens, tees and bunkers. Great new menu at our Sandwedges Restaurant. Noted for large true greens and use of every club in bag. 20 minutes outside Providence, RI. Call golf course for weekday specials.

	1	2	3	4	5	6	7	8	9
PAR	4	5	3	5	4	4	4	3	4
YARDS	380	500	155	550	400	310	300	155	410
	10	11	12	13	14	15	16	17	18
PAR	5	4	3	4	4	4	3	5	4
YARDS	500	345	205	380	330	270	170	540	440

Directions: From Providence: East on Route 44 to Route 118; turn left and 1st left to course. From Taunton: West on Route 44 to Route 118. Turn right, 1st left to course. From Attleboro: East on Route 118, right on Fairview to Homestead. Right, then 1st left onto Perryville.

Rochester Golf Club ○○ ▶ 45

323 Rounseville Road
Rochester, MA (508) 763-5155
www.rochestergolf.net

Club Pro: Rusty Gunnerson, PGA
Payment: Cash Only
Tee Times: 2 days adv. (Sat, Sun, & holidays)
Fee 9 Holes: Weekday: $15
Fee 18 Holes: Weekday: $25
Twilight Rates: No
Cart Rental: $20/18, $10/9 per cart
Lessons: $60/45 min.; Private **Schools:** No
Membership: No
Other: Snack Bar

Tees	Holes	Yards	Par	USGA	Slope
BACK	18	5280	69	66	119
MIDDLE	18	4830	69	64	114
FRONT	18	4032	69	64	107

Weekend: $16
Weekend: $27
Discounts: None
Driving Range: No
Junior Golf: Yes
Architect/Yr Open: 1969
GPS:

Course is challenging with beautiful scenery. New sandtraps. Accuracy at premium, not long but tight. "Heavy forest and water on 14 holes define the challenge. Think twice about pulling out the big dawg." –AP

	1	2	3	4	5	6	7	8	9
PAR	3	4	4	4	3	5	4	4	3
YARDS	156	386	258	252	128	435	250	312	116
	10	11	12	13	14	15	16	17	18
PAR	4	3	4	4	3	4	4	4	5
YARDS	280	110	272	290	180	260	280	373	492

Directions: I-195 to Rochester exit, follow Route 105 approximately 4 miles north on right.

Sandwich Hollows Golf Club ○○ ▶ 46

1 Round Hill Road
East Sandwich, MA
(508) 888-3384 x0
www.sandwichhollows.com

Club Pro: Jesse Schechtman, PGA
Payment: MC, Visa, Check
Tee Times: 3 week adv.

Tees	Holes	Yards	Par	USGA	Slope
BACK	18	6220	71	70.4	124
MIDDLE	18	5891	71	68.6	120
FRONT	18	4894	71	68.1	115

Fee 9 Holes: Weekday: $20, $29 ride   **Weekend:** $22, $31 ride
Fee 18 Holes: Weekday: $37.95 M/T/Th w/cart **Weekend:** $62 w/cart
Twilight Rates: $30 after 2pm w/cart; $24 after 4pm w/cart
Discounts: None
Cart Rental: Included   **Driving Range:** $5 bucket, all grass tees
Lessons: $40/half hour **Schools:** Adult Intro. **Junior Golf:** Yes
Membership: Full and Seasonal (wkdays only) **Architect/Yr Open:** Richard Cross/1972
Other: Clubhouse / Restaurant / Lounge / Function Facilities

COUPON

The course is hilly. Accurate shots are essential. Open year round. All-day special on Wednesday includes greens fee and cart. Pleasant views of Cape Cod Bay.

	1	2	3	4	5	6	7	8	9
PAR	5	4	3	4	4	5	3	4	4
YARDS	485	325	120	305	347	570	177	340	401
	10	11	12	13	14	15	16	17	18
PAR	4	4	3	4	5	3	4	4	4
YARDS	300	380	175	285	520	160	340	355	330

Directions: Located between Exits 3 and 4 on Route 6 (Mid-Cape Highway) on service road.

Siasconset Golf Course

260 Milestone Road
Nantucket, MA (508) 257-6596
www.siasconsetgolf.com

Tees	Holes	Yards	Par	USGA	Slope
BACK					
MIDDLE	9	2582	34		
FRONT					

Club Pro: Phillip Truono
Payment: Visa, MC, Amex, Disc, Checks
Tee Times: No
Fee 9 Holes: Weekday: $35   **Weekend:** $35
Fee 18 Holes: Weekday: $60   **Weekend:** $60
Twilight Rates: No   **Discounts:** Junior
Cart Rental: Walking carts $5   **Driving Range:** No
Lessons: No **Schools:** No   **Junior Golf:** No
Membership: Yes   **Architect/Yr Open:** John Grout/1894
Other: **GPS:** Yes

A historic golf course with small greens. The fairways are not irrigated taking the golfer back in time with a feel for what golf used to be. A must-play when on Nantucket.

	1	2	3	4	5	6	7	8	9
PAR	3	5	3	5	3	4	3	4	4
YARDS	200	480	217	450	140	245	215	325	310
PAR									
YARDS									

Directions: From Nantucket Town Center drive 7 miles on Milestone Road.

Stone-E-Lea Golf Course

1411 County Street
Attleboro, MA (508) 222-9735
www.selgc.com

Tees	Holes	Yards	Par	USGA	Slope
BACK					
MIDDLE	18	6251	69	69.5	116
FRONT	18	6030	69	67.8	112

Club Pro:
Payment: Cash or Credit
Tee Times: No
Fee 9 Holes: Weekday: $16   **Weekend:** $20
Fee 18 Holes: Weekday: $24   **Weekend:** $32
Twilight Rates: Yes   **Discounts:** Seniors and Juniors
Cart Rental: $24/18, $12/9 per cart **Driving Range:** No
Lessons: No **Schools:** No   **Junior Golf:** Yes
Membership: No   **Architect/Yr Open:**
Other: Value Packages   **GPS:**

Discounts for seniors over 62 after 2pm Monday through Friday. Open year round. Clubhouse is newly renovated. "Easy course to walk." –FP

	1	2	3	4	5	6	7	8	9
PAR	4	4	4	3	4	4	3	4	4
YARDS	360	350	310	185	330	420	175	380	430
	10	**11**	**12**	**13**	**14**	**15**	**16**	**17**	**18**
PAR	5	4	4	4	4	3	4	4	3
YARDS	490	390	410	390	265	190	390	325	240

Directions: I-95 to Exit 3 to 123 West. At first light take left onto Tiffany Street. Next light take right onto County Street. Course is at top of hill on right.

Sun Valley Golf Course ✪ ▸ 49

329 Summer Street
Rehoboth, MA (508) 336-8686

Tees	Holes	Yards	Par	USGA	Slope
BACK	18	6734	71	71.0	118
MIDDLE	18	6383	71	71.0	118
FRONT	18	5654	71	71.0	N/A

Club Pro:
Payment: Cash Only
Tee Times: No
Fee 9 Holes: Weekday: $20
Fee 18 Holes: Weekday: $25
Twilight Rates: After 2pm
Cart Rental: $26/18, $14/9 per cart
Lessons: No **Schools:** No
Membership: No
Other: Restaurant / Clubhouse / Bar-Lounge / Lockers / Snack Bar / Showers

Weekend:
Weekend: $30
Discounts: Seniors play for $18
Driving Range:
Junior Golf: No
Architect/Yr Open: Benjamin J. Wihry/1961

Sig. hole: #12, dogleg right, green to the left, brook runs through it. Flat, willow-tree-lined, large fairways (wide); some brooks, greens excellent. Open March - November.

	1	2	3	4	5	6	7	8	9
PAR	4	4	5	3	4	3	5	4	4
YARDS	345	336	475	180	380	155	510	415	400
	10	11	12	13	14	15	16	17	18
PAR	4	5	4	3	4	4	3	4	4
YARDS	365	450	425	172	380	400	195	385	415

Directions: Route I-195 West to Route 114A to Route 44 East for 3 miles. Take right on Lake Street. Go 1 mile to course.

Swansea Country Club ✪✪ ▸ 50

299 Market Street
Swansea, MA (508) 379-9886 x1
www.swanseacountryclub.com

Tees	Holes	Yards	Par	USGA	Slope
BACK	18	6840	72	72.8	126
MIDDLE	18	6429	72	70.9	125
FRONT	18	5598	72	69.4	113

Club Pro: Shane Drury, PGA
Payment: Visa, MC, Disc, Amex, Cash
Tee Times: 6 days adv. (508) 379-9886 x1
Fee 9 Holes: Weekday: $24
Fee 18 Holes: Weekday: $32
Twilight Rates: After 5:45pm
Cart Rental: $15pp/18, $8pp/9
Lessons: Yes **Schools:** Yes
Membership: See website for details
Other: Clubhouse / Snack Bar / Restaurant / Bar-Lounge / Outdoor Patio & Tent Seating for 200

Weekend: $28
Weekend: $42
Discounts: Senior & Junior, wkdys
Driving Range: Yes, grass tees
Junior Golf: Yes
Architect/Yr Open: Geoffrey Cornish/1963

2nd hole redesigned. Improved irrigation and new sets of tees in 2012. Great value, excellent course conditions. Just 10 minutes outside Providence. Great for large groups and outings. Look for the lunch specials.

	1	2	3	4	5	6	7	8	9
PAR	4	5	4	3	4	3	4	5	4
YARDS	331	496	415	206	353	118	366	475	419
	10	11	12	13	14	15	16	17	18
PAR	4	3	4	5	4	3	4	5	4
YARDS	323	170	366	615	291	203	368	478	436

Directions: I-195 East or West to Exit #2 (Massachusetts). South on Route 136 for 1 mile. Golf course is on right.

SE MA/ CAPE

Swansea Executive Par 3 ✪✪ ▶ 51

299 Market Street
Swansea, MA (508) 379-9886
www.swanseacountryclub.com

Tees	Holes	Yards	Par	USGA	Slope
BACK	9	1378	27	54.8	84
MIDDLE	9	1196	27	54..8	84
FRONT	9	957	27	57.0	89

Club Pro: Shane Drury, PGA
Payment: Most Major Cards, No Checks
Tee Times:
Fee 9 Holes: Weekday: $12   **Weekend:** $12
Fee 18 Holes: Weekday: $18   **Weekend:** $18
Twilight Rates: No   **Discounts:** None
Cart Rental: $12pp/18, $7pp/9   **Driving Range:** Yes
Lessons: Yes **Schools:** Yes   **Junior Golf:** Yes
Membership: Yes   **Architect/Yr Open:** M. Weremay/1997
Other: **GPS:**

A fine track in the beautiful setting of Narragansett Bay. Inquire about member rates: Family, Adult, Junior. Single-rider cart rates. 10 min. to downtown Providence.

	1	2	3	4	5	6	7	8	9
PAR	3	3	3	3	3	3	3	3	3
YARDS	153	115	160	128	134	141	101	122	142
PAR									
YARDS									

Directions: MA Exit 2 off I-195. Course is 1 mile south of freeway.

Touisset Country Club ✪✪✪ ▶ 52

221 Pearse Road
Swansea, MA (508) 679-9577
www.touissetcc.com

Tees	Holes	Yards	Par	USGA	Slope
BACK	9	3182	36	69.1	111
MIDDLE	9	3024	35	69.1	111
FRONT	9	2776	36	71.1	114

Club Pro:
Payment: Cash, Visa, MC, Disc
Tee Times: No
Fee 9 Holes: Weekday: $18.50   **Weekend:** $20.50
Fee 18 Holes: Weekday: $23   **Weekend:** $28
Twilight Rates: After 4pm   **Discounts:** Senior/Junior/Military
Cart Rental: $18pp/18, $13pp/9   **Driving Range:** No
Lessons: $19/half hour **Schools:** Yes   **Junior Golf:** Yes
Membership: Yes   **Architect/Yr Open:** Raymond H. Brigham/1961
Other: Snack Bar / Restaurant / Bar-Lounge / Clubhouse / Lockers / Practice Area and Putting Greens

COUPON

9 hole course with 4 sets of tees. Fairly flat but challenging. Open year round, weather permitting. Newly renovated pro shop with competitive pricing.

	1	2	3	4	5	6	7	8	9
PAR	4	4	4	4	3	4	3	5	4
YARDS	324	291	373	388	118	448	160	534	388
PAR									
YARDS									

Directions: Exit 3 off I-195, Route 6 West. Left at first traffic light onto Maple Street. Straight ¾ mile to 221 Pearse Road.

Twin Brooks Golf Course ✪✪✪

35 Scudder Avenue
Hyannis, MA (508) 862-6980
www.twinbrooksgolf.net

Tees	Holes	Yards	Par	USGA	Slope
BACK					
MIDDLE	18	2621	54		
FRONT	18	2230	54		

Club Pro:
Payment: Visa, MC, Amex, Diner's, Cash
Tee Times: Call
Fee 9 Holes: Weekday:
Fee 18 Holes: Weekday: $28 M-Th
Twilight Rates: $25 after 4pm M-Th
Cart Rental: $12pp/18, $4/pull
Lessons: Yes **Schools:** Yes
Membership: Yes
Other: Restaurant / Hotel / Bar-Lounge / Showers

Weekend:
Weekend: $33 F/S/S
Discounts: Senior/Junior $25
Driving Range: No
Junior Golf: No
Architect/Yr Open: Cornish & Robinson/1965
GPS:

COUPON

New home of Cape Cod Golf School facility. Perfect for all ages. Very challenging. Open year round. Rates subject to change. Guest rates available. Pull carts, drive carts, and rentals available.

	1	2	3	4	5	6	7	8	9
PAR	3	3	3	3	3	3	3	3	3
YARDS	135	90	165	144	110	102	175	140	135
	10	11	12	13	14	15	16	17	18
PAR	3	3	3	3	3	3	3	3	3
YARDS	190	140	150	115	170	215	150	160	135

Directions: Take Route 6 to Exit 6 (Hyannis), follow Route 132 to Hyannis, follow signs to West End - Hyannis. At rotary, you will see the resort and confence center.

Wampanoag Golf Club NR

168 Old Providence Road
North Swansea, MA (508) 379-9832
www.wampanoaggolfcouse.com

Tees	Holes	Yards	Par	USGA	Slope
BACK					
MIDDLE	9	2775	35	69.5	112
FRONT	9	2439	37	69.5	112

Club Pro:
Payment: Cash Only
Tee Times: No
Fee 9 Holes: Weekday: $15
Fee 18 Holes: Weekday: $20
Twilight Rates: No
Cart Rental: $14pp/18, $7pp/9
Lessons: No **Schools:** No
Membership: Yes
Other: Snack Bar / Bar-Lounge

Weekend: $20
Weekend: $25
Discounts: Senior & Junior
Driving Range: No
Junior Golf: No
Architect/Yr Open: Aljenon Barney/1931
GPS:

COUPON

Good mix of long par 3s and short par 5s. Long ball hitters have a definite advantage. Play front and back tees for an enjoyable 18 holes. Open year round. Yardage markers, superb greens & improved drainage.

	1	2	3	4	5	6	7	8	9
PAR	4	3	4	4	4	3	5	4	4
YARDS	305	115	343	400	397	150	417	301	343
PAR									
YARDS									

Directions: Take I-95 to Exit 2 (Warren/Newport), turn right onto Route 6. Turn left at Mason Street. At stop sign turn right on Old Providence Road.

Wentworth Hills Country Club ✪✪✪½   ▶ 55

27 Bow Street
Plainville, MA (508) 316-0240
www.wentworthhillsgc.com

Club Pro: Jimmy Bombard, Golf Instructor
Payment: Visa, MC, Amex
Tee Times: 7 days adv.
Fee 9 Holes: Weekday: $24
Fee 18 Holes: Weekday: $32
Twilight Rates: After 3pm
Cart Rental: $17pp/18, $9pp/9
Lessons: Yes **Schools:** Yes
Membership: No
Other: Restaurant / Clubhouse / Bar-Lounge

Tees	Holes	Yards	Par	USGA	Slope
BACK	18	6202	71	71.0	128
MIDDLE	18	5817	71	68.0	125
FRONT	18	5325	71	65.3	120

Weekend: $29
Weekend: $42
Discounts: Senior
Driving Range: Yes
Junior Golf: Yes
Architect/Yr Open: Howard Maurer/2001
GPS:

COUPON

Featuring the Barrie Bruce Golf School. "Tight oak and pine tree lined fairways with solid, fast running greens that hold your approach shots. Numerous interesting holes. A real gem." –GG

	1	2	3	4	5	6	7	8	9
PAR	4	3	4	4	5	4	4	3	4
YARDS	334	88	368	350	440	366	282	125	328
	10	11	12	13	14	15	16	17	18
PAR	4	4	5	4	4	5	3	3	4
YARDS	396	320	448	244	268	460	130	122	256

Directions: From Route 495, take Route 1A. Follow 1A South for 1 mile, right on Cross Street. Follow 1 mile to "T" intersection stop sign. Left at "T" intersection (High Street.) Proceed 1 mile, then right on Hancock Street. Follow .4 miles, then left on Bow Street to golf course entrance on right.

Whaling City Golf Course   ✪½   ▶ 56

581 Hathaway Road
New Bedford, MA (508) 996-9393
www.johnsongolfmanagement.com

Club Pro: Bill Allan, PGA
Payment: Cash, Credit Cards
Tee Times: 7 days adv.
Fee 9 Holes: Weekday: $17
Fee 18 Holes: Weekday: $29
Twilight Rates: No
Cart Rental: $15pp/18, $8pp/9
Lessons: Yes **Schools:** No
Membership: Yes
Other: Snack Bar / Restaurant / Bar-Lounge

Tees	Holes	Yards	Par	USGA	Slope
BACK	18	6780	72	73	131
MIDDLE	18	6527	72	70.2	126
FRONT	18	6457	74	70.1	118

Weekend: $19
Weekend: $33
Discounts: Junior and Resident
Driving Range: Yes
Junior Golf: No
Architect/Yr Open: Donald Ross/1946
GPS:

New tees. Municipal course. Managed by Johnson Management. Reasonable value. "Nice layout." –FP

	1	2	3	4	5	6	7	8	9
PAR	4	4	4	4	3	4	5	3	5
YARDS	448	382	409	343	190	381	530	140	453
	10	11	12	13	14	15	16	17	18
PAR	5	4	4	3	5	4	4	3	4
YARDS	535	379	436	163	499	333	356	179	331

Directions: Take Route 140 in New Bedford to Exit 3. Bear right.

Agawam Municipal CC	1	GEAA Golf Club	33	Quaboag Country Club	65
Amherst Golf Club	2	Grandview GC	34	Quail Hollow Golf & CC	66
Ashfield Community Golf Club	3	Green Hill Municipal GC	35	Ranch Golf Club, The	67
Bas Ridge Golf Course	4	Greenock Country Club	36	Red Tail Golf Club	68
Bay Path Golf Course	5	Groton Pool & GC	37	Settlers Crossing Golf Course	69
Beaver Brook Country Club	6	Hemlock Ridge GC	38	Shaker Farms CC	70
Bedrock Golf Club	7	Heritage Country Club	39	Shaker Hills Golf Club	71
Berlin Country Club	8	Hickory Ridge CC	40	Skyline Country Club	72
Blackstone National Golf Club	9	Highfields Golf & CC	41	Southampton CC	73
Blissful Meadows GC	10	Hillcrest Country Club	42	Southwick CC	74
Cherry Hill GC	11	Holden Hills CC	43	St. Anne Country Club	75
Chicopee Municipal GC	12	Holyoke Country Club	44	St. Mark's Golf Club	76
Clearview Golf Course	13	Hopedale CC	45	Taconic Golf Club	77
Cold Spring Country Club	14	Indian Meadows Golf Club	46	Tekoa Country Club	78
Country Club of Greenfield	15	Juniper Hill GC (Lakeside)	47	Templewood Golf Course	79
Country Club of Wilbraham	16	Juniper Hill GC (Riverside)	48	The International (The Oaks)	80
Cranwell Resort, Spa & GC	17	Kettle Brook Golf Club	49	Thomas Memorial Golf & CC	81
Crestview CC	18	Ledges Golf Club	50	Townsend Ridge CC	82
Crumpin-Fox Club	19	Leicester Country Club	51	Twin Springs Golf Club	83
Cyprian Keyes Golf Club	20	Links at Lancaster Golf, The	52	Tyngsboro CC	84
Cyprian Keyes GC, Par 3	21	Meadows Golf Club, The	53	Veteran's Golf Club	85
Donnybrook CC	22	Mill Valley Links	54	Wachusett CC	86
Dudley Hill Golf Club	23	Monoosnock CC	55	Wahconah CC	87
Dunroamin CC	24	North Adams CC	56	Waubeeka Golf Links	88
East Mountain CC	25	Northfield CC	57	Westborough CC	89
Edge Hill GC	26	Oak Ridge Golf Club	58	Westminster CC	90
Edgewood Golf Club	27	Oak Ridge GC-Gill	59	Westover Golf Course	91
Egremont Country Club	28	Pakachoag Golf Course	60	Winchendon School CC	92
Ellinwood CC	29	Pine Grove Golf Club	61	Woods of Westminster CC	93
Forest Park CC	30	Pine Knoll Par 3	62	Worthington GC	94
Franconia Muni. GC	31	Pine Ridge Country Club	63		
Gardner Municipal GC	32	Pontoosuc Lake CC	64		

KEY TO THE STAR RATINGS:
5✪ = Outstanding   4✪ = Excellent   3✪ = Very Good   2✪ = Good   1✪ = Average   **NR** = Not Rated

Agawam Municipal Country Club ○○

128 Southwick Street (Route 57)
Feeding Hills, MA (413) 786-2194
www.agawamgc.com

Club Pro: Ron Dunn, PGA
Payment: Cash, Visa, MC
Tee Times: 7 days adv.
Fee 9 Holes: Weekday: $13
Fee 18 Holes: Weekday: $17
Twilight Rates: After 12pm
Cart Rental: $13pp/18, $7pp/9
Lessons: Private & Group **Schools:** No
Membership: No
Other: Snack Bar / Bar-Lounge

Tees	Holes	Yards	Par	USGA	Slope
BACK					
MIDDLE	18	6119	71	67.0	110
FRONT	18	5345	71	71.2	110

Weekend: $15
Weekend: $20
Discounts: Senior & Junior
Driving Range: No
Junior Golf: Yes
Architect/Yr Open: Richard Leao/1929
GPS:

A friendly course. No water holes but 1 creek and 8 sand traps. Total irrigation. The 9th hole is referred to as "Cardiac Hill," and for good reason. Weekend specials before 8am and after 12pm. "Great bang for the buck." –FP

	1	2	3	4	5	6	7	8	9
PAR	5	4	3	4	3	4	4	5	3
YARDS	480	375	144	465	121	360	385	560	175
	10	11	12	13	14	15	16	17	18
PAR	5	4	4	3	4	3	5	5	3
YARDS	475	395	348	160	322	145	554	475	180

Directions: I-90 (Mass Pike) to I-91 to Route 57 (Agawam). Go west on Route 57. Club is in the town of Feeding Hills.

Amherst Golf Club ○○

365 South Pleasant Street
Amherst, MA (413) 256-6894
www.amherstgolfclub.org

Club Pro: Dave Twohig, PGA
Payment: Visa, MC
Tee Times: No
Fee 9 Holes: Weekday: $25
Fee 18 Holes: Weekday: $25
Twilight Rates: No
Cart Rental: $25/18 per cart
Lessons: $45/half hour **Schools:** No
Membership: Wait list
Other: Clubhouse / Lockers / Showers / Snack Bar

Tees	Holes	Yards	Par	USGA	Slope
BACK					
MIDDLE	9	3055	35	68.9	117
FRONT	9	2774	36	68.9	122

Weekend: $25
Weekend: $25
Discounts: None
Driving Range: No
Junior Golf: No
Architect/Yr Open: Walter Hatch/1900

COUPON

Sig. Hole #9 is a long, uphill par 3 with a sloping green. Collared shirts. Course is short in length with small greens, but in good shape. Old New England course.

	1	2	3	4	5	6	7	8	9
PAR	4	4	4	3	4	4	5	4	3
YARDS	390	375	405	160	350	340	525	310	200
PAR									
YARDS									

Directions: Take Mass Pike to Route 181 to Route 9 into Amherst. Course is located by Amherst College.

Ashfield Community Golf Club   NR

143 Norton Hill Road
Ashfield, MA (413) 628-4413

Club Pro:
Payment: Cash or Check
Tee Times: No
Fee 9 Holes: Weekday: $13
Fee 18 Holes: Weekday: $16
Twilight Rates: No
Cart Rental: $10pp/18, $7pp/9
Lessons: No **Schools:** No
Membership: Yes
Other: Clubhouse / Snack Bar

Tees	Holes	Yards	Par	USGA	Slope
BACK					
MIDDLE	9	2077	33		
FRONT	9	1729	33		

Weekend: $12
Weekend: $16
Discounts: None
Driving Range: No
Junior Golf: Yes
Architect/Yr Open: 1927
GPS:

Improved tee boxes. Honor system for play during the week, instructions for payment on clubhouse door. Attendant on weekends and holidays.

	1	2	3	4	5	6	7	8	9
PAR	4	4	3	4	3	4	4	4	3
YARDS	286	289	201	317	102	200	185	341	156

PAR									
YARDS									

Directions: I-91 North to Exit 24. Off ramp, go north on Route 5 and 10. Pass Yankee Candle to Route 116 West to center of Ashfield, MA. Turn left at Norton Hill Road, golf course up the hill on the right.

Bas Ridge Golf Course   ✪

151 Plunkett Street
Hinsdale, MA (413) 655-2605
www.basridge.com

Club Pro: Gary Norton, PGA
Payment: Cash Only
Tee Times: Recommended
Fee 9 Holes: Weekday: $12
Fee 18 Holes: Weekday: $15
Twilight Rates: After 4pm
Cart Rental: $10pp/18, $5pp/9
Lessons: Yes **Schools:**
Membership: Limited
Other: Clubhouse / Bar-Lounge

Tees	Holes	Yards	Par	USGA	Slope
BACK					
MIDDLE	18	5051	70	63.7	111
FRONT	18	4369	70	65.9	110

Weekend: $15
Weekend: $20
Discounts: Senior weekdays
Driving Range: No
Junior Golf: Yes
Architect/Yr Open: Rowland Armacost/1998
GPS:

"A shorter course, but fun." "Each hole is more beautiful and the greens are incredible." –BB
Open April 1 - November 1. New solar panels for club house plus computerized sprinkler system.

	1	2	3	4	5	6	7	8	9
PAR	4	4	3	4	3	4	4	4	4
YARDS	335	269	193	280	170	224	233	331	276
	10	11	12	13	14	15	16	17	18
PAR	4	4	3	4	5	3	5	4	4
YARDS	270	336	187	313	451	112	466	278	327

Directions: Take Mass Pike to Lee exit, go east on Route 20 about 8 miles. Left onto Route 8 North about 10 miles to Plunkett Street. Course is on the left.

Bay Path Golf Course

⭐½ 5 ▶

193 North Brookfield Road
East Brookfield, MA (508) 867-8161
www.baypathgolf.com

Club Pro:
Payment: Visa, MC
Tee Times: No
Fee 9 Holes: Weekday: $15
Fee 18 Holes: Weekday: $21
Twilight Rates: No
Cart Rental: $15pp/18, $10pp/9
Lessons: No **Schools:** No
Membership: Yes, limited
Other: Clubhouse / Snack Bar / Bar-Lounge

Tees	Holes	Yards	Par	USGA	Slope
BACK	9	2952	36	67.4	109
MIDDLE	9	2640	36	66.0	107
FRONT	9	2298	36	67.6	107

Weekend: $17
Weekend: $26
Discounts: Junior & Senior
Driving Range: No
Junior Golf: No
Architect/Yr Open: Don Hoenig/1962
GPS: No

COUPON

Player Comments: "Great deal for the money. Nice friendly staff and lounge." Very flat and easy to walk. Open April - November 15. Proper attire required.

	1	2	3	4	5	6	7	8	9
PAR	4	4	5	4	3	5	4	3	4
YARDS	297	273	456	305	131	426	270	151	331
PAR									
YARDS									

Directions: Mass. Pike to Route 20 East (Sturbridge exit). Then take Route 20 East to Route 49 North to Route 9 West to Route 67 North (North Brookfield Road). Course is approximately ¼ mile on left.

Beaver Brook Country Club

NR 6 ▶

183 Main Street
Haydenville, MA (413) 268-7229
www.beaverbrookma.com

Club Pro: Hiroshi Akimoto
Payment: Visa, MC
Tee Times: Yes
Fee 9 Holes: Weekday: $16
Fee 18 Holes: Weekday: $24
Twilight Rates: After 4pm
Cart Rental: Available
Lessons: No **Schools:** No
Membership: Yes
Other: Clubhouse / Snack Bar / Bar-Lounge

Tees	Holes	Yards	Par	USGA	Slope
BACK					
MIDDLE	9	3046	36	68.1	110
FRONT	9	2480	36	67.7	107

Weekend: $17
Weekend: $25
Discounts: Junior & Senior
Driving Range: No
Junior Golf: Yes
Architect/Yr Open: 1964
GPS:

COUPON

Beautifully laid out and maintained 9-hole course. The course sports 2 brooks and 4 ponds. Special Mon-Sat: 2 players w/cart 9 holes $37, 18 holes $58 until 2pm.

	1	2	3	4	5	6	7	8	9
PAR	4	4	5	3	4	4	4	3	5
YARDS	343	315	496	146	367	370	287	167	490
PAR									
YARDS									

Directions: I-91 to Exit 19 North. Continue to end; make right. Course is 2 miles on State Road (Route 9 West).

Bedrock Golf Club

87 Barre Paxton Road
Rutland, MA (508) 886-0202
www.bedrockgolfclub.com

Club Pro: Joe Carr, PGA
Payment: Visa, MC, Cash, Amex
Tee Times: Weekends
Fee 9 Holes: Weekday: $15
Fee 18 Holes: Weekday: $25
Twilight Rates: $15 after 12pm/$25 wknds
Cart Rental: $20pp/18, $10pp/9
Lessons: No **Schools:** No
Membership: Yes
Other: Clubhouse / Bar-Lounge / Snack Bar

Tees	Holes	Yards	Par	USGA	Slope
BACK					
MIDDLE	9	3131	36	69.8	127
FRONT					

Weekend: $25
Weekend: $40
Discounts: Junior, wkdys $12pp/18
Driving Range: No
Junior Golf: No
Architect/Yr Open: Green & Whitehead/1992
GPS:

COUPON

New tees. Gently rolling, narrow landing areas. Small, undulating greens, challenging. Collared shirts required. "Absolutely loved it." Open April - November.

	1	2	3	4	5	6	7	8	9
PAR	4	5	4	3	4	5	3	4	4
YARDS	340	460	380	184	355	487	166	348	411
PAR									
YARDS									

Directions: I-90 (Mass Pike) to Auburn Exit (10). Then take Route 20 West to Route 56 North to Route 122 In Paxton. Course is 4 miles on left.

Berlin Country Club

✪✪½ 8

25 Carr Road
Berlin, MA (978) 838-2733
www.berlincountryclub.com

Club Pro: James Calderwood, GM
Payment: Cash, Credit, Debit
Tee Times: No
Fee 9 Holes: Weekday: $14
Fee 18 Holes: Weekday: $21
Twilight Rates: After 6pm
Cart Rental: $14pp/18, $9pp/9
Lessons: No **Schools:** No
Membership: Yes - Annual/Seasonal
Other:

Tees	Holes	Yards	Par	USGA	Slope
BACK					
MIDDLE	9	2433	33	32	108
FRONT	9	2072	33	31.4	104

Weekend: $16
Weekend: $26
Discounts: Sr./Jr./Early Bird/Month
Driving Range: No
Junior Golf: Yes - Weekdays
Architect/Yr Open: 1954
GPS:

COUPON

Mildly sloping fairways with challenging greens. Golf shirts and golf shoes required. Open March - November. "Nice, friendly staff." –FP

	1	2	3	4	5	6	7	8	9
PAR	4	4	4	3	4	4	3	4	3
YARDS	312	326	332	127	264	349	108	282	133
PAR									
YARDS									

Directions: From I-495 take Exit 26 to Route 62 West to Berlin Center. Take a right at Center Street and continue onto Highland Street. Turn left at Randall Road, then right at Carr Road, and follow to course.

CTRL/
WEST
MA

Blackstone National GC ✪✪✪✪ ▶ 9

227 Putnam Hill Road
Sutton, MA (508) 865-2111
www.bngc.net

Club Pro: Matt Stephens, PGA
Payment: Visa, MC, Amex, Disc
Tee Times: 5 days adv.
Fee 9 Holes: Weekday: $23
Fee 18 Holes: Weekday: $39
Twilight Rates: After 1:30pm
Cart Rental: $20pp/18, $12pp/9
Lessons: Yes **Schools:** Yes
Membership: Yes **GPS:** Yes

Tees	Holes	Yards	Par	USGA	Slope
BACK	18	6909	72	73.5	132
MIDDLE	18	6396	72	71.2	127
FRONT	18	5203	72	70.0	122

Weekend:
Weekend: $75 (inc. cart)
Discounts: Junior
Driving Range: Yes
Junior Golf: Yes
Architect/Yr Open: Rees Jones/2000
Other: Full Restaurant / Clubhouse / Lockers / Showers / Bar-Lounge /
Henry-Griffitts Precision Golf Club Fitting

Player Comments: "Elevated tees and greens call for lots of club decisions—pick the right tees or you'll wish you did. Great scenery." –JD

	1	2	3	4	5	6	7	8	9
PAR	4	5	3	4	4	4	3	5	4
YARDS	331	575	154	393	346	425	196	480	363
	10	11	12	13	14	15	16	17	18
PAR	4	3	4	3	4	4	5	4	5
YARDS	396	160	358	190	387	481	568	372	480

Directions: Mass Pike to Exit 10A to Route 146 South. Go 6 miles and take Central Turnpike toward Oxford 3 miles, to 4-way stop. Take left. Course is on top of hill.

Blissful Meadows Golf Club ✪✪½ ▶ 10

801 Chockalog Road
Uxbridge, MA (508) 278-6113
www.blissfulmeadows.com

Club Pro: Matthew Griffith, PGA
Payment: Visa, MC, Amex, Disc
Tee Times: 7 days adv.
Fee 9 Holes: Weekday: $20 M-Th
Fee 18 Holes: Weekday: $31 M-Th
Twilight Rates: After 3:30pm
Cart Rental: $17pp/18, $10pp/9
Lessons: Yes **Schools:** No
Membership: Yes

Tees	Holes	Yards	Par	USGA	Slope
BACK	18	6700	72	73.4	136
MIDDLE	18	6210	72	71.3	131
FRONT	18	5065	72	70.0	126

Weekend: Fri $24, $30 S/S
Weekend: Fri $39, $51 S/S
Discounts: Sr. & Jr. lunch specials
Driving Range: $7/lg., $4.50/sm.
Junior Golf: Yes
Architect/Yr Open: Brian Silva/1992
Other: Meadowview Tavern / Clubhouse / Bar-Lounge / Available for Outings

Bent grass greens and tees. Many holes quite isolated. Front 9 gently rolling with lots of character, Back 9 wild and very hilly. The 3 finishing holes are great. Each replay you'll enjoy it more. Scenic and challenging.

	1	2	3	4	5	6	7	8	9
PAR	4	3	5	4	3	4	4	5	4
YARDS	325	148	520	343	132	368	312	572	350
	10	11	12	13	14	15	16	17	18
PAR	5	4	4	3	4	3	5	4	4
YARDS	499	343	375	155	306	176	525	375	398

Directions: Take Route 146 to Route 16 West. Take first left onto West Street. Follow signs for 3 miles. Take right at dead end.

Cherry Hill Golf Course

NR

323 Montague Road
Amherst, MA (413) 256-4071
www.cherryhillgolf.org

Club Pro:
Payment: Visa, MC
Tee Times: No
Fee 9 Holes: Weekday: $15
Fee 18 Holes: Weekday: $21
Twilight Rates: After 5pm
Cart Rental: $24/18, $14/9 per cart
Lessons: No **Schools:** No
Membership: Yes
Other: Snack Bar

Tees	Holes	Yards	Par	USGA	Slope
BACK	9	2944	36	65.7	101
MIDDLE	9	2604	35	65.3	111
FRONT	9	2292	36	66.6	111

Weekend: $17
Weekend: $23
Discounts: Senior & Junior
Driving Range: No
Junior Golf: No
Architect/Yr Open: Dave Maxson/1963
GPS:

Improvements to bunkers, greens, approaches. A great course for everyone. Incredibly beautiful views of the Berkshires.

	1	2	3	4	5	6	7	8	9
PAR	5	4	3	4	4	4	5	3	3
YARDS	452	265	155	382	290	247	525	130	158

PAR									
YARDS									

Directions: Take I-91 to Hadley exit, right on Route 9 into Amherst. Go north on Route 16 for 3 miles, turn right at light onto Pine Street and onto Route 63. Course is ½ mile on right.

Chicopee Municipal Golf Course ✪✪½

12 ▶

1290 Burnett Road
Chicopee, MA (413) 594-9295
www.chicopeecc.org

Club Pro: Thomas DiRico, PGA
Payment: Cash, Credit Cards
Tee Times: Yes
Fee 9 Holes: Weekday: $15
Fee 18 Holes: Weekday: $25 (7 day, non-res.)
Twilight Rates: After 2pm
Cart Rental: $14pp/18, $9pp/9
Lessons: Yes **Schools:** No
Membership: No
Other: Clubhouse / Snack Bar

Tees	Holes	Yards	Par	USGA	Slope
BACK	18	6742	71	73.0	126
MIDDLE	18	6109	71	70.4	120
FRONT	18	5123	71	72.4	115

Weekend: $18
Weekend: $25
Discounts: Senior/Residents
Driving Range: Yes
Junior Golf: No
Architect/Yr Open: Geoffrey Cornish/1965
GPS:

Player Comments: "Course provides the opportunity to hit every club. "A solid test of your skills from tee to green. Between the design and condition, this is one of the region's very best values." –JD Voted by *Golf Digest* and *USA Today* Best Value In Massachusetts.

	1	2	3	4	5	6	7	8	9
PAR	4	5	3	4	4	4	5	3	4
YARDS	382	481	173	316	433	354	535	193	285
	10	**11**	**12**	**13**	**14**	**15**	**16**	**17**	**18**
PAR	4	3	3	4	4	5	3	5	4
YARDS	362	157	160	340	391	473	173	534	367

Directions: I-90 (Mass Pike) to Exit 6, turn right at light; course is 2.5 miles on left.

Clearview Golf Course

NR **13** ▶

66 Park Hill Avenue
Millbury, MA (508) 754-5654
www.clearviewcountryclub.com

Tees	Holes	Yards	Par	USGA	Slope
BACK	9	2999	36	67.7	112
MIDDLE	9	2724	35	66.3	107
FRONT	9	2724	35	66.3	107

Club Pro: Neil Loomis
Payment: Visa, MC, Amex, Discover, Cash
Tee Times: 1 week adv.
Fee 9 Holes: Weekday: $10 9am-1pm   **Weekend:** $18 9am-2pm
Fee 18 Holes: Weekday: $18 9am-2pm   **Weekend:** $26 9am-2pm
Twilight Rates: **Discounts:** Pre-game
Cart Rental: $16pp/18, $8pp/9   **Driving Range:** No
Lessons: Yes **Schools:** Yes   **Junior Golf:** Yes
Membership: Yes   **Architect/Yr Open:** 1962
Other: Snack Bar / Bar-Lounge / Ice Cold Beer   **GPS:**

New asphalt paths. Friendly service, great greens. Cold beer. "Play the view"

	1	2	3	4	5	6	7	8	9
PAR	3	5	5	3	5	3	4	4	3
YARDS	147	472	484	192	477	135	348	290	179
PAR									
YARDS									

Directions: I-90 (Mass Pike) to Exit 10A (Route 146). Look for Route 20 East. At first traffic light, go right onto Park Hill Avenue. Course is ½ mile on left.

Cold Spring Country Club

✪✪✪½ **14** ▶

336 Chauncey Walker Street
Belchertown, MA (413) 323-4888
www.coldspringcountryclub.com

Tees	Holes	Yards	Par	USGA	Slope
BACK	18	6491	71	71.7	130
MIDDLE	18	5894	71	69.6	125
FRONT	18	4698	71	65.0	112

Club Pro: Mark Klotz, PGA
Payment: Visa, MC, AMEX, Cash
Tee Times: 7 days adv.
Fee 9 Holes: Weekday: Call   **Weekend:** Call
Fee 18 Holes: Weekday: Call   **Weekend:** Call
Twilight Rates: After 2pm   **Discounts:** Senior/Junior/College
Cart Rental: Call   **Driving Range:** Yes
Lessons: Yes **Schools:** Yes   **Junior Golf:** Yes
Membership: Yes   **Architect/Yr Open:** 2012
Other: Full Restaurant / Clubhouse / Bar-Lounge / Snack Bar / Lockers / Showers

A world-class semi-private course in a spectacular New England setting. Open to the public on weekdays and weekends after 1pm. Playable for all levels of golfers. "Take the ride and give it a try." –FP

	1	2	3	4	5	6	7	8	9
PAR	4	5	4	3	4	3	5	3	4
YARDS	421	540	387	206	409	145	456	162	305
	10	11	12	13	14	15	16	17	18
PAR	3	5	3	5	4	3	5	4	3
YARDS	197	490	106	479	384	230	460	325	192

Directions: I-90 (Mass Pike) to Exit 7. Take a right and follow Route 21 for 7.5 miles. The entrance to the club is on the left.

Country Club of Greenfield ✪✪½ 15 ▶

Country Club Road
Greenfield, MA (413) 773-7530
www.countryclubofgreenfield.net

Club Pro: Kevin Piecuch, PGA
Payment: Cash, Visa
Tee Times: No
Fee 9 Holes: Weekday: $25
Fee 18 Holes: Weekday: $35
Twilight Rates: No
Cart Rental: $27pp/18, $13.50pp/9
Lessons: Yes **Schools:** No
Membership: Yes
Other: Full Restaurant / Clubhouse / Bar-Lounge / Snack Bar / Showers

Tees	Holes	Yards	Par	USGA	Slope
BACK	18	6450	72	70.1	117
MIDDLE	18	6210	72	68.6	114
FRONT	18	5444	73	70.6	119

Weekend: $30
Weekend: $45
Discounts: Senior & Junior
Driving Range: Yes
Junior Golf: Yes
Architect/Yr Open: R. Alex Findlay/1896

COUPON

Built in 1896. Easy drive from all over New England.

	1	2	3	4	5	6	7	8	9
PAR	4	3	4	4	3	5	4	5	4
YARDS	380	144	421	380	130	565	283	455	362
	10	11	12	13	14	15	16	17	18
PAR	4	3	5	4	5	3	4	4	4
YARDS	357	185	470	280	570	145	315	387	320

Directions: I-91, take Exit 27. Turn right at Route 5 and 10. Take right at first set of lights onto Silver Street. Country Club Road is fourth street on right.

Country Club of Wilbraham ✪✪½ 16 ▶

859 Stony Hill Road
Wilbraham, MA (413) 596-8887
www.countryclubofwilbraham.com

Club Pro: Pete Chapman
Payment: Cash, Credit Card
Tee Times: No
Fee 9 Holes: Weekday: $40/res, $50/non-res, $18/guest
Weekend: $45/res, $55/non-res
Fee 18 Holes: Weekday: $40/res, $30/guest **Weekend:** $45/res
Twilight Rates: After 6pm weekdays; after 5pm weekends $25
Discounts: Senior discount Mondays $23
Cart Rental: $15pp/18, $7.50pp/9
Lessons: $60/half hour **Schools:** No
Membership: Yes
Other: Clubhouse / Practice Green

Tees	Holes	Yards	Par	USGA	Slope
BACK	18	6380	72	71.2	130
MIDDLE	18	5967	72	68.9	125
FRONT	18	5168	72	65.4	115

Driving Range: Yes
Junior Golf: For residents
Architect/Yr Open: Willie Org/1927
GPS:

Semi-private. Residents of Wilbraham after 3pm, or as a guest with a member. Challenging even from the middle tees.

	1	2	3	4	5	6	7	8	9
PAR	4	3	4	4	3	5	4	5	4
YARDS	375	162	364	416	142	481	258	528	359
	10	11	12	13	14	15	16	17	18
PAR	3	5	4	4	3	4	4	4	5
YARDS	136	445	383	304	167	327	295	350	475

Directions: Take I-90 (Mass Pike) West to Exit 7, Belchertown/Ludlow. Turn left at end of ramp. Take Route 21 South. Follow signs to Wilbraham. Go left on Route 20 to Stony Hill Road.

Cranwell Resort, Spa, and GC ✪✪✪✪½ 17

55 Lee Road
Lenox, MA (413) 637-2563
www.cranwell.com

Tees	Holes	Yards	Par	USGA	Slope
BACK	18	6346	70	70	123
MIDDLE	18	6169	70	69.4	120
FRONT	18	5602	72	70.2	121

Club Pro: David Strawn, PGA
Payment: Visa, MC, Amex, Disc, Cash
Tee Times: Yes
Fee 9 Holes: Wkday: **Weekend:**
Fee 18 Holes: Wkday: $53, $99/Sum, $40/Fall **Weekend:** $53, $104/Sum, $48/Fall
Twilight Rates: After 1pm **Discounts:** Junior 18 under, $30
Cart Rental: Included **Driving Range:** $5/bucket
Lessons: $50/half hour, $100/hour **Schools:** Yes **Junior Golf:** No
Membership: Yes **Architect/Yr Open:** Stiles & Van Kleek/1926
Other: Hotel / Lockers / Showers / Snack Bar / Restaurant / Bar-Lounge/ Major Golf School

COUPON

Beautiful par 70 with Berkshire Mountain views, tree lined fairways and challenging contoured greens. Spring and Fall play all day specials; $39 to $48 includes carts. Your group will love the experience.

	1	2	3	4	5	6	7	8	9
PAR	4	5	3	4	3	4	4	4	4
YARDS	384	463	144	373	218	370	360	340	405
	10	**11**	**12**	**13**	**14**	**15**	**16**	**17**	**18**
PAR	4	4	3	4	4	5	3	4	4
YARDS	263	390	195	426	315	495	148	315	375

Directions: I-90 (Mass Pike) to Exit 2, take Route 20 West. Course is 10 minutes up the road.

Crestview Country Club ✪✪✪✪½ 18

281 Shoemaker Lane
Agawam, MA (413) 786-0917
www.crestviewcc.org

Tees	Holes	Yards	Par	USGA	Slope
BACK	18	6902	72	74.2	133
MIDDLE	18	6297	72	71.0	128
FRONT	18	5571	72	73.4	130

Club Pro: Richard Fleury, PGA
Payment: Visa, MC, Amex, Cash
Tee Times: 7 days adv.
Fee 9 Holes: Weekday: $29 **Weekend:** $35 F/S/S
Fee 18 Holes: Weekday: $49 **Weekend:** $59 F/S/S
Twilight Rates: **Discounts:** Senior, Military
Cart Rental: $17pp/18, $11pp/9 **Driving Range:** Yes
Lessons: Yes **Schools:** Yes **Junior Golf:** Yes
Membership: Yes **Architect/Yr Open:** Geoffrey Cornish/1958
Other: Restaurant / Bar-Lounge / Clubhouse / Lockers / Showers / Al Fresca Dining & Music

COUPON

Challenging and enjoyable premier championship course. Full service pro shop. Private club conditions. 10 minutes to Bradley Airport. "Great greens, great layout." –FP

	1	2	3	4	5	6	7	8	9
PAR	4	5	3	4	4	3	5	4	4
YARDS	401	526	144	356	373	174	467	359	398
	10	**11**	**12**	**13**	**14**	**15**	**16**	**17**	**18**
PAR	4	3	5	4	3	4	4	5	4
YARDS	338	145	447	366	143	383	414	490	373

Directions: I-90 (Mass Pike) to Exit 6 (I-91 South) to Exit 3 (Agawam). Go halfway around rotary to Route 57 to Route 75 South. At third light turn right onto Shoemaker Lane. Course is ¾ mile on left.

Crumpin-Fox Club

○○○○½

Parmenter Road
Bernardston, MA (413) 648-9101
www.golfthefox.com

Tees	Holes	Yards	Par	USGA	Slope
BACK	18	7007	72	73.8	141
MIDDLE	18	6508	72	71.3	136
FRONT	18	5432	72	71.5	131

Club Pro: Michael Zaranek, PGA
Payment: Visa, MC, Amex, Disc
Tee Times: golfthefox.com
Fee 9 Holes: Weekday: $47 w/cart
Fee 18 Holes: Weekday: $89 w/cart
Twilight Rates: After 4pm
Cart Rental: Included
Lessons: $45/half hour **Schools:** Jr. & Sr.
Membership: Yes

Weekend: $50 w/cart
Weekend: $95 w/cart
Discounts: Senior & Junior
Driving Range: $5/bag
Junior Golf: Yes
Architect/Yr Open: Roger Rulewich/1978

COUPON

Other: Restaurant / Clubhouse / Hotel / Bar-Lounge / Lockers / Snack Bar / Showers / Tennis Courts / Pond

Player Comments: "Must play." –JD "Variety of holes. You really need to think before you hit. Beautiful landscape. Great staff and atmosphere. Immaculate. The rustic clubhouse and pro shop, the tall trees surrounding the entrance—it just doesn't get any better." –LB

	1	2	3	4	5	6	7	8	9
PAR	4	4	3	4	5	4	4	5	3
YARDS	386	338	165	345	501	402	353	568	177
	10	11	12	13	14	15	16	17	18
PAR	4	3	4	4	5	3	4	5	4
YARDS	394	150	374	370	506	172	410	508	389

Directions: I-91 to Exit 28A (between Brattleboro, VT and Greenfield, MA). Follow Route 10 North for 1 mile; take left on Parmenter Road and follow signs to club.

Cyprian Keyes Golf Club

○○○½

284 East Temple Street
Boylston, MA (508) 869-9900
www.cypriankeyes.com

Tees	Holes	Yards	Par	USGA	Slope
BACK	18	6871	72	74.4	136
MIDDLE	18	6134	72	72.4	132
FRONT	18	5029	72	71.2	126

Club Pro: Scott Hickey, PGA
Payment: Visa, MC, Amex, Disc, Cash
Tee Times: 5 days adv.
Fee 9 Holes: Weekday:
Fee 18 Holes: Weekday: $54 M-F
Fee 18 Holes: Weekend: $59 before 11am, $54 after 11am S/S/H
Twilight Rates: After 3pm
Cart Rental: $18pp/18
Lessons: Yes **Schools:** Yes
Membership: Yes

Weekend:

Discounts: Senior & Junior
Driving Range: $8/bucket
Junior Golf: Yes
Architect/Yr Open: Mark Mungeam/1997

Other: Restaurant / Clubhouse / Showers / Lockers / Bar-Lounge / Custom Club Fitting

Among many great holes, the short, risky 13th and the challenging 11th. Custom fitting center featuring trackman fiting system. Exceptional dining room and outdoor patio. Great pro shop and learning center.

	1	2	3	4	5	6	7	8	9
PAR	4	4	5	5	4	3	4	4	3
YARDS	332	367	510	476	376	180	357	369	155
	10	11	12	13	14	15	16	17	18
PAR	5	3	4	4	4	4	3	4	5
YARDS	486	175	350	318	406	348	162	297	470

Directions: Route 290 to Exit 23B (Route 140 North). Go 1 mile and take third right onto East Temple Street.

Cyprian Keyes Golf Club, Par 3 ✪✪✪ ▶ 21

284 East Temple Street
Boylston, MA (508) 869-9900
www.cypriankeyes.com

Club Pro: Scott Hickey, PGA
Payment: Visa, MC, Amex, Disc
Tee Times: 5 days adv.
Fee 9 Holes: Weekday: $15 M-F
Fee 18 Holes: Weekday: $18
Twilight Rates: No
Cart Rental: $9pp
Lessons: Yes **Schools:** Yes
Membership: Juniors

Tees	Holes	Yards	Par	USGA	Slope
BACK					
MIDDLE	9	1230	27		
FRONT					

Weekend: $18/S/S/H
Weekend:
Discounts: Jr. and Sr.
Driving Range: $8 bucket
Junior Golf: Yes
Architect/Yr Open: Mark Mungeam/1997

Other: Clubhouse / Restaurant/ Function Facilities / Golf School / Custom Club Fitting

Sig. Hole: #9 is a picturesque 165-yard hole framed by trees with water to the left. It provides the golfer with many options. Custim fitting center featuring trackman fitting system. Player comments: "There are some great holes here. They could be part of any full-sized course." –JD Home

	1	2	3	4	5	6	7	8	9
PAR	3	3	3	3	3	3	3	3	3
YARDS	155	85	165	105	135	120	155	145	165
PAR									
YARDS									

Directions: Route 290 to Exit 23B (Route 140 North). Go 1 mile and take third right onto East Temple Street.

Donnybrook Country Club NR ▶ 22

775 Williams Town Road
Lanesborough, MA (413) 499-7888
www.donnybrookgolf.com

Club Pro:
Payment: All Types
Tee Times: Yes
Fee 9 Holes: Weekday: $35/with cart
Fee 18 Holes: Weekday: $45/with cart
Twilight Rates: Yes, time varies
Cart Rental: $10-$15
Lessons: No **Schools:** No
Membership: Yes

Tees	Holes	Yards	Par	USGA	Slope
BACK	9	3338	36	74.2	139
MIDDLE	9	3038	36	70.8	135
FRONT	9	2426	36	69.2	124

Weekend: $40
Weekend: $50
Discounts: Senior and Junior
Driving Range: No
Junior Golf: Yes
Architect/Yr Open: Vinnie Bartlett/2008

Other: Restaurant / Club-House / Showers / Bar-Lounge / Pro Shop / Putting Course

A great 9 hole course with multiple tee boxes providing a very different experience for a round of 18 holes. Beautiful, scenic, well mantained.

	1	2	3	4	5	6	7	8	9
PAR	4	4	5	3	5	4	4	3	4
YARDS	333	357	553	135	416	348	393	174	329
PAR									
YARDS									

Directions: I-90 (Mass Pike) to Exit 2 (Lee) to Route 20 North to Route 7 North. Travel 9.2 miles and the course is on the left.

Dudley Hill Golf Club ✪✪½ 23 ▶

80 Airport Road
Dudley, MA (508) 943-4538
www.dudleyhill.org

Club Pro:
Payment: Visa, MC
Tee Times: Daily
Fee 9 Holes: Weekday: $20
Fee 18 Holes: Weekday: $30 M-Th
Twilight Rates: After 6pm
Cart Rental: $12pp/18, $6pp/9
Lessons: No **Schools:** No
Membership: Yes
Other: Snack Bar / Bar-Lounge

Tees	Holes	Yards	Par	USGA	Slope
BACK					
MIDDLE	9	3279	36	71.4	123
FRONT	9	2848	36	71.3	115

Weekend: $20
Weekend: $35 F/S/S
Discounts: Junior
Driving Range: No
Junior Golf: Yes
Architect/Yr Open: Devereux Emmett/1926
GPS:

Hidden secret, semi-private. Open to public weekdays and after 1pm on weekends. Weekdays before 12pm, $20 for 9 holes with cart and lunch, $35 for 18 holes with cart and lunch. Distances below from back tees.

	1	2	3	4	5	6	7	8	9
PAR	4	4	3	4	4	3	4	5	5
YARDS	373	380	164	398	321	186	428	509	474
PAR									
YARDS									

Directions: I-395 to Exit 2 (West) in Webster, MA. Head east approximately 4.5 miles (Dudley) to Airport Road. Course is on right at Cumberland Farms.

Dunroamin Country Club NR 24 ▶

262 Lower Road
Gilbertville, MA (413) 477-0004
www.dunroamincc.com

Club Pro: Bob Lemoine
Payment: Cash or Credit Card
Tee Times: Weekends/Holidays
Fee 9 Holes: Weekday: $16
Fee 18 Holes: Weekday: $30
Twilight Rates: No
Cart Rental: $16pp/18, $8pp/9
Lessons: Yes **Schools:** No
Membership: Yes
Other: Clubhouse / Lockers / Showers / Snack Bar / Bar-Lounge

Tees	Holes	Yards	Par	USGA	Slope
BACK					
MIDDLE	9	2863	35	68.6	117
FRONT	9	2401	35	66.8	106

Weekend: $15
Weekend: $30
Discounts: Junior
Driving Range: $3/bucket
Junior Golf: Yes
Architect/Yr Open: Manuel Francis/1966

COUPON

Come try us.

	1	2	3	4	5	6	7	8	9
PAR	3	4	4	5	4	4	4	3	4
YARDS	204	331	393	493	322	310	367	166	277
PAR									
YARDS									

Directions: Mass Pike to Exit 8. Take Route 32 North for 15 miles.

East Mountain Country Club ✪✪

1458 East Mountain Road
Westfield, MA (413) 568-1539
www.eastmountaincc.com

Tees	Holes	Yards	Par	USGA	Slope
BACK	18	6118	71	69.4	120
MIDDLE	18	5819	71	68.3	113
FRONT	18	4564	71	65.4	104

Club Pro: Ted Perez Jr., PGA
Payment: Visa, MC, Amex, Cash
Tee Times: 1 week adv.
Fee 9 Holes: Weekday: $15
Fee 18 Holes: Weekday: $23
Twilight Rates: After 5pm
Cart Rental: $13.50pp/18, $7.50pp/9
Lessons: Yes **Schools:** Yes
Membership: Full or Associate
Other: Clubhouse / Snack Bar / Lounge

Weekend: $16
Weekend: $26
Discounts: Sr. & Jr: $16 wkdys $9.50/9 holes
Driving Range: Yes
Junior Golf: Yes
Architect/Yr Open: Ted Perez Sr./1963
GPS:

SR 7200 Velvet Bent Greens seeded in 2003 – fantastic putting surface. Fees subject to change.

	1	2	3	4	5	6	7	8	9
PAR	4	4	3	5	4	4	4	4	3
YARDS	305	361	149	495	372	426	319	352	175
	10	11	12	13	14	15	16	17	18
PAR	3	5	5	3	4	5	4	3	4
YARDS	159	492	481	168	394	536	429	174	331

Directions: I-90 (Mass Pike) to Exit 3, follow Route 202 North to East Mountain Road. Course is 1.5 miles on right.

Edge Hill Golf Club NR

298 Barnes Road
Ashfield, MA (413) 625-6018
www.edgehillgolfcourse.com

Tees	Holes	Yards	Par	USGA	Slope
BACK	18	5708	71		
MIDDLE	18	5293	71	NOT	
FRONT	18	4188	71	YET	

Club Pro:
Payment: Cash, Visa, MC, Disc
Tee Times: Yes
Fee 9 Holes: Weekday: $16
Fee 18 Holes: Weekday: $20
Twilight Rates: No
Cart Rental: $30pp/18, $15pp/9
Lessons: No **Schools:** No
Membership: Yes
Other: Full Restaurant / Clubhouse / Bar-Lounge

Weekend: $19
Weekend: $24
Discounts: Junior
Driving Range: Yes
Junior Golf: No
Architect/Yr Open: Mark Graves/1994

COUPON

Very challenging course demands playing positional golf. Open May - November.

	1	2	3	4	5	6	7	8	9
PAR	5	4	3	4	4	3	5	4	4
YARDS	520	300	150	320	370	160	520	370	400
PAR									
YARDS									

Directions: I-91 Southbound: take Exit 26 (Route 2 West) to Route 112 South. Left on Route 116 to course. Follow signs. I-91 Northbound: take Exit 24 (Route 116/South Deerfield) to Conway-Ashfield. Turn right in Ashfield at Baptist Corner Road. Follow signs.

Edgewood Golf Club ✪✪

161 Sheep Pasture Road
Southwick, MA (413) 569-6826
www.edgewood4golf.com

Tees	Holes	Yards	Par	USGA	Slope
BACK	18	6510	71	69.1	115
MIDDLE	18	6050	71	67.6	113
FRONT	18	5580	71	71.8	109

Club Pro: Mike Grigley, PGA
Payment: Visa, MC
Tee Times: 4 days adv.
Fee 9 Holes: Weekday: $14   **Weekend:** $18
Fee 18 Holes: Weekday: $22   **Weekend:** $26
Twilight Rates: After 6pm $6/M-F, after 5pm $10/weekend
Discounts: Senior & Junior
Cart Rental: $16pp/18, $9.50pp/9   **Driving Range:** $7/lg, $4/sm bucket
Lessons: $40/half hour   **Schools:** No   **Junior Golf:** Yes, clinics
Membership: Yes   **Architect/Yr Open:** Geoffrey Cornish/1963
Other: Clubhouse / Showers / Snack Bar / Restaurant / Bar-Lounge

Picturesque, easy walk, fairly open.

**CTRL/
WEST
MA**

	1	2	3	4	5	6	7	8	9
PAR	5	4	4	5	4	3	4	3	4
YARDS	450	415	315	523	385	170	390	205	340
	10	**11**	**12**	**13**	**14**	**15**	**16**	**17**	**18**
PAR	4	3	4	3	5	5	4	3	4
YARDS	295	160	375	150	545	480	355	150	340

Directions: I-90 (Mass Pike) to Exit 3 (Springfield). Route 57 to Southwick. Route 57 goes through Routes 10 and 202. Go through center of town. Take a left on Depot. Right onto Sheep Pasture Road, follow it around to the right.

Egremont Country Club ✪✪✪½

Route 23
Great Barrington, MA
(413) 528-4222
www.egremontcountryclub.com

Tees	Holes	Yards	Par	USGA	Slope
BACK	18	6036	71	68.7	122
MIDDLE	18	5771	71	67.5	120
FRONT	18	4894	71	68.1	113

Club Pro:
Payment: Cash, MC Visa, Amex
Tee Times: 7 days adv. 413-528-4222 x1
Fee 9 Holes: Weekday: $17   **Weekend:** $25
Fee 18 Holes: Weekday: $26   **Weekend:** $45
Twilight Rates: After 4pm   **Discounts:** Senior & Junior
Cart Rental: $18pp/18, $9pp/9   **Driving Range:** $7/lg, $5/sm
Lessons: No   **Schools:** No   **Junior Golf:** Yes
Membership: Yes   **Architect/Yr Open:** 1920
Other: Clubhouse / Lockers / Showers / Snack Bar / Restaurant / Bar-Lounge

COUPON

Sig. Hole: #18 Double-tiered, elevated tee area, framed by large maples. Some claim the feel of #18th hole 'chute' at Augusta. Green guarded by 2 bunkers. Accurate approach shots a must. Tanglewood nearby.

	1	2	3	4	5	6	7	8	9
PAR	4	4	3	4	5	3	4	4	3
YARDS	335	245	175	389	497	140	320	325	151
	10	**11**	**12**	**13**	**14**	**15**	**16**	**17**	**18**
PAR	4	4	5	5	3	4	4	4	4
YARDS	338	275	532	538	152	320	325	353	361

Directions: I-90 (Mass Pike) to Exit 2 (Lee) Route 7. Follow Route 102 West to Route 7 South. Turn right on Route 23 for 3 miles.

Ellinwood Country Club

○○½

1928 Pleasant Street
Athol, MA (978) 249-7460
www.ellinwoodcc.com

Tees	Holes	Yards	Par	USGA	Slope
BACK	18	6195	71	69.5	123
MIDDLE	18	5891	71	68.8	119
FRONT	18	5031	72	69.1	118

Club Pro:
Payment: Visa, MC, Cash
Tee Times: Yes
Fee 9 Holes: Weekday: $20   **Weekend:** $25
Fee 18 Holes: Weekday: $30   **Weekend:** $40
Twilight Rates: After 5pm   **Discounts:** Junior
Cart Rental: Yes   **Driving Range:** No
Lessons: Yes **Schools:** No   **Junior Golf:** Yes
Membership: Yes   **Architect/Yr Open:** Ross/1929; Cornish/1968
Other: Clubhouse / Snack Bar / Bar-Lounge / Banquet Hall

COUPON

Immaculate, fast greens. No back and forth holes. Every hole offers a different challenge. 9 holes by Donald Ross in 1929. 9 holes by Geoff Cornish in 1968. Fully irrigated in 2004. "A Hidden Gem of Worcester County."

	1	2	3	4	5	6	7	8	9
PAR	4	4	3	5	5	3	4	3	4
YARDS	400	321	148	477	414	158	405	150	369
	10	11	12	13	14	15	16	17	18
PAR	3	4	3	5	3	4	5	4	4
YARDS	215	278	150	441	136	398	472	416	517

Directions: Route 2 to Exit 17. Take right off exit, follow ½ mile on right to Woodlawn Road. Go all the way to the end; clubhouse is on the right.

Forest Park Country Club

NR

1928 Pleasant Street
Adams, MA (413) 743-3311
www.forestparkadams.com

Tees	Holes	Yards	Par	USGA	Slope
BACK					
MIDDLE	9	2555	34	63.8	110
FRONT	9	2323	34	63.8	110

Club Pro:
Payment: Cash or Check Only
Tee Times: No
Fee 9 Holes: Weekday: $15   **Weekend:** $15
Fee 18 Holes: Weekday: $20   **Weekend:** $20
Twilight Rates: No   **Discounts:** None
Cart Rental: $13.50pp/18, $7.50pp/9 **Driving Range:** No
Lessons: No **Schools:** No   **Junior Golf:** Yes
Membership: Yes   **Architect/Yr Open:** Alex Findlay/1900
Other: Clubhouse / Lockers / Showers / Snack Bar / Bar-Lounge/ Banquet Hall

COUPON

Sig. Hole: #5 is a 157-yard par 3: all carry, well bunkered, small sloping green. Tricky to birdie. Ongoing clubhouse renovations. Scenic 9 holes at the foot of Mt. Greylock.

	1	2	3	4	5	6	7	8	9
PAR	4	4	3	4	3	4	4	4	4
YARDS	270	341	157	327	147	333	314	389	277
PAR									
YARDS									

Directions: I-90 (Mass Pike) to Exit 2 (Lee). Take Route 20 East to Route 8 to Adams. Take left at statue on Park Street to Maple Street. Take first left onto Forest Park Avenue.

Franconia Municipal Golf Course ✪✪✪

618 Dwight Road
Springfield, MA (413) 734-9334
www.franconiagolfcourse.com

Club Pro: Kevin Kennedy, PGA
Payment: Most Major Credit Cards
Tee Times: Weekends

Tees	Holes	Yards	Par	USGA	Slope
BACK	18	6153	71	68.7	118
MIDDLE	18	5825	71	67.1	115
FRONT	18	5348	71	67.1	115

Fee 9 Holes: Weekday: **Weekend:**
Fee 18 Holes: Weekday: $21   **Weekend:** $22
Twilight Rates: After 3pm   **Discounts:** Sr. & Jr. Weekdays
Cart Rental: $26/18, $14/9 per cart   **Driving Range:** No
Lessons: $24/half hour   **Schools:** No   **Junior Golf:** Yes
Membership: Yes   **Architect/Yr Open:** Stiles & Van Kleek/1929
Other: Clubhouse / Snack Bar / Restaurant / Bar-Lounge

Rates are for all-day play. Several challenging par 5s. Good mix of holes. Discount for town residents. Great shape. Re-landscaped in 2001. Well maintained.

	1	2	3	4	5	6	7	8	9
PAR	4	4	4	5	3	4	4	3	4
YARDS	314	307	349	557	124	412	360	162	387
	10	11	12	13	14	15	16	17	18
PAR	5	4	5	4	3	4	4	3	4
YARDS	491	307	468	368	132	350	282	173	282

Directions: I-91 to Longmeadow exit. At 2nd light take a left onto Converse Street. At end, take left onto Dwight Road. Follow to course.

Gardner Municipal Golf Course ✪✪½

152 Eaton Street
Gardner, MA (978) 632-9703
www.gardner-ma.gov

Club Pro: Ben Egan, PGA
Payment: Cash Only
Tee Times: Weekends, Holidays

Tees	Holes	Yards	Par	USGA	Slope
BACK	18	6106	71	68.9	124
MIDDLE	18	5857	71	67.6	120
FRONT	18	5557	75	71.7	122

Fee 9 Holes: Weekday: $15   **Weekend:**
Fee 18 Holes: Weekday: $30   **Weekend:** $35
Twilight Rates: After 4pm weekday; after 3pm weekend
Discounts: Junior
Cart Rental: $13.50pp/18, $8pp/9   **Driving Range:** Yes
Lessons: $40/half hour   **Schools:**   **Junior Golf:** Yes
Membership: Yes   **Architect/Yr Open:** 1936
Other: Clubhouse / Snack Bar / Restaurant / Bar-Lounge

Player Comments: "Lesser known to those outside the area, but well worth the trip." New tee on #8, provides new angle of approach to green, requires carry over bunker.

	1	2	3	4	5	6	7	8	9
PAR	4	4	3	4	5	3	5	3	4
YARDS	320	297	215	316	525	137	530	142	406
	10	11	12	13	14	15	16	17	18
PAR	4	5	4	4	3	5	3	4	4
YARDS	300	450	323	370	136	478	207	352	353

Directions: Route 2 to Exit 24B (Route 140 North). Follow signs to Mount Wachusett Community College. Course is across street from front of college.

GEAA Golf Club

303 Crane Avenue
Pittsfield, MA (413) 443-5746
www.geaagolf.com

Club Pro: Jay Abir, PGA
Payment: All Types
Tee Times: Yes
Fee 9 Holes: Weekday: $14
Fee 18 Holes: Weekday: $22
Twilight Rates: No
Cart Rental: $22pp/18, $14pp/9
Lessons: Yes **Schools:** No
Membership: Yes

Weekend: $14
Weekend: $22
Discounts: None
Driving Range: For Members
Junior Golf: Yes
Architect/Yr Open: Rowland Armacost/1930

Other: Restaurant / Clubhouse / Snack Bar / Bar-Lounge / Lockers / Showers

Tees	Holes	Yards	Par	USGA	Slope
BACK	9	3180	36	70.0	118
MIDDLE	9	3079	36	69.6	115
FRONT	9	2637	36	69.4	110

Gently rolling hills and windy all year round. Tree-lined fairways with beautiful view of Mt. Greylock.

	1	2	3	4	5	6	7	8	9
PAR	3	4	4	4	5	5	4	3	4
YARDS	170	379	348	276	443	539	332	134	391
PAR									
YARDS									

Directions: I-90 (Mass Pike) to Lee exit. Follow Route 7 North through Lee and Lenox. ½ mile past Reed Middle School is Crane Street; take right to the course.

Grandview Golf Course

449 Wachusett Street
Leominster, MA (978) 537-9151
www.grandviewgolfleominster.com

Club Pro: Sue Tourigny, Golf Manager
Payment: Visa, MC, Disc, Check, Cash
Tee Times: 7 days adv.
Fee 9 Holes: Weekday: $14
Fee 18 Holes: Weekday: $23
Twilight Rates: No
Cart Rental: $13pp/18, $10pp/9
Lessons: No **Schools:** No
Membership: Yes
Other: Snack Bar

Weekend: $17
Weekend: $26
Discounts: Senior and Junior
Driving Range: No
Junior Golf: No
Architect/Yr Open:

Tees	Holes	Yards	Par	USGA	Slope
BACK					
MIDDLE	9	3357	36	68.8	113
FRONT	9	3103	36		

Grandview is a scenic, public golf course that has been owned and operated by the Vachon Family since 1965. The 9 hole course is friendly, yet challenging for players of all levels. The course offers beautiful views of Wachusett Mountain and borders the Vachon Wildlife Sanctuary.

	1	2	3	4	5	6	7	8	9
PAR	4	4	3	4	3	4	5	4	5
YARDS	337	358	195	425	175	440	491	397	539
PAR									
YARDS									

Directions: Route 2 West to Exit 33 (I-190 South). Left onto Route 12. Straight onto Pleasant Street. Travel 2.1 miles and take a right onto Wachusett Street. Course is 1.3 miles on right.

Green Hill Municipal Golf Course ✪✪✪½ 35

1929 Skyline Drive
Worcester, MA (508) 799-1359
www.greenhillgc.com

Tees	Holes	Yards	Par	USGA	Slope
BACK	18	6485	72	71.4	130
MIDDLE	18	6054	72	69.6	127
FRONT	18	5424	72	66.5	122

Club Pro: Matthew Moison, PGA
Payment: Visa, MC, Disc, Check, Cash
Tee Times: 7 days (508) 799-1545
Fee 9 Holes: Weekday: $20
Fee 18 Holes: Weekday: $35
Twilight Rates: No
Cart Rental: $15pp/18, $10pp/9
Lessons: No **Schools:** Yes
Membership: Yes
Other: Clubhouse / Bar-Lounge / Snack Bar

Weekend: $30
Weekend: $40
Discounts: Seniors (62), Juniors (under 18)
Driving Range: No
Junior Golf: Yes
Architect/Yr Open: Ted Robinson/1929

Green Hill Golf Course is one of the older courses in the area. Our sloping greens and classic layout are attractive to golfers of many different styles and skill levels. Sitting atop one of Worcester's Seven Hills contributes a scenic pleasure to your golf game.

	1	2	3	4	5	6	7	8	9
PAR	4	4	5	4	4	3	4	3	5
YARDS	375	334	418	347	342	190	330	157	452
	10	11	12	13	14	15	16	17	18
PAR	4	3	4	5	4	3	5	4	4
YARDS	358	198	328	482	385	140	458	371	389

Directions: From Rt. 9 - East or West - Turn into Green Hill Park at Skyline Drive.

Greenock Country Club ✪✪✪ 36

220 West Park Street
Lee, MA (413) 243-3323
www.greenockcc.com

Tees	Holes	Yards	Par	USGA	Slope
BACK					
MIDDLE	9	3070	35	68.9	120
FRONT	9	2843	37	72.2	123

Club Pro: Bob Mucha, PGA
Payment: Visa, MC, Cash, Check
Tee Times: Sat. and Sun., call
Fee 9 Holes: Weekday: $18
Fee 18 Holes: Weekday: $26
Twilight Rates: After 5pm wkdys
Cart Rental: $9.50pp/18, $7.50pp/9
Lessons: $55/hour **Schools:** No
Membership: Yes
Other: Clubhouse / Lockers / Showers / Snack Bar / Restaurant / Bar-Lounge

Weekend: $25
Weekend: $42
Discounts: None
Driving Range: No
Junior Golf: Yes
Architect/Yr Open: Donald Ross/1927

Postage stamp-size greens. Donald Ross design, one of the first 100 courses built in the United States. New irrigation.

	1	2	3	4	5	6	7	8	9
PAR	4	3	4	4	4	5	3	4	4
YARDS	330	158	391	300	423	464	168	360	364
PAR									
YARDS									

Directions: I-90 (Mass Pike) to Exit 2 (Lee). Take right on Housatonic Street to the center of Lee. Come to the stop sign next to town park. Take West Park Street up the hill over the RR tracks. Course on right.

Groton Pool and Golf Center ✪½ 37

94 Lovers Lane
Groton, MA (978) 448-2564
www.grotoncountryclub.com

Club Pro: Rod Van Guilder
Payment: Most Major Credit Cards
Tee Times: 7 days adv.

Tees	Holes	Yards	Par	USGA	Slope
BACK	9	3003	35	66.5	116
MIDDLE	9	2709	35	66.5	116
FRONT	9	2409	36		

Fee 9 Holes: Weekday: $19   **Weekend:** $20
Fee 18 Holes: Weekday: $27   **Weekend:** $32
Twilight Rates: 6pm wkday/5pm wknd ($10)   **Discounts:** Senior & Junior
Cart Rental: $15pp/18, $9pp/9   **Driving Range:**
Lessons: Yes **Schools:** Yes   **Junior Golf:** Yes
Membership: Yes   **Architect/Yr Open:** 1950
Other: Full Restaurant / Clubhouse / Bar-Lounge / Snack Bar / Showers

Resident-discounted rates. Collared shirts are required. New Golf Cart and Cart Paths. Open April - November.

	1	2	3	4	5	6	7	8	9
PAR	4	4	4	3	3	4	4	5	4
YARDS	330	260	325	140	210	326	335	450	300
PAR									
YARDS									

Directions: I-495 to Route 119 West to Groton.

Hemlock Ridge Golf Course ✪✪½ 38

220 Holland Road
Fiskdale, MA (508) 347-9935
www.hemlockridgegolfcourse.com

Club Pro:
Payment: Visa, MC
Tee Times: Weekends Only

Tees	Holes	Yards	Par	USGA	Slope
BACK					
MIDDLE	9	3136	36	70.6	117
FRONT	9	2603	36	69.0	109

Fee 9 Holes: Weekday: $16   **Weekend:** $18
Fee 18 Holes: Weekday: $24   **Weekend:** $27
Twilight Rates: No   **Discounts:** Senior $1 off
Cart Rental: $9pp/18, $7pp/9   **Driving Range:** No
Lessons: No **Schools:** No   **Junior Golf:** Yes
Membership: Yes   **Architect/Yr Open:** Philip Wogan/1965
Other: Clubhouse / Snack Bar / Showers   **GPS:**

Hilly and scenic. Conditions good for both fairways and greens. No dress code. Open April 1 - November 1. "Great country course, worth the trip." –FP

	1	2	3	4	5	6	7	8	9
PAR	4	4	3	4	4	5	4	3	5
YARDS	308	382	154	449	370	471	317	170	515
PAR									
YARDS									

Directions: Route 20 West through Sturbridge to Holland Road, turn left. Course is 1 mile up Holland Road.

Heritage Country Club

85 Sampson Road
Charlton, MA (508) 248-5111
www.heritagecountryclub.com

Tees	Holes	Yards	Par	USGA	Slope
BACK	18	6677	71	69.3	118
MIDDLE	18	6138	71	67.3	113
FRONT	18	5415	72	70.3	114

Club Pro: Liz Farland, PGA
Payment: Cash, Credit Cards
Tee Times: 7 days adv.
Fee 9 Holes: Weekday: $21
Fee 18 Holes: Weekday: $33
Twilight Rates: After 4pm
Cart Rental: $14pp/18, $8pp/9
Lessons: $35/half hour **Schools:** Yes
Membership: Yes
Other: Clubhouse / Lockers / Showers / Snack Bar / Bar-Lounge

Weekend: $25 after 3pm
Weekend: $41
Discounts: Senior & Junior
Driving Range: $7/bucket
Junior Golf: Yes
Architect/Yr Open: Don Hoeing/1963

Player comments: "Good value. Hilly but fun and fair. Enjoy the views." "Worth a new visit." Early-bird and late-afternoon specials. Weekend after 6pm – $10/walk, $15/ride, unlimited. New man-made pond and new trees, bunkers, and tees.

	1	2	3	4	5	6	7	8	9
PAR	4	4	3	4	4	5	3	4	4
YARDS	365	372	176	360	352	525	166	319	443
	10	11	12	13	14	15	16	17	18
PAR	4	4	5	3	4	4	3	5	4
YARDS	393	364	580	155	297	381	175	564	360

Directions: Located on Route 20 in Charlton. 3 miles east of Old Sturbridge Village. Easy to reach from Worcester, Boston, Springfield, Hartford, or Providence.

Hickory Ridge Country Club

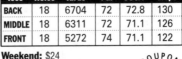

191 West Pomeroy Lane
Amherst, MA (413) 230-3360
www.hickoryridgecc.com

Tees	Holes	Yards	Par	USGA	Slope
BACK	18	6704	72	72.8	130
MIDDLE	18	6311	72	71.1	126
FRONT	18	5272	74	71.1	122

Club Pro: Bill Rosenblum
Payment: Visa, Amex, MC
Tee Times: 7 days adv.
Fee 9 Holes: Weekday: $20
Fee 18 Holes: Weekday: $30
Twilight Rates: No
Cart Rental: $16pp/18, $10pp/9
Lessons: Yes **Schools:** No
Membership: Yes
Other: Clubhouse / Lockers / Showers / Snack Bar / Restaurant

Weekend: $24
Weekend: $39
Discounts: Junior
Driving Range: $4/sm.
Junior Golf: Yes
Architect/Yr Open: Cornish & Robinson/1970

Generous landing areas, big greens, challenge for all playing abilities.

	1	2	3	4	5	6	7	8	9
PAR	5	4	4	4	3	5	4	3	4
YARDS	501	380	329	394	193	500	344	158	405
	10	11	12	13	14	15	16	17	18
PAR	4	5	4	4	4	3	5	3	4
YARDS	372	447	401	342	349	140	466	182	438

Directions: I-91 to Route 9 East from Northampton to Route 116 in Amherst. Go South on Route 116 for 2.5 miles to West Pomeroy Lane. Right onto West Pomeroy for ½ mile.

Highfields Golf & Country Club ✪✪✪✪

41

42 Magill Drive (off Route 122)
Grafton, MA (508) 839-1945
www.highfieldsgolfcc.com

Tees	Holes	Yards	Par	USGA	Slope
BACK	18	7021	72	74.5	140
MIDDLE	18	6474	72	72.2	136
FRONT	18	6024	72	69.9	131

Club Pro: Roger Adams
Payment: Visa, MC, Amex, Disc
Tee Times: Yes
Fee 9 Holes: Weekday: $28 walk, $36 ride   **Weekend:** $28 walk, $36 ride
Fee 18 Holes: Weekday: $54 ride   **Weekend:** $61 ride
Twilight Rates: **Discounts:** Senior & Junior M-F
Cart Rental: Included   **Driving Range:** Irons only
Lessons: Yes **Schools:** Yes   **Junior Golf:** Yes
Membership: Many levels   **Architect/Yr:** Cornish, Silva, & Mungeam/2002
Other: Clubhouse / Lockers / Showers / Snack Bar / Restaurant / Bar-Lounge

COUPON

Championship course designed by Cornish, Silva and Mungeam complements a beautiful residential project. Breathtaking views all around. Playable for all skill levels and abilities. Great conditions. Beautiful new clubhouse.

	1	2	3	4	5	6	7	8	9
PAR	5	3	4	4	3	4	4	4	5
YARDS	516	138	399	365	218	389	383	339	570
	10	11	12	13	14	15	16	17	18
PAR	4	3	4	4	4	5	4	3	5
YARDS	411	145	325	385	321	501	441	121	507

Directions: I-90 (Mass Pike) to Exit 11 (Route 122). Go right off ramp (122 South). 4.5 miles to Magill Drive on left. Follow Magill Drive 1.5 miles to clubhouse on left.

Hillcrest Country Club

✪½

42

325 Pleasant Street
Leicester, MA (508) 892-0963

Tees	Holes	Yards	Par	USGA	Slope
BACK	9	3068	35	67.1	103
MIDDLE	9	3138	35	67.1	103
FRONT	9	2388	36	67.2	113

Club Pro: George Poaskis
Payment: Cash Only
Tee Times: Recommended
Fee 9 Holes: Weekday: $14   **Weekend:** $14
Fee 18 Holes: Weekday: $18   **Weekend:** $18
Twilight Rates: No   **Discounts:** Junior
Cart Rental: $16pp/18, $8pp/9   **Driving Range:** No
Lessons: No **Schools:** No   **Junior Golf:** No
Membership: No   **Architect/Yr Open:** Robert B. Harris/1964
Other: Clubhouse / Snack Bar / Restaurant / Bar-Lounge

Ongoing improvements. Friendly staff and personnel. Under new management.

	1	2	3	4	5	6	7	8	9
PAR	5	4	4	4	3	5	3	3	4
YARDS	500	402	345	340	355	475	110	136	475
PAR									
YARDS									

Directions: I-90 (Mass Pike) to Exit 10 (Auburn). Take right onto Route 12, follow 3 miles. Take right onto Route 20, follow 3 miles; take right onto Route 56, 4 miles.

Holden Hills Country Club ✪✪

 43 ▶

1800 Main Street
Jefferson, MA (508) 829-3129
www.holdenhillsgolf.com

Tees	Holes	Yards	Par	USGA	Slope
BACK	18	6088	71	70.7	132
MIDDLE	18	5878	71	69.4	129
FRONT	18	5390	74	73.0	128

Club Pro: Jeff Bailey
Payment: MC, Visa, Amex
Tee Times: Weekends, 1 week adv.
Fee 9 Holes: Weekday: $25 w/cart
Fee 18 Holes: Weekday: $35 w/cart
Twilight Rates: After 5pm
Car Rental: $18pp/18, $10pp/9
Lessons: Yes **Schools:** No
Membership: Yes
Other: Clubhouse / Snack Bar / Restaurant / Bar-Lounge

Weekend: $25 w/cart
Weekend: $40 w/cart
Discounts: $15 after 5pm; $25 w/cart
Driving Range: No
Junior Golf: Yes
Architect/Yr Open: William F. Mitchell/1957

Picturesque course set among hills, ponds, and streams. New cart path and bunkers. While not long, the holes demand good placement and are challenging. Early-bird before 8am. Golf and cart special – $30 M-F before 12pm.

	1	2	3	4	5	6	7	8	9
PAR	4	5	3	4	4	3	4	5	4
YARDS	354	592	170	309	312	147	340	484	348
	10	11	12	13	14	15	16	17	18
PAR	3	4	4	5	4	4	4	4	3
YARDS	164	269	256	444	369	348	425	327	220

Directions: I-290 to Route 190 North. Take second exit (Holden). Go straight through lights, then bear right. Bear left at next light, up hill. Right on Main Street to Route 122A North. Course is 5 miles on right.

Holyoke Country Club

NR 44 ▶

Route 5 at Delaney House
Holyoke, MA (413) 534-1933
www.holyokecountryclub.com

Tees	Holes	Yards	Par	USGA	Slope
BACK					
MIDDLE	9	3495	36	71	118
FRONT	9	2723	37	N/A	N/A

Club Pro: Via Whightman, PGA
Payment: Visa, MC
Tee Times: S/S Members
Fee 9 Holes: Weekday: $12
Fee 18 Holes: Weekday: $20
Twilight Rates: No
Cart Rental: $18pp/18, $9pp/9
Lessons: $30/45 min. **Schools:** Yes
Membership: No
Other: Clubhouse / Lockers / Showers / Snack Bar / Restaurant / Bar-Lounge

Weekend: $12
Weekend: $20
Discounts: Please call
Driving Range: No
Junior Golf: Yes
Architect/Yr Open: 1896

Second hole is difficult with a quick green, hitting up 2 levels. If you are on the top level of the green, and flag is on the bottom, easy to bogey or double bogey.

	1	2	3	4	5	6	7	8	9
PAR	4	4	4	4	5	4	4	3	4
YARDS	343	356	409	292	472	407	323	121	347
PAR									
YARDS									

Directions: I-91 to Exit 17A to traffic light. Turn left onto Route 5, approximately 2½ miles. At the Delaney Restaurant go through entrance, past restaurant 50 yards, then turn left to country club.

Hopedale Country Club ✪✪ ▶ 45

90 Mill Street
Hopedale, MA (508) 473-9876
www.hopedalecc.com

Tees	Holes	Yards	Par	USGA	Slope
BACK	9	3050	35	69	125
MIDDLE	9	2972	35	69	118
FRONT	9	2741	35	70.8	121

Club Pro: Joe Potty, PGA
Payment: Visa, MC, Cash
Tee Times: No
Fee 9 Holes: Weekday: $20 before 3pm **Weekend:** No public play
Fee 18 Holes: Weekday: $35 before 1pm M-Th **Weekend:** No public play
Twilight Rates: No **Discounts:** None
Cart Rental: $14pp/18, $7pp/9 **Driving Range:** No
Lessons: $40/half hour **Schools:** No **Junior Golf:** Yes
Membership: Yes **Architect/Yr Open:** Geoffrey Cornish/1953
Other: Clubhouse / Bar-Lounge / Snack Bar **GPS:**

New clubhouse. 9 holes, 2 sets of tees. Public play welcome on weekdays, except holidays.

	1	2	3	4	5	6	7	8	9
PAR	4	5	3	4	4	4	4	4	3
YARDS	374	508	140	371	362	316	304	381	216
PAR									
YARDS									

Directions: I-495 to Route 85 Milford. Turn right onto Route 85 and right onto Route 16 through center of Milford to Hopedale. At lights go left onto Hopedale Street to end. Take right onto Green Street to course.

Indian Meadows Golf Club ✪✪ ▶ 46

275 Turnpike Road
Westboro, MA (508) 836-5460
www.indianmeadowsgolf.com

Tees	Holes	Yards	Par	USGA	Slope
BACK	9	3265	36	71.7	124
MIDDLE	9	3019	36	69.4	119
FRONT	9	2468	36	67.0	107

Club Pro: Art Billingham
Payment: Cash, Visa, MC, Discover
Tee Times: 1 day adv.
Fee 9 Holes: Weekday: $20 **Weekend:** $22
Fee 18 Holes: Weekday: $30 **Weekend:** $32
Twilight Rates: After 5pm **Discounts:** Sr & Jr (weekday only)
Cart Rental: $16pp/18, $8pp/9 **Driving Range:** No
Lessons: Yes **Schools:** No **Junior Golf:** Yes
Membership: Yes **Architect/Yr Open:** Art Billingham/1990
Other: Restaurant / Clubhouse / Bar-Lounge / Snack Bar

COUPON

Great atmosphere. Water on every hole. Shirts with collars required. Open April - December. Semi-private.

	1	2	3	4	5	6	7	8	9
PAR	5	4	4	4	3	5	4	3	4
YARDS	451	340	420	316	136	455	415	173	313
PAR									
YARDS									

Directions: I-495 to Route 9 West (Turnpike Road). Follow Route 9 for 3 miles West to Westboro.

Juniper Hill Golf Club (Lakeside) ✪✪✪½ 47 ▶

202 Brigham Street
Northboro, MA (508) 393-2444
www.juniperhillgc.com

Club Pro: Ken Chrzan, PGA
Payment: Visa, MC, Amex, Cash, Debit
Tee Times: 7 days adv.
Fee 9 Holes: Weekday: $23 Mon-Fri
Fee 18 Holes: Weekday: $40 Mon-Fri
Twilight Rates: No
Cart Rental: $20pp/18, $13pp/9
Lessons: Yes **Schools:** Jr. & Sr.
Membership: No

Tees	Holes	Yards	Par	USGA	Slope
BACK	18	6289	71	70.3	126
MIDDLE	18	5378	71	66.0	117
FRONT	18	5272	71	70.5	118

Weekend: $26 S/S/H
Weekend: $45 S/S/H
Discounts: Before 1pm, Sr. (M-Th) & Jr. (M-Th)
Driving Range: Practice green
Junior Golf: Yes
Architect/Yr: Phil Wogan, Homer Darling/1991

Other: Clubhouse / Lockers / Showers / Snack Bar / Bar-Lounge / Teaching Facility

18 holes of championship caliber with a lot of character. Collared shirts required. Noted for golf professional and friendly staff. Better year after year.

	1	2	3	4	5	6	7	8	9
PAR	3	5	4	4	3	4	5	3	4
YARDS	187	524	313	392	169	314	522	146	307
	10	**11**	**12**	**13**	**14**	**15**	**16**	**17**	**18**
PAR	4	4	4	4	3	5	4	5	3
YARDS	377	365	336	420	206	482	441	602	179

Directions: I-90 (Mass Pike) to I-495 North. Exit to Route 9 West and continue onto Route 135 West. Follow for 1.4 miles. Right onto Brigham Street. Follow for 1 mile to course.

Juniper Hill Golf Club (Riverside) ✪✪✪½ 48 ▶

202 Brigham Street
Northboro, MA (508) 393-2444
www.juniperhillgc.com

Club Pro: Ken Chrzan, PGA
Payment: Visa, MC, Amex, Cash, Debit
Tee Times: 7 days adv.
Fee 9 Holes: Weekday: $23 Mon-Fri
Fee 18 Holes: Weekday: $40 Mon-Fri
Twilight Rates: No
Cart Rental: $20pp/18, $13pp/9
Lessons: Yes **Schools:** Jr. & Sr.
Membership: No

Tees	Holes	Yards	Par	USGA	Slope
BACK	18	6245	71	70.5	126
MIDDLE	18	5379	71	66.0	117
FRONT	18	5272	71	70.5	118

Weekend: $26 S/S/H
Weekend: $45 S/S/H
Discounts: Before 1pm, Sr. & Jr. (M-F)
Driving Range: Practice green
Junior Golf: Yes

Architect/Yr Open: Homer Darling & Geoff Cornish/1931
Other: Clubhouse / Lockers / Showers / Snack Bar / Bar-Lounge / Teaching Facility

Player comments: "36 holes well-maintained for public play." "Some open fairways are inviting for your driver. Lots of variety." "Short overall but that doesn't mean easy. Number 17 is a dangerous and daunting par 3." Continually upgrading the facilities.

	1	2	3	4	5	6	7	8	9
PAR	4	4	5	4	3	4	3	4	4
YARDS	370	336	495	387	193	330	156	405	350
	10	**11**	**12**	**13**	**14**	**15**	**16**	**17**	**18**
PAR	5	4	4	4	4	3	4	3	5
YARDS	490	391	367	381	371	157	391	220	476

Directions: I-90 (Mass Pike) to I-495 North. Exit to Route 9 West and continue onto Route 135 West. Follow for 1.4 miles. Right onto Brigham Street. Follow for 1 mile to course.

Kettle Brook Golf Club ✪✪✪½

136 Marshall Street
Paxton, MA (508) 799-4653
www.kettlebrookgolfclub.com

Tees	Holes	Yards	Par	USGA	Slope
BACK	18	6912	72	73.1	125
MIDDLE	18	6203	72	70.3	121
FRONT	18	5105	72	70.2	118

Club Pro: Tim Suitum
Payment: Visa, MC, Amex, Cash, Checks
Tee Times: 7 days adv.
Fee 9 Holes: Weekday: $30
Fee 18 Holes: Weekday: $55 w/cart M-Th
Twilight Rates: After 3pm
Cart Rental: $14pp
Lessons: No **Schools:** No
Membership: Inner club
Other: Clubhouse / Bar / Snack Bar / Function Room for Outings

Weekend:
Weekend: $60 w/cart
Discounts: Senior & Junior
Driving Range: No
Junior Golf: No
Architect/Yr Open: Brian Silva/1999

Player Comments: "Very good course—another Brian Silva gem. 3 of the best opening holes and 2 of the best closing holes anywhere." "Challenging but fun. Playable and friendly." "Awesome test of golf. Plays tougher than the slope rating. All they lack is a practice range."

	1	2	3	4	5	6	7	8	9
PAR	4	5	4	4	4	3	5	3	4
YARDS	366	522	359	327	339	170	485	132	452
	10	11	12	13	14	15	16	17	18
PAR	4	5	3	4	5	4	4	3	4
YARDS	346	485	164	251	481	338	379	196	411

Directions: I-290, exit to Route 9 to Worcester Center. Follow signs to Worcester airport. Take left off of Route 122 into airport rotary. First right to Bailey Street. Go 3 miles on right.

Ledges Golf Club ✪✪½

18 Mulligan Drive
South Hadley, MA (413) 532-2307
www.ledgesgc.com

Tees	Holes	Yards	Par	USGA	Slope
BACK	18	6507	72	72.2	133
MIDDLE	18	6110	72	70.9	129
FRONT	18	5001	72	69.5	125

Club Pro: Doug Juhasz, PGA
Payment: Visa, MC, Amex, Disc
Tee Times: 7 days adv.
Fee 9 Holes: Weekday: $19
Fee 18 Holes: Weekday: $30
Twilight Rates: After 3pm
Cart Rental: $10pp/18, $7pp/9
Lessons: Yes **Schools:** Yes
Membership: Yes
Other: Snack Bar / Bar / Restaurant

Weekend: $22
Weekend: $35
Discounts: Sr./Jr./Military/Student
Driving Range: No
Junior Golf: Yes
Architect/Yr Open: Howard Maurer/2001
GPS:

COUPON

Picturesque championship golf course. 78 strategically placed bunkers, 4 sets of tees. Well-maintained with thick rough and fast greens. New pro shop and a full-service restaurant.

	1	2	3	4	5	6	7	8	9
PAR	4	4	3	4	5	4	3	4	5
YARDS	386	424	96	276	456	300	123	349	528
	10	11	12	13	14	15	16	17	18
PAR	5	4	3	4	3	4	4	4	5
YARDS	564	405	215	397	176	270	273	372	500

Directions: I-91 to Exit 16. Follow signs for Route 202 toward South Hadley. At rotary, take 3rd right onto West Summit Street. Follow signs.

Leicester Country Club ✪✪✪ 51

1430 Main Street
Leicester, MA (508) 892-1390
www.leicestercc.com

Club Pro: Cheryl Orrico, PGA
Payment: Visa, MC, Amex
Tee Times: 7 days adv.
Fee 9 Holes: Weekday: $20
Fee 18 Holes: Weekday: $30
Twilight Rates: After 6pm
Cart Rental: $16pp/18, $8pp/9
Lessons: No **Schools:** No
Membership: Yes
Other: Snack Bar / Bar-Lounge / Banquet Facility

Tees	Holes	Yards	Par	USGA	Slope
BACK					
MIDDLE	18	6026	70	69.8	126
FRONT	18	4559	70	67.4	121

Weekend: $24
Weekend: $36
Discounts: Junior
Driving Range: No
Junior Golf: Yes
Architect/Yr Open: 1864

COUPON

CTRL/ WEST MA

Noted for excellent greens and some new ladies tees. Pro customer service and very friendly.

	1	2	3	4	5	6	7	8	9
PAR	4	5	3	4	4	4	3	4	3
YARDS	437	489	201	345	371	328	179	309	173
	10	11	12	13	14	15	16	17	18
PAR	4	4	3	4	5	4	5	3	4
YARDS	314	317	165	411	545	403	515	183	341

Directions: I-90 (Mass Pike) to Exit 10 (Auburn). Take Route 12 West to Route 20 to Route 56 North. Follow Route 56 for 7 miles to Route 9. Turn left (west) at the light and continue for 1 mile. Club is on the right at the top of the hill ¼ mile past the Castle Restaurant.

Links at Lancaster Golf, The NR 52

438 Old Union Turnpike
Lancaster, MA (978) 537-8922
www.lancastergolfcenter.com

Club Pro: Dennis Lanciani
Payment: Visa, MC, Amex, Disc, Checks
Tee Times:
Fee 9 Holes: Weekday: $10
Fee 18 Holes: Weekday: $13
Twilight Rates: No
Cart Rental:
Lessons: $45/half hour **Schools:**
Membership: Yes
Other:

Tees	Holes	Yards	Par	USGA	Slope
BACK					
MIDDLE	9	1125	27		
FRONT					

Weekend: $13
Weekend: $16
Discounts: Senior & Junior
Driving Range: Yes
Junior Golf: League & Summer Program
Architect/Yr Open: Gurall and Cronin/1996
GPS:

COUPON

Our range is rated a top 100 in USA by Golf Range Association. New longer first hole. We welcome beginners and junior golfers every day. Seniors pay ½ price greens fees Monday until 3pm. Women pay ½ price greens fees Tuesday until 3pm. Junior rate is $8 M-F. Excellent range.

	1	2	3	4	5	6	7	8	9
PAR	3	3	3	3	3	3	3	3	3
YARDS	133	69	98	64	150	206	170	105	130
PAR									
YARDS									

Directions: Exit 34 off Route 2.

Meadows Golf Club, The ✪

398 Deerfield Street
Greenfield, MA (413)773-9047
www.meadowsgreenfield.com

Club Pro:
Payment: Visa, MC
Tee Times: No
Fee 9 Holes: Weekday: $10
Fee 18 Holes: Weekday: $15
Twilight Rates: No
Cart Rental: 18/$12pp,$5 pull, 9/$8pp, $3 pull
Lessons: No **Schools:** No
Membership: Yes
Other: Bar-Lounge / Restaurant Open All Year

Tees	Holes	Yards	Par	USGA	Slope
BACK	9	2858	36	66.6	106
MIDDLE	9	2800	36	66.6	106
FRONT	9	2547	36	66.6	106

Weekend: $16
Weekend: $22
Discounts: Seniors every day
Driving Range: No
Junior Golf: $10/14 yrs. old or under
Architect/Yr Open: 1933
GPS:

See us on Facebook. Player Comments: "Great condition. Pretty elevation changes which also make for a challenging round. Extremely friendly and helpful staff." Rates may change.

	1	2	3	4	5	6	7	8	9
PAR	5	3	4	4	4	3	5	4	4
YARDS	475	155	320	280	255	135	470	365	345
PAR									
YARDS									

Directions: I-91 to Route 2. Take Route 5 South, through Greenfield Center. Course is 1.5 - 2 miles on right after Greenfield Center.

Mill Valley Golf Links ✪✪

380 Mill Valley Road
Belchertown, MA (413) 323-4079
www.millvalleygolflinks.com

Club Pro:
Payment: MC, Visa
Tee Times: 1 day adv.
Fee 9 Holes: Weekday: $15
Fee 18 Holes: Weekday: $20
Twilight Rates: No
Cart Rental: $14pp/18, $7/pp9
Lessons: No **Schools:** Yes
Membership: Yes
Architect/Yr Open: Armstrong Golf Associates/1963
Other: Restaurant / Bar-Lounge / Clubhouse

Tees	Holes	Yards	Par	USGA	Slope
BACK	18	6583	72	72.2	131
MIDDLE	18	6076	72	70.5	125
FRONT	18	5546	72	72.0	131

Weekend: $15
Weekend: $25
Discounts: Sr., Jr. before 12pm, M-F
Driving Range: No
Junior Golf: Yes

GPS: Garmin

Scenic challenging golf course with tree-lined fairways. 14th hole features 200 feet drop from tee to fairway. Play our double dog-leg 16th, and the 17th is the hardest par 4 in Western Massachusetts.

	1	2	3	4	5	6	7	8	9
PAR	3	4	4	4	4	4	5	4	4
YARDS	206	319	382	316	468	362	552	422	323
	10	11	12	13	14	15	16	17	18
PAR	5	5	4	4	3	4	4	4	3
YARDS	500	517	331	311	240	321	400	400	172

Directions: I-90 (Mass Pike) to Route 32 to Route 181 North. Course is about 2 miles on right.

Monoosnock Country Club ✪✪✪ 55 ▶

40 Monoosnock Avenue
Leominster, MA (978) 537-1872
www.monoosnockcountryclub.com

Club Pro: John M. Novak
Payment: Visa, MC
Tee Times: No
Fee 9 Holes: Weekday: $16
Fee 18 Holes: Weekday: $26
Twilight Rates: No
Cart Rental: $16pp/18, $8pp/9
Lessons: Yes **Schools:** Night classes
Membership: Yes
Other: Clubhouse / Restaurant / Bar-Lounge

Weekend: $18 after 2pm
Weekend: $30 after 2pm
Discounts: None
Driving Range: $11/jumbo, $6/large
Junior Golf: Yes
Architect/Yr Open: 1919
GPS:

Tees	Holes	Yards	Par	USGA	Slope
BACK					
MIDDLE	9	3051	35	69.5	120
FRONT	9	2823	36	71.0	115

Course is open to public play on Monday - Friday until 3pm (except holidays). The fairways are narrow and brooks cross through 5 holes. 2 new bunkers on 5th hole and greens are in great shape. Full practice area with grass tees. Open April 1 - November 30.

	1	2	3	4	5	6	7	8	9
PAR	4	5	4	3	3	5	4	3	4
YARDS	335	515	378	158	235	450	387	214	379
PAR									
YARDS									

Directions: Route 2 to Route 13 North. Go north 1 mile and take right onto Monoosnock Avenue. Follow to pro shop.

North Adams Country Club ✪✪ 56 ▶

641 River Road
Clarksburg, MA (413) 664-7149
www.northadamscountryclub.com

Club Pro: Gary Cyr
Payment: Cash, Check
Tee Times: Weekends & Holidays
Fee 9 Holes: Weekday: $14
Fee 18 Holes: Weekday: $22
Twilight Rates: No
Cart Rental: $16pp/18, $8pp/9
Lessons: Yes **Schools:** No
Membership: Yes
Other: Snack Bar / Bar-Lounge

Weekend: $14
Weekend: $22
Discounts: M-Sat, 7am-11am
Driving Range: No
Junior Golf: Yes
Architect/Yr Open: Orrin E. Smith/1903
GPS:

Tees	Holes	Yards	Par	USGA	Slope
BACK	9	2899	36	67.0	119
MIDDLE	9	2782	36	67.0	119
FRONT	9	2503	36	68.4	122

Traditional course in the midst of the Berkshires features small, fast greens requiring a good short game. Well-conditioned course with a great value for the price. Near the Mass MOCA museum.

	1	2	3	4	5	6	7	8	9
PAR	4	3	4	4	5	4	4	3	5
YARDS	339	143	364	257	484	360	273	143	419
PAR									
YARDS									

Directions: Route 2 to Route 8; go north 2 miles. Course is on left side.

Northfield Country Club ✪✪½ 57

31 Holten Street
East Northfield, MA
(413) 498-2432
www.northfieldcountryclub.com

Club Pro:
Payment: Visa, MC, Amex
Tee Times: No
Fee 9 Holes: Weekday: $12
Fee 18 Holes: Weekday: $20
Twilight Rates: No
Cart Rental: $24pp/18, $12pp/9
Lessons: No **Schools:** No
Membership: Yes
Other: Snack Bar / Clubhouse

Tees	Holes	Yards	Par	USGA	Slope
BACK					
MIDDLE	9	2760	36	66.2	121
FRONT	9	2405	36	68.0	121

Weekend: $15
Weekend: $25
Discounts: None
Driving Range: Net hitting area
Junior Golf: Yes
Architect/Yr Open: Alex Findlay/1912
GPS:

Challenging layout. Very difficult to shoot the course rating. Open April - November. "Terrific greens" –FP

	1	2	3	4	5	6	7	8	9
PAR	5	4	4	4	5	3	3	4	4
YARDS	430	300	370	260	450	170	130	270	380
PAR									
YARDS									

Directions: I-91 to Route 2 East to Routes 10 and 63 North, 1 mile north of the center of Northfield. Take Holton Street, turn right into parking lot.

Oak Ridge Golf Club ✪✪ 58

850 South Westfield Street
Feeding Hills, MA (413) 789-7307
www.oakridgegc.com

Club Pro: Tony Strycharz
Payment: MC, Visa, Amex, Disc
Tee Times: 7 days adv.
Fee 9 Holes: Weekday: $17
Fee 18 Holes: Weekday: $26
Twilight Rates: After 2pm
Cart Rental: $14pp/18 $8pp/9
Lessons: Yes **Schools:** No
Membership: Yes
Other: Clubhouse / Lockers / Showers / Bar-Lounge / Snack Bar

Tees	Holes	Yards	Par	USGA	Slope
BACK	18	6702	70	72.2	124
MIDDLE	18	6390	70	70.2	121
FRONT	18	5297	70	70.8	124

Weekend:
Weekend: $35
Discounts: Senior weekdays
Driving Range:
Junior Golf: Yes
Architect/Yr Open: Tom Fazio/1974

Excellent condition, flowers throughout course make for a real New England beauty. Open March 1 to December 1. Reduced rates after 2pm on weekends.

	1	2	3	4	5	6	7	8	9
PAR	4	4	4	3	4	5	4	3	4
YARDS	379	379	395	191	378	570	385	151	387
	10	**11**	**12**	**13**	**14**	**15**	**16**	**17**	**18**
PAR	4	3	5	3	4	4	5	3	4
YARDS	431	195	559	176	352	363	493	200	406

Directions: I-91 to Exit 3 Agawam/Southwick. Take Route 57 West to end. Take left onto Route 187 South then first left at Oak Ridge sign. Course ¼ mile on right.

Oak Ridge Golf Club-Gill

231 West Gill Road
Gill, MA (413) 863-9693
www.oakridgegolfclub.net

Tees	Holes	Yards	Par	USGA	Slope
BACK	9	2952	36	68.7	117
MIDDLE	9	2861	36	68.7	117
FRONT	9	2595	36	70.0	117

Club Pro:
Payment: Visa, MC
Tee Times: No
Fee 9 Holes: Weekday: $14   **Weekend:** $16
Fee 18 Holes: Weekday: $18   **Weekend:** $22
Twilight Rates: No   **Discounts:** Senior & Junior
Cart Rental: $12pp/18, $8pp/9   **Driving Range:** No
Lessons: No **Schools:** No   **Junior Golf:** No
Membership: Yes   **Architect/Yr Open:** 1963
Other: Full Restaurant/Clubhouse / Bar-Lounge / New Deck for Patio Dining

Scenic rolling hills, well groomed. Special rates for seniors (60+) and weekdays prior to 11am.
Open March - November.

	1	2	3	4	5	6	7	8	9
PAR	4	4	5	4	4	4	4	4	3
YARDS	290	319	481	364	300	329	410	240	128
PAR									
YARDS									

Directions: I-91 to Exit 27 East and follow signs to golf course.

Pakachoag Golf Course

Upland Street
Auburn, MA (508) 755-3291
www.johnsongolfmanagement.com

Tees	Holes	Yards	Par	USGA	Slope
BACK					
MIDDLE	9	3255	36	70.0	119
FRONT					

Club Pro:
Payment: Cash or Credit Card
Tee Times: Weekends & Holidays am only
Fee 9 Holes: Weekday: $17   **Weekend:** $20
Fee 18 Holes: Weekday: $27   **Weekend:** $30
Twilight Rates: No   **Discounts:** Senior & Junior
Cart Rental: $30/18, $15/9 per cart   **Driving Range:** No
Lessons: Yes **Schools:** No   **Junior Golf:** Yes
Membership: Yes   **Architect/Yr Open:** 1932
Other: Snack Bar   **GPS:**

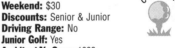

Sig. Hole: #9, a dogleg left, has 3 ways to play. Short hitters - right of pond. Medium hitters - 180 yard carry. Big hitters - 270 yards over stone wall. "Nice greens, some very challenging holes." –GM

	1	2	3	4	5	6	7	8	9
PAR	4	4	4	3	5	4	4	3	5
YARDS	376	329	395	143	563	372	377	189	511
PAR									
YARDS									

Directions: From Route 20 to Greenwood Street to Upland Street. From I-290 use Auburn Street exit to Route 12 (Southbridge Street). Left at lights. ¼ mile right, take Burnap Street up hill to Pakachoag Street and go left. 2 miles to Upland Street.

Pine Grove Golf Club

254 Old Wilson Road
Florence, MA (413) 584-4570

Tees	Holes	Yards	Par	USGA	Slope
BACK					
MIDDLE	18	6115	72	69.0	122
FRONT	18	4890	72	68.4	110

Club Pro:
Payment: Cash Only
Tee Times: 1 day adv.
Fee 9 Holes: Weekday: $14
Fee 18 Holes: Weekday: $22
Twilight Rates: After 4 pm
Cart Rental: $16pp/18, $8 pp/9 per cart
Lessons: Yes **Schools:** Yes
Membership: Yes
Other: Clubhouse / Snack Bar / Bar-Lounge

Weekend: $17
Weekend: $25
Discounts: Senior & Junior
Driving Range: No
Junior Golf: No
Architect/Yr Open: 1972
GPS:

A scenic and challenging 18 hole public golf course in a beautiful New England setting.

	1	2	3	4	5	6	7	8	9
PAR	4	5	5	3	4	3	4	4	4
YARDS	315	475	500	140	350	165	370	385	335
	10	11	12	13	14	15	16	17	18
PAR	4	3	4	4	5	3	4	5	4
YARDS	375	125	370	330	470	140	360	600	310

Directions: I-91 to Exit 18. Left off exit, Route 5 North about 1.5 miles to light. Left onto Route 9 West to next light. Straight through light, then bear left onto Route 66 for 3 miles, and bear left onto Wilson Road.

Pine Knoll Par 3 Golf Course

380 Porter Road
East Longmeadow, MA
(413) 525-4444 x5

Tees	Holes	Yards	Par	USGA	Slope
BACK					
MIDDLE	18	1567	54		
FRONT					

Club Pro:
Payment: Cash or Credit
Tee Times: No
Fee 9 Holes:
Fee 18 Holes: Weekday: $9
Twilight Rates: No
Cart Rental: $1.50/pull
Lessons: Yes **Schools:** No
Membership: No
Other: First Tee Facility

Weekend:
Weekend: $10
Discounts: Senior & Junior
Driving Range: Yes
Junior Golf: No
Architect/Yr Open: 1950
GPS:

Easy walker. Great for short game practice. Very scenic. Open March - November. First Tee facility. At Fenway Batting cages complex.

	1	2	3	4	5	6	7	8	9
PAR	3	3	3	3	3	3	3	3	3
YARDS	86	64	80	92	78	60	72	60	102
	10	11	12	13	14	15	16	17	18
PAR	3	3	3	3	3	3	3	3	3
YARDS	74	96	48	130	114	124	115	85	87

Directions: I-91 to Exit 4. Sumner Avenue (Route 21) East. Go to end of Sumner Avenue, bear right by McDonald's onto Allen Street. ½ mile to Porter Road. Left turn onto Porter to course entrance on left.

Pine Ridge Country Club

★★½ 63

28 Pleasant Street
North Oxford, MA (508) 892-9188
www.pineridgegolf.net

Club Pro: Betty Donovan, LPGA
Payment: Visa, MC, Amex, Disc
Tee Times: 7 days adv.
Fee 9 Holes: Weekday: $17
Fee 18 Holes: Weekday: $29
Twilight Rates: After 3pm
Cart Rental: $15pp/18, $9pp/9
Lessons: $50/hour **Schools:** Yes
Membership: Yes
Other: Clubhouse / Lockers / Showers / Snack Bar / Restaurant / Bar-Lounge

Tees	Holes	Yards	Par	USGA	Slope
BACK	18	6002	71	69.7	120
MIDDLE	18	5763	71	68.3	117
FRONT	18	5307	72	69.6	117

Weekend: $20
Weekend: $38
Discounts: Senior & Junior
Driving Range: No
Junior Golf: No
Architect/Yr Open: Phil Wogan/1969

COUPON

Tournament friendly. Great value. New outdoor patio with access to the lounge. Great course for business outings with complete amenities.

	1	2	3	4	5	6	7	8	9
PAR	4	3	4	3	4	5	4	4	3
YARDS	295	144	437	161	382	390	330	358	148
	10	11	12	13	14	15	16	17	18
PAR	4	3	5	4	5	3	4	4	5
YARDS	270	188	431	403	482	166	354	344	480

Directions: I-90 (Mass Pike) Exit 10 or I-290 Exit 6B. Route 20 West to Route 56 North, go right. Take Route 56 North for 1 mile, club on left.

Pontoosuc Lake Country Club

★★ 64

Kirkwood Drive
Pittsfield, MA (413) 445-4217
www.plcc.biz

Club Pro: Bob Dastoli, PGA
Payment: Cash, Check
Tee Times: Weekends & Holidays
Fee 9 Holes: Weekday: $14
Fee 18 Holes: Weekday: $22 all day
Twilight Rates: After 5pm
Cart Rental: $23pp/18, $11.50pp/9
Lessons: Yes **Schools:** No
Membership: Yes
Other: Snack Bar / Bar-Lounge / Hot Dogs

Tees	Holes	Yards	Par	USGA	Slope
BACK					
MIDDLE	18	6207	70	68.1	114
FRONT					

Weekend: $17
Weekend: $25 all day
Discounts: Jr. & Sr., weekdays only
Driving Range: No
Junior Golf: No
Architect/Yr Open: A.W. Tillinghast/1920
GPS:

COUPON

Sig. Hole: #9 links hole with large mounds and hills leading to a highly elevated green. Considered moderately difficult. No one under 14 unless accompanied by an adult. Prices subject to change.

	1	2	3	4	5	6	7	8	9
PAR	4	4	5	3	4	4	4	3	4
YARDS	367	295	597	137	372	284	404	223	361
	10	11	12	13	14	15	16	17	18
PAR	4	3	4	4	3	5	3	4	5
YARDS	411	152	386	355	173	593	196	360	541

Directions: I-90 (Mass Pike) to Route 7 North to Hancock Road (left). Approximately 1 mile to Ridge Avenue (right), turn left on Kirkwood Drive.

Quaboag Country Club

NR 65

Route 32
Monson, MA (413) 267-5294
www.quaboagcountryclub.com

Tees	Holes	Yards	Par	USGA	Slope
BACK					
MIDDLE	9	2880	34	67.2	116
FRONT	9	2610	35	69.2	113

Club Pro: Greg Farland
Payment: Cash, Credit
Tee Times: 7 days adv.
Fee 9 Holes: Weekday: $18
Fee 18 Holes: Weekday: $25
Twilight Rates: After 2pm weekends
Cart Rental: $10pp/9, $15pp/18
Lessons: $40/half hour **Schools:** No
Membership: $595/year
Other: Bar-Lounge / Banquet / Snack Bar / Lockers / Showers

Weekend: $30 w/cart
Weekend: $45 w/cart
Discounts: Senior & Junior
Driving Range: No
Junior Golf: Yes
Architect/Yr Open: 1900

COUPON

Course is over 100 years old. Brimfield Flea Market and the Big "E" are area attractions.

	1	2	3	4	5	6	7	8	9
PAR	4	3	4	4	4	4	4	3	4
YARDS	350	225	435	430	360	350	250	130	350
PAR									
YARDS									

Directions: I-90 to Exit 8 in Palmer. Turn right onto Route 32 South. Go 2 lights, turn left. Go 3 miles to golf course on right.

Quail Hollow Golf & CC

★★½ 66

1822 Old Turnpike Road
Oakham, MA (508) 882-5516
www.quailhollowgolf.net

Tees	Holes	Yards	Par	USGA	Slope
BACK	18	5896	70	68.6	123
MIDDLE	18	5567	70	67.0	120
FRONT	18	4839	71	68.9	120

Club Pro:
Payment: Visa, MC, Cash
Tee Times: Recommended
Fee 9 Holes: Weekday: $10
Fee 18 Holes: Weekday: $20
Twilight Rates Weekends: After 1pm
Cart Rental: $16pp/18, $8pp/9
Lessons: Yes **Schools:** No
Membership: Yes
Other: Clubhouse/ Bar-Lounge / Snack Bar

Weekend: $17
Weekend: $25
Discounts: Junior
Driving Range: Yes
Junior Golf: Yes
Architect/Yr Open: Philip Wogan/1990
GPS: Yes - Skycaddie

Cart paths are complete. Beautiful view. Hole #10 is a great short par 4. Super early morning weekday specials.

	1	2	3	4	5	6	7	8	9
PAR	4	4	4	3	5	3	4	4	4
YARDS	296	290	230	174	500	140	415	299	310
	10	11	12	13	14	15	16	17	18
PAR	4	3	4	4	4	4	5	3	4
YARDS	324	178	361	340	347	408	511	115	320

Directions: I-290 to Worcester to Route 122 North to Oakham to Old Turnpike Road. Course is 3.5 miles off Route 122.

Ranch Golf Club, The   ✪✪✪✪   67 ▶

65 Sunnyside Road
Southwick, MA (413) 569-9333
www.theranchgolfclub.com

Tees	Holes	Yards	Par	USGA	Slope
BACK	18	7174	72	75.0	139
MIDDLE	18	6103	72	69.6	130
FRONT	18	4983	72	69.7	125

Club Pro: Hope Kelley, PGA
Payment: Visa, MC, Amex, Checks, Cash
Tee Times: 7 days adv.
Fee 9 Holes: Weekday: $35   **Weekend:** $40
Fee 18 Holes: Weekday: $55 M-Th   **Weekend:** $75 F/S/S/H
Twilight Rates: After 2pm   **Discounts:** Senior & Junior
Cart Rental: $20pp/18; $15pp/9   **Driving Range:** Yes
Lessons: $45/30min., $80/50min. **Schools:** Jr. **Junior Golf:** Yes
Membership: Yes   **Architect/Yr Open:** Damian Pascuzzo/2001
Other: Clubhouse / Lockers / Showers / Bar-Lounge / Restaurant / Golf Shop
GPS: Yes

One of *Golf Digest's* "Best Places to Play". Great condition, great layout, great service — great fun!

	1	2	3	4	5	6	7	8	9
PAR	5	4	4	4	3	4	4	3	5
YARDS	480	341	365	404	146	334	369	180	502
	10	11	12	13	14	15	16	17	18
PAR	4	4	3	5	4	4	5	3	4
YARDS	406	366	181	540	419	357	578	170	404

Directions: I-90 (Mass Pike) to Exit 3. Go South on Routes 10/202 to Southwick. After Southwick Country Club, take right on Sunnyside Road. Club is 1 mile on left.

Red Tail Golf Club   ✪✪✪✪✪   68 ▶

15 Bulge Road
Devens, MA (978) 772-3273
www.redtailgolf.net

Tees	Holes	Yards	Par	USGA	Slope
BACK	18	7006	72	73.9	138
MIDDLE	18	6292	72	70.1	129
FRONT	18	5049	72	69.4	120

Club Pro: Jim Pavlik, PGA
Payment: Visa, MC, Amex, Disc, Checks, Cash
Tee Times: 7 days adv.
Fee 9 Holes: Weekday: **Weekend:**
Fee 18 Holes: Weekday: $95 cart incl. M-Th   **Weekend:** $105 cart incl. F/S/S
Twilight Rates: After 2pm   **Discounts:** None
Cart Rental: Yes   **Driving Range:** Yes
Lessons: Yes **Schools:** Sr. & Jr.   **Junior Golf:** Yes
Membership: Yes   **Architect/Yr:** Brian Silva/2002
Other: Bar-Lounge / Restaurants / Clubhouse / Showers / Spring Hill Suites - Devens
GPS:

Site of 2009 U.S.G.A. Women's Amateur National Public Links Championship. "Top 50 Public Course in America," *Golf World*. A true championship course.

	1	2	3	4	5	6	7	8	9
PAR	4	5	3	5	3	4	4	4	4
YARDS	354	516	170	512	161	331	400	306	374
	10	11	12	13	14	15	16	17	18
PAR	5	3	4	4	4	3	4	4	5
YARDS	507	154	352	342	380	157	329	385	499

Directions: I-495 to Route 2 West to Jackson Road, Devens exit. North on Jackson Road to Patton Road. Right on Patton Road to Bulge Road. Left on Bulge to clubhouse.

Settlers Crossing Golf Course ✪½ ▶ 69

994 Northfield Road
Lunenburg, MA (978) 582-6694

Tees	Holes	Yards	Par	USGA	Slope
BACK					
MIDDLE	9	2685	35	63.9	106
FRONT	9	2520	35	66.5	105

Club Pro: Don Lyons, PGA
Payment: Visa, MC, Amex, Disc, Cash
Tee Times:
Fee 9 Holes: Weekday: $15   **Weekend:** $17
Fee 18 Holes: Weekday: $25   **Weekend:** $27
Twilight Rates: After 6pm   **Discounts:** Senior & Juniors
Cart Rental: $13pp/18, $8pp/9   **Driving Range:** No
Lessons: $50/40 min. **Schools:** Yes   **Junior Golf:** Yes
Membership: Yes   **Architect/Yr Open:** 1961
Other: Clubhouse / Snack Bar / Restaurant / Bar-Lounge

Junior and family friendly. "Friendly staff, new management. Improvements should be forthcoming." –GM

	1	2	3	4	5	6	7	8	9
PAR	4	3	4	4	4	4	3	4	5
YARDS	230	130	350	320	310	340	175	350	490
PAR									
YARDS									

Directions: Route 2 to Route 13 North. Take right, ⅛ mile to top of hill. Take left back on Route 13 North, go 2 miles to Northfield Road. Take left, go 1 mile. Clubhouse on right.

Shaker Farms Country Club ✪✪ ▶ 70

866 Shaker Road
Westfield, MA (413) 568-4087
www.shakerfarmscc.com

Tees	Holes	Yards	Par	USGA	Slope
BACK	18	6285	72	69.4	119
MIDDLE	18	6096	72	68.3	116
FRONT	18	5271	72	70.2	119

Club Pro:
Payment: Visa, MC, Amex, Check
Tee Times: 1-7 days adv.
Fee 9 Holes: Weekday: $15 walk, $21 ride   **Weekend:** $17 walk, $25 ride
Fee 18 Holes: Weekday: $21 walk, $29 ride   **Weekend:** $25 walk, $36 ride
Twilight Rates: After 5pm   **Discounts:** Junior
Cart Rental: Included   **Driving Range:** Yes
Lessons: Yes **Schools:** Yes   **Junior Golf:** Yes
Membership: Yes   **Architect/Yr Open:** Geoffrey Cornish/1953
Other: Restaurant / Clubhouse / Lockers / Showers / Bar-Lounge
GPS:

Each hole has its own personality with natural slopes, breathtaking scenery, doglegs, and strategically placed bunkers. The back 9 is Cornish at his very best.

	1	2	3	4	5	6	7	8	9
PAR	5	4	4	5	4	5	3	4	3
YARDS	510	340	329	461	388	577	215	375	156
	10	11	12	13	14	15	16	17	18
PAR	4	4	3	4	3	4	4	5	4
YARDS	311	360	140	314	137	342	405	447	290

Directions: I-90 (Mass Pike) to Exit 3 Westfield. Follow Routes 10 and 202 South to Route 20. Stay on Route 20 East passing Westfield shops. Turn right on Route 187 at blinking light. Follow to course.

Shaker Hills Country Club ✪✪✪✪✪

146 Shaker Road
Harvard, MA (978) 772-3330
www.shakerhills.com

Tees	Holes	Yards	Par	USGA	Slope
BACK	18	7015	72	74.0	137
MIDDLE	18	6524	72	71.2	129
FRONT	18	6044	72	69.4	124

Club Pro: Jeff Friel, PGA
Payment: MC, Visa, Amex, Disc, Cash
Tee Times: 7 days adv.
Fee 9 Holes: Weekday: $40 before 8am
Fee 18 Holes: Weekday: $75 M-T
Twilight Rates: $54 after 3pm
Cart Rental: Included
Lessons: $40-$45/half hour **Schools:** No
Membership: Yes
Weekend: $40 before 8am
Weekend: $89 F/S/S
Discounts: Senior and Junior
Driving Range: Yes, $5/bucket
Junior Golf: Yes
Architect/Yr Open: Silva & Mungeam/1991
Other: Clubhouse / Restaurant / Bar-Lounge / Lockers / Showers
GPS:

A true test at golf for players of all abilities. Tremendous new renovations to the golf course and clubhouse. Great conditions and a great layout. Shaker Hill staff makes everyone feel like a member at a private course for the day. Check out Shaker Hills' unique 5 and 10 play discount cards.

	1	2	3	4	5	6	7	8	9
PAR	4	5	3	4	5	3	4	4	4
YARDS	342	507	186	449	558	172	333	390	347
	10	11	12	13	14	15	16	17	18
PAR	4	4	4	3	4	5	3	4	5
YARDS	396	378	380	149	300	538	224	315	560

Directions: I-495 to Exit 30 (Route 2A West). 4 miles left onto Shaker Road. Course is ½ mile on left.

Skyline Country Club

NR

405 South Main Street (Route 7)
Lanesborough, MA (413) 445-5584
www.skyline-cc.com

Tees	Holes	Yards	Par	USGA	Slope
BACK	18	6250	71	68.8	117
MIDDLE	18	6100	72	66.9	113
FRONT	18	4900	71	67.5	114

Club Pro: Jim Mitus
Payment: MC, Visa, Cash
Tee Times: 1 week adv.
Fee 9 Holes: Weekday: $16
Fee 18 Holes: Weekday: $25
Twilight Rates: After 3pm
Cart Rental: $15pp/18, $8pp/9 per cart
Lessons: $40/half hour **Schools:** No
Membership: Yes
Other: Snack Bar / Bar-Lounge
Weekend: $17
Weekend: $27
Discounts: None
Driving Range: Yes
Junior Golf: Yes
Architect/Yr Open: Rowland Armacost/1962
GPS:

The course is somewhat hilly; considered moderately difficult.

	1	2	3	4	5	6	7	8	9
PAR	4	5	3	4	4	4	3	5	4
YARDS	369	487	127	331	363	390	196	540	379
	10	11	12	13	14	15	16	17	18
PAR	4	3	5	4	4	3	5	4	4
YARDS	395	167	490	343	295	167	432	362	379

Directions: I-90 (Mass Pike) to Exit 2 (Lee). Go North on Route 7. Course is approximately 20 miles on right.

Southampton Country Club ✪✪½ 73

329 College Highway (Route 10)
Southampton, MA (413) 527-9815

Club Pro:
Payment: Cash, Check
Tee Times: S/S 1 wk. adv.
Fee 9 Holes: Weekday: $13
Fee 18 Holes: Weekday: $19
Twilight Rates: After 4pm
Cart Rental: $14pp/18, $8pp/9
Lessons: No **Schools:** No
Membership: Yes
Other: Snack Bar / Restaurant / Bar-Lounge

Tees	Holes	Yards	Par	USGA	Slope
BACK	18	6585	72	72.6	126
MIDDLE	18	6135	72	69.1	120
FRONT	18	5422	72	66.6	116

Weekend: $16
Weekend: $26
Discounts: None
Driving Range: No
Junior Golf: No
Architect/Yr Open: John Strychary/1950
GPS:

Sig. Hole: #4, 165-yard par 3. This meticulously maintained course is moderately easy with large greens, rolling hills and panoramic views. Rated 3½ stars by *Golf Digest*. New clubhouse completed in 2010.

	1	2	3	4	5	6	7	8	9
PAR	4	3	4	3	4	5	4	4	5
YARDS	325	165	380	165	310	455	400	390	460
	10	11	12	13	14	15	16	17	18
PAR	3	5	5	3	4	4	4	4	4
YARDS	140	485	460	200	340	365	405	325	365

Directions: I-90 (Mass Pike) to Exit 3 West (Westfield exit). Take left onto Route 10/Route 202, course is 5 miles on right.

Southwick Country Club ✪✪✪ 74

739 College Highway
Southwick, MA (413) 569-0136
www.southwickcountryclub.com

Club Pro: Frank Powers, Manager
Payment: Cash, Credit Cards
Tee Times: 1 day adv.
Fee 9 Holes: Weekday: $15
Fee 18 Holes: Weekday: $22
Twilight Rates: After 6pm
Cart Rental: $13pp/18, $8pp/9
Lessons: Yes **Schools:** No
Membership: Yes
Other: Snack Bar / Restaurant / Lounge / Weekday Specials

Tees	Holes	Yards	Par	USGA	Slope
BACK					
MIDDLE	18	6100	71	64.8	102
FRONT	18	5570	71	64.7	103

Weekend: $20
Weekend: $26
Discounts: Senior & Junior
Driving Range: No
Junior Golf: Yes
Architect/Yr Open: 1928

The other course in Southwick. The course is flat and wide open; considered an easy walker. Greens and course in excellent condition.

	1	2	3	4	5	6	7	8	9
PAR	4	5	3	4	4	3	4	4	4
YARDS	410	525	175	400	430	120	325	300	355
	10	11	12	13	14	15	16	17	18
PAR	5	4	4	4	3	4	4	4	4
YARDS	490	290	320	315	125	450	415	310	345

Directions: I-90 (Mass Pike) Exit 3, Westfield; turn right onto Route 202. Course is approximately 4 miles south of Westfield.

St. Anne Country Club

★★½ **75**

781 Shoemaker Lane
Feeding Hills, MA (413) 786-2088
www.stannecc.com

Club Pro: Paul Napolitan
Payment: Most Major
Tee Times: 1 week adv.
Fee 9 Holes: Weekday: $18
Fee 18 Holes: Weekday: $23
Twilight Rates: No
Cart Rental: $28/18, $14/9 per cart
Lessons: Yes **Schools:** No
Membership: Open
Other: Snack Bar / Bar-Lounge

Tees	Holes	Yards	Par	USGA	Slope
BACK	18	6608	72	70.8	120
MIDDLE	18	5927	72	69.5	118
FRONT	18	5566	72	70.0	118

Weekend: $21
Weekend: $27
Discounts: Senior
Driving Range: No
Junior Golf: No
Architect/Yr Open: Joe Napolitan/1963
GPS:

CTRL/
WEST
MA

"Looks and feels like an arboretum with overviews of the course from elevated tees and level fairways. Easy layout that is great for beginners." –GG

	1	2	3	4	5	6	7	8	9
PAR	4	4	3	4	5	4	4	5	3
YARDS	385	312	141	342	500	381	394	420	171
	10	11	12	13	14	15	16	17	18
PAR	4	3	4	4	4	3	5	4	5
YARDS	310	133	315	315	273	185	467	360	523

Directions: I-91 to Route 57 West to Route 187. Turn right. First right is Shoemaker Lane, The club is ½ mile on the right.

St. Mark's Golf Club

★★ **76**

32 Cordaville Road
Southborough, MA (508) 460-0946
www.stmarksgolfclub.com

Club Pro:
Payment: Cash or Credit
Tee Times: Weekends, Holidays
Fee 9 Holes: Weekday: $18
Fee 18 Holes: Weekday: $28
Twilight Rates: Yes
Cart Rental: $13pp/18, $8pp/9
Lessons: No **Schools:** No
Membership: Yes
Other: Leagues welcome

Tees	Holes	Yards	Par	USGA	Slope
BACK					
MIDDLE	9	2905	35	67.1	117
FRONT	9	2670	35	67.1	117

Weekend: $20
Weekend: $30
Discounts: Senior & Junior
Driving Range: Practice area
Junior Golf: No
Architect/Yr Open: 1895
GPS:

COUPON

Scottish links styling, rolling terrain, long grass and sand pot bunkers, adjacent to scenic Sudbury reservoir.

	1	2	3	4	5	6	7	8	9
PAR	4	3	5	4	4	4	3	4	4
YARDS	325	155	445	345	375	335	195	320	410
PAR									
YARDS									

Directions: Route 9 to Route 85 North. Course is .8 mile after intersection.

Taconic Golf Club

✪✪✪✪½ **77**

19 Meachum Street
Williamstown, MA (413) 458-3997
www.taconicgolf.com

Tees	Holes	Yards	Par	USGA	Slope
BACK	18	6808	71	73.5	136
MIDDLE	18	6410	71	72.1	127
FRONT	18	5143	71	71.4	122

Club Pro: Rick Pohle, PGA
Payment: Credit Cards, Checks, Cash
Tee Times: 7 days adv.
Fee 9 Holes: Weekday: No   **Weekend:** No
Fee 18 Holes: Weekday: $145 (incl. cart)   **Weekend:** $145 (incl. cart)
Twilight Rates: No   **Discounts:** None
Cart Rental: Included in greens fee   **Driving Range:** Yes
Lessons: $50/45 min. **Schools:**   **Junior Golf:** Yes
Membership: No   **Architect/Yr Open:** Stiles & Van Kleek/1896
Other: Clubhouse / Lockers / Showers / Snack Bar / Bar-Lounge

Player Comments: "Outstanding course. Worth high rating. Nice people. Course was in super shape."
"If you come to golf in Western New England or Eastern New York, you need to come to Taconic." –ER

	1	2	3	4	5	6	7	8	9
PAR	5	4	4	4	3	4	4	4	3
YARDS	470	355	383	346	157	356	368	382	167
	10	11	12	13	14	15	16	17	18
PAR	5	4	4	4	3	4	4	3	5
YARDS	498	449	363	377	152	426	430	221	510

Directions: Route 2 to Williamstown; left on Route 43 South; 3rd street on right.

Tekoa Country Club

✪✪ **78**

459 Russell Road
Westfield, MA (413) 568-1064
www.tekoacc.com

Tees	Holes	Yards	Par	USGA	Slope
BACK	18	6438	71	70.1	123
MIDDLE	18	5917	71	69.2	121
FRONT	18	5201	71	69.3	112

Club Pro: E.J. Altobello
Payment: Visa, MC, Amex, Disc
Tee Times: 7 days adv.
Fee 9 Holes: Weekday: $16   **Weekend:** $20
Fee 18 Holes: Weekday: $25   **Weekend:** $28
Twilight Rates: After 5pm   **Discounts:** Senior & Junior
Cart Rental: $10pp/18, $6pp/9   **Driving Range:** No
Lessons: $35/half hour, $50/hour **Schools:** No **Junior Golf:** Yes
Membership: Yes   **Architect/Yr Open:** Donald Ross/1923
Other: Clubhouse / Restaurant / Sports Bar / Banquet Facilities

COUPON

Donald Ross design. Scenic views of Tekoa Mountain and Westfield River. Easy walking, short but challenging.

	1	2	3	4	5	6	7	8	9
PAR	4	4	3	5	4	3	5	4	4
YARDS	356	398	157	461	342	202	445	377	346
	10	11	12	13	14	15	16	17	18
PAR	4	3	5	4	5	4	3	4	3
YARDS	361	146	477	389	479	339	145	415	187

Directions: Take Mass Pike to Exit 3. Bear right onto Routes 10/202 South. Travel 2 miles into the center of Westfield. Bear right onto Route 20 West. Course is 2 miles on the right.

Templewood Golf Course   ✪✪½

160 Brooks Road
Templeton, MA (978) 939-5031
www.templewoodgolfcourse.com

Tees	Holes	Yards	Par	USGA	Slope
BACK	18	6067	70		
MIDDLE	18	5691	70		
FRONT	18	4882	70		

Club Pro: John Ross
Payment: Visa, MC, Amex, Disc, Check, Cash
Tee Times: 1 week adv.
Fee 9 Holes: Weekday: $14
Fee 18 Holes: Weekday: $20
Twilight Rates: Yes
Cart Rental: $15pp/18, $11pp/9
Lessons: Yes **Schools:** No
Membership: Yes
Other: Clubhouse / Lounge / New Pavillion / Practice Net

Weekend: $22
Weekend: $35
Discounts: No
Driving Range: No
Junior Golf: Yes
Architect/Yr Open: Cornish/Maurer/1998

Inspiring views of surrounding terrain. Panoramic view of Mt. Monadnock. Friendly staff. Beautiful course.

	1	2	3	4	5	6	7	8	9
PAR	5	3	4	3	5	4	3	4	4
YARDS	515	135	375	135	455	405	135	245	345
	10	11	12	13	14	15	16	17	18
PAR	5	3	4	4	3	4	3	4	5
YARDS	479	158	373	262	154	382	186	400	552

Directions: Route 2 to Exit 20. Follow Trailblazing signs.

The International (The Oaks)   ✪✪✪✪✪   80

159 Ballville Road
Bolton, MA (978) 779-6910
www.theinternational.com

Tees	Holes	Yards	Par	USGA	Slope
BACK	18	6944	72	73.5	132
MIDDLE	18	6565	72	72.5	129
FRONT	18	5243	71	70.8	126

Club Pro: Chris Kasheta, Dir. of Golf
Payment: Visa, MC, Amex, Disc
Tee Times: Yes
Fee 9 Holes: Weekday:
Fee 18 Holes: Weekday: $129
Twilight Rates: $85 after 3pm
Cart Rental: Included
Lessons: Yes **Schools:** Yes
Membership: Yes
Other: Clubhouse / Restaurant / Hotel / Lockers / Showers / Bar-Lounge

Weekend:
Weekend: $129
Discounts: No
Driving Range: Yes
Junior Golf: Yes
Architect/Yr Open: Tom Fazio/2001

The first and only Tom Fazio designed golf course in New England. A natural wonder that provides a unique experience that celebrates the ebb and flow of the geography. Visage GPS on all carts.

	1	2	3	4	5	6	7	8	9
PAR	5	3	4	3	4	4	4	5	4
YARDS	494	163	330	161	325	375	405	515	436
	10	11	12	13	14	15	16	17	18
PAR	4	3	5	3	5	4	4	3	5
YARDS	428	200	537	144	515	401	402	194	540

Directions: Route 495 to Exit 27 (Route 117). West on 117 for 1.5 miles. Left onto Wilder Road. Left onto Ballville Road. Club is ½ mile on right.

Thomas Memorial Golf & CC   NR 81 ▶

29 Country Club Lane
Turners Falls, MA (413) 863-8003
www.tmgcc.net

Tees	Holes	Yards	Par	USGA	Slope
BACK					
MIDDLE	9	2688	35	66.0	113
FRONT	9	2424	35	68.0	113

Club Pro:
Payment: Visa, MC, Disc
Tee Times: No
Fee 9 Holes: Weekday: $15   **Weekend:** $17
Fee 18 Holes: Weekday: $21   **Weekend:** $23
Twilight Rates: No   **Discounts:** None
Cart Rental: $12.50pp/18, $8.50pp/9   **Driving Range:** No
Lessons: Schools: No   **Junior Golf:** Yes
Membership: Yes   **Architect/Yr Open:** Walter B. Hatch/1959
Other: Bar-Lounge / Snack Bar   **GPS:**

COUPON

Course layout is interesting: hilly, several blind holes, narrow fairways, and some water hazards, 2 holes have 2 separate greens.

	1	2	3	4	5	6	7	8	9
PAR	4	4	4	4	5	4	3	4	3
YARDS	360	323	235	280	460	352	128	256	145
PAR									
YARDS									

Directions: Route 2 to lights at Turners Falls. Turn South on Avenue A to Turners Falls, left on 3rd Street. Right on L Street. At fork, bear left onto Montague. Right onto Griswold. Course .25 mile on right.

Townsend Ridge Country Club ✪✪✪½ 82 ▶

40 Scales Lane
Townsend, MA (978) 597-8400
www.townsendridge.com

Tees	Holes	Yards	Par	USGA	Slope
BACK	18	6231	70	70.4	126
MIDDLE	18	5819	70	68.6	121
FRONT	18	4685	71	68.5	115

Club Pro: Derick Fors
Payment: Visa, MC, Amex
Tee Times: 7 days adv.
Fee 9 Holes: Weekday: $18   **Weekend:** $21 (after 11am)
Fee 18 Holes: Weekday: $33   **Weekend:** $46
Twilight Rates: After 2pm wkdy; after 11am wknd   **Discounts:** Sr., 55+ & Jr.,18-
Cart Rental: $18pp/18, $9pp/9   **Driving Range:** $6/bucket
Lessons: $45/half hour; $75/hour   **Schools:** Yes
Junior Golf: Yes
Membership: Yes   **Architect/Yr:** T. Manning & Mary Mills/1996
Other: Clubhouse / 19th Hole Lounge / Full Bar / Restaurant

COUPON

Picturesque and well groomed course. Challenging for players of all ability levels with a wide variety of holes ranging in difficulty. Membership and outings encouraged!

	1	2	3	4	5	6	7	8	9
PAR	4	4	3	4	5	4	3	4	4
YARDS	312	375	126	390	469	308	156	349	351
	10	11	12	13	14	15	16	17	18
PAR	4	4	5	4	4	3	4	3	4
YARDS	375	377	460	328	407	135	367	170	364

Directions: I-495 to Exit 31. Go west on Route 119 for 15 miles. Take first left after Townsend Ford onto Scales Lane.

Twin Springs Golf Club ✪✪

83

295 Wilder Road
Bolton, MA (978) 779-5020
www.twinspringsgolf.com

Club Pro: Robert Keene, PGA
Payment: MC, Visa, Amex
Tee Times: 1 week adv.

Tees	Holes	Yards	Par	USGA	Slope
BACK					
MIDDLE	9	2592	34	64.8	113
FRONT	9	2432	35	67.2	106

Fee 9 Holes: Weekday: $16
Fee 18 Holes: Weekday: $24
Twilight Rates: No
Cart Rental: $12.75pp/18, $7.75pp/9
Driving Range: Sm./$3.50, Med./$7, Jumbo/$10.50
Lessons: $60/hour **Schools:** Yes
Membership: Senior & Junior
Other: Snack Bar/ Range

Weekend: $18
Weekend: $28
Discounts: Sr. & Jr. wkdy; Jr. wknd

COUPON

Junior Golf: Yes
Architect/Yr Open: 1932
GPS:

CTRL/ WEST MA

Sig. Hole: #4 is a devilish par 3 with a great view of Wachusett Mountain, fronted by a creek. "Fun for all levels of golfers." –FP

	1	2	3	4	5	6	7	8	9
PAR	4	4	4	3	3	4	4	4	4
YARDS	327	294	300	140	161	318	368	320	384
PAR									
YARDS									

Directions: I-495 to Exit 27 to Route 117 West into center of Bolton. Go straight for .7 mile. Turn left up hill at Wilder Road. Course is 2 miles on right.

Tyngsboro Country Club ✪½

84

48 Sherburne Avenue
Tyngsboro, MA (978) 649-7334

Club Pro: Allan Pottle
Payment: Cash Only
Tee Times: 5 days adv. weekends

Tees	Holes	Yards	Par	USGA	Slope
BACK	9	2590	35	65.2	104
MIDDLE	9	2397	35	63.2	104
FRONT	9	2023	35	62.6	97

Fee 9 Holes: Weekday: $17
Fee 18 Holes: Weekday: $28
Twilight Rates: No
Cart Rental: $25/18, $14/9 per cart
Lessons: No **Schools:** Yes
Membership: 7 day and weekday available
Other: Snack Bar / Bar-Lounge

Weekend: $19
Weekend: $31
Discounts: None
Driving Range: No
Junior Golf: No
Architect/Yr Open: 1933
GPS:

The course requires accurate shots and is easy to walk. Dress code required. Specials: Wednesday after 2pm - $12 for 9 holes; Tuesday, Thursday, and Friday after 6pm - $15 for 9 holes; Saturday and Sunday after 2pm - $15 for 9 holes.

	1	2	3	4	5	6	7	8	9
PAR	4	4	3	5	3	5	4	4	3
YARDS	320	314	216	446	160	463	282	249	140
PAR									
YARDS									

Directions: I-95 to Route 3 North to Exit 35 (onto Route 113 East); go approximately 2.5 miles to course.

Veteran's Memorial Golf Course ✪✪½ 85

1059 South Branch Pkwy
Springfield, MA (413) 787-6449
www.springfieldcityhall.com/Park

Tees	Holes	Yards	Par	USGA	Slope
BACK	18	6433	72	71.7	126
MIDDLE	18	5901	72	68.7	121
FRONT	18	4810	72	68.3	121

Club Pro: Kevin Kennedy, PGA
Payment: Cash, Visa, MC
Tee Times: Wknd, call Wed
Fee 9 Holes: Weekday: **Weekend:**
Fee 18 Holes: Weekday: $22   **Weekend:** $23
Twilight Rates: After 3pm   **Discounts:** Senior & Junior
Cart Rental: $13pp/18, $7pp/9 per cart   **Driving Range:** No
Lessons: Yes **Schools:**   **Junior Golf:** No
Membership: No   **Architect/Yr Open:** Geoffrey Cornish/1963
Other: Restarurant / Bar-Lounge   **GPS:**

Good value. Worth exploring.

	1	2	3	4	5	6	7	8	9
PAR	4	4	5	4	3	4	3	4	5
YARDS	261	341	431	331	194	343	145	273	485
	10	11	12	13	14	15	16	17	18
PAR	4	4	5	4	5	3	4	4	3
YARDS	362	405	498	345	472	166	288	324	157

Directions: I-95 (Exit 2), Sumner Ave. (3.8 miles), left on Bradley Road (0.4 miles). Right onto South Branch Parkway. Course is on left.

Wachusett Country Club ✪✪✪½ 86

187 Prospect Street
West Boylston, MA (508) 835-2264
www.wachusettcc.com

Tees	Holes	Yards	Par	USGA	Slope
BACK	18	6608	72	71.4	124
MIDDLE	18	6206	72	71.7	123
FRONT	18	6216	73	70.0	120

Club Pro: Nick Marrone, PGA
Payment: Visa, MC, Amex, Discover
Tee Times: 7 days adv.
Fee 9 Holes: Weekday: $20/walk, $30/ride M-Th (9am-3pm)
Fee 18 Holes: Weekday: $40/walk, $57/ride **Weekend:** $45/walk (after 12 noon), $62/ride
Twilight Rates: After 3pm & before 9am M-F **Discounts:** Jr. after 3pm M-F
Cart Rental: $17pp/18, $12pp/9   **Driving Range:** Yes
Lessons: Yes **Schools:** Junior Camp   **Junior Golf:** Yes
Membership: Yes, wait list   **Architect/Yr Open:** Donald Ross/1927
Other: Snack Bar / Bar-Lounge / Banquet Facilities

Donald Ross design. Reduced rates after 3pm on weekdays. "Beautifully maintained with nice views. Definitely give this course a try." –FP

	1	2	3	4	5	6	7	8	9
PAR	4	5	4	3	5	3	4	4	4
YARDS	388	518	380	145	507	175	360	436	426
	10	11	12	13	14	15	16	17	18
PAR	5	4	4	3	4	5	4	4	3
YARDS	494	430	426	203	330	508	316	374	192

Directions: I-90 (Mass Pike) to I-290 to I-190, Exit 4 onto Route 12 North. Approximately 2 miles to Franklin Street, turn left. At end of road turn left onto Prospect.

Wahconah Country Club ✪✪✪ 87 ▶

15 Orchard Road
Dalton, MA (413) 684-1333
www.wahconahcountryclub.com

Tees	Holes	Yards	Par	USGA	Slope
BACK	18	6553	71	72.5	135
MIDDLE	18	6229	71	71.6	132
FRONT	18	5831	73	73	128

Club Pro: James Underdown, PGA
Payment: Cash, Check, Visa, MC
Tee Times: 1 week adv.
Fee 9 Holes: Weekday: $45
Fee 18 Holes: Weekday: $70
Twilight Rates: No
Cart Rental: $15pp/18, 2 riders
Lessons: $40/half hour **Schools:** Yes
Membership: No waiting list
Other: Clubhouse / Restaurant / Bar-Lounge / Landscaped Patio

Weekend:
Weekend: $80
Discounts: None
Driving Range: $5/lg., $3/sm.
Junior Golf: Yes
Architect/Yr Open: Wayne Stiles/1930

CTRL/
WEST
MA

A beautiful, very challenging, semi-private course with fast greens. Considered to be moderately difficult. Open April 15 - November 15. "Excellent conditions." –FP

	1	2	3	4	5	6	7	8	9
PAR	4	3	4	4	4	3	5	4	4
YARDS	382	206	398	300	360	147	476	390	388
	10	11	12	13	14	15	16	17	18
PAR	4	4	4	3	5	4	4	3	5
YARDS	368	340	371	203	480	349	430	177	458

Directions: I-90 (Mass Pike) to Exit 2. Follow Route 9 North from Amherst into Dalton. In Dalton, take left onto Orchard Road. Course is approximately ½ mile on left.

Waubeeka Golf Links ✪✪✪ 88 ▶

137 New Ashford Road (Route 7)
South Williamstown, MA
(413) 458-8355
www.waubeeka.com

Tees	Holes	Yards	Par	USGA	Slope
BACK	18	6368	71	70.8	128
MIDDLE	18	5972	71	69.2	124
FRONT	18	5210	71	70.2	121

Club Pro:
Payment: Cash, Amex, MC, Visa, Disc
Tee Times: 7 days adv.
Fee 9 Holes: Weekday: $25
Fee 18 Holes: Weekday: $45
Twilight Rates: After 4pm, S/S/M/T
Cart Rental: $20pp/18, $10pp/9
Lessons: $30/45 min., $125/5 lessons
Schools: Jr./Women
Membership: Yes
Other: Clubhouse / Lockers / Showers / Snack Bar / Restaurant / Bar-Lounge

COUPON

Weekend: $30
Weekend: $55
Discounts: Junior and Seniors

Driving Range: New, plus practice facility
Junior Golf: Yes
Architect: Redesign Mungeam 2009/2010

Renovation of Back 9 and Front. Cart paths added to every hole. Well-groomed, scenic, Audubon Society member. Open April - November. "Rolling hills with scenic views. Great condition." –GM

	1	2	3	4	5	6	7	8	9
PAR	4	4	3	5	4	4	3	5	4
YARDS	365	443	181	494	435	400	176	487	386
	10	11	12	13	14	15	16	17	18
PAR	3	4	4	4	3	5	3	5	4
YARDS	230	420	369	305	155	532	162	501	327

Directions: I-90 (Mass Pike) to Exit 2 (Lee) to Route 20 North to Route 7 North. Go north about 45 minutes. Course is on left.

Westborough Country Club ✪✪½ 89

121 West Main Street
Westborough, MA (508) 366-9947
www.westborocountryclub.com

Tees	Holes	Yards	Par	USGA	Slope
BACK	9	3172	36	35.5	123
MIDDLE	9	2978	36	34.3	119
FRONT	9	2706	36	33.3	115

Club Pro: Jack A. Negoshian, PGA
Payment: Visa, MC, Amex, Disc
Tee Times: Weekends/Holidays, call Friday
Fee 9 Holes: Weekday: $18   **Weekend:** $32
Fee 18 Holes: Weekday: $30   **Weekend:** $32
Twilight Rates: After 6pm   **Discounts:** Senior & Junior
Cart Rental: $18pp/18, $9pp/9   **Driving Range:** No
Lessons: Yes   **Schools:** No   **Junior Golf:** No
Membership: Yes   **Architect/Yr Open:** Howe/1921
Other: Restaurant / Bar-Lounge / Clubhouse / Showers/Pro Shop / Putting Course

COUPON

Expanded Fairways in front of greens for easy run-ups. Hilly Course.

	1	2	3	4	5	6	7	8	9
PAR	5	4	5	4	3	4	3	4	4
YARDS	412	262	491	325	169	345	150	409	415
PAR									
YARDS									

Directions: Route 9 to Route 30 toward Westborough. Take a right at the stop sign. Course is 1 mile past center of town on the right. From 495, Exit 23B, Route. 9 West - Worcester - right onto Route 30. West toward Westborough/North Grafton - straight through Rotary, club is 1 mile on right.

Westminster Country Club ✪✪✪ 90

51 Ellis Road
Westminster, MA (978) 874-5938
www.westminstercountryclub.com

Tees	Holes	Yards	Par	USGA	Slope
BACK	18	6491	71	70.9	133
MIDDLE	18	6223	71	69.5	123
FRONT	18	5453	71	70.0	115

Club Pro: Michael Leblanc
Payment: Most Major
Tee Times: 4 days adv.
Fee 9 Holes: Weekday: $15   **Weekend:** $35
Fee 18 Holes: Weekday: $30   **Weekend:** $35
Twilight Rates: No   **Discounts:** Sr. & Jr. during "off" hrs.
Cart Rental: $16pp/18, $8pp/9   **Driving Range:** No
Lessons: Yes   **Schools:** No   **Junior Golf:** Yes
Membership: Yes   **Architect/Yr Open:** LeBlanc and Francis/1957
Other: Clubhouse / Lockers / Showers / Snack Bar / Restaurant / Bar-Lounge / Lodging Partner

COUPON

A great blue collar golf course with exceptional value. "Friendly and fair with a good mix of holes." –FP

	1	2	3	4	5	6	7	8	9
PAR	4	4	4	4	4	4	4	4	3
YARDS	422	396	344	384	353	316	333	312	173
	10	**11**	**12**	**13**	**14**	**15**	**16**	**17**	**18**
PAR	3	4	3	4	5	4	5	3	5
YARDS	131	381	224	452	532	314	548	157	451

Directions: Route 2 to Route 140 East. Take an immediate right after bridge, through Westminster Center. Follow 2 miles. Left onto Nichols. Bear right at fork onto Ellis. Course is 1 mile on right.

Westover Golf Course ✪✪ 91 ▶

181 South Street
Granby, MA (413) 547-8610
www.westovergolfcourse.com

Tees	Holes	Yards	Par	USGA	Slope
BACK	18	7025	72	74.0	131
MIDDLE	18	6610	72	71.9	129
FRONT	18	5580	72	71.9	117

Club Pro: Bill Kubinski, PGA
Payment: Cash, Visa, MC, Amex, Disc
Tee Times: 7 days adv.
Fee 9 Holes: Weekday: $16   **Weekend:** $19
Fee 18 Holes: Weekday: $23   **Weekend:** $26
Twilight Rates: After 4pm   **Discounts:** Senior & Junior
Cart Rental: $13pp/18, $8pp/9   **Driving Range:** Yes
Lessons: $45/50 min. **Schools:** No   **Junior Golf:** Yes
Membership: No   **Architect/Yr Open:** Orin Smith/1959
Other: Clubhouse / Lockers / Snack Bar / Bar-Lounge

Player Comments: "A great challenge for a reasonable price." Fantastic layout, very challenging. Dress code: no cutoffs or tank tops. Lessons for all ages and abilities. Open April 1 - December.

	1	2	3	4	5	6	7	8	9
PAR	4	4	4	3	4	4	5	3	5
YARDS	390	410	335	207	396	419	489	163	532
	10	11	12	13	14	15	16	17	18
PAR	3	4	5	3	4	4	4	4	5
YARDS	160	422	490	160	364	405	373	354	541

Directions: I-90 to Exit 5. Go left on Route 33 North, follow for approximately 5 miles to New Ludlow Road. Take right and go 3 miles to South Street.

Winchendon School Golf Club ✪✪½ 92 ▶

435 Spring Street
Winchendon, MA (978) 297-9897
www.winchgolf.com

Tees	Holes	Yards	Par	USGA	Slope
BACK	18	5512	70	67.8	122
MIDDLE	18	5348	70	67.2	119
FRONT	18	4693	72	70.5	124

Club Pro: Tom Borden, PGA
Payment: Visa, MC, Amex, Disc, Check, Cash
Tee Times: 7 days adv.

Fee 9 Holes: Weekday: $14, $21 ride   **Weekend:** $16, $23 ride
Fee 18 Holes: Weekday: $25, $39 ride   **Weekend:** $30, $44 ride
Twilight Rates: After 2pm   **Discounts:** Senior and Junior
Cart Rental: $16pp/18, $8pp/9   **Driving Range:** Yes
Lessons: Yes **Schools:** Yes   **Junior Golf:** Yes
Membership: Yes   **Architect/Yr Open:** Donald Ross/1926
Other: Clubhouse / Bar-Lounge / Snack Bar / Banquets / Outings Welcome

Improvements include a new clubhouse and pro shop. New driving range. Some short par 4's and long par 3's. "Nice, friendly staff." –FP

	1	2	3	4	5	6	7	8	9
PAR	4	5	4	4	3	4	3	3	4
YARDS	278	423	242	288	245	233	211	175	314
	10	11	12	13	14	15	16	17	18
PAR	5	4	4	4	4	4	3	5	3
YARDS	472	388	381	377	372	285	161	502	165

Directions: Route 2 to Route 140 North to Route 12 North. ½ mile down on your left.

Woods of Westminster ✪✪✪ ▶ 93

90 Bean Porridge Hill Road
Westminster, MA (978) 874-0500
www.woodsofwestminster.com

Tees	Holes	Yards	Par	USGA	Slope
BACK	18	6060	72	67.2	121
MIDDLE	18	5505	72	65.7	117
FRONT	18	4765	72	66.6	111

Club Pro: Dan Bartkus
Payment: Visa, MC
Tee Times: 5 days adv.
Fee 9 Holes: Weekday: $16   **Weekend:** $18
Fee 18 Holes: Weekday: $24   **Weekend:** $34
Twilight Rates: No   **Discounts:** Senior & Junior
Cart Rental: $16pp/18, $10pp/9   **Driving Range:** $7/lg., $5/sm.
Lessons: Yes **Schools:** Yes **Junior Golf:** Yes
Membership: Yes   **Architect/Yr Open:** Al Zikorus/1998
Other: Bar-Lounge   **GPS:**

COUPON

The best course and the friendliest people you'll ever play and meet.

	1	2	3	4	5	6	7	8	9
PAR	5	4	5	4	4	3	4	3	4
YARDS	460	275	525	295	345	175	405	145	320
	10	11	12	13	14	15	16	17	18
PAR	5	4	4	5	3	4	3	4	4
YARDS	345	220	330	435	145	315	130	300	340

Directions: From Routes I-95, I-495 or I-190: take Route 2 West, turn left off ramp onto 2A. Follow 2 miles, turn left onto South Ashburnham Road, follow for 1 mile. Turn right onto Bean Porridge Hill Road for 1 mile. Woods of Westminster is on the left at the top of the hill.

Worthington Golf Course NR ▶ 94

113 Ridge Road
Worthington, MA (413) 238-4464
www.worthingtongolfclub.net

Tees	Holes	Yards	Par	USGA	Slope
BACK	9	2782	35	33.3	115
MIDDLE	9	2797	70	66.8	116
FRONT	9	2797	35	33.5	121

Club Pro: Karl Enroth, PGA
Payment: Cash, Credit
Tee Times: 1 week adv.
Fee 9 Holes: Weekday: $13   **Weekend:** $17
Fee 18 Holes: Weekday: $26   **Weekend:** $30
Twilight Rates: No   **Discounts:** None
Cart Rental: $30/18, $18/9 per cart   **Driving Range:** Yes
Lessons: Yes **Schools:** Yes **Junior Golf:** Yes
Membership: Yes   **Architect/Yr Open:** A.P. Taylor/1904
Other: Clubhouse / Snack Bar / Restaurant / Bar-Lounge

COUPON

Sig. Hole: #6, par 3, 2 trees guarding fairway. 2 sand traps in front and 2-tiered green. Call ahead for tee times. 2 sets of tees makes an interesting 18. The 8th hole is the highest elevated golf hole in all of Massachusetts.

	1	2	3	4	5	6	7	8	9
PAR	4	4	4	4	3	3	5	5	3
YARDS	333	322	340	301	201	148	528	476	148
PAR									
YARDS									

Directions: I-91 to Northampton. Exit 19, depart Route 9 West toward Williamsburg, turn left onto Route 143 West. Follow to the traffic light at Worthington Four Corners. Go straight through intersection up Buffington Hill Road. Turn left onto Ridge Road to the course.

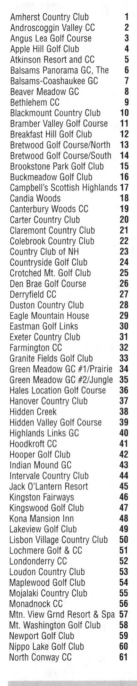

Course	No.
Amherst Country Club	1
Androscoggin Valley CC	2
Angus Lea Golf Course	3
Apple Hill Golf Club	4
Atkinson Resort and CC	5
Balsams Panorama GC, The	6
Balsams-Coashaukee GC	7
Beaver Meadow GC	8
Bethlehem CC	9
Blackmount Country Club	10
Bramber Valley Golf Course	11
Breakfast Hill Golf Club	12
Bretwood Golf Course/North	13
Bretwood Golf Course/South	14
Brookstone Park Golf Club	15
Buckmeadow Golf Club	16
Campbell's Scottish Highlands	17
Candia Woods	18
Canterbury Woods CC	19
Carter Country Club	20
Claremont Country Club	21
Colebrook Country Club	22
Country Club of NH	23
Countryside Golf Club	24
Crotched Mt. Golf Club	25
Den Brae Golf Course	26
Derryfield CC	27
Duston Country Club	28
Eagle Mountain House	29
Eastman Golf Links	30
Exeter Country Club	31
Farmington CC	32
Granite Fields Golf Club	33
Green Meadow GC #1/Prairie	34
Green Meadow GC #2/Jungle	35
Hales Location Golf Course	36
Hanover Country Club	37
Hidden Creek	38
Hidden Valley Golf Course	39
Highlands Links GC	40
Hoodkroft CC	41
Hooper Golf Club	42
Indian Mound GC	43
Intervale Country Club	44
Jack O'Lantern Resort	45
Kingston Fairways	46
Kingswood Golf Club	47
Kona Mansion Inn	48
Lakeview Golf Club	49
Lisbon Village Country Club	50
Lochmere Golf & CC	51
Londonderry CC	52
Loudon Country Club	53
Maplewood Golf Club	54
Mojalaki Country Club	55
Monadnock CC	56
Mtn. View Grnd Resort & Spa	57
Mt. Washington Golf Club	58
Newport Golf Club	59
Nippo Lake Golf Club	60
North Conway CC	61

Course	No.
Oak Hill Golf Course	62
Oaks Golf Links, The	63
Overlook GC	64
Owl's Nest Golf Club	65
Passaconaway CC	66
Pease Golf Course	67
Pembroke Pines CC	68
Pheasant Ridge CC	69
Pine Grove Springs CC	70
Pine Valley Golf Links	71
Ponemah Green Family Center	72
Portsmouth CC	73
Ragged Mountain Resort	74
Ridgewood Country Club	75
Rochester Country Club	76
Rockingham CC	77
Sagamore-Hampton GC	78
Shattuck GC, The	79

Course	No.
Souhegan Woods GC	80
Stonebridge Country Club	81
Sunset Hill Golf Course	82
Twin Lake Villa Golf Course	83
Waterville Valley	84
Waukewan Golf Club	85
Waumbek Golf Club	86

Course	No.
Wentworth Resort GC	87
Whip-Poor-Will GC	88
White Mountain CC	89
Windham Country Club	90

KEY TO THE STAR RATINGS:
5✪ = Outstanding   4✪ = Excellent   3✪ = Very Good   2✪ = Good   1✪ = Average   **NR** = Not Rated

Amherst Country Club   ✪✪✪

72 Ponemah Road
Amherst, NH (603) 673-9908
www.amherstcountryclub.com

Tees	Holes	Yards	Par	USGA	Slope
BACK	18	6543	72	70.8	124
MIDDLE	18	6036	72	67.5	117
FRONT	18	5590	74	72.1	117

Club Pro:
Payment: Visa, MC, Amex, Disc, Cash, Check
Tee Times: 5 days adv.
Fee 9 Holes: Weekday: $25   **Weekend:** $27
Fee 18 Holes: Weekday: $40   **Weekend:** $50
Twilight Rates: Check for availability   **Discounts:** Senior (wkdys) & Junior (after 12pm)
Cart Rental: $15pp/18, $8pp/9   **Driving Range:** Yes
Lessons: Yes **Schools:** Yes   **Junior Golf:** Yes
Membership: Yes   **Architect/Yr Open:** William Mitchell/1965
Other: Bar-Lounge / Restaurant / Clubhouse / Showers
GPS:

With a reputation for excellent conditions and quality customer service, Amherst Country Club is an 18-hole premier golf destination for all levels of play. Accomodates all levels of play with 4 sets of tees.

	1	2	3	4	5	6	7	8	9
PAR	4	5	3	5	4	4	3	4	4
YARDS	300	475	188	460	370	338	183	412	373
	10	**11**	**12**	**13**	**14**	**15**	**16**	**17**	**18**
PAR	4	4	4	3	5	3	5	4	4
YARDS	350	260	344	135	455	135	508	391	359

Directions: Route 3 (Everett Turnpike) to Exit 7W-Rowe 101A West; Go 7 miles on Route 101A West to Route 122; turn right on 122. Amherst Country Club is ½ mile on right.

Androscoggin Valley CC   ✪✪✪½

2 Main Street (Route 2)
Gorham, NH (603) 466-9468
www.avccgolf.com

Tees	Holes	Yards	Par	USGA	Slope
BACK	18	6110	70	67.9	118
MIDDLE	18	5715	70	66.5	115
FRONT	18	5131	70	71.0	122

Club Pro: Gary A. Riff
Payment: Visa, MC, Amex, Disc
Tee Times: 1 day adv.
Fee 9 Holes: Weekday: $20   **Weekend:** $25
Fee 18 Holes: Weekday: $30   **Weekend:** $35
Twilight Rates: After 1pm   **Discounts:** Junior
Cart Rental: $40/18, $20/9 per cart   **Driving Range:** $10/lg, $5/sm
Lessons: $50/hour **Schools:**   **Junior Golf:** Yes
Membership:
Architect/Yr Open: Alex Chisolm & Horace Smith/2004
Other: Clubhouse / Snack Bar / Bar-Lounge / Lockers / Showers

Scenic, open layout with good greens makes this a joy to play and score on. Some holes border the Androscoggin River. Open May 1 - October 31.

	1	2	3	4	5	6	7	8	9
PAR	5	4	3	5	4	3	3	4	5
YARDS	475	375	165	475	310	190	170	325	520
	10	**11**	**12**	**13**	**14**	**15**	**16**	**17**	**18**
PAR	4	4	4	3	5	3	4	3	4
YARDS	375	370	350	145	480	155	290	195	350

Directions: I-93 to Route 3 through Twin Mountain to Route 115 East to Route 2. Take Route 2 to Gorham. At light, take a right through town. Cross bridge, club is on left.

Angus Lea Golf Course

NR 3

126 West Main Street
Hillsboro, NH (603) 464-5404
www.anguslea.com

Tees	Holes	Yards	Par	USGA	Slope
BACK					
MIDDLE	9	2319	33	60.0	94
FRONT	9	2097	33	62.3	104

Club Pro: Curtis R. Niven, PGA
Payment: Visa, MC
Tee Times: Weekends/Holidays
Fee 9 Holes: Weekday: $18.95   **Weekend:** $18.95
Fee 18 Holes: Weekday: $33   **Weekend:** $33
Twilight Rates: No
Discounts: M-Th 11-2pm $16/Student (w/proper ID); $15/Junior
Cart Rental: $28/18, $16/9 per cart   **Driving Range:** No
Lessons: $40/hour **Schools:** No   **Junior Golf:** Yes
Membership: Yes   **Architect/Yr Open:** Ed Bedell/1964
Other: Snack Bar / Bar-Lounge / Full Pro Shop   **GPS:**

Bordered by the Contoocook River, the course plays around water and through the woods. Beautiful view from large screened porch.

	1	2	3	4	5	6	7	8	9
PAR	4	3	3	4	4	4	4	3	4
YARDS	283	150	160	300	310	435	245	161	275
PAR									
YARDS									

Directions: I-89 to Exit #5. Located on Main Street (Route 202/9) in Hillsboro. ½ mile on left after traffic light in downtown.

Apple Hill Golf Club

⊙⊙ 4

69 East Road (Route 107)
E. Kingston, NH (603) 642-4414
www.applehillgolf.com

Tees	Holes	Yards	Par	USGA	Slope
BACK	18	6184	70	69.6	120
MIDDLE	18	5875	70	68.2	117
FRONT	18	4767	70	68.4	118

Club Pro: Steve Lundquist, PGA
Payment: Visa, MC, Disc, Checks
Tee Times: 1 week adv.
Fee 9 Holes: Weekday: $18   **Weekend:** $20
Fee 18 Holes: Weekday: $30   **Weekend:** $35
Twilight Rates: Sunday after 2pm   **Discounts:** Senior & Junior
Cart Rental: $15pp/18, $8pp/9   **Driving Range:** No
Lessons: Yes **Schools:** No   **Junior Golf:** Yes
Membership: Yes   **Architect/Yr Open:**
Other: Clubhouse / Snack Bar / Bar-Lounge   **GPS:**

COUPON

Now 27 holes, including Apple Hill 9-hole par 3 course, 715 yards. Both courses are well maintained. Rates for the 9 hole course are $10 every day.

	1	2	3	4	5	6	7	8	9
PAR	4	3	4	3	5	4	4	4	4
YARDS	365	145	377	165	479	415	368	358	357
	10	11	12	13	14	15	16	17	18
PAR	5	3	4	5	3	4	4	3	4
YARDS	458	181	363	420	169	294	356	136	410

Directions: I-95 to Exit 1 in New Hampshire (Route 107). The course is 6 miles on right. From Route 125 Kingston take Route 107 South, go 3½ miles.

Atkinson Resort and CC ✪✪✪✪

 5

85 Country Club Drive
Atkinson, NH (603) 362-8700
www.atkinsonresort.com

Club Pro: Peter Doherty, PGA
Payment: Visa, MC, Amex, Checks
Tee Times: 5 days adv.
Fee 9 Holes: Weekday: $28
Fee 18 Holes: Weekday: $52
Twilight Rates: After 5:30pm weekdays
Cart Rental: $18pp/18, $10pp/9
Lessons: Yes **Schools:** Yes
Membership: Yes

Tees	Holes	Yards	Par	USGA	Slope
BACK	18	6580	72	73.1	135
MIDDLE	18	6088	72	70.3	131
FRONT	18	4867	72	68.6	117

Weekend: $33
Weekend: $62
Discounts: Sr, Jr, Military
Driving Range: Yes
Junior Golf: Yes
Architect/Yr Open: Lewis Group/1996

COUPON

Other: Snack Bar / Clubhouse / Lockers / Showers / Restaurant / Bar-Lounge / Hotel

A championship 18-hole golf course with a fully equipped pro shop. GPS-guided carts, a state-of-the-art practice facility, the area's most sophisticated indoor virtual golf simulators, family-friendly 9-hole Par 3 course, and the Willowcreek Golf Academy—all open to the public seven days a week.

	1	2	3	4	5	6	7	8	9
PAR	4	5	3	4	4	5	4	3	4
YARDS	310	485	180	350	400	481	366	185	380
	10	11	12	13	14	15	16	17	18
PAR	4	3	5	4	3	4	5	4	4
YARDS	346	144	477	317	127	370	466	370	334

Directions: Route 495 to Exit 50 (Route 97). Left off exit, follow 4 miles, take right onto Hampstead Road. Course is 2.3 miles on right.

Balsams Panorama Golf Club ✪✪✪½

6

1000 Cold Spring Road
Dixville Notch, NH (603) 255-4961
www.thebalsams.com

Club Pro: Douglas A. Ruttle, PGA
Payment: Visa, MC, Amex, Disc
Tee Times: 7 days adv.
Fee 9 Holes: Weekday: $52
Fee 18 Holes: Weekday: $99
Twilight Rates: $65 after 2pm
Cart Rental: Included
Lessons: $85/hour **Schools:** Yes
Membership: Yes

Tees	Holes	Yards	Par	USGA	Slope
BACK	18	6804	72	72.8	130
MIDDLE	18	6097	72	69.1	122
FRONT	18	5069	72	67.8	115

Weekend: $52
Weekend: $99
Discounts: Afternoon only
Driving Range: $5/lg.
Junior Golf: No
Architect/Yr Open: Donald Ross/1912

Other: Clubhouse / Restaurant / Lockers / Showers / Bar-Lounge / Resort Hotel

Closed for renovations. Expected to open summer 2015.

	1	2	3	4	5	6	7	8	9
PAR	4	5	4	4	3	5	3	4	4
YARDS	366	457	376	363	175	463	157	346	316
	10	11	12	13	14	15	16	17	18
PAR	4	4	4	4	3	5	3	4	5
YARDS	320	302	323	423	191	501	173	365	480

Directions: 1) Take I-93 North to Exit 35, Route 3 North to Colebrook, east on Route 26 for 10 miles; or 2) Take I-91 to exit at St. Johnsbury, Route 2. Go east on Route 2 to Lancaster. Take Route 3 North to Colebrook, and east on Route 26 for 10 miles.

Balsams-Coashaukee Golf Course ✪✪

7 ▶

1000 Cold Spring Road
Dixville Notch, NH (603) 255-4961
www.thebalsams.com

Club Pro: Douglas A. Ruttle
Payment: MC, Visa, Disc, Amex
Tee Times: None required
Fee 9 Holes: Weekday:
Fee 18 Holes: Weekday: $25
Twilight Rates: No
Cart Rental: $25pp/18, $17pp/9
Lessons: Yes **Schools:** Sr.
Membership: Yes
Other:

Tees	Holes	Yards	Par	USGA	Slope
BACK					
MIDDLE	9	1917	32	59.1	87
FRONT					

Weekend:
Weekend: $25
Discounts: None
Driving Range: No
Junior Golf: No
Architect/Yr Open: James Smith/1965
GPS:

Closed for renovations. Expected to open summer 2015.

	1	2	3	4	5	6	7	8	9
PAR	4	3	3	4	4	4	3	4	3
YARDS	304	147	174	223	265	236	145	313	110

PAR									
YARDS									

Directions: 1) Take I-93 North to Exit 35, Route 3 North to Colebrook, east on Route 26 for 10 miles; or 2) Take I-91 to exit at St. Johnsbury, Route 2. Go east on Route 2 to Lancaster. Take Route 3 North to Colebrook, and east on Route 26 for 10 miles.

Beaver Meadow Golf Club ✪✪¹⁄₂

8 ▶

1 Beaver Meadow Drive
Concord, NH (603) 228-8954
beavermeadowgolfcourse.com

Club Pro: Julie Donlon, PGA
Payment: Visa, MC
Tee Times: Weekends, 2 days adv.
Fee 9 Holes: Weekday: $25
Fee 18 Holes: Weekday: $40
Twilight Rates: After 3pm
Cart Rental: $16pp/18, $8pp/9
Lessons: $50/45 min. **Schools:** No
Membership: Yes
Other: Clubhouse / Snack Bar / Bar-Lounge

Tees	Holes	Yards	Par	USGA	Slope
BACK	18	6356	72	70.8	127
MIDDLE	18	6034	72	69.2	121
FRONT	18	6519	72	71.8	123

Weekend: $25
Weekend: $40
Discounts: Srs. on annual basis
Driving Range: Yes
Junior Golf: City Rec. Dept.
Architect/Yr Open: Willie Campbell/1896
GPS:

COUPON

Newly renovated practice facility with grass tee. Host site 2009 USI Championship. An official event on the Duramed Futures Tour, road to the LPGA.

	1	2	3	4	5	6	7	8	9
PAR	4	5	3	5	4	3	4	4	4
YARDS	341	480	153	474	336	138	366	414	315
	10	**11**	**12**	**13**	**14**	**15**	**16**	**17**	**18**
PAR	5	4	4	3	4	4	5	3	4
YARDS	527	320	301	130	347	400	560	156	276

Directions: I-93 to Exit 15 West (North Main Street). At second light, take right onto Route 3 North. Course is 3.1 miles on right.

Bethlehem Country Club

NR 9

1901 Main Street
Bethlehem, NH (603) 869-5745
www.bethlehemccnhgolf.com

Club Pro:
Payment: Visa, MC, Cash
Tee Times: Required

Tees	Holes	Yards	Par	USGA	Slope
BACK	18	5808	70	67.9	110
MIDDLE	18	5586	70	66.6	110
FRONT	18	5008	70	63.0	98

Fee 9 Holes: Weekday: $19 (12 holes)
Fee 18 Holes: Weekday: $28
Twilight Rates: After 3pm
Cart Rental: $15pp/18, $11pp/12
Lessons: Yes **Schools:** No
Membership: Yes
Other: Restaurant/ Snack Bar / Retail

Weekend: $25 (12 holes)
Weekend: $33
Discounts: Junior
Driving Range: No
Junior Golf: Yes
Architect/Yr: W. Lilywhite/1898; D. Ross/1910
GPS:

COUPON

Player Comments: "Generous fairways and light rough will have you blasting your driver on all long holes. Accuracy is required on the 4 par 3 holes." –AP

	1	2	3	4	5	6	7	8	9
PAR	4	4	3	4	4	4	3	4	4
YARDS	413	319	210	264	402	399	157	328	288
	10	11	12	13	14	15	16	17	18
PAR	3	5	3	4	4	5	4	4	4
YARDS	95	487	153	417	260	501	270	296	360

Directions: I-93 to Exit 40 East. 2.5 miles on Route 302 East.

Blackmount Country Club

★★ 10

400 Clark Pond Road
North Haverhill, NH (603) 787-6564
www.blackmountcountryclub.com

Club Pro: Bill Grimes
Payment: Cash or Check
Tee Times: No

Tees	Holes	Yards	Par	USGA	Slope
BACK	9	3015	36	34.8	114
MIDDLE	9	2658	36	33.3	110
FRONT	9	2316	36	35.7	121

Fee 9 Holes: Weekday: $12
Fee 18 Holes: Weekday: $20
Twilight Rates: No
Cart Rental: $24/18, $15/9 per cart
Lessons: Yes **Schools:** No
Membership: Yes
Other: Clubhouse / Snack Bar / Gazebo / Beer & Wine

Weekend: $16
Weekend: $24
Discounts: Senior, Junior, Ladies
Driving Range: Yes
Junior Golf: No
Architect/Yr Open: Robert Stoddard

COUPON

Outstanding greens. Beautiful course. Play & Stay package with the Hayloft Inn B&B adjacent to 1st hole.

	1	2	3	4	5	6	7	8	9
PAR	3	5	4	5	4	4	4	3	4
YARDS	150	400	333	383	217	317	350	142	366
PAR									
YARDS									

Directions: I-91 to Bradford, VT. Exit to NH Route 10 to village of North Haverhill, NH. Turn onto Clark Pond Road, across from Aldrich's General Store. Bear right for 1.5 miles.

Bramber Valley Golf Course ✪✪ ▶ 11

75 Bramber Valley Drive
Greenland, NH (603) 436-4288
www.brambervalleygolf.com

Club Pro: Scott Marceau
Payment: Cash, Check, Credit Cards
Tee Times: No
Fee 9 Holes: Weekday: $20
Fee 18 Holes: Weekday: $32
Twilight Rates: Fall only, after 2pm
Cart Rental: $24pp/18, $14pp/9
Lessons: Yes **Schools:** Jr.
Membership: No
Other: Clubhouse / Bar-Lounge

Weekend: $20
Weekend: $32
Discounts: Senior & Junior
Driving Range: $8/lg., $4/sm.
Junior Golf: Yes
Architect/Yr Open: James Petropolus/1994
GPS:

Tees	Holes	Yards	Par	USGA	Slope
BACK					
MIDDLE	9	2114	32	61.4	103
FRONT					

Great playing surfaces, friendly staff, wonderful practice facility, and low prices. Improvements ongoing. Full-service restaurant and bar. Beaches nearby.

	1	2	3	4	5	6	7	8	9
PAR	3	4	3	4	3	4	4	3	4
YARDS	133	333	107	312	160	260	315	180	314
PAR									
YARDS									

Directions: I-95 to Exit 3A. Go west on Route 33 for about 3 miles. Blue sign for club is after Golf & Ski Warehouse.

Breakfast Hill Golf Club ✪✪✪ ▶ 12

399 Breakfast Hill Road
Greenland, NH (603) 436-5001
www.breakfasthill.com

Club Pro: Nathan Bridges
Payment: Visa, MC, Disc, Checks
Tee Times: 7 days adv.
Fee 9 Holes: Weekday: $31
Fee 18 Holes: Weekday: $47
Twilight Rates: After 5 pm
Cart Rental: $17pp/18, $12pp/9
Lessons: Yes **Schools:** No
Membership: Yes, Season Pass
Other: Restaurant / Clubhouse / Bar-Lounge

Weekend: $31
Weekend: $54
Discounts: Senior (see website)
Driving Range: Yes
Junior Golf: Yes, pay your age under 18
Architect/Yr Open: Brian Silva/2000
GPS:

Tees	Holes	Yards	Par	USGA	Slope
BACK	18	6493	71.5	77.6	131
MIDDLE	18	5981	69.0	74.7	128
FRONT	18	4994	69.3	64.7	121

18 unique holes with rolling fairways and contoured greens. Brian Silva design. Rated Top Five in state by *Golf Week*.

	1	2	3	4	5	6	7	8	9
PAR	4	5	4	3	5	3	4	4	4
YARDS	350	465	365	149	489	124	364	332	350
	10	11	12	13	14	15	16	17	18
PAR	4	4	5	4	3	4	4	3	4
YARDS	309	460	526	296	165	322	378	143	394

Directions: I-95 to Exit 3 (Greenland/Portsmouth). Left onto Route 33. Left onto Route 151 South for 1.4 miles. Go left onto Breakfast Hill Road. Course is 1 mile on left.

Bretwood Golf Course (North) ✪✪✪½

635 East Surry Road
Keene, NH (603) 352-7626
www.bretwoodgolf.com

Tees	Holes	Yards	Par	USGA	Slope
BACK	18	6974	72	73.9	132
MIDDLE	18	6434	72	71.5	129
FRONT	18	5822	72	68.9	125

Club Pro: Matt Barrett, PGA
Payment: Visa, MC, Disc
Tee Times: Weekends, 3 days adv.
Fee 9 Holes: Weekday: $20   **Weekend:** $24
Fee 18 Holes: Weekday: $38   **Weekend:** $42
Twilight Rates: No   **Discounts:** None
Cart Rental: $13pp/18, $8pp/9 (all day $24)   **Driving Range:** $8/lg., $6/med., $4/sm.
Lessons: Yes   **Schools:** No   **Junior Golf:** Yes
Membership: Yes   **Architect/Yr Open:** Hugh Barrett/1968
Other: Clubhouse / Snack Bar / Group Outings for all Sizes.

Player Comments: "Gets better every year. Favorite hole # 13 island green." "Scenic. Great layouts."
"Excellent fairways and greens. River meanders through course and comes into play often. Covered
bridges, great value." –GG

	1	2	3	4	5	6	7	8	9
PAR	4	5	3	4	5	4	5	3	4
YARDS	413	552	187	340	505	390	480	138	400
	10	**11**	**12**	**13**	**14**	**15**	**16**	**17**	**18**
PAR	4	4	4	3	4	4	3	5	4
YARDS	400	340	372	130	380	379	154	501	373

Directions: I-91 North to Route 9 East to Keene. Follow hospital signs to Court Street. East Surry
Road is off Upper Court Street. 1.5 miles to course.

Bretwood Golf Course (South) ✪✪✪

635 East Surry Road
Keene, NH (603) 352-7626
www.bretwoodgolf.com

Tees	Holes	Yards	Par	USGA	Slope
BACK	18	6952	72	73.2	133
MIDDLE	18	6345	72	70.7	124
FRONT	18	5645	70	68.0	119

Club Pro: Matt Barrett, PGA
Payment: Visa, MC, Disc
Tee Times: Weekends, 3 days adv.
Fee 9 Holes: Weekday: $20   **Weekend:** $24
Fee 18 Holes: Weekday: $38   **Weekend:** $42
Twilight Rates: No   **Discounts:** None
Cart Rental: $13pp/18, $8pp/9 (all day $24)   **Driving Range:** $8/lg., $6/med., $4/sm. bucket
Lessons: Yes   **Schools:** No   **Junior Golf:** Yes
Membership: Yes   **Architect/Yr:** Geoffrey Cornish, Hugh Barrett/1968
Other: Clubhouse / Snack Bar / Group Outings for all Sizes.
GPS: Yes

Front nine lulls you into submission as the back nine tests you metal as you wind your way through
Jurasic Park (holes #15, #17).

	1	2	3	4	5	6	7	8	9
PAR	5	5	3	4	4	4	3	4	4
YARDS	477	530	168	364	288	305	181	394	383
	10	**11**	**12**	**13**	**14**	**15**	**16**	**17**	**18**
PAR	5	4	3	5	4	4	3	4	4
YARDS	472	372	133	536	371	340	176	410	445

Directions: I-91 North to Route 9 East to Keene. Follow hospital signs to Court Street. East Surry
Road is off Upper Court Street. 1.5 miles to course.

Brookstone Park Golf Course

14 Route 111
Derry, NH (603) 894-7336
www.brookstone-park.com

Tees	Holes	Yards	Par	USGA	Slope
BACK	9	2422	27		
MIDDLE	9	1892	27		
FRONT	9	1502	27		

Club Pro: Joe Kobrenski, Manager
Payment: All Types
Tee Times: 7 days adv.
Fee 9 Holes: Weekday: $13
Fee 18 Holes: Weekday: $23
Twilight Rates: No
Cart Rental: $12pp/18, $7pp/9
Lessons: Yes **Schools:** Yes
Membership: Yes
Other: Clubhouse / Snack Bar

Weekend: $15
Weekend: $26
Discounts: Senior & Junior
Driving Range: Yes
Junior Golf: Yes
Architect/Yr Open: Howard Maurer/2005
GPS:

The course has large greens, sand traps, rolling hills and water hazards that are strategically placed to create "target style" greens.

	1	2	3	4	5	6	7	8	9
PAR	3	3	3	3	3	3	3	3	3
YARDS	96	119	125	84	125	116	76	72	133
PAR									
YARDS									

Directions: I-93 to Exit 3 in NH, head east on Route 111. Go about 4.5 miles. Golf course is on left.

Buckmeadow Golf Club

30 Route 101A
Amherst, NH (603) 673-7077

Tees	Holes	Yards	Par	USGA	Slope
BACK	9	2425	33	61.8	101
MIDDLE	9	2340	33	60.9	100
FRONT	9	2280	34	66.2	103

Club Pro:
Payment: Cash, Check
Tee Times: Public/Members
Fee 9 Holes: Weekday: $14
Fee 18 Holes: Weekday: $26
Twilight Rates: No
Cart Rental: $14pp/18, $7pp/9
Lessons: Yes **Schools:** No
Membership: Limited/100 max.
Other: Bar-Lounge / Snack Bar

Weekend: $16
Weekend: $28
Discounts: Senior & Junior
Driving Range: No
Junior Golf: No
Architect/Yr Open: M.E. Young/1979
GPS:

"Six dogleg par 4s and 3 interesting 1-shot holes make for a challenging round on this nicely maintained venue." –AP

	1	2	3	4	5	6	7	8	9
PAR	4	3	4	4	4	3	4	3	4
YARDS	320	120	190	335	345	175	330	185	340
PAR									
YARDS									

Directions: Route 3 to Route 101A West. Course is 1.5 miles off Route 101 outside of Milford.

Campbell's Scottish Highlands ✪✪✪½

79 Brady Avenue
Salem, NH (603) 894-4653
www.scottishhighlandsgolf.com

Tees	Holes	Yards	Par	USGA	Slope
BACK	18	6249	71	70.1	121
MIDDLE	18	5746	71	67.6	113
FRONT	18	5056	71	68.9	116

Club Pro: Geoff Williams
Payment: Visa, MC, Disc
Tee Times: 5 days adv. 603-894-4653 x13
Fee 9 Holes: Weekday: $24   **Weekend:** $29
Fee 18 Holes: Weekday: $40   **Weekend:** $50
Twilight Rates: Yes   **Discounts:** Sr. cart; Jr. twilgt. w/adult
Cart Rental: $18pp/18, $10pp/9   **Driving Range:** Yes
Lessons: $60/half hour   **Schools:**   **Junior Golf:** Yes
Membership: Season Passes   **Architect/Yr:** MHF Design & G. Sargent/1994
Other: Clubhouse / Bar-Lounge / Lockers / Shower / Snack Bar

COUPON

NGCOA - Beginner-friendly certified. Noted for friendly staff, well-maintained turf. Open, rolling fairways and 'true rolling' velvet greens, some of them very large. Links-style course with well-placed hazards.

	1	2	3	4	5	6	7	8	9
PAR	4	5	3	4	5	4	3	4	4
YARDS	341	454	185	418	482	358	167	260	352
	10	11	12	13	14	15	16	17	18
PAR	4	3	4	4	4	3	4	4	5
YARDS	295	162	330	322	395	125	303	305	492

Directions: I-93 to Exit 2. Bear right off ramp. Right onto South Policy Street. Next light, right onto Route 38. Straight through next set of lights, left on to Brady Avenue for .5 miles.

Candia Woods ✪✪½ 18

313 South Road
Candia, NH (603) 483-2307
www.candiawoods.com

Tees	Holes	Yards	Par	USGA	Slope
BACK	18	6540	71	70.9	118
MIDDLE	18	6317	71	69.8	117
FRONT	18	5367	71	69.8	116

Club Pro: Craig McLaughlin, PGA
Payment: Visa, MC, Disc, Amex
Tee Times: 5 days adv.
Fee 9 Holes: Weekday: $30   **Weekend:** $35
Fee 18 Holes: Weekday: $50   **Weekend:** $60
Twilight Rates: After 6pm, $20   **Discounts:** Senior & Junior
Cart Rental: $17pp/18, $9pp/9   **Driving Range:** $5/sm., $8/lg. bucket
Lessons: $50/half hour   **Schools:** No   **Junior Golf:** Yes
Membership: Yes   **Architect/Yr Open:** Phil Wogan/1964
Other: Restaurant / Bar-Lounge / Lockers / Showers / Snack Bar / Pavilion / Outings

10 minutes from Manchester Airport and Mall of NH. Multiple tees allow for all skill levels, user-friendly layout. Private club conditions and service.

	1	2	3	4	5	6	7	8	9
PAR	4	4	4	4	3	4	4	3	5
YARDS	409	359	355	389	183	357	382	195	521
	10	11	12	13	14	15	16	17	18
PAR	5	4	4	4	4	3	5	3	4
YARDS	464	443	394	309	308	158	540	146	405

Directions: I-93, Exit 7 to Route 101 East. Take Exit 3. Straight at stop sign, right at next stop sign. Club is ⅛ mile on left at top of hill.

Canterbury Woods Country Club ✪✪✪

15 West Road
Canterbury, NH (603) 783-9400
www.canterburywoodscc.com

Tees	Holes	Yards	Par	USGA	Slope
BACK	18	6650	72	71.7	136
MIDDLE	18	6134	72	69.2	130
FRONT	18	5535	72	66.1	118

Club Pro: Walter Reeves, PGA
Payment: Visa, MC
Tee Times: 5 days adv.
Fee 9 Holes: Weekday: $20 walk, $30 ride after 12pm
            Weekend: $25 walk, $35 ride after 12pm
Fee 18 Holes: Weekday: $35 walk, $50 ride   **Weekend:** $42 walk, $58 ride
Twilight Rates: Yes   **Discounts:** Senior & Junior
Cart Rental: $15pp/18, $10pp/9   **Driving Range:** Yes
Lessons: Yes **Schools:** Yes   **Junior Golf:** Clinics
Membership: Yes   **Architect/Yr Open:** Ross Forbes/2003
Other: Restaurant / Clubhouse/ Snack Bar / Bar-Lounge

COUPON

Site of the 2006 NH State Amateur Championship. Bent grass greens, tees, and fairways. Outstanding playing conditions. New tee box #7 and drainage in fairways.

	1	2	3	4	5	6	7	8	9
PAR	4	5	4	5	4	3	4	3	4
YARDS	394	488	364	518	264	128	353	208	347

	10	11	12	13	14	15	16	17	18
PAR	5	3	4	3	4	5	5	3	4
YARDS	456	180	381	176	340	516	474	138	409

Directions: I-93 to Exit 18. Turn left on to West Road. Continue left at fork ½ mile from exit ramp. Course entrance is on the left just beyond Sloping Acres Farm (approximately ½ mile) from fork.

Carter Country Club

257 Mechanic Street
Lebanon, NH (603) 448-4483
www.cartercc.com

Tees	Holes	Yards	Par	USGA	Slope
BACK	9	2800	36	68.1	116
MIDDLE	9	2760	36	66.1	114
FRONT	9	2565	36	71.7	127

Club Pro: Rich Parker, PGA
Payment: Most Major
Tee Times: No
Fee 9 Holes: Weekday: $15   **Weekend:** $15
Fee 18 Holes: Weekday: $24   **Weekend:** $24
Twilight Rates: No   **Discounts:** None
Cart Rental: $13pp/18, $7pp/9   **Driving Range:** No
Lessons: Yes **Schools:** No   **Junior Golf:** Yes
Membership: Yes   **Architect/Yr Open:** Donald Ross/1923
Other: Restaurant / Clubhouse / Bar-Lounge   **GPS:**

Semi-hilly course, very scenic, especially nice in the Fall, small greens, very sloped. Men's League on Thursday. Open April - November. New drainage makes the course much drier.

	1	2	3	4	5	6	7	8	9
PAR	4	3	5	4	4	5	4	4	3
YARDS	350	155	470	365	280	480	265	285	110

PAR									
YARDS									

Directions: Just a short pitch off I-89, Exit 19.

Claremont Country Club

NR 21

Maple Avenue
Claremont, NH (603) 542-9550
www.claremontcountryclubnh.com

Tees	Holes	Yards	Par	USGA	Slope
BACK	9	2647	34	64.7	104
MIDDLE	9	2415	34		
FRONT	9	2335	34		

Club Pro:
Payment: Cash or Check
Tee Times: No
Fee 9 Holes: Weekday: $16
Fee 18 Holes: Weekday: $25
Twilight Rates: No
Cart Rental: $25pp/18, $15pp/9
Lessons: **Schools:** No
Membership: Yes
Other: Clubhouse / Bar-Lounge / Snack Bar / Lockers / Showers

Weekend: $18
Weekend: $28
Discounts: None
Driving Range: Yes
Junior Golf: Yes
Architect/Yr Open: 1917

Old-style course. Small greens. Hilly, with woods.

	1	2	3	4	5	6	7	8	9
PAR	4	4	4	4	4	3	4	3	4
YARDS	420	328	273	262	275	174	434	169	312
PAR									
YARDS									

Directions: I-91 to Claremont exit. Follow signs to downtown Claremont. Take Pleasant Street to Maple Avenue. Right onto Maple. Go ½ mile to course.

Colebrook Country Club

NR 22

15 Abenaki Lane
Colebrook, NH (603) 237-5566
www.colebrookcountryclub.com

Tees	Holes	Yards	Par	USGA	Slope
BACK	9	3001	36	67.1	114
MIDDLE	9	2897	36	67.1	114
FRONT	9	2114	36	72.3	114

Club Pro:
Payment: Visa, MC, Amex, Disc
Tee Times: No
Fee 9 Holes: Weekday: $18
Fee 18 Holes: Weekday: $18
Twilight Rates: After 5pm
Cart Rental: $30/18, $20/9 per cart
Lessons: No **Schools:**
Membership: Yes
Other: Restaurant / Bar-Lounge / Motel

Weekend: $22
Weekend: $22
Discounts: Senior, Junior, Women
Driving Range: No
Junior Golf: Yes
Architect/Yr Open: 1927
GPS:

COUPON

Tee #3 rebuilt August, 2010. Beautifully maintained. Hole #5 is 612 yards. Discounts after 5pm daily and on Mondays and Wednesdays. 9 holes with 2 sets of tees. Hole #7 has been rebuilt in June 2007.

	1	2	3	4	5	6	7	8	9
PAR	4	4	3	4	6	3	5	3	4
YARDS	345	328	191	289	612	192	518	122	300
PAR									
YARDS									

Directions: From I-93 or I-91, take Route 3 North from Littleton, NH. When in Colebrook, take right onto Route 26 East about ½ mile. Club is on left.

Country Club of New Hampshire ✪✪½ 23 ►

178 Kearsarge Road
North Sutton, NH (603) 927-4246
www.playgolfne.com

Club Pro: Dave Krumenacker
Payment: Visa, MC, Amex, Disc, Checks, Cash
Tee Times: 1 week adv.

Tees	Holes	Yards	Par	USGA	Slope
BACK	18	6743	72	72.5	134
MIDDLE	18	6256	72	70.3	126
FRONT	18	5416	72	71.7	127

Fee 9 Holes: Weekday: $18
Fee 18 Holes: Weekday: $35
Twilight Rates: After 2pm
Cart Rental: $17pp/18, $10pp/9
Lessons: $45/half hour **Schools:** No
Membership: Yes
Other: Clubhouse / Showers / Snack Bar / Restaurant / Bar-Lounge / Hotel

Weekend: $25
Weekend: $43
Discounts: None
Driving Range: $12/lg,$6/md.$4/sm
Junior Golf: Yes
Architect/Yr Open: Stiles & Van Kleek/1930

COUPON

The front 9 is level, the back is hilly. Located at the base of 3000 ft, Mt. Kearsarge.

NH

	1	2	3	4	5	6	7	8	9
PAR	4	3	5	4	4	3	4	5	4
YARDS	380	160	495	330	346	169	376	452	380
	10	**11**	**12**	**13**	**14**	**15**	**16**	**17**	**18**
PAR	4	3	4	5	4	3	4	4	5
YARDS	410	124	351	471	366	169	412	400	465

Directions: One mile off I-89 at Exit 10. Follow signs to Winslow State Park.

Countryside Golf Club   NR 24 ►

20 Country Club Drive (Route 13)
Dunbarton, NH (603) 774-5031
www.countrysidegolfnh.com

Club Pro:
Payment: Visa, MC, Cash
Tee Times: Weekends only

Tees	Holes	Yards	Par	USGA	Slope
BACK	9	3157	36	69.3	128
MIDDLE	9	3001	36	69.2	126
FRONT	9	2758	36	71.5	126

Fee 9 Holes: Weekday: $16
Fee 18 Holes: Weekday: $26
Twilight Rates: No
Cart Rental: Per person, call for price
Lessons: Yes **Schools:** No
Membership: Yes
Other: Clubhouse / Snack Bar / Bar-Lounge / Deck

Weekend: $19
Weekend: $29
Discounts: Sr & Jr weekdays
Driving Range: Yes
Junior Golf: Yes
Architect/Yr Open: Bill Mitchell/1964

COUPON

Scenic views and friendly staff under new management/ownership.

	1	2	3	4	5	6	7	8	9
PAR	4	4	3	5	4	4	4	3	5
YARDS	305	369	138	485	386	365	344	143	466
PAR									
YARDS									

Directions: Route 101 to Route 114 toward Goffstown. Take Route 13 North at Sully's Superette. Go 4 miles. Club is on left.

Crotched Mountain Golf Club ✪✪✪¹/₂ ▶ 25

740 2nd NH Turnpike North
Francestown, NH (603) 588-2923
www.crotchedmountaingolfclub.com

Tees	Holes	Yards	Par	USGA	Slope
BACK	18	6111	71	69.2	125
MIDDLE	18	5530	71	66.7	118
FRONT	18	4604	71	67.4	117

Club Pro: Matthew Bradbury, PGA
Payment: Visa, MC, Amex, Disc, Check, Cash
Tee Times: 10 days adv.
Fee 9 Holes: Weekday: $18   **Weekend:** $18
Fee 18 Holes: Weekday: $25   **Weekend:** $35
Twilight Rates: After 2pm   **Discounts:** None
Cart Rental: $14pp/18, $8pp/9   **Driving Range:** Yes
Lessons: $45/30 min. **Schools:** Yes   **Junior Golf:** Yes
Membership: Yes   **Architect/Yr Open:** Donald Ross/1929
Other: Restaurant / Clubhouse / Bar-Lounge / Function Room / Lodging Partner

COUPON

A scenic NH Mountain course. Beautifully manicured. Small sloping greens. A hidden gem. CMGC has a dress code – no denims, proper golf shirt.

	1	2	3	4	5	6	7	8	9
PAR	4	4	3	5	4	3	5	4	4
YARDS	338	310	145	479	339	184	416	333	374
	10	11	12	13	14	15	16	17	18
PAR	4	4	4	5	4	4	3	4	3
YARDS	347	289	342	383	328	277	186	290	170

Directions: From I-93, Route 114 to Route 13 South. In New Boston take 136 to Francestown. In Francestown take 47 West, 4 miles on right is Crotched Mountain Resort.

Den Brae Golf Course ✪✪¹/₂ ▶ 26

80 Prescott Road
Sanbornton, NH (603) 934-9818
www.denbrae.com

Tees	Holes	Yards	Par	USGA	Slope
BACK	9	3095	36		
MIDDLE	9	2959	36	67.0	112
FRONT	9	2663	36	70.0	123

Club Pro: Tom Gilley
Payment: Visa, MC
Tee Times: Weekends, Holidays
Fee 9 Holes: Weekday: $15   **Weekend:** $16
Fee 18 Holes: Weekday: $25   **Weekend:** $27
Twilight Rates: After 3pm   **Discounts:** None
Cart Rental: $14pp/18, $8pp/9   **Driving Range:** $6.50/lg., grass tees
Lessons: $27/hour **Schools:** No   **Junior Golf:** Yes
Membership: Yes   **Architect/Yr Open:** Henry Homan/1958
Other: Clubhouse / Snack Bar / Bar-Lounge   **GPS:**

COUPON

New 6500-square-foot 7th green is pure putting purgatory! Open April - October. New women's tees make course more woman-friendly. New greens on course. New target greens on driving range.

	1	2	3	4	5	6	7	8	9
PAR	4	4	3	5	4	4	4	4	4
YARDS	380	241	170	490	270	370	288	355	395
PAR									
YARDS									

Directions: I-93 to Exit 22, go south on Route 127 for 1.1 miles. Right on Prescott Road, .3 miles on left.

Derryfield Country Club ✪✪ 27 ▶

625 Mammoth Road
Manchester, NH (603) 669-0235
www.derryfieldgolf.com

Club Pro: Mike Ryan, PGA
Payment: Cash, Visa, MC, Discover
Tee Times: S/S/H
Fee 9 Holes: Weekday: $23
Fee 18 Holes: Weekday: $38
Twilight Rates: After 6pm
Cart Rental: $15pp/18, $9pp/9
Lessons: $40/half hour **Schools:** No
Membership: Yes
Other: Snack Bar / Restaurant / Bar-Lounge

Tees	Holes	Yards	Par	USGA	Slope
BACK	18	6143	70	69.1	121
MIDDLE	18	5852	70	67.9	118
FRONT	18	5174	70	69.1	111

Weekend: $23
Weekend: $38
Discounts: None
Driving Range: No
Junior Golf: Yes
Architect/Yr Open: 1932
GPS:

COUPON

Because course is hilly with small greens, approach shots are key. Wide-open fairways let you open up.
Major improvements planned for 2014.

NH

	1	2	3	4	5	6	7	8	9
PAR	4	4	3	4	4	4	4	3	4
YARDS	302	386	176	349	361	363	349	159	313
	10	11	12	13	14	15	16	17	18
PAR	4	4	3	4	4	4	4	5	4
YARDS	312	409	146	238	327	327	320	504	374

Directions: I-93 to Exit 8. Bear right at the bottom of the ramp. At second set of lights, take a left.
Course is on the left.

Duston Country Club NR 28 ▶

40 Country Club Road
Hopkinton, NH (603) 746-4234
www.dustoncc.com

Club Pro:
Payment: Visa, MC, Disc
Tee Times: Weekends & Holidays
Fee 9 Holes: Weekday: $15
Fee 18 Holes: Weekday: $24
Twilight Rates: After Labor Day
Cart Rental: $24pp/18, $15pp/9
Lessons: Schools: No
Membership: Yes
Other: Clubhouse / Grill / Bar-Lounge

Tees	Holes	Yards	Par	USGA	Slope
BACK					
MIDDLE	9	2109	32	61.4	100
FRONT	9	2065	33	64.4	106

Weekend: $16
Weekend: $26
Discounts: Senior & Junior
Driving Range: No
Junior Golf: Yes
Architect/Yr Open: 1926
GPS:

COUPON

Scottish-style bunkers and lush greens. Some hills. Greens are small to medium in size. Open April -
November. Family run.

	1	2	3	4	5	6	7	8	9
PAR	4	3	4	3	4	4	3	4	3
YARDS	295	117	353	133	265	299	194	273	180
PAR									
YARDS									

Directions: I-89 to Exit 5 onto Routes 202 & 9 for 3 miles. Take Country Club Road exit.

Eagle Mountain House

Carter Notch Road
Jackson, NH (603) 383-9090
www.eaglemt.com

Club Pro: Bob McGraw PGA
Payment: Cash, Visa, MC, Amex, Disc
Tee Times: 1 week adv.
Fee 9 Holes: Weekday: $22
Fee 18 Holes: Weekday: $32
Twilight Rates: After 3pm
Cart Rental: $15pp/18, $10pp/9
 Lessons: Yes **Schools:** No
Membership: Yes

Tees	Holes	Yards	Par	USGA	Slope
BACK					
MIDDLE	9	2120	32	61	102
FRONT	9	1539	32	61	102

Weekend: $22
Weekend: $32
Discounts: Junior
Driving Range: Full
Junior Golf: Yes
Architect/Yr Open: Arthur Gae/1931

Other: Hotel / Lockers / Showers / Snack Bar / Restaurant / Bar-Lounge

Family Friendly. Breathtaking views of mountains and river. Grass driving range. Always improving. Open early May - end of October.

	1	2	3	4	5	6	7	8	9
PAR	4	3	4	5	3	3	3	3	4
YARDS	270	188	331	395	143	152	160	188	293
PAR									
YARDS									

Directions: I-95 to Route 16 North. 9 miles north of North Conway. Continue through covered bridge into Jackson, ½ mile up Carter Notch Road.

Eastman Golf Links

6 Clubhouse Lane
Grantham, NH (603) 863-4500
www.eastmangolflinks.com

Club Pro: Mark Larrabee, PGA
Payment: Visa, MC, Amex, Disc, Checks
Tee Times: Up to 5 days adv.
Fee 9 Holes: Weekday: $30
Fee 18 Holes: Weekday: $49
Twilight Rates: No
Cart Rental: $18pp/18, $12pp/9
Lessons: Yes, 3 teachers **Schools:** No
Membership: Limited

Tees	Holes	Yards	Par	USGA	Slope
BACK	18	6731	71	72.8	129
MIDDLE	18	6338	71	71.0	127
FRONT	18	5499	73	72.7	125

Weekend: $30
Weekend: $49
Discounts: Junior after 2pm
Driving Range: $6/bucket
Junior Golf: Yes
Architect/Yr Open: Geoffrey Cornish/1973

COUPON

Other: Clubhouse / Lockers / Showers / Snack Bar / Restaurant / Bar-Lounge

Golf carts are required Friday, Saturday and Sunday before 2pm. Hosted 2010 NHGA Men's State Amateur. Book tee times online and by mobile device @ www.eastmangolflinks.com/mobile. "A great public golf course with the feel of a private club." –FP

	1	2	3	4	5	6	7	8	9
PAR	4	5	3	4	4	4	3	5	4
YARDS	354	544	167	353	389	409	189	493	395
	10	11	12	13	14	15	16	17	18
PAR	4	4	4	3	4	3	5	4	4
YARDS	322	384	443	189	384	113	441	385	384

Directions: Take I-89 to Exit 13; left off ramp from North, right off ramp from South. ¼ mile on right is entrance to course.

Exeter Country Club ⭐⭐

31

58 Jady Hill Avenue
Exeter, NH (603) 772-4752
www.exetercountryclub.com

Club Pro: Joel Jenkins, PGA
Payment: Visa, MC, Disc
Tee Times: Yes
Fee 9 Holes: Weekday: $20
Fee 18 Holes: Weekday: $35
Twilight Rates: After 5pm
Cart Rental: $18pp/18, $9pp/9
Lessons: $45/half hour **Schools:** Yes
Membership: $1150/$249 Junior
Other: Restaurant / Clubhouse / Snack Bar / Showers / Bar-Lounge

Tees	Holes	Yards	Par	USGA	Slope
BACK					
MIDDLE	9	2721	35	70.1	117
FRONT	9	2553	35	68.9	114

Weekend: $25
Weekend: $40
Discounts: None
Driving Range: Yes
Junior Golf: Yes
Architect/Yr Open: 1889; M. Francis/1950

COUPON

Player Comments: "A placement course. Makes you think about each shot." Rolling terrain with a variety of challenges. Not overly difficult. Open April 1 - December 1.

	1	2	3	4	5	6	7	8	9
PAR	4	3	5	4	4	4	4	3	4
YARDS	379	160	460	361	365	250	281	165	300
PAR									
YARDS									

Directions: I-95 to Hampton, NH exit to Route 101 West, exit to Route 108 to Stratham, Exeter. Bear left. Go right at 3rd light, take 1st left, then the next right.

Farmington Country Club

NR 32

188 Main Street (Route 153)
Farmington, NH (603) 755-2412
www.farmingtoncountryclubnh.com

Club Pro: James Pollini, PGA
Payment: Visa, MC
Tee Times: Weekends
Fee 9 Holes: Weekday: $17
Fee 18 Holes: Weekday: $25
Twilight Rates: No
Cart Rental: $25/18, $17/9 per cart
Lessons: $40/half hour **Schools:** Yes
Membership: Yes
Other: Clubhouse / Snack Bar/ Bar-Lounge / Beverage Cart

Tees	Holes	Yards	Par	USGA	Slope
BACK					
MIDDLE	9	3152	36	69.7	125
FRONT	9	2739	36	70.7	123

Weekend: $21
Weekend: $31
Discounts: None
Driving Range: Yes
Junior Golf: Yes
Architect/Yr Open: 1924, 1996

Challenging redesigned course. 9 holes, 2 sets of tees. Highly improved conditions.

	1	2	3	4	5	6	7	8	9
PAR	4	4	3	5	4	3	5	4	4
YARDS	350	350	140	491	375	135	516	406	345
PAR									
YARDS									

Directions: From Spaulding Turnpike (Route 16), take Route 11 West. Then to Route 153 North. Approximately 1.5 miles on the right is club.

NH

Granite Fields Golf Club ✪✪½ ▶ 33

7 Route 125
Kingston, NH (603) 642-9977
www.granitefields.com

Tees	Holes	Yards	Par	USGA	Slope
BACK	18	6518	72	71.6	131
MIDDLE	18	6018	72	68.7	124
FRONT	18	4695	72	116	68.0

Club Pro:
Payment: Most Major Credit Cards
Tee Times: 5 days adv.
Fee 9 Holes: Weekday: $20   **Weekend:** $25
Fee 18 Holes: Weekday: $25   **Weekend:** $40
Twilight Rates: Yes   **Discounts:** Senior & Junior
Cart Rental: $15pp/18, $10pp/9   **Driving Range:** Yes
Lessons: Yes **Schools:** No   **Junior Golf:**
Membership: Yes   **Architect/Yr Open:** Steve Cummings/2005
Other: Clubhouse / Bar-Lounge   **GPS:**

Has matured into a real winner. Very scenic and challenging, too. Distances below are from the Blue tees.

	1	2	3	4	5	6	7	8	9
PAR	4	4	4	3	4	5	4	3	5
YARDS	356	323	305	175	354	493	380	150	450
	10	11	12	13	14	15	16	17	18
PAR	4	3	4	3	5	5	4	4	4
YARDS	344	133	369	151	479	478	387	319	352

Directions: I-495 to Exit 51B. North on Route 125. 5.3 miles on right. From 101: take 125 South. Approximately 11 miles on left.

Green Meadow GC #1, The Prairie ✪✪ ▶ 34

55 Steele Road
Hudson, NH (603) 889-1555
www.greenmeadowgolfclub.com

Tees	Holes	Yards	Par	USGA	Slope
BACK	18	6160	70	68.4	113
MIDDLE	18	5810	70	66.7	110
FRONT	18	4877	70	66.6	106

Club Pro: Brian Doyle, PGA
Payment: Cash, MC, Visa, Disc, Amex
Tee Times: Weekends, 1 week adv.
Fee 9 Holes: Weekday: $21   **Weekend:**
Fee 18 Holes: Weekday: $32   **Weekend:** $39
Twilight Rates: 12pm   **Discounts:** Senior/$26 & Junior/$10
Cart Rental: $14pp/18, $9pp/9   **Driving Range:** $7/lg. bucket
Lessons: $45/half hour **Schools:** No **Junior Golf:** Yes
Membership: No   **Architect/Yr Open:** Philip Friel/1959
Other: Clubhouse / Snack Bar / Bar-Lounge / Showers

Lots of room and very forgiving. Junior discounts.

	1	2	3	4	5	6	7	8	9
PAR	4	4	3	4	4	3	5	4	4
YARDS	334	328	141	376	341	169	471	411	364
	10	11	12	13	14	15	16	17	18
PAR	4	3	4	3	4	4	4	4	5
YARDS	353	158	324	153	329	410	313	329	506

Directions: Take Route 3 to Exit 2. Follow the signs toward Hudson, NH. At the end of the bridge bear to the right onto Route 3A South. At the third set of lights, which is Steele Road, take a right. This road leads directly into the Green Meadow parking lot.

Green Meadow GC #2, The Jungle ✪✪½   35 ▶

55 Steele Road
Hudson, NH (603) 889-1555
www.greenmeadowgolfclub.com

Tees	Holes	Yards	Par	USGA	Slope
BACK	18	6940	72	71.5	124
MIDDLE	18	6394	72	68.9	120
FRONT	18	5352	72	69.7	114

Club Pro: Brian Doyle, PGA
Payment: Cash, MC, Visa, Disc, Amex
Tee Times: Weekends, 1 week adv.
Fee 9 Holes: Weekday: $21
Fee 18 Holes: Weekday: $32
Twilight Rates: Noon, 2pm, 5pm
Cart Rental: $14pp/18, $9pp/9
Lessons: $45/half hour **Schools:** No
Membership: No
Other: Clubhouse / Snack Bar / Bar-Lounge / Showers

Weekend:
Weekend: $39
Discounts: Senior/$26; Junior/$10
Driving Range: $7/lg.
Junior Golf: Yes
Architect/Yr Open: Philip Friel/1959

Junior discounts 7 days a week. Course set along the Merrimac River. More challenging than the Prairie Course. Junior discounts with no restrictions.

	1	2	3	4	5	6	7	8	9
PAR	4	4	5	3	4	4	4	3	5
YARDS	368	341	513	164	351	405	366	185	479
	10	11	12	13	14	15	16	17	18
PAR	4	3	4	5	4	4	3	4	5
YARDS	358	137	370	538	382	368	142	415	512

Directions: Take Route 3 to Exit 2. Follow the signs toward Hudson, NH. At the end of the bridge bear to the right onto Route 3A South. At the third set of lights, which is Steele Road, take a right. This road leads directly into the Green Meadow parking lot.

Hales Location Golf Course ✪✪½   36 ▶

87 Fairway Drive
North Conway, NH (603) 356-2140
www.haleslocationgolf.com

Tees	Holes	Yards	Par	USGA	Slope
BACK	9	3025	36	68.8	122
MIDDLE	9	2816	36	66.8	115
FRONT	9	2508	36	67.4	113

Club Pro: Julie Rivers
Payment: Visa, MC, Disc
Tee Times: May 1st for season
Fee 9 Holes: Weekday: $35
Fee 18 Holes: Weekday: $47
Twilight Rates: After 3pm
Cart Rental: $17pp/18, $11pp/9
Lessons: Yes **Schools:** Yes
Membership: Yes
Other: Clubhouse / Hotel / Restaurant / Bar-Lounge / Snack Bar / Lockers / Showers
GPS: Yes

Weekend: $38
Weekend: $50
Discounts: Senior and Junior
Driving Range: No
Junior Golf: Yes
Architect/Yr Open: Al Zikorus/1990

COUPON

Special holes: #1 and #9. Great 9-hole layout with breathtaking views of the White Mountains. Bent grass fairways and greens. Golf rates vary seasonally. Open May-November.

	1	2	3	4	5	6	7	8	9
PAR	5	4	3	4	5	3	4	4	4
YARDS	458	312	148	256	468	130	334	368	342
PAR									
YARDS									

Directions: Route 16 to traffic light in Conway. Turn onto Washington Street, then right onto West Side Road; 5 miles on left.

Hanover Country Club　　✪✪✪½　▶ 37

36 Hilton Field Lane
Hanover, NH (603) 646-2000
www.golf.dartmouth.edu

Tees	Holes	Yards	Par	USGA	Slope
BACK	18	6472	71	70.8	131
MIDDLE	18	6142	71	70.8	131
FRONT	18	5330	72	71.5	128

Club Pro: Alex Kirk, PGA
Payment: Visa, MC, Amex
Tee Times: 3 days adv.
Fee 9 Holes: Weekday:
Fee 18 Holes: Weekday: $49
Twilight Rates: $30 after 3pm
Cart Rental: $16pp/18
Lessons: $40/half hour **Schools:** No
Membership: Yes
Other: Clubhouse / Snack Bar / Leagues

Weekend:
Weekend: $59
Discounts: Junior
Driving Range: Yes
Junior Golf: Yes
Architect/Yr Open: O. Smith/1899
GPS:

COUPON

Home of Dartmouth golf team. "Course greens in great shape, fast, challenging, and fun." Parkland-style with old-growth trees.

	1	2	3	4	5	6	7	8	9
PAR	4	4	4	3	3	4	4	4	5
YARDS	400	408	290	115	183	341	405	283	572
	10	11	12	13	14	15	16	17	18
PAR	4	4	3	4	3	4	4	5	5
YARDS	385	315	177	308	142	425	358	467	457

Directions: I-91 to bridge into Hanover. 1st left after lights, then 2nd left onto Maynard Street. Next right onto Rope Ferry Road. Follow to end.

Hidden Creek Golf Course　　NR　▶ 38

17 Morgan Road
Litchfield, NH (603) 262-9272
www.hiddencreekgolfnh.com

Tees	Holes	Yards	Par	USGA	Slope
BACK	9	3252	36	70.5	127
MIDDLE	9	3114	36	68.5	126
FRONT	9	2858	36	68.0	124

Club Pro: Frank Carpentino, Pro Shop Mgr.
Payment: Visa, MC
Tee Times: Yes
Fee 9 Holes: Weekday: $30
Fee 18 Holes: Weekday: $39
Twilight Rates: After 6pm
Cart Rental: $15pp/18, $10pp/9
Lessons: No **Schools:** No
Membership: Yes
Other:

Weekend: $33
Weekend: $45
Discounts: Senior
Driving Range: Yes
Junior Golf: No
Architect/Yr Open: 2005
GPS:

Opened late 2006. Sister course to Passaconaway.

	1	2	3	4	5	6	7	8	9
PAR	4	4	3	5	4	4	3	5	4
YARDS	371	345	190	565	330	283	140	500	390
PAR									
YARDS									

Directions: I-93 North to Exit 5 (Route 28). Go South 1.3 miles, turn right at Stonehenge Road. Go left at Bartley Hill Road for 3.5 miles (becomes Corning Road). Turn left at Charles Bancroft Highway (Route 3A), turn left at Albuquerque Avenue and left at Morgan Road.

Hidden Valley Golf Course   ✪½   **39** ▶

81 Damren Road
Derry, NH (603) 887-7888
www.hiddenvalleyrv.com

Club Pro:
Payment: Visa, MC, Cash
Tee Times: 7 days adv.
Fee 9 Holes: Weekday: $15 w/o cart
Fee 18 Holes: Weekday: $25 w/o cart
Twilight Rates: After 4pm
Cart Rental: $15pp/18, $10pp/9
Lessons: No **Schools:** No
Membership: Yes
Other: RV Campsites / Canobie Lake Park

Tees	Holes	Yards	Par	USGA	Slope
BACK	18	6280	72	70.8	126
MIDDLE	18	5823	72	67.8	124
FRONT	18	5175	72	65.3	109

Weekend: $20 w/o cart
Weekend: $35 w/o cart
Discounts: Senior & Junior
Driving Range: No
Junior Golf: Yes
Architect/Yr Open: Ed Simonsen/1993
GPS:

COUPON

Rates subject to change. RV sites at course. Nice big greens. Added 9-hole par 3 courses. Southern NH's most scenic, well-maintained 18-hole championship course. Friendly staff, leagues, tournaments.

	1	2	3	4	5	6	7	8	9
PAR	3	4	3	5	4	4	4	5	4
YARDS	150	310	155	420	355	345	345	505	275

	10	11	12	13	14	15	16	17	18
PAR	5	4	3	5	4	4	3	4	4
YARDS	420	325	190	530	365	308	155	355	330

Directions: Take Exit 4 on Route 93. Go east until the Derry Rotary Circle. Take East Derry Road for 4½ miles. Go left onto Damren Road to Course.

Highlands Links Golf Club   ✪✪   **40** ▶

339 Mt. Prospect Road
Holderness, NH (603) 536-3452

Club Pro: Joe Clark Sr., PGA
          Brian Desilets, Pro
Payment: Cash, Credit
Tee Times: No
Fee 9 Holes: Weekday: $15
Fee 18 Holes: Weekday: $22
Twilight Rates: No
Cart Rental: $25/18, $15/9 per cart
Lessons: Yes **Schools:** Yes
Membership: Yes
Other: Clubhouse / Custom Club Fitting

Tees	Holes	Yards	Par	USGA	Slope
BACK					
MIDDLE	9	1485	27	59.0	97
FRONT	9	1355	27		

Weekend: $15
Weekend: $22
Discounts: Junior
Driving Range: No
Junior Golf: Yes
Architect/Yr Open:
GPS:

COUPON

Sig. Hole: #8, 190-yard par 3 called "Ballybunion." Elevated tee with rolling fairway — outstanding Southwest view.

	1	2	3	4	5	6	7	8	9
PAR	3	3	3	3	3	3	3	3	3
YARDS	210	185	140	165	145	130	165	190	155

PAR									
YARDS									

Directions: I-93 to Exit 25, turn left at end of ramp. Follow ¼ mile to Route 175 South. At stop sign, opposite Holderness Prep School, take left onto Mt. Prospect Road. Follow 1.5 mile to course.

Hoodkroft Country Club ✪✪ ▶ 41

121 East Broadway
Derry, NH (603) 434-0651
www.hoodkroftcc.com

Tees	Holes	Yards	Par	USGA	Slope
BACK	9	3283	36	35.5	125
MIDDLE	9	3856	36	33.4	116
FRONT	9	2434	36	33.9	110

Club Pro: Tony Zdunko, PGA
Payment: Visa, MC, Disc
Tee Times: Tues. for weekend
Fee 9 Holes: Weekday: $24
Fee 18 Holes: Weekday: $35
Twilight Rates: After 5pm
Cart Rental: $16pp/18, $10pp/9
Lessons: Yes **Schools:** No
Membership: Available
Other: Clubhouse / Bar-Lounge / Snack Bar / Showers

Weekend: $25
Weekend: $39
Discounts: Senior, weekdays only
Driving Range: No
Junior Golf: Yes
Architect/Yr Open: Philip Wogan/1971

COUPON

Mostly flat, open fairways, lots of water. Large open greens. New chipping area. Open April 1 - November 30 (or snow). New middle tee for 2014.

	1	2	3	4	5	6	7	8	9
PAR	4	4	3	5	4	4	4	3	5
YARDS	335	430	187	555	355	400	340	180	456
	10	11	12	13	14	15	16	17	18
PAR	4	4	3	5	4	4	4	3	5
YARDS	355	420	224	538	375	380	360	155	456

Directions: I-93 to Exit 4 in NH, head east on Route 102. Go about 2 miles. Golf course is on right-hand side.

Hooper Golf Club ✪✪✪ ▶ 42

166 Prospect Hill
Walpole, NH (603) 756-4080
www.hoopergolfclub.com

Tees	Holes	Yards	Par	USGA	Slope
BACK					
MIDDLE	9	3033	71	68.9	123
FRONT	9	2709	36	71.2	121

Club Pro: Ron Rosko, PGA
Payment: Visa, MC, Amex, Cash
Tee Times: Yes
Fee 9 Holes: Weekday: $22
Fee 18 Holes: Weekday: $41
Twilight Rates: No
Cart Rental: $19pp/18, $11pp/9
Lessons: Yes **Schools:** No
Membership: $670/Adult, $1050/Couple
Other: Full Restaurant / Clubhouse / Bed and Breakfast Hotel

Weekend: $22
Weekend: $41
Discounts: None
Driving Range: No
Junior Golf: No
Architect/Yr Open: Stiles & Van Kleek/1927

Named 11th best 9 hole course in US by "Golf World." Historic clubhouse and bed & breakfast. Call ahead to this busy course. Open April - October. On weekends opens at 10:30am to non-members.

	1	2	3	4	5	6	7	8	9
PAR	5	4	4	3	5	3	4	4	4
YARDS	456	427	285	155	474	194	311	381	350
	10	11	12	13	14	15	16	17	18
PAR	4	4	4	3	5	3	4	4	4
YARDS	435	427	275	155	481	194	311	381	336

Directions: I-91 to Exit 5. Take Route 5 South to 1st left, onto Route 123 to Route 12. Turn right onto Route 12 South, take 1st left onto South Street to Prospect Hill Road, ¾ mile on Prospect. Golf course on right.

Indian Mound Golf Club ✪✪ ▶ 43

Route 16B
Center Ossipee, NH (603) 539-7733
www.indianmoundgc.com

Tees	Holes	Yards	Par	USGA	Slope
BACK	18	5675	70	68.1	120
MIDDLE	18	5360	70	67.1	118
FRONT	18	4713	70	67.5	117

Club Pro: Jonathan Rivers
Payment: Most Major Credit Cards, Checks
Tee Times: Yes
Fee 9 Holes: Weekday: $29
Fee 18 Holes: Weekday: $45
Twilight Rates: After 3pm
Cart Rental: Wkdy: $30pp/18, $20pp/9, Wknd: $32pp/18, $22pp/9
Driving Range: No
Lessons: Yes **Schools:** No
GPS: Golf Logic
Other: Clubhouse / Restaurant / Bar-Lounge / Lodging Partner

Weekend: $31
Weekend: $50
Discounts: Juniors after 11am
Junior Golf: Yes
Membership: Yes
Architect/Yr Open: Philip Wogan/1968

COUPON

Lots of upgrades, great course for all abilities, groups. Tournaments welcome, great food and beverage, very friendly staff. Newly renovated 1st hole and great finishing hole.

NH

	1	2	3	4	5	6	7	8	9
PAR	4	5	4	3	4	4	4	3	4
YARDS	295	465	355	118	288	276	295	170	365
	10	11	12	13	14	15	16	17	18
PAR	4	3	4	4	5	4	3	5	3
YARDS	340	113	303	400	433	360	104	495	185

Directions: From West or East, Route 25 or Route 28 to Route 16 to Center Ossipee exit. Course is .5 mile on left.

Intervale Country Club ✪✪ ▶ 44

1491 Front Street
Manchester, NH (603) 647-6811
www.intervalecc.com

Tees	Holes	Yards	Par	USGA	Slope
BACK					
MIDDLE	9	3086	36	69.6	115
FRONT	9	2740	36	71..0	120

Club Pro: Matt Thibeault, PGA
Payment: Credit Cards, Cash or Check
Tee Times: No
Fee 9 Holes: Weekday: $25
Fee 18 Holes: Weekday: $35
Twilight Rates: No
Cart Rental: $13pp/18, $7pp/9
Lessons: $50/hour **Schools:** No
Membership: Yes
Architect/Yr Open: A. Findlay/1903; W.B. Booth/2004
Other: Restaurant / Bar-Lounge

Weekend: $25
Weekend: $35
Discounts: Junior
Driving Range: No
Junior Golf: Yes

Semi-private. Call for details. Open April - November. Classic design, course is over 100 years old. New green added over water hazard. Tee enlargement #2, #7, #9. Host of NHPGA Pro-Pro Championship.

	1	2	3	4	5	6	7	8	9
PAR	3	4	4	5	4	4	4	3	5
YARDS	222	338	334	463	441	342	284	137	516
PAR									
YARDS									

Directions: I-293 North to Exit 7. Course is ½ mile on right. From the north take Exit 10 off I-93. Take left and course is 2 miles on left.

Jack O'Lantern Resort ✪✪ ▶ 45

Route 3
Woodstock, NH (603) 745-3636
www.jackolanternresort.com

Club Pro: James Gelunas
Payment: Visa, MC, Amex, Disc
Tee Times: 24 hours adv.
Fee 9 Holes: Weekday: $25
Fee 18 Holes: Weekday: $45
Twilight Rates: After 3pm
Cart Rental: $18pp/18, $11pp/9
Lessons: $30/half hour **Schools:** Yes
Membership: Yes

Tees	Holes	Yards	Par	USGA	Slope
BACK					
MIDDLE	18	6003	70	68.6	117
FRONT	18	4917	71	67.0	113

Weekend: $30
Weekend: $48
Discounts: Junior
Driving Range: No
Junior Golf: Yes
Architect/Yr Open: Bob Keating/1948

COUPON

Other: Restaurant / Hotel / Bar-Lounge / Snack Bar / Horses / Bear Shows / Caves / Parks

Players will enjoy and be challenged by the may dogleg turns. River golf holes over road. Bridge over water, 360 degree views of mountains. Maintained by golf professionals. Best conditions in area. Master winner – Doug Ford on premises.

	1	2	3	4	5	6	7	8	9
PAR	4	4	4	4	3	4	4	4	3
YARDS	370	365	414	362	175	421	335	395	160
	10	11	12	13	14	15	16	17	18
PAR	5	4	4	3	4	5	4	3	4
YARDS	519	292	305	140	410	520	320	175	325

Directions: I-93 to Exit 30, right there on the right!

Kingston Fairways Golf Club ✪✪ ▶ 46

65 Depot Road (Route 107)
Kingston, NH (603) 642-7722
www.kingstonfairwaysgolf.com

Club Pro: Mike Andersen
Payment: Cash, Visa, MC
Tee Times: No
Fee 9 Holes: Weekday: $16
Fee 18 Holes: Weekday: $27
Twilight Rates: After 5pm
Cart Rental: $28/18, $14/9 per cart
Lessons: No **Schools:** No
Membership: No
Other: Clubhouse / Snack Bar

Tees	Holes	Yards	Par	USGA	Slope
BACK					
MIDDLE	18	5670	71	67.4	114
FRONT	18	5078	71		

Weekend: $19
Weekend: $33
Discounts: Senior & Junior
Driving Range: No
Junior Golf: Yes
Architect/Yr Open: Frank Colanton/1994
GPS:

	1	2	3	4	5	6	7	8	9
PAR	3	5	4	4	4	4	4	4	4
YARDS	125	505	315	329	347	300	300	330	381
	10	11	12	13	14	15	16	17	18
PAR	3	4	4	3	4	4	5	4	4
YARDS	154	429	300	135	240	380	470	252	378

Directions: Route 107 off Route 125 in Kingston, ¼ of a mile. Or Exit 1 in Seabrook off of Route I-95. Go 10 miles West on Route 107.

Kingswood Golf Club

37 Kingswood Road
Wolfeboro, NH (603) 569-3569
www.kingswoodgolfclub.com

Club Pro: Kristy Gleason
Payment: Visa, MC, Amex, Disc
Tee Times: 5 days adv.
Fee 9 Holes: Contact Pro Shop
Fee 18 Holes: Contact Pro Shop
Twilight Rates: After 3pm
Cart Rental: $22pp/18, $12pp/9
Lessons: $60/hour, $35/half hour **Schools:** No
Membership: Yes
Other: Snack Bar / Bar-Lounge

Tees	Holes	Yards	Par	USGA	Slope
BACK	18	6366	72	71.4	134
MIDDLE	18	5934	72	69.3	128
FRONT	18	5448	72	69.7	118

Weekend: Contact Pro Shop
Weekend: Contact Pro Shop
Discounts: None
Driving Range: $7/bucket
Junior Golf: Yes
Architect/Yr Open: Donald Ross/1915
GPS:

COUPON

Classic New England mountain course with great views. The course is hilly with 5 ponds. Has an excellent new range (230-yard range). Reduced fees after 3pm without cart. Open April - October 31.

	1	2	3	4	5	6	7	8	9
PAR	4	5	3	4	4	3	4	4	4
YARDS	380	420	163	372	310	138	367	297	337
	10	11	12	13	14	15	16	17	18
PAR	4	5	4	3	4	4	5	4	4
YARDS	334	461	367	175	349	284	464	360	356

Directions: Route 28 North .25 mile past Kingswood High School. Turn left onto Kingswood Road.

Kona Mansion Inn/Golf

Moultonborough Neck Road
Center Harbor, NH (603) 253-4900
www.konamansioninn.com

Club Pro:
Payment: Visa, MC, Disc
Tee Times: No
Fee 9 Holes: Weekday: $15
Fee 18 Holes: Weekday: $15
Twilight Rates: No
Cart Rental: $3/pull
Lessons: No **Schools:** No
Membership: Yes, seasonal
Other: Hotel / Full-Service Restaurant

Tees	Holes	Yards	Par	USGA	Slope
BACK					
MIDDLE	9	1170	27		
FRONT					

Weekend: $15
Weekend: $15
Discounts: None
Driving Range:
Junior Golf: No
Architect/Yr Open: N.P. Nelson/1903
GPS:

A resort on Lake Winnipesaukee. Par 3 course. New driving range.

	1	2	3	4	5	6	7	8	9
PAR	3	3	3	3	3	3	3	3	3
YARDS	105	150	130	135	128	150	162	125	85
PAR									
YARDS									

Directions: I-93 to Exit 23 (Meredith). Go 11 miles, take a left on Route 3 to lights, take right on Route 25. Go 9 miles to Moultonboro Neck Road on right. Go right, 2.5 miles to Kona Road on right. Follow signs.

Lakeview Golf Club

NR **49**

89 Ladd Hill Road
Belmont, NH (603) 524-2220

Tees	Holes	Yards	Par	USGA	Slope
BACK					
MIDDLE	9	3615	35	69	
FRONT	9	2270	37	72.0	

Club Pro:
Payment: Cash or Check
Tee Times: No
Fee 9 Holes: Weekday: $15
Fee 18 Holes: Weekday: $22
Twilight Rates: After 3pm $13pp/9 M-F
Cart Rental: $10pp/18, $6pp/9
Lessons: No **Schools:** No
Membership: Yes

Weekend: $15
Weekend: $22
Discounts: None
Driving Range: No
Junior Golf: No
Architect/Yr Open: 1925

Beautiful 9-hole golf course overlooks a panorama of lakes and mountains. Good walking course. Dress code. Twilight rates for 9 holes after 3pm - $12.

	1	2	3	4	5	6	7	8	9
PAR	5	4	4	4	3	4	3	5	3
YARDS	505	315	290	425	220	435	175	550	195
PAR									
YARDS									

Directions: I-93 North to Exit 20, then East toward Laconia on Routes 3 & 11. Cross Winnisquam bridge and follow 1 mile to set of lights. Take right, across from Belknap Mall.

Lisbon Village Country Club

NR **50**

621 Bishop Road
Lisbon, NH (603) 838-6004
www.lisbongolf.com

Tees	Holes	Yards	Par	USGA	Slope
BACK					
MIDDLE	9	2900	36	69.7	126
FRONT	9	2466	36	70.6	127

Club Pro: Steve Schultz
Payment: Cash or Check
Tee Times: Suggested
Fee 9 Holes: Weekday: $17
Fee 18 Holes: Weekday: $25
Twilight Rates: After 4pm
Cart Rental: $16pp/18, $9pp/9
Lessons: Yes **Schools:** No
Membership: Yes
Other: Club House/ Bar-Lounge / Snack Bar

Weekend: $20
Weekend: $28
Discounts: Junior
Driving Range: $5/lg, $3/sm
Junior Golf: Yes
Architect/Yr Open: Ralph Barten/1927
GPS:

COUPON

Scenic White Mt. course that is the epitome of target golf, noted for elevated tees and greens. 9 holes with 18 different tees. Par will change on some holes. Requires a deft touch with irons and woods. Juniors under 7 play for free. Open mid-April through October.

	1	2	3	4	5	6	7	8	9
PAR	4	5	4	4	3	4	5	4	3
YARDS	255	535	310	397	211	248	440	350	148
PAR									
YARDS									

Directions: Route 302 West from I-93 interchange approximately 9 miles to Lyman Road on right. Take Bishop Road .25 mile on left. Entrance to golf course .5 mile on right.

Lochmere Golf & Country Club ✪✪✪½ 51 ▶

360 Laconia Road
Tilton, NH (603) 528-4653
www.lochmeregolf.com

Club Pro: Vic Stanfield, PGA
Payment: Visa, MC
Tee Times: 7 days adv.

Tees	Holes	Yards	Par	USGA	Slope
BACK	18	6660	72	71.7	128
MIDDLE	18	6227	72	69.4	123
FRONT	18	5227	72	68.9	120

Fee 9 Holes: Weekday: $18   **Weekend:** $25
Fee 18 Holes: Weekday: $32, $47 w/cart   **Weekend:** $45, $61 w/cart
Twilight Rates: After 4pm   **Discounts:** Seasonal specials
Cart Rental: $16pp/18, $9pp/9   **Driving Range:** $3/$5/$7 bucket
Lessons: $45/half hour **Schools:** No   **Junior Golf:** Yes
Membership: Yes   **Architect/Yr Open:** Wogan & Sargent/1992
Other: Restaurant / Clubhouse / Bar-Lounge / Snack Bar / Function Room / Gazebo
GPS: Yes

Player Comments: "Great challenging course, friendly staff, just gets better every visit." –FP
Renovated hole #5 has greater landing area. Tuesday is senior citizen day. Four-Star *Golf Digest* facility.

	1	2	3	4	5	6	7	8	9
PAR	4	4	3	4	4	4	5	3	4
YARDS	330	340	140	350	368	363	480	163	390
	10	11	12	13	14	15	16	17	18
PAR	4	5	4	3	4	4	4	4	5
YARDS	350	500	310	160	410	401	377	323	472

Directions: I-93 to Exit 20 (Laconia/Tilton). Go 1.5 miles East on Route 3. Course is on left.

Londonderry Country Club ✪✪ 52 ▶

56 Kimball Road
Londonderry, NH (603) 432-9789
www.londonderrycountryclub.com

Club Pro: Helga Kimball, GM
Payment: Cash, Visa, MC
Tee Times: Thurs. am for weekend

Tees	Holes	Yards	Par	USGA	Slope
BACK					
MIDDLE	18	3897	62	60.7	102
FRONT	18	3258	62	58.5	92

Fee 9 Holes: Weekday: $20   **Weekend:** $24
Fee 18 Holes: Weekday: $30   **Weekend:** $34
Twilight Rates: No   **Discounts:** Senior & Junior
Cart Rental: $22/18, $14pp/9 per cart **Driving Range:** No
Lessons: Yes **Schools:** No   **Junior Golf:** Yes
Membership: No   **Architect/Yr Open:** Forrest & Tom Kimball/1969
Other: Nuttfield Lounge and Snack Bar **GPS:**

Lots of improvements in last two years. Beautiful condition due to the new improvements! Friendly staff.
"Great course for your irons." –FP

	1	2	3	4	5	6	7	8	9
PAR	3	3	4	4	3	3	3	3	3
YARDS	210	165	235	215	135	165	177	123	165
	10	11	12	13	14	15	16	17	18
PAR	3	3	4	4	4	4	4	4	3
YARDS	155	115	300	310	340	235	370	345	135

Directions: I-93 to Exit 4, left onto Route 102 West, follow to Route 128 North. Follow 4 miles to traffic light. Left on Litchfield Road. Go 1.7 miles, take left onto Kimball Road. Club is 1 mile on right.

NH

Loudon Country Club

$\star\star^{1}/_{2}$ **53** ▶

653 Route 106
Loudon, NH (603) 783-3372
www.loudoncc.com

Tees	Holes	Yards	Par	USGA	Slope
BACK	18	6298	72	70.4	120
MIDDLE	18	5959	72	68.7	115
FRONT	18	5132	72	69	118

Club Pro: Bob Bean, PGA
Payment: Most Major Credit Cards, Cash
Tee Times: 6 days adv.
Fee 9 Holes: Weekday: $20   **Weekend:** $24
Fee 18 Holes: Weekday: $34   **Weekend:** $40
Twilight Rates: After 3:30pm   **Discounts:** Senior & Junior M-W
Cart Rental: $16pp/18, $10pp/9   **Driving Range:** $7/lg., $5/sm.
Lessons: Yes **Schools:** Yes   **Junior Golf:** Yes
Membership: Yes   **Architect/Yr Open:** William Leombruno/1993
Other: Full Restaurant / Bar-Lounge / Clubhouse

Challenging, yet playable. Very scenic and great conditions.

	1	2	3	4	5	6	7	8	9
PAR	4	5	4	3	4	5	4	3	4
YARDS	271	497	365	169	389	484	404	168	429
	10	11	12	13	14	15	16	17	18
PAR	4	3	5	3	4	4	4	4	4
YARDS	339	210	485	166	298	359	482	415	381

Directions: From Route I-93 North or South: Exit 15 East (Route 4) – go 3 miles to Exit 3 (Route 106). Take left – approximately 6 miles on left.

Maplewood Golf Club

$\star\star$ **54** ▶

Route 302
Bethlehem, NH (603) 869-3335
www.maplewoodgolfresort.com

Tees	Holes	Yards	Par	USGA	Slope
BACK	18	6200	72	69.2	125
MIDDLE	18	6001	72	69.2	123
FRONT	18	5013	71	68.8	113

Club Pro: Trevor Howard, Golf Dir.
Payment: Most Major Credit Cards
Tee Times: Yes
Fee 9 Holes: Weekday: $22   **Weekend:** $28
Fee 18 Holes: Weekday: $39   **Weekend:** $49
Twilight Rates: After 4pm wkdy, 5pm wknd   **Discounts:** Junior
Cart Rental: $16pp/18, $10pp/9   **Driving Range:**
Lessons: No **Schools:** No   **Junior Golf:** No
Membership: Yes   **Architect/Yr Open:** Donald Ross/1914
Other: 1890 Restored Clubhouse / Showers / Lockers / Bar-Lounge / Hotel

Recently restored classic Donald Ross course. Stay and Play packages. Ladies' Day on Wednesday. Cart required 8am - 2pm on weekends. New tees on holes 3 and 6.

	1	2	3	4	5	6	7	8	9
PAR	5	4	4	4	4	4	4	3	4
YARDS	445	399	277	388	367	373	319	150	355
	10	11	12	13	14	15	16	17	18
PAR	4	3	3	4	4	5	6	4	3
YARDS	355	163	201	321	279	527	651	287	144

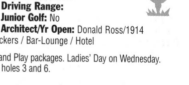

Directions: I-93 Exit 40 onto Route 302 East. Approximately 5 miles.

Mojalaki Country Club

321 Prospect Street
Franklin, NH (603) 934-3033
www.mojalaki.com

Tees	Holes	Yards	Par	USGA	Slope
BACK	18	5820	70	69.9	113
MIDDLE	18	5342	70	66.2	106
FRONT	18	4802	70	63.5	104

Club Pro: Bob Warren
Payment: Visa, MC, Disc
Tee Times: 5 days adv.
Fee 9 Holes: Weekday: $15
Fee 18 Holes: Weekday: $23
Twilight Rates: After 2pm
Cart Rental: $17pp/18, $11pp/9
Lessons: Yes **Schools:** Yes
Membership: Yes

Weekend: $15
Weekend: $23
Discounts: Senior & Junior
Driving Range: Yes
Junior Golf: Yes
Architect/Yr Open: Stiles & Sargent/1920, 2003

COUPON

Other: Complete Function Facility Holds 180 / Snack Bar / Large Outings Welcome / Gazebo Available For Weddings

Beautiful views and a combination of contemporary and traditional design with tees to complement every skill level. Driving range, putting and chipping green.

	1	2	3	4	5	6	7	8	9
PAR	4	3	4	3	5	4	3	4	4
YARDS	312	93	352	135	465	344	140	307	250
	10	11	12	13	14	15	16	17	18
PAR	4	4	3	5	4	4	5	3	4
YARDS	258	322	140	478	407	319	454	179	387

Directions: I-93 to Exit 19 traveling North, Exit 20 traveling South. Route 3 South to downtown Franklin, left onto Prospect Street. Golf course 1 mile on right.

Monadnock Country Club

49 High Street
Peterborough, NH (603) 924-7769
www.monadnockcc.com

Tees	Holes	Yards	Par	USGA	Slope
BACK					
MIDDLE	9	1576	29	54.0	76
FRONT	9	1576	32	54.0	76

Club Pro: Dana Hennessey
Payment: Visa, MC
Tee Times: No
Fee 9 Holes: Weekday: $15
Fee 18 Holes: Weekday: $24
Twilight Rates: After 4pm
Cart Rental: $25/18, $14/9 per cart
Lessons: Yes **Schools:** No
Membership: Yes

Weekend: $16
Weekend: $26
Discounts: Senior & Junior
Driving Range: No
Junior Golf: Yes
Architect/Yr Open: S. Anderson & Son/1901

Other: Clubhouse / Snack Bar / Bar-Lounge / Banquet Facility

While the men's par is 29 and the women's 32, don't be fooled. This course can be challenging for both veterans and beginners. The scenic beauty alone is worth the trip. Clubhouse recently renovated.

	1	2	3	4	5	6	7	8	9
PAR	4	3	3	3	3	4	3	3	3
YARDS	241	108	205	150	166	257	134	162	153
PAR									
YARDS									

Directions: From East or West, Route 101. From North or South, Route 202. Located on High Street.

NH

Mountain View Grand Resort & Spa ✪½ ▶ 57

101 Mountain View Road
Whitefield, NH (603) 837-0076
www.mountainviewgrand.com

Club Pro:
Payment: Visa, MC, Amex, Disc
Tee Times: 7 days adv.
Fee 9 Holes: Weekday: $20
Fee 18 Holes: Weekday: $30
Twilight Rates: After 3pm
Cart Rental: $15pp/18, $10pp/9
Lessons: No **Schools:** No
Membership: Yes
Other: Restaurant / Clubhouse / Showers / Hotel / Bar / Lounge / Tennis

Weekend: $25
Weekend: $35
Discounts: Junior
Driving Range: No
Junior Golf:
Architect/Yr Open: Ralph Barton/1900

Tees	Holes	Yards	Par	USGA	Slope
BACK					
MIDDLE	9	2930	35	66	112
FRONT	9	2873	35	66	112

COUPON

Challenging course in the heart of the White Mountains. Majestic views 360 degrees and historic hotel with great accommodations. Historic 9 holes completely renovated in 1998. Additional holes in planning stage.

	1	2	3	4	5	6	7	8	9
PAR	4	4	5	4	4	3	4	3	4
YARDS	449	398	472	326	316	126	342	123	321
PAR									
YARDS									

Directions: I-93 North to Exit 35. 21 miles north on Route 3.

Mt. Washington Golf Club ✪✪✪✪½ ▶ 58

210 Mt. Washington Hotel Road
Bretton Woods, NH (603) 278-4653
www.mountwashingtonresort.com

Club Pro: John Pawlak
Payment: Visa, MC, Amex, Disc, Checks
Tee Times: Yes, 603-278-GOLF
Fee 9 Holes: Weekday: 2 for $59 after 2pm (Sun-Th)
Fee 18 Holes: Weekday: $85 ($75 resort)
Twilight Rates: 2 for $99 after 2pm (Sun-Th)
Cart Rental: Included
Lessons: Private and Group **Schools:** Yes
Membership: Yes
Architect/Yr Open: Donald Ross/1915, Cornish & Silva 9-hole course/1989
Other: Resort / Golf Packages / Restaurant / Clubhouse / Bar-Lounge / Lockers / Showers

Weekend: $85 ($75 resort)
Discounts: Senior & Junior
Driving Range: Yes
Junior Golf: Yes

Tees	Holes	Yards	Par	USGA	Slope
BACK	27/18	6974	72	73.7	124
MIDDLE	27/18	6378	72	67.0	122
FRONT	27/18	5336	71	70.2	120

COUPON

Spectacular Donald Ross layout set at the foot of the Presidential Mountains. Brilliant design fully restored by Brian Silva in 2008. *Golfweek's* #1 Course You Can Play in NH.

	1	2	3	4	5	6	7	8	9
PAR	4	4	4	4	3	5	4	4	4
YARDS	347	337	298	279	167	461	313	396	342
	10	11	12	13	14	15	16	17	18
PAR	5	5	4	4	3	4	3	4	4
YARDS	450	461	241	340	174	243	154	322	340

Directions: From I-93 take Exit 35 to Route 3N. Follow to Twin Mountain. Turn right at Route 302 and follow to Mount Washington Resort.

Newport Golf Club ✪✪ 59

112 Unity Road
Newport, NH (603) 863-7787
www.newport-golf.com

Tees	Holes	Yards	Par	USGA	Slope
BACK	18	6509	71	72.7	126
MIDDLE	18	6083	71	70.4	125
FRONT	18	4738	71	62.7	108

Club Pro: Vince Molesky, Dir. of Golf
Payment: Visa, MC, Cash
Tee Times: 3 days adv.
Fee 9 Holes: Weekday: $20
Fee 18 Holes: Weekday: $34
Twilight Rates: After 2pm
Cart Rental: $15pp/18, $10pp/9
Lessons: $35/half hour **Schools:** No
Membership: Yes
Other: Clubhouse / Snack Bar / Bar-Lounge / Lockers

Weekend: $38 includes cart
Weekend: $59 includes cart
Discounts: Junior
Driving Range: 2006
Junior Golf: Yes
Architect/Yr Open: Raph Barton/1922

COUPON

Improvements: recently completed full renovations. New hole number 5. Area attractions include, Mt. Sunapee, great hiking, and stream fishing.

	1	2	3	4	5	6	7	8	9
PAR	5	4	4	3	4	4	3	4	4
YARDS	511	326	388	179	373	375	145	269	369
	10	11	12	13	14	15	16	17	18
PAR	5	3	4	4	4	4	3	4	5
YARDS	477	138	387	379	375	341	169	375	507

Directions: I-91 to Exit 8. East to Claremont, then Route 11 toward Newport, ¾ mile take right onto Unity Road. Or, I-89 North to Exit 9. Follow Route 103 to Route 11 to center of town on Route 11 & 10 to lights, take right toward Claremont, first left after next light onto Unity Road, ¾ mile on left.

Nippo Lake Golf Club ✪✪✪ 60

88 Stagecoach Road
Barrington, NH (603) 664-7616
www.nippolake.com

Tees	Holes	Yards	Par	USGA	Slope
BACK	18	5594	70	66.5	121
MIDDLE	18	5307	70	64.9	117
FRONT	18	4513	70	85.4	104

Club Pro: Chris Mowers, PGA
Payment: Visa, MC
Tee Times: 7 days adv.
Fee 9 Holes: Weekday: $20
Fee 18 Holes: Weekday: $35
Twilight Rates: After 4pm
Cart Rental: $16pp/18, $10pp/9
Lessons: $45/30 min. **Schools:** Jr.
Membership: Yes
Other: Clubhouse / Snack Bar / Restaurant / Bar-Lounge / Video instruction

Weekend: $24
Weekend: $42
Discounts: Junior & Senior
Driving Range: Yes
Junior Golf: Yes
Architect/Yr Open:

COUPON

You will enjoy the majestic beauty of this backwoods links through the serene mountain setting and the friendly staff.

	1	2	3	4	5	6	7	8	9
PAR	4	5	3	5	4	3	4	4	3
YARDS	314	518	150	505	371	130	329	344	135
	10	11	12	13	14	15	16	17	18
PAR	5	4	3	4	4	4	4	3	4
YARDS	476	333	171	315	316	351	365	180	291

Directions: Spaulding Turnpike North to Exit 13 (Route 202 North). Take right onto Route 126. Go ¼ mile, then take a left onto Province Road.

NH

North Conway Country Club

76 Norcross Circle
North Conway, NH (603) 356-9391
www.northconwaycountryclub.com

Club Pro: Larry Gallagher, PGA
Payment: Visa, MC, Disc
Tee Times: 5 days adv.

Tees	Holes	Yards	Par	USGA	Slope
BACK	18	6659	71	71.9	125
MIDDLE	18	6266	71	70.3	121
FRONT	18	5530	71	70.7	118

Fee 9 Holes: Weekday:
Fee 18 Holes: Wkdy: $46 walk, $60 ride, M-Th
Twilight Rates: After 4pm
Cart Rental: $14pp/18
Lessons: By appointment **Schools:** Junior
Membership: Yes
Other: Restaurant / Bar-Lounge / Clubhouse

Weekend:
Weekend: $70 w/cart F/S/S/H
Discounts: Sr. & Jr. after 1pm M-Th
Driving Range: Yes, natural grass
Junior Golf: Yes
Architect/Yr: Alex Findlay & Phil Wogan/1895
GPS:

COUPON

Scenic and golfer friendly, well condition. Host to NH Ladies and Men Amateur, NH Open and NH PGA Championship.

	1	2	3	4	5	6	7	8	9
PAR	4	4	4	3	4	4	3	5	4
YARDS	406	399	354	130	328	362	208	497	376
	10	11	12	13	14	15	16	17	18
PAR	4	5	4	3	4	3	4	5	4
YARDS	349	475	385	150	420	147	357	528	337

Directions: Route 16 to Main Street, North Conway. Next to scenic railroad station.

Oak Hill Golf Course

159 Pease Road
Meredith, NH (603) 279-4438
www.oakhillgc.com

Club Pro:
Payment: Cash, Visa, MC
Tee Times: No

Tees	Holes	Yards	Par	USGA	Slope
BACK	9	2347	34	63.4	97
MIDDLE	9	2210	34	62.4	94
FRONT	9	1890	34	60.0	98

Fee 9 Holes: Weekday: $14
Fee 18 Holes: Weekday: $24
Twilight Rates: After 3pm
Cart Rental: $24/18, $14/9 per cart
Lessons: No **Schools:** No
Membership: Yes
Other: Snack Bar / Bar-Lounge

Weekend: $14
Weekend: $24
Discounts: None
Driving Range: No
Junior Golf: No
Architect/Yr Open: Harry Page/1963
GPS:

COUPON

Short regulation New England course. Good challenge for your irons. Wooded and scenic. Features such as stonewalls, scenic beauty, and its four hidden greens give Oak Hill an abundance of character. Our greens fees are the most reasonable around and our friendly atmosphere will tempt you to stay awhile. No tank tops. Open late April to November.

	1	2	3	4	5	6	7	8	9
PAR	4	3	4	4	3	4	3	4	5
YARDS	255	136	258	298	159	229	118	300	457
PAR									
YARDS									

Directions: I-93 to Exit 23 Route 104 East, 7.5 miles to stop light. Turn right onto Pease Road 1.5 miles. Parking on left, golf course on right.

Oaks Golf Links, The ✪✪✪½ 63 ▶

100 Hideaway Place
Somersworth, NH (603) 692-6257
www.theoaksgolflinks.com

Club Pro: Susan Bishop
Payment: Most Major Credit Cards
Tee Times: 5 days adv.
Fee 9 Holes: Weekday: $30
Fee 18 Holes: Weekday: $50
Twilight Rates: Ater 5:30pm
Cart Rental: $18pp/18, $9pp/9
Lessons: Yes **Schools:** Yes
Membership: Yes
Other: Restaurant / Bar and Grille / Clubhouse

Tees	Holes	Yards	Par	USGA	Slope
BACK	18	6825	71	72.1	126
MIDDLE	18	6165	71	69.4	123
FRONT	18	4880	71	69.7	112

Weekend: $35
Weekend: $60
Discounts: Senior & Junior, wkdys only
Driving Range: Yes
Junior Golf: Yes
Architect/Yr Open: Brad Booth/2005
GPS:

Beautifully manicured tight fairways and fast greens make The Oaks a must play. Dual memberships available with our sister course, Candia Woods. A public course with the private club feel. Top notch practice facility.

	1	2	3	4	5	6	7	8	9
PAR	4	4	3	5	3	4	4	4	4
YARDS	346	320	169	555	149	400	398	324	390
	10	**11**	**12**	**13**	**14**	**15**	**16**	**17**	**18**
PAR	4	5	4	3	4	4	3	4	5
YARDS	360	518	306	133	359	327	150	392	562

Directions: I-95 in Portsmouth to Route 16 North (Spaulding Turnpike) to Exit 9. Bear right off ramp and then move to left lane at Weeks Crossings intersection (about .3 miles). North on Route 108 for 3.6 miles; club on right.

Overlook Golf Club ✪✪✪½ 64 ▶

5 Overlook Drive
Hollis, NH (603) 465-2909
www.overlookgolfclub.com

Club Pro: Dan Diskin
Payment: Visa, MC, Amex, Disc
Tee Times: 7 days adv.
Fee 9 Holes: Weekday: $25
Fee 18 Holes: Weekday: $42
Twilight Rates: After 1pm
Cart Rental: $15pp/18, $10pp/9
Lessons: Yes **Schools:** No
Membership: Inner Club
Other: Clubhouse / Snack Bar / Bar-Lounge

Tees	Holes	Yards	Par	USGA	Slope
BACK	18	6624	71	70.1	126
MIDDLE	18	6103	71	68.2	119
FRONT	18	5255	72	69.2	114

Weekend: $30
Weekend: $52
Discounts: Senior & Junior
Driving Range: No
Junior Golf: Yes
Architect/Yr Open: 1989
GPS:

Player Comments: "Enjoyable for all abilities." "Use all clubs in bag." The front 9 are fairly hilly, back 9 are somewhat flat. New 6th hole. Front and back women's tees. Friendly atmosphere, great conditions. Nice practice area with bunkers and huge putting green.

	1	2	3	4	5	6	7	8	9
PAR	5	4	4	4	3	4	4	3	4
YARDS	535	299	433	390	177	371	292	167	326
	10	**11**	**12**	**13**	**14**	**15**	**16**	**17**	**18**
PAR	5	4	4	4	3	4	4	3	5
YARDS	522	376	346	390	164	341	320	138	516

Directions: From Route 495 take Exit to Route 3 North to Exit 5W (Route 111 West). Follow Route 111 West approximately 3½ miles. Course is on the right.

Owl's Nest Golf Club

✪✪✪½ **65**

40 Clubhouse Lane
Campton, NH (603) 726-3076
www.owlsnestgolf.com

Club Pro: Charles Wheeler
Payment: Visa, MC, Amex, Disc
Tee Times: 7 days adv., 1-888-OWL-NEST
Fee 9 Holes: Weekday: $34
Fee 18 Holes: Weekday: $64
Twilight Rates: After 3pm
Cart Rental: $18pp/18, $18pp/9
Lessons: $45/half hour; $75/hr. **Schools:** No
Membership: Yes
Other: Off-season rates as low as $44/18

Tees	Holes	Yards	Par	USGA	Slope
BACK	18	6818	72	74.0	133
MIDDLE	18	6110	72	69.7	124
FRONT	18	5174	72	67.8	117

Weekend: $34
Weekend: $64
Discounts: Junior 50% M-Th
Driving Range: $5
Junior Golf: Yes
Architect/Yr Open: Cornish & Mungeam/1998
GPS:

COUPON

Player Comments: "Great greens" "Nice layout, well-maintained, courteous staff." "Excellent customer service." "A true destination course." Discount rates in early and late seasons (call ahead). One of the best layouts in New England. Best scenic view around; staff will make you feel welcome.

	1	2	3	4	5	6	7	8	9
PAR	4	4	4	5	3	4	4	4	5
YARDS	370	366	395	503	160	311	350	335	483
	10	**11**	**12**	**13**	**14**	**15**	**16**	**17**	**18**
PAR	3	4	4	5	3	5	4	5	4
YARDS	127	316	391	489	160	259	435	488	348

Directions: I-93 to Exit 28, West on Route 49, then north on Owl Street.

Passaconaway Country Club

✪✪✪½ **66**

12 Midway Avenue (Route 3A)
Litchfield, NH (603) 424-4653
passaconawaycc.com

Club Pro: Joe Healey
Payment: Cash, Visa, MC
Tee Times: 5 days adv.
Fee 9 Holes: Weekday: $31
Fee 18 Holes: Weekday: $45
Twilight Rates: After 6pm
Cart Rental: $18pp/18, $11pp/9
Lessons: $45/half hour **Schools:** No
Membership: Yes, Inner Club
Other: Restaurant / Showers

Tees	Holes	Yards	Par	USGA	Slope
BACK	18	6855	71	72.6	132
MIDDLE	18	6462	71	70.5	128
FRONT	18	5369	71	70.9	118

Weekend: $34 after 10am only
Weekend: $56
Discounts: Sr., Jr., & Ladies wkdys
Driving Range: $10/lg, $5/sm
Junior Golf: Yes
Architect/Yr Open: Cornish & Silva/1989
GPS:

COUPON

Player Comments: "Links-style. Clubhouse staff very friendly. Course is well-maintained, very plush, greens outstanding and true. Plenty of water on the course. Bring the driver: long par 4's."

	1	2	3	4	5	6	7	8	9
PAR	5	3	4	3	5	4	4	3	4
YARDS	532	150	424	172	556	454	443	169	428
	10	**11**	**12**	**13**	**14**	**15**	**16**	**17**	**18**
PAR	4	4	4	3	5	4	4	4	4
YARDS	352	327	395	203	502	348	321	379	307

Directions: Route 93 North to Exit 4. Left on Route 102 for 5.5 miles to yellow blinking light. Take right on West Road, for 3 miles to the end. Left on Hillcrest for 3 miles, the course is straight ahead.

Pease Golf Course

200 Grafton Road
Portsmouth, NH (603) 433-1331
www.peasegolf.com

Tees	Holes	Yards	Par	USGA	Slope
BACK	27/18	6346	71	70.3	126
MIDDLE	27/18	5901	71	68.8	120
FRONT	27/18	5243	71	69.5	124

Club Pro: Tim Riese, PGA
Payment: Visa, MC, Amex, Cash
Tee Times: 7 days adv.
Fee 9 Holes: Weekday: $22
Fee 18 Holes: Weekday: $40
Twilight Rates: After 4pm
Cart Rental: $14pp/18, $8pp/9
Lessons: $35-$50/half hour **Schools:** Jr.
Membership: Yes
Other: Clubhouse / Bar-Lounge / Snack Bar / Showers / Lockers

Weekend: $25
Weekend: $44
Discounts: Senior & Junior
Driving Range: $11/lg., $4/sm.
Junior Golf: Yes
Architect/Yr Open: Arthur Findlay/1901

COUPON

27 holes available. Blue course 9 demanding for all levels: rating, 35.0/slope/120. Carts mandatory only for new 9. Scorecard below from the middle tees Red and White courses.

	1	2	3	4	5	6	7	8	9
PAR	5	5	3	4	4	4	4	4	3
YARDS	465	471	160	315	343	310	370	364	150
	10	11	12	13	14	15	16	17	18
PAR	4	3	4	5	3	5	3	4	4
YARDS	322	185	385	535	143	481	162	365	375

Directions: I-95 North to Exit 3, at light turn left, take 1st right. From Route I-95 South take Exit 3A, at stop sign turn right.

Pembroke Pines Country Club

42 Whittemore Road
Pembroke, NH (603) 210-1365
www.pembrokecc.net

Tees	Holes	Yards	Par	USGA	Slope
BACK	18	6572	72	62.4	130
MIDDLE	18	6162	72	61.4	125
FRONT	18	5419	72	71.0	122

Club Pro: Matt Delois, PGA
Payment:
Tee Times: 5 days adv.
Fee 9 Holes: Weekday: $24
Fee 18 Holes: Weekday: $40
Twilight Rates: After 4pm
Cart Rental: $16pp/18, $10pp/9
Lessons: Yes **Schools:** No
Membership: Yes
Other:

Weekend: $26
Weekend: $45
Discounts: Senior
Driving Range: Yes
Junior Golf: Yes
Architect/Yr Open: 1963
GPS:

COUPON

Two different experiences at one course. A wide-open front 9 with room to recover from wayward shots. "While the back 9 with picturesque views and tight fairways are a shot-makers paradise." –FP

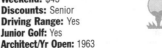

	1	2	3	4	5	6	7	8	9
PAR	5	4	4	3	4	3	4	4	5
YARDS	451	393	343	148	441	165	346	386	474
	10	11	12	13	14	15	16	17	18
PAR	4	4	5	3	5	4	3	4	4
YARDS	387	399	545	164	516	306	125	328	245

Directions: I-293, to Route 101 West to Amherst. Then take Route 122 to the course located ½ mile past Amherst Country Club.

NH

Pheasant Ridge Country Club ✪✪ 69

140 Country Club Road
Gilford, NH (603) 524-7808
www.playgolfne.com

Club Pro: Jim Swarthout, PGA
Payment: Visa, MC, Disc, Amex
Tee Times: 7 days adv.
Fee 9 Holes: Weekday: $20
Fee 18 Holes: Weekday: $34
Twilight Rates: After 2pm
Cart Rental: $32/18 per cart
Lessons: Yes **Schools:** No
Membership: Season Pass
Other: Snack Bar / Bar-Lounge / 400-seat Function Hall

Tees	Holes	Yards	Par	USGA	Slope
BACK	18	6402	70	69.3	115
MIDDLE	18	6004	70	67.2	112
FRONT	18	5192	70	68.6	112

Weekend: $26
Weekend: $44
Discounts: None
Driving Range: Yes
Junior Golf: No
Architect/Yr Open: Geoffrey Cornish/1962

"Course reflects both the late Phil Friel's skill as a golfer and as a developer." –Paul Harber. Beautiful views. A Golf Management Company course.

	1	2	3	4	5	6	7	8	9
PAR	4	3	4	4	4	5	4	3	4
YARDS	340	150	370	410	290	535	329	163	370
	10	**11**	**12**	**13**	**14**	**15**	**16**	**17**	**18**
PAR	5	4	4	3	4	4	4	4	3
YARDS	480	385	380	190	340	360	360	376	176

Directions: I-93 to Exit 20 (3 North), follow 9 miles onto Laconia Bypass. Take 2nd exit, right off ramp then next right onto Country Club Road. Course is ½ mile up hill on left.

Pine Grove Springs Country Club NR 70

292 Route 9A
Spofford, NH (603) 363-4433
www.pgscc.com

Club Pro: Jim Hillier
Payment: Disc, Visa, MC, Disc, Check
Tee Times: No
Fee 9 Holes: Weekday: $16
Fee 18 Holes: Weekday: $18
Twilight Rates: After 4pm
Cart Rental: $15pp/18, $10pp/9
Driving Range: No
Lessons: Yes **Schools:** No
Membership: Yes
Other: Snack Bar / Bar-Lounge

Tees	Holes	Yards	Par	USGA	Slope
BACK					
MIDDLE	9	2924	36	69.7	124
FRONT	9	2630	36	72.2	120

Weekend: $17
Weekend: $25
Discounts: Senior over 65
                  Junior 18 and under

Junior Golf: Yes
Architect/Yr Open: 1900

COUPON

Sig. Hole: #3 is a par 5 with 3 water hazards, dogleg right, rolling fairways, and elevated green. Open April – October. Plus 5-hole pitch and putt course.

	1	2	3	4	5	6	7	8	9
PAR	4	4	5	4	3	4	5	4	3
YARDS	269	368	541	345	148	347	420	318	168
PAR									
YARDS									

Directions: I-91 to Exit 3, 6 miles east of Brattleboro, VT.

Pine Valley Golf Links   ✪½   **71** ▶

247 Main Street
Pelham, NH 03076
(603) 635-7979, (603) 635-8305
www.pinevalleygolflinks.com

Club Pro: Rob Hardy
Payment: All Cards Accepted
Tee Times: Weekends only
Fee 9 Holes: Weekday: $17
Fee 18 Holes: Weekday: $22
Twilight Rates: $17 after 3pm/wkdy; $19/wknd
Cart Rental: $14pp/18, $8pp/9
Lessons: No   **Schools:** No
Membership: Yes
Other: Snack Bar / Bar-Lounge

Tees	Holes	Yards	Par	USGA	Slope
BACK	9	3015	35	90	128
MIDDLE	9	2805	35	66.8	113
FRONT	9	2675	36	69	122

Weekend: $19
Weekend: $27
Discounts: None
Driving Range: No
Junior Golf: Yes
Architect/Yr Open: Todd Madden/1961
GPS:

COUPON

Course is well-trapped and wooded. Easy to walk. Extended tee on #7. Fast greens and lots of trees and water. Dress code. No tanktops.

NH

	1	2	3	4	5	6	7	8	9
PAR	4	3	5	4	4	4	4	4	3
YARDS	290	200	510	295	335	410	350	320	125
PAR									
YARDS									

Directions: I-93 to Exit 1 (Rockingham Park). Follow signs to Route 38 South (Pelham). Course is located 4 miles up on left.

Ponemah Green Family Center   ✪✪½   **72** ▶

55 Ponemah Road
Amherst, NH (603) 672-4732
www.amherstcountryclub.com

Club Pro:
Payment: Visa, MC, Disc
Tee Times: 5 days adv.
Fee 9 Holes: Weekday: $16
Fee 18 Holes: Weekday: $25
Twilight Rates: After 4pm, weekends only
Cart Rental: $9pp/9
Lessons: $69/hour, $40/half hour   **Schools:** No
Membership: Yes
Other: Clubhouse / Snack Shop

Tees	Holes	Yards	Par	USGA	Slope
BACK	9	2210	34	62.4	110
MIDDLE	9	2160	34	61.4	107
FRONT	9	1804	34	71.0	106

Weekend: $16
Weekend: $25
Discounts: Junior
Driving Range: $5/sm., $8/lg.
Junior Golf: Yes
Architect/Yr Open: Geoffrey Cornish/1989
GPS:

Executive 9-hole golf course with small undulating greens. Accuracy a must. Open April until first snow. Now with mini-golf.

	1	2	3	4	5	6	7	8	9
PAR	3	3	4	4	4	4	4	4	4
YARDS	111	129	252	238	394	251	292	229	314
PAR									
YARDS									

Directions: I-293, to Route 101 West to Amherst. Then take Route 122 to the course located ½ mile past Amherst Country Club.

Portsmouth Country Club ✪✪✪✪   73

80 Country Club Lane
Greenland, NH (603) 436-9719
www.portsmouthcc.net

Club Pro: Bill Andrews, PGA
Payment: Visa, MC, Amex, Disc, Cash
Tee Times: 3 day adv.

Tees	Holes	Yards	Par	USGA	Slope
BACK	18	7153	72	73.8	124
MIDDLE	18	6222	72	70.6	119
FRONT	18	5134	75	64.8	111

Fee 9 Holes: Weekday: $47.50
Fee 18 Holes: Weekday: $85
Twilight Rates: No
Cart Rental: $18pp/18, $13pp/9
Lessons: $80/hour **Schools:** No
Membership: Yes
Other: Clubhouse / Restaurant / Bar-Lounge / Lockers / Showers

Weekend: $47.50
Weekend: $85
Discounts: Sat/Sun before 10am
Driving Range: Yes
Junior Golf: No
Architect/Yr Open: Robert Trent Jones Jr./1957

COUPON

Championship layout! 8 holes played along Great Bay. You will play shots over the ocean, around the ocean and often into the ocean! Magnificently manicured with traditional fast greens in excellent condition. You will not be disappointed.

	1	2	3	4	5	6	7	8	9
PAR	4	4	4	5	3	4	5	3	4
YARDS	370	378	349	471	139	403	474	210	368
	10	11	12	13	14	15	16	17	18
PAR	4	5	4	3	5	4	3	4	4
YARDS	395	483	423	130	432	310	117	376	394

Directions: I-95 to Route 33 West (Greenland exit). Follow (tiny) signs. Course is approximately 2 miles from I-95.

Ragged Mountain Resort ✪✪½ 74

620 Ragged Mountain Road
Danbury, NH (603) 768-3600
www.raggedmountainresort.com

Club Pro: Ian Willikens, PGA
Payment: Visa, MC
Tee Times: 7 days adv.

Tees	Holes	Yards	Par	USGA	Slope
BACK	18	6482	72	72.5	136
MIDDLE	18	5762	72	69.3	125
FRONT	18	4963	72	65.1	118

Fee 9 Holes: Weekday: $35 ride
Fee 18 Holes: Weekday: $49 ride
Twilight Rates: $35 after 3pm
Cart Rental: Included
Lessons: Schools: No
Membership: No
Other: Full Restaurant / Clubhouse / Bar Lounge

Weekend: $35 ride
Weekend: $59 ride
Discounts: None
Driving Range: $4.50/bucket
Junior Golf: No
Architect/Yr Open: Jeff Julian/1999

Player Comments: "Great mountain course. Beautiful setting." Spectacular views under 2 hours from Boston. 4 sets of tees. Ask about early season rates.

	1	2	3	4	5	6	7	8	9
PAR	4	5	4	4	3	4	3	5	4
YARDS	305	432	377	290	143	302	112	497	302
	10	11	12	13	14	15	16	17	18
PAR	4	5	4	3	4	3	4	5	4
YARDS	342	438	307	136	349	188	412	500	330

Directions: Route 93 North to Exit 23. Take Route 104 West for 20 minutes, through town of Bristol. Follow signs for Ragged Mountain access road on left. Follow road for 2 miles to course.

Ridgewood Country Club ✪✪✪½ 75 ▶

258 Gov. Wentworth Highway
Moultonborough, NH
(603) 476-5930
www.ridgewoodcc.net

Club Pro: Mike Uhlman
Payment: Visa, MC, Amex, Discover
Tee Times: 5 days adv.
Fee 9 Holes: Weekday: $29
Fee 18 Holes: Weekday: $32
Twilight Rates: After 3pm
Cart Rental: $17pp/18, $10pp/9
Lessons: Yes **Schools:** Yes
Membership: Yes, yearly/monthly/weekly
Other: Full-Service Restaurant

Weekend: $39
Weekend: $42
Discounts: No
Driving Range: Yes
Junior Golf: Yes
Architect/Yr Open: John Ponko/1998
GPS:

Tees	Holes	Yards	Par	USGA	Slope
BACK	18	6573	72	71.8	130
MIDDLE	18	6044	72	69.2	124
FRONT	18	4473	72	66.9	112

COUPON

18 championship holes, full-service golf shop, custom club fitting, short game practice area.

NH

	1	2	3	4	5	6	7	8	9
PAR	4	4	5	4	3	4	3	4	
YARDS	302	336	470	393	173	371	178	288	530
	10	11	12	13	14	15	16	17	18
PAR	3	5	4	4	4	4	4	3	5
YARDS	173	517	347	359	361	340	349	128	438

Directions: Route I-93, Exit 23 to Route 104. Left at Route 3 in Meredith to Route 25 East Moultonboro to Route 109 South. 1.5 mile on right. Please see website.

Rochester Country Club ✪✪✪½ 76 ▶

94 Church Street
Rochester, NH (603) 332-9892
www.rochestercc.com

Club Pro: Bill Cassell
Payment: Visa, MC, Amex, Disc, Cash, Check
Tee Times: 7 days adv.
Fee 9 Holes: Weekday: $20
Fee 18 Holes: Weekday: $35
Twilight Rates: After 4pm
Cart Rental: $16pp/18, $10pp/9
Lessons: $45/30 min. **Schools:** Jr
Membership: Yes
Architect/Yr Open: William Mitchell & Philip Wogan/1939
Other: Restaurant / Lockers / Showers / Snack Bar / Bar-Lounge / Function Room

Weekend: $24
Weekend: $42
Discounts: Senior & Juniors
Driving Range: No
Junior Golf: Yes

Tees	Holes	Yards	Par	USGA	Slope
BACK	18	6687	72	72.0	131
MIDDLE	18	6344	72	70.2	128
FRONT	18	5187	72	69.9	121

COUPON

"Great public course with a private flair. Continued improvements being made all the time. Every hole is unique." –FP & MH

	1	2	3	4	5	6	7	8	9
PAR	4	5	4	3	4	5	3	4	4
YARDS	322	481	447	205	306	516	134	407	324
	10	11	12	13	14	15	16	17	18
PAR	4	5	3	4	4	5	3	4	4
YARDS	362	548	168	421	328	487	193	393	302

Directions: From Route 16 (Spaulding Turnpike): take 125 South for 2 miles and turn left onto Church Street.

Rockingham Country Club

77

200 Exeter Road
Newmarket, NH (603) 659-9956
www.rockinghamgolf.com

Club Pro:
Payment: Visa, MC, Amex, Disc, Cash, Check
Tee Times: 7 days adv. (non-members)
Fee 9 Holes: Weekday: $22
Fee 18 Holes: Weekday: $31
Twilight Rates: No
Cart Rental: $28/18, $14/9 per cart
Lessons: Yes **Schools:** No
Membership: Yes
Other:

Tees	Holes	Yards	Par	USGA	Slope
BACK					
MIDDLE	9	2875	35	65.3	104
FRONT	9	2622	37	69.4	104

Weekend: $22
Weekend: $31
Discounts: Senior & Juniors weekdays
Driving Range: No
Junior Golf: No
Architect/Yr Open: 1933

The course is level and well-kept with 2 water holes.

	1	2	3	4	5	6	7	8	9
PAR	4	4	3	4	4	4	3	4	5
YARDS	386	315	175	393	315	380	125	306	480
PAR									
YARDS									

Directions: I-95 to Hampton Exit (Route 101 West) to Route 108. North to course.

Sagamore-Hampton Golf Club ✪✪½

78

101 North Road
North Hampton, NH (603) 964-5341
www.sagamoregolf.com

Club Pro: Laura Shanahan Rowe, LPGA
Payment: Visa, MC, Amex
Tee Times: 1 week adv.
Fee 9 Holes: Weekday: $26
Fee 18 Holes: Weekday: $42
Twilight Rates: After 3pm/wknds; 5pm/wkdys
Cart Rental: $17pp/18, $10pp/9
Driving Range: Off-site, 603-964-8393
Lessons: Yes **Schools:** No
Membership: No
Other:

Tees	Holes	Yards	Par	USGA	Slope
BACK	18	6041	71	68.6	118
MIDDLE	18	5647	71	67.1	115
FRONT	18	4886	71	67.5	112

Weekend: $28
Weekend: $47
Discounts: Senior/Junior/College

COUPON

Junior Golf: Yes
Architect/Yr Open: Christopher Luff/1962

A Seacoast favorite for 50 years, featuring great golf, a friendly staff, and unbeatable golf value. Rated a "4-star" course by *Golf Digest* and voted "Best on the Seacoast." New bunkers added to the 7th and 14th hole. An ideal course for any level of golfer, featuring a spacious Front 9 combined with a tree-lined Back 9.

	1	2	3	4	5	6	7	8	9
PAR	4	4	4	3	4	5	3	5	3
YARDS	291	325	352	135	300	463	192	424	166
	10	11	12	13	14	15	16	17	18
PAR	5	3	4	5	3	4	5	3	4
YARDS	527	172	380	446	125	284	456	190	419

Directions: I-95 to Exit 2, right to 101 West. First exit, go right onto 111 East, then follow 2.5 miles. Left onto 151 North, follow 1 mile, right onto North Road.

Shattuck Golf Course, The ✪✪½ 79

53 Dublin Road
Jaffrey, NH (603) 532-4300
www.sterlinggolf.com

Tees	Holes	Yards	Par	USGA	Slope
BACK	18	6764	71	73.5	153
MIDDLE	18	6077	71	70.9	141
FRONT	18	4632	71	73.9	139

Club Pro: Brad Durrin, PGA
Payment: MC, Visa, Amex, Cash
Tee Times: 7 days adv.
Fee 9 Holes: Weekday: $30 (includes cart) **Weekend:** $35 (includes cart)
Fee 18 Holes: Weekday: $49 (includes cart) **Weekend:** $60 (includes cart)
Twilight Rates: After 4pm **Discounts:** Senior & Junior
Cart Rental: **Driving Range:** Yes
Lessons: Yes **Schools:** Yes **Junior Golf:** Yes
Membership: Yes **Architect/Yr Open:** Brian Silva/1991
Other: Bar-Lounge / Weddings / Large Functions

Player Comments: "Every-club-in-the-bag course. Very challenging." "Believe the slope rating—this is a monster. Helpful Player's Guide on website. Uncrowded." Under Sterling Golf Management. Brian Silva course designed in 1991. *Golf Digest* Ranked 43rd of the 50 toughest golf courses in the U.S.

	1	2	3	4	5	6	7	8	9
PAR	4	3	4	4	5	5	3	4	4
YARDS	357	146	343	312	551	508	183	373	356
	10	11	12	13	14	15	16	17	18
PAR	4	4	3	4	3	5	4	4	4
YARDS	394	407	155	303	121	508	367	313	380

Directions: I-90 (Mass Pike) to 495 North to Route 2 West. Take Exit 24B Route 140 North to Route 12 North. Take a left, go .9 mile. Go right on Route 202 North to Jaffrey, NH. Go left on Route 124. Follow West 2.2 miles. Go right at Mount Monadnock sign. Club is on the left.

Souhegan Woods Golf Club ✪✪✪ 80

65 Thornton's Ferry Road
Amherst, NH (603) 673-0200
www.playgolfne.com

Tees	Holes	Yards	Par	USGA	Slope
BACK	18	6507	72	70	118
MIDDLE	18	6122	72	68.3	115
FRONT	18	5286	71/69	70.6	123

Club Pro: Adam Nelson
Payment: Most Major
Tee Times: 7 days adv.
Fee 9 Holes: Weekday: $23 **Weekend:**
Fee 18 Holes: Weekday: $35 **Weekend:** $48
Twilight Rates: After 3pm **Discounts:** Senior & Junior
Cart Rental: $15pp/18, $10pp/9 **Driving Range:** $10/lg, $6/sm bucket
Lessons: $95/hour **Schools:** No **Junior Golf:** Yes - $10
Membership: No **Architect/Yr Open:** Phil Friel/1992
Other: Clubhouse / Bar-Lounge / Snack Bar / Showers

Designed to challenge all golfers. In very good condition and well spread out. Open April - November. A Golf Management Company course.

	1	2	3	4	5	6	7	8	9
PAR	4	4	3	5	4	5	4	3	4
YARDS	375	312	168	445	402	501	337	149	355
	10	11	12	13	14	15	16	17	18
PAR	4	3	4	4	5	4	4	3	5
YARDS	312	153	343	368	510	349	406	166	469

Directions: Route 3 (Everett Turnpike) in NH take Exit 11. Turn left at end of ramp and proceed under the highway. Take your very first right onto Amherst Road and proceed 4.3 miles. Take a right onto Stillwater Road. Course is a ¼ mile on the right.

Stonebridge Country Club ✪✪✪¹/₂

81

161 Gorham Pond Road
Goffstown, NH (603) 497-8633
www.golfstonebridgecc.com

Tees	Holes	Yards	Par	USGA	Slope
BACK	18	6808	72	72.9	136
MIDDLE	18	6388	72	71.0	133
FRONT	18	4747	72	67.6	116

Club Pro: Ken Hamel, PGA
Payment: Visa, MC, Amex, Disc
Tee Times: 5 days adv.
Fee 9 Holes: Weekday: $29   **Weekend:** $39
Fee 18 Holes: Weekday: $44   **Weekend:** $55
Twilight Rates: $29 after 2pm; $20 after 6pm   **Discounts:** Jr., M-Th before 3pm
Cart Rental: $17pp/18, $12pp/9   **Driving Range:** $7/bucket
Lessons: $40/half hour **Schools:** No   **Junior Golf:** Yes
Membership: Yes   **Architect/Yr Open:** Phil Wogan/1998
Other: Full Restaurant / Clubhouse / Lockers / Showers / Bar-Lounge

Player Comments: "Challenging greens. Beautiful landscape." "Demanding layout from middle and back tees." Newly paved cart paths, new carts, and other renovations completed in 2008. Hole no. 6, the short but dangerous par 3, was voted number 1 golf hole in NH by WMUR-TV viewers.

	1	2	3	4	5	6	7	8	9
PAR	5	4	4	3	4	3	4	4	4
YARDS	480	398	370	152	366	136	332	408	417
	10	11	12	13	14	15	16	17	18
PAR	5	4	4	3	5	4	3	5	4
YARDS	496	325	349	193	526	369	150	521	400

Directions: I-93 to Route 101 West to Route 114 North for 9 miles, through Goffstown center. After Sully's Superette, go 1.5 mile and take right onto Parker Station Road. Immediate right onto Gorham Pond Road. Course is ¾ mile on left.

Sunset Hill Golf Course

NR **82**

234 Sunset Hill Road
Sugar Hill, NH (603) 823-7244
www.sunsethillgolf.com

Tees	Holes	Yards	Par	USGA	Slope
BACK	9	2002	33		
MIDDLE	9	1690	33		
FRONT	9	1379	33		

Club Pro:
Payment: Visa, MC, Amex, Disc, Checks
Tee Times: Yes
Fee 9 Holes: Weekday: $15   **Weekend:** $20
Fee 18 Holes: Weekday: $20   **Weekend:** $30
Twilight Rates: After 5pm   **Discounts:** Junior
Cart Rental: $25pp/18, $15pp/9 weekday; $30pp/18, $20pp/9 weekend
Driving Range: No
Lessons: $30/half hour **Schools:** Yes   **Junior Golf:** Yes
Membership: Yes   **Architect/Yr Open:** Ted Bonar/1897
Other: Snack Bar / Restaurant / Hotel Along 1st Hole / Functions

"Particularly friendly for families, beginners, and seniors. Hassle-free golf the way we remember it." Oldest 9-hole course in NH, built in 1897. Antique clubhouse restored in 2007. A really fun place to play golf.

	1	2	3	4	5	6	7	8	9
PAR	4	4	4	4	3	4	3	4	3
YARDS	267	288	234	260	173	211	156	267	176
PAR									
YARDS									

Directions: I-93 to Exit 38. Go left at bottom of ramp, take right at blinking light. Go ½ mile then left on Route 117. Go uphill for 2 miles and turn left onto Sunset Hill Road. Course is ½ mile on the left.

Twin Lake Villa Golf Course

83

164 Twin Lake Villa Road
New London, NH (603) 526-2034
www.twinlakevillage.com

Club Pro:
Payment: Personal Checks
Tee Times: 3 days adv.
Fee 9 Holes: Weekday: $12
Fee 18 Holes: Weekday: $16
Twilight Rates: No
Cart Rental: No
Lessons: Arranged off-site **Schools:** No
Membership: Yes
Other:

Tees	Holes	Yards	Par	USGA	Slope
BACK	9	1515	27		
MIDDLE	9	1356	27		
FRONT	9	1149	27		

Weekend: $12
Weekend: $16
Discounts: Senior, $2 off
Driving Range: No
Junior Golf: No
Architect/Yr Open: Henry Kidder/1948
GPS:

Open May 1 - October 31.

	1	2	3	4	5	6	7	8	9
PAR	3	3	3	3	3	3	3	3	3
YARDS	141	113	118	109	190	197	180	177	131
PAR									
YARDS									

Directions: I-89 to Exit 12. Go East 2 miles to New London. At blinking light, turn left onto Country Road. At first stop sign, turn left onto Little Sunapee Road for 1 mile. Bear right onto Twin Lake Villa Road and follow up hill to Hotel and Golf Shop.

Waterville Valley Golf Club

NR 84

3 Lost Pass Road
Waterville Valley, NH
(603) 236-4805
www.waterville.com

Club Pro:
Payment: Visa, MC, Amex, Disc
Tee Times: 48 hours adv.
Fee 9 Holes: Weekday: $25
Fee 18 Holes: Weekday: $35
Twilight Rates: No
Cart Rental: $26pp/18, $18pp/9
Lessons: Yes **Schools:** No
Membership: Yes
Other: Clubhouse / Snack Bar / Club Storage / Resort

Tees	Holes	Yards	Par	USGA	Slope
BACK					
MIDDLE	9	1700	30	63	105
FRONT					

COUPON

Weekend: $25
Weekend: $35
Discounts: None
Driving Range: No
Junior Golf: Yes
Architect/Yr Open: 1898

Interesting, newly designed golf course with 3 holes on the top of the hill. Spectacular view. Mountain resort. Open May 27 - October 15. Inquire about junior clinics. New clubhouse.

	1	2	3	4	5	6	7	8	9
PAR	4	3	3	3	3	4	3	4	3
YARDS	294	185	105	128	118	317	136	312	105
PAR									
YARDS									

Directions: I-93 to Exit 28; follow Route 49 for 12 miles.

Waukewan Golf Club

⭐⭐½   **85**

166 Waukewan Road
Center Harbor, NH (603) 279-6661
www.waukewan.com

Tees	Holes	Yards	Par	USGA	Slope
BACK	18	5885	72	68.7	118
MIDDLE	18	5415	72	68.3	117
FRONT	18	4695	72	64.6	113

Club Pro: Chuck Yeager
Payment: Cash or Credit Card
Tee Times: Up to 7 days adv. 6am-3pm
Fee 9 Holes: Weekday: $25
Fee 18 Holes: Weekday: $40
Twilight Rates: $15 after 3pm walking
Cart Rental: $16pp/18, $10pp/9
Lessons: Available **Schools:** Yes
Membership: Yes
Other: Clubhouse / Snack Bar / Bar-Lounge

Weekend: $30
Weekend: $50
Discounts: None
Driving Range: $6/lg, $3/sm bucket
Junior Golf: Yes
Architect/Yr Open: Melvin D. Hale Sr./1958
GPS:

COUPON

Located in the Lakes Region of New Hampshire, this scenic course is nestled within a beautiful mountain range. The redsigned 13th green is our latest accomplishment. The friendly staff will only add to your relaxing golf experience.

	1	2	3	4	5	6	7	8	9
PAR	4	4	3	4	4	5	3	5	4
YARDS	360	305	130	230	230	530	160	430	370
	10	**11**	**12**	**13**	**14**	**15**	**16**	**17**	**18**
PAR	4	3	4	4	4	5	3	5	4
YARDS	260	180	245	400	280	440	180	430	215

Directions: I-93 to Exit 23. Route 104 to Meredith. Route 3 North toward Plymouth. At 3 miles from Meredith traffic junction, left turn onto Waukewan Road.

Waumbek Golf Club

NR   **86**

28 Waumbek Street
Jefferson, NH (603) 586-7777
www.playgolfne.com

Tees	Holes	Yards	Par	USGA	Slope
BACK	18	6128	71	67.0	117
MIDDLE	18	5792	71	65	111
FRONT	18	4772	71	67.8	111

Club Pro: Larry Fellows
Payment: Visa, MC, Amex, Disc, Cash
Tee Times: Yes
Fee 9 Holes: Weekday: $17
Fee 18 Holes: Weekday: $26
Twilight Rates: After 3pm, $15
Cart Rental: $13pp/18, $8pp/9
Lessons: Yes **Schools:** Yes
Membership: Yes
Other: Restaurant / Bar-Lounge / Lodging Patner

Weekend: $20
Weekend: $32
Discounts: Junior & Senior
Driving Range:
Junior Golf: Yes
Architect/Yr Open: Willy Norton/1895
GPS:

COUPON

New Hampshire's oldest 18 hole course. Scottish link style course. 90% of greens slope toward Cherry Mountain. Located on back side of the Presidential Range Mountains. Breathtaking views on every hole.

	1	2	3	4	5	6	7	8	9
PAR	4	4	5	4	4	4	4	3	3
YARDS	333	370	500	310	320	390	290	200	195
	10	**11**	**12**	**13**	**14**	**15**	**16**	**17**	**18**
PAR	4	5	4	4	3	4	4	5	3
YARDS	310	465	387	280	110	340	335	490	170

Directions: I-93 to Exit 35 (Route 3 North). Follow Route 3 for 12 miles, then take a right onto Route 115 North. Follow Route 115 North for 6.7 miles. Take a left onto Route 115A. Golf course is 4 miles down on the right.

Wentworth Resort Golf Club   ✪✪   ▶ 87

Route 16A
Jackson, NH (603) 383-9641
www.wentworthgolf.com

Tees	Holes	Yards	Par	USGA	Slope
BACK					
MIDDLE	18	5581	69	66.0	115
FRONT	18	5087	70	66.7	114

Club Pro: Kevin Walker PGA
Payment: MC, Visa, Amex, Disc
Tee Times: Yes
Fee 9 Holes: Weekday: **Weekend:**
Fee 18 Holes: Weekday: $35   **Weekend:** $45 F/S/S/H
Twilight Rates: After 3pm   **Discounts:** Junior
Cart Rental: $15pp/18, $9pp/9   **Driving Range:** No
Lessons: $45/45 min **Schools:** No   **Junior Golf:** Yes
Membership: Yes   **Architect/Yr:** Wayne Stiles/1895, Arthur Hill/1998
Other: Snack Bar / Restaurant / Bar-Lounge   **GPS:**

COUPON

Challenging course situated in Jackson Village. Enjoy the rolling hills and the covered bridge crossing the Ellis River on the White Mountains' 2nd oldest course.

	1	2	3	4	5	6	7	8	9
PAR	4	4	4	3	3	4	4	4	5
YARDS	305	337	349	304	147	411	291	307	479
	10	11	12	13	14	15	16	17	18
PAR	4	4	4	4	3	5	3	3	4
YARDS	333	359	336	365	185	454	180	144	295

Directions: I-95 to Spaulding Turnpike. Take Route 16 North to Jackson Village. Or I-93 to Route 25 to Route 16 North to Jackson Village.

Whip-Poor-Will Golf Club   ✪✪✪½   ▶ 88

55 Marsh Road
Hudson, NH (603) 889-9706

Tees	Holes	Yards	Par	USGA	Slope
BACK	9	3015	36	67.8	120
MIDDLE	9	2990	36	67.8	120
FRONT	9	2547	36	69.9	119

Club Pro: Lori Brooks, Manager
Payment: Visa, MC, Amex, Disc
Tee Times: 7 days adv.
Fee 9 Holes: Weekday: $21   **Weekend:** $24
Fee 18 Holes: Weekday: $30   **Weekend:** $35
Twilight Rates: After 3pm wknds   **Discounts:** Senior & Junior
Cart Rental: $12.50pp/18, $8pp/9   **Driving Range:** No
Lessons: Schools: No   **Junior Golf:** No
Membership: No   **Architect/Yr Open:** Manuel Francis/1959
Other: Clubhouse / Snack Bar / Bar Lounge   **GPS:**

An enjoyable well-maintained 9-hole course, perfect for an early afternoon off. A Golf Management Company course. New senior tees.

	1	2	3	4	5	6	7	8	9
PAR	4	3	4	4	5	4	4	5	3
YARDS	330	170	345	315	485	402	280	498	165
PAR									
YARDS									

Directions: I-93 to Exit 4 to Route 102 West approximately 7 miles. Course is on left at Marsh Road just after Alverine High School.

NH

White Mountain Country Club ✪✪½ 89

North Ashland Road
Ashland, NH (603) 536-2227
www.playgolfne.com

Club Pro: Gregg Sufat
Payment: Visa, MC, Amex, Disc
Tee Times: 1 week adv.

Tees	Holes	Yards	Par	USGA	Slope
BACK	18	6428	71	70.4	122
MIDDLE	18	5963	112	67.9	119
FRONT	18	5350	72	69.6	118

Fee 9 Holes: Weekday: $20
Fee 18 Holes: Weekday: $33
Twilight Rates: After 3pm
Cart Rental: $16pp/18, $9pp/9
Lessons: $30/half hour, $50/hour **Schools:** No
Membership: No
Other: Bar-Lounge / Snack Bar / Townhouse Rentals

Weekend: $32
Weekend: $43
Discounts: None
Driving Range: $8/lg, $4/sm bucket
Junior Golf: No
Architect/Yr Open: Cornish & Silva/1975

Player Comments: "Great course in the Fall." Golfer-friendly, challenging, well-cared-for. Expanded driving range and recent reversal of dogleg on hole #2. A Golf Management Company course.

	1	2	3	4	5	6	7	8	9
PAR	4	4	4	3	5	4	3	5	4
YARDS	327	334	325	174	524	300	172	508	312
	10	11	12	13	14	15	16	17	18
PAR	4	3	4	4	4	4	4	4/5	4
YARDS	356	154	356	374	321	301	359	410	356

Directions: I-93 North to Exit 24, left off ramp for 1 mile. Right onto North Ashland Road, 2.5 miles on left.

Windham Country Club ✪✪✪ 90

1 Country Club Road
Windham, NH (603) 434-2093
www.windhamcc.com

Club Pro: Joanne Flynn, PGA
Payment: Visa, MC, Disc
Tee Times: 7 days a week, 7 days in adv.

Tees	Holes	Yards	Par	USGA	Slope
BACK	18	6442	72	71.2	135
MIDDLE	18	6033	72	69.1	129
FRONT	18	5584	72	67.4	122

Fee 9 Holes: Weekday: $24
Fee 18 Holes: Weekday: $42
Twilight Rates: After 3pm wknds
Cart Rental: $18pp/18, $9pp/9
Lessons: $50/half hour **Schools:** Yes
Membership: Season passes available
Other: Clubhouse / Bar-Lounge

Weekend: $29
Weekend: $50
Discounts: Senior & Junior
Driving Range: Yes
Junior Golf: Yes
Architect/Yr Open: William Flynn/1995

Noted for great overall condition and challenging layout. Open year round (when possible). Year round Golf Academy with 3 heated bays and professional golf technology.

	1	2	3	4	5	6	7	8	9
PAR	5	4	3	4	5	3	4	4	3
YARDS	522	374	158	365	578	136	398	369	165
	10	11	12	13	14	15	16	17	18
PAR	4	4	5	4	3	5	4	4	4
YARDS	280	354	440	304	166	444	382	335	306

Directions: I-93 to Exit 3. Take Route 111 West 1.5 miles. Then right on Church Street to fire station; then right onto North Lowell for 1 mile. Left onto Londonderry Road .5 mile and left on Country Club Road.

Beaver River Golf Club	1	Goddard State Park GC	13	Pinecrest Golf Course	25
Bristol Golf Club	2	Green Valley CC	14	Richmond Country Club	26
Button Hole	3	Harbor Lights Golf & CC	15	Rolling Greens GC	27
Country View Golf Club	4	Jamestown Golf & CC	16	Rose Hill Golf Course	28
Coventry Pines Golf Club	5	Laurel Lane Country Club	17	Triggs Memorial GC	29
Cranston Country Club	6	Lindhbrook GC	18	West Warwick CC, The	30
Crystal Lake GC of RI	7	Meadow Brook	19	Windmill Hill Golf Course	31
East Greenwich CC	8	Melody Hill Golf Course	20	Winnapaug Golf Course	32
Exeter Country Club	9	Midville Country Club	21	Wood River Golf	33
Fairlawn Golf Course	10	Montaup Country Club	22	Woodland Greens GC	34
Fenner Hill Golf Club	11	Newport National Golf Club	23		
Foster Country Club	12	North Kingstown Muni. GC	24		

Beaver River Golf Club   ✪✪½   1 ▶

343 Kingstown Road
Richmond, RI (401) 539-2100
www.beaverrivergolf.com

Club Pro:
Payment: Visa, MC
Tee Times: 7 days adv.

Tees	Holes	Yards	Par	USGA	Slope
BACK	18	6086	70	67.1	123
MIDDLE	18	5802	70	65.7	123
FRONT	18	5410	70	70.8	115

Fee 9 Holes: Weekday: $19/Sr; $15/Jr   **Weekend:** $21
Fee 18 Holes: Weekday: $34   **Weekend:** $40
Twilight Rates: After 3pm   **Discounts:** Senior and Military
Cart Rental: $16pp/18, $8pp/9   **Driving Range:** No
Lessons: No **Schools:** Yes   **Junior Golf:** Yes
Membership: Yes   **Architect/Yr Open:** Michael Weremay/2001
Other: Clubhouse / Bar-Lounge   **GPS:**

COUPON

Bent grass from tee to green. Excellent conditions and service. South County course. New cosmetic improvements. Scenic fall views.

	1	2	3	4	5	6	7	8	9
PAR	5	4	3	4	4	5	3	4	4
YARDS	477	334	150	326	318	485	201	411	332
	10	11	12	13	14	15	16	17	18
PAR	4	3	4	4	4	3	4	4	4
YARDS	328	146	433	379	300	170	265	367	380

Directions: I-95 to Exit 3A. Take Route 138, 3 miles east.

Bristol Golf Club   NR   2 ▶

95 Tupelo Road
Bristol, RI (401) 253-9844

Club Pro:
Payment: Cash Only
Tee Times: No

Tees	Holes	Yards	Par	USGA	Slope
BACK					
MIDDLE	9	2273	33	69.9	118
FRONT					

Fee 9 Holes: Weekday: $10   **Weekend:** $12
Fee 18 Holes: Weekday: $10   **Weekend:** $12
Twilight Rates: No   **Discounts:** None
Cart Rental: $10pp/18, $5/pull   **Driving Range:** No
Lessons: No **Schools:** No   **Junior Golf:** No
Membership: Yes   **Architect/Yr Open:** 1964
Other: Snack Bar / Bar-Lounge   **GPS:**

A good course for beginners.

	1	2	3	4	5	6	7	8	9
PAR	3	4	3	3	3	4	5	4	4
YARDS	137	254	148	130	167	337	480	320	300
PAR									
YARDS									

Directions: I-195 East to Exit 2, follow Route 136 to Tupelo Street, take right and course is on left.

RI

Button Hole ⊗⊗ ▶3

1 Button Hole Drive
Providence, RI (401) 421-1664
www.buttonhole.org

Club Pro: Dan Gaughan
Payment: Visa, MC, Amex, Disc
Tee Times:

Tees	Holes	Yards	Par	USGA	Slope
BACK					
MIDDLE	9	1035	27	50.9	
FRONT	9	780	27	48.6	

Fee 9 Holes: Weekday: $10
Fee 18 Holes: Weekday: $15
Twilight Rates: No
Cart Rental: $3/pull
Lessons: Yes* **Schools:** Yes
Membership: Range and Course
Weekend: $10
Weekend: $15
Discounts: Senior/Junior/Military
Driving Range: $10/lg., $6/sm.
Junior Golf: Yes
Architect/Yr Open: Ron Pritchard, P.B. Dye/1998
Other: Clubhouse / Patio / Snacks / 16,000 sq ft Putting Green / Chipping Area

Short course and teaching center designed to lower cost, provide easy access and playing time. "Not just a beginner's layout. Shots and putts have to be made to score." –RW

*Lessons priced according to age. Inquire!

	1	2	3	4	5	6	7	8	9
PAR	3	3	3	3	3	3	3	3	3
YARDS	70	118	60	90	95	62	110	90	85
PAR									
YARDS									

Directions: I-95 to Route 6 West to Route 6A West-Hartford Avenue exit. Take left (East) on Hartford Avenue. Go .7 miles and take right on Glenbridge Avenue. Go .3 miles and take left on Button Hole Drive. Facility on right.

Country View Golf Club ⊗⊗ ▶4

49 Club Lane
Harrisville, RI (401) 568-7157
www.countryviewgolf.net

Club Pro: Rick Finlayson, PGA
Payment: Visa, MC, Disc, Cash
Tee Times: 7 days adv.

Tees	Holes	Yards	Par	USGA	Slope
BACK	18	6067	70	68.2	117
MIDDLE	18	5721	70	66.5	113
FRONT	18	5060	70	67.4	108

Fee 9 Holes: Weekday: $18
Fee 18 Holes: Weekday: $30
Twilight Rates: After 5:30pm
Cart Rental: $17pp/18, $9pp/9
Lessons: $35/half hour **Schools:** No
Membership: Yes
Weekend: $25
Weekend: $38
Discounts: Senior & Junior
Driving Range: No
Junior Golf: No
Architect/Yr Open: Carl Dexter/1965

Other: Clubhouse / Lockers / Showers / Snack Bar / Restaurant / Bar-Lounge

With a great mixture of holes, Country View provides a challenge for all players. Improved drainage on the front 9. New ladies tees (4, 6, 18). New, redesigned holes (12, 14, 17). Quiet country atmosphere to enjoy your round.

	1	2	3	4	5	6	7	8	9
PAR	4	3	4	4	4	5	3	4	4
YARDS	318	126	341	347	315	461	137	344	348
	10	11	12	13	14	15	16	17	18
PAR	4	4	5	3	4	4	4	3	4
YARDS	379	281	485	178	332	392	386	184	367

Directions: I-295 to Exit 8 (Route 7 North). Follow 5 miles past Bryant University, take left onto Mattity Road follow to end. Take left onto Tarkiln Road. Follow 600 yards take left onto Colewell Road, entrance is ½ mile on right.

Coventry Pines Golf Club

NR 5

1065 Harkney Hill Road
Coventry, RI (401) 397-9482

Tees	Holes	Yards	Par	USGA	Slope
BACK					
MIDDLE	9	3170	36	68.0	113
FRONT	9	3120	36	70.0	113

Club Pro:
Payment: Cash Only
Tee Times: No
Fee 9 Holes: Weekday: $13
Fee 18 Holes: Weekday: $23
Twilight Rates: After 6pm
Cart Rental: $32/18, $16/9 per cart
Lessons: No **Schools:** No
Membership: No
Other: Snack Bar

Weekend: $17
Weekend: $26
Discounts: Senior M-F
Driving Range: Practice field
Junior Golf: No
Architect/Yr Open: 1959
GPS:

A very scenic course with rolling hills and tree-lined fairways. 3 water holes. Noted for the par 5 sixth which has 2 different greens, men's and women's. South County course. Open March - December.

	1	2	3	4	5	6	7	8	9
PAR	4	4	3	5	4	5	4	3	4
YARDS	375	308	169	484	408	520	357	187	362
PAR									
YARDS									

Directions: I-95 to RI Exit 6 (Route 3). Continue north on Route 3 for 1 mile. Take a left on Harkney Hill Road. The course is 2 miles on the left.

Cranston Country Club

✪✪✪½ 6

69 Burlingame Road
Cranston, RI (401) 826-1683
www.cranstoncc.com

Tees	Holes	Yards	Par	USGA	Slope
BACK	18	6914	71	73.5	130
MIDDLE	18	6493	71	70.8	125
FRONT	18	6109	71	69.1	122

Club Pro: Tom Palmer, Dir. of Golf
Payment: Visa, MC, Cash
Tee Times: Yes
Fee 9 Holes: Weekday: $28
Fee 18 Holes: Weekday: $40
Twilight Rates: $28 after 3pm wknds
Cart Rental: $18pp/18, $9pp/9
Lessons: No **Schools:** No
Membership: Yes
Other: Clubhouse / Lockers / Showers / Snack Bar / Bar / Banquet Facilities

Weekend: $28
Weekend: $46
Discounts: Senior M-F $30
Driving Range: Grass
Junior Golf: Yes
Architect/Yr Open: Geoffrey Cornish/1974

COUPON

Hole #8 is an island green. Scenic country setting. W-i-d-e fairways. Lots of room to hit driver. 4 finishing holes are a fun challenge!

	1	2	3	4	5	6	7	8	9
PAR	5	4	4	3	4	4	4	3	4
YARDS	529	348	375	180	338	346	344	173	410
	10	11	12	13	14	15	16	17	18
PAR	4	4	3	5	4	3	4	5	4
YARDS	345	377	125	475	349	166	369	545	355

Directions: I-95 to Route 37 West (Exit 14). Go to end of Route 37, turn left. Go .2 mile to intersection, turn right; .4 mile to stop sign, bear right. Proceed .2 mile to crossroads and turn left (Phoenix Avenue). Go 2 miles to golf course.

RI

Crystal Lake Golf Course of RI ✪✪✪

7

100 Broncos Highway (Route 102)
Mapleville, RI (401) 567-4500
www.crystallakegolfclub.com

Tees	Holes	Yards	Par	USGA	Slope
BACK	18	6349	71	70.0	120
MIDDLE	18	5892	71	68.2	116
FRONT	18	5035	71	69.9	115

Club Pro: Tony DiGiorgio, PGA
Payment: Cash, MC, Visa, Amex, Discover
Tee Times: 6 days adv.
Fee 9 Holes: Weekday: $18   **Weekend:** $24
Fee 18 Holes: Weekday: $32   **Weekend:** $44 ($30 Friday)
Twilight Rates: After 6pm   **Discounts:**
Cart Rental: $16pp/18, $9pp/9   **Driving Range:** Yes
Lessons: Yes **Schools:** Yes   **Junior Golf:** Yes
Membership: Yes   **Architect/Yr Open:** Howard Maurer/2003
Other: Clubhouse / Restaurant / Bar / Function Facility

COUPON

Clubhouse with 4-star restaurant. Lunch Special: $46 for 18 holes, cart, $5 lunch voucher. Great views and better greens. "18-hole course with great variety of holes wrapped around Crystal Lake. Lots of elevation changes and doglegs make for interesting round." –JD

	1	2	3	4	5	6	7	8	9
PAR	4	3	4	4	5	5	4	3	4
YARDS	347	165	375	358	535	450	415	170	292
	10	11	12	13	14	15	16	17	18
PAR	4	3	4	4	5	3	4	4	4
YARDS	407	178	295	275	460	130	315	372	353

Directions: 146 North or South to Route 102 West, 8 miles to Crystal Lake on right.

East Greenwich Country Club ✪✪½

8

1646 Division Street
East Greenwich, RI (401) 884-5656
www.eastgreenwichgolfclub.com

Tees	Holes	Yards	Par	USGA	Slope
BACK	9	3315	36		127
MIDDLE	9	3125	36		124
FRONT	9	2875	36		119

Club Pro: Larry Rittmann
Payment: Cash, Visa, MC, Amex
Tee Times: No
Fee 9 Holes: Weekday: $19   **Weekend:** $24
Fee 18 Holes: Weekday: $29   **Weekend:** $34
Twilight Rates: After 5pm   **Discounts:** Senior
Cart Rental: $15pp/18, $12pp/9   **Driving Range:** No
Lessons: Yes **Schools:** Yes   **Junior Golf:** Yes
Membership: Yes   **Architect/Yr Open:** Michael Kroian/1963
Other: Snack Bar / Bar-Lounge / Restaurant   **GPS:**

Rated as one of the more challenging 9-hole courses in N.E. Private club conditions. Fantastic greens, trees, and scenic ponds.

	1	2	3	4	5	6	7	8	9
PAR	4	4	5	4	4	3	5	4	3
YARDS	365	325	500	360	385	160	475	380	175
PAR									
YARDS									

Directions: I-95 to Exit 8 (East Greenwich). Take right off exit (Route 2). Head South for 300 yards to traffic light. Take right (Division Road). Course is ½ mile on left.

Exeter Country Club   ✪✪½ ▶ 9

320 Pen Rod Road
Exeter, RI (401) 295-8212
www.exetercc.com

Club Pro:
Payment: Visa, MC ($15 Minimum)
Tee Times: 1 day adv., call after 8am
Fee 9 Holes: Weekday: $20 M-Th 1pm
Fee 18 Holes: Weekday: $35 walk/$50 ride
Twilight Rates: After 4pm
Cart Rental: $15pp/18, $9pp/9
Lessons: No **Schools:** No
Membership: Yes, waiting list

Tees	Holes	Yards	Par	USGA	Slope
BACK	18	6919	72	72.3	123
MIDDLE	18	6390	72	69.9	116
FRONT	18	5733	72	72.1	115

Weekend: $25 F/S/S/H 3:30pm
Weekend: $40 walk/$55 ride F/S/S/H
Discounts: Junior
Driving Range: $8/lg., $5/med.
Junior Golf: No
Architect/Yr Open: Geoffrey Cornish/1969

Other: Clubhouse / Snack Bar / Lockers / Bar-Lounge / Full Restaurant

Course has a beautiful layout with strategically placed hazards. Wide fairways – bring your driver. Friendly staff. Open March - November. South County course.

	1	2	3	4	5	6	7	8	9
PAR	4	5	3	5	3	4	4	4	4
YARDS	350	530	190	510	180	360	420	370	400
	10	11	12	13	14	15	16	17	18
PAR	4	3	4	4	5	4	4	3	5
YARDS	400	150	330	310	480	350	370	200	490

Directions: I-95 to Route 4 (Exit 5B South) into Exeter (approximately 4-5 miles), take Route 102 North. Course is 2.5 miles on left. From South, take I-95 North to Exit 4. Take Route 3 North, at intersection of Route 102, go right. Course is 5 miles on right side.

Fairlawn Golf Course   NR ▶ 10

3 Sherman Avenue
Lincoln, RI (401) 334-3937
www.fairlawngolfcourse.com

Club Pro:
Payment: Cash Only
Tee Times: No
Fee 9 Holes: Weekday: $13
Fee 18 Holes: Weekday: $18
Twilight Rates:
Cart Rental: $13pp/18; $6.50pp/9
Lessons: No **Schools:** No
Membership: Yes
Other: Clubhouse / Beer and Wine

Tees	Holes	Yards	Par	USGA	Slope
BACK					
MIDDLE	9	2534	27	52.2	N/A
FRONT					

Weekend: $15
Weekend: $20
Discounts: Senior
Driving Range: No
Junior Golf: No
Architect/Yr Open: Adams/1963
GPS:

COUPON

Beautiful and affordable course.

	1	2	3	4	5	6	7	8	9
PAR	3	3	3	3	3	3	3	3	3
YARDS	133	181	121	167	91	110	110	161	193
PAR									
YARDS									

Directions: I-95 North to Route 146 North to Sherman Avenue exit. Course is on right —you can't miss it.

Fenner Hill Golf Club   ✪✪½   11 ▶

33 Wheeler Lane
Hope Valley, RI (401) 539-8000
www.fennerhill.com

Tees	Holes	Yards	Par	USGA	Slope
BACK	18	6636	72	71.4	134
MIDDLE	18	6262	72	70.1	125
FRONT	18	5893	72	68.4	124

Club Pro:
Payment: Visa, MC
Tee Times: 3 days adv.
Fee 9 Holes: Weekday: $21   **Weekend:** $23
Fee 18 Holes: Weekday: $34   **Weekend:** $42
Twilight Rates: After 3pm   **Discounts:** Sr. & Jr. Weekdays
Cart Rental: $16pp/18, $10pp/9 **Driving Range:** No
Lessons: No **Schools:** No   **Junior Golf:** No
Membership: Full, Weekday, Inner Club   **Architect/Yr Open:** Ron & Dennis Levesque/1999
Other: Restaurant / Bar-Lounge / Banquet Facilities / Corporate Outings

Player Comments: "Looks easy from the road, but watch out. Walkable." The beauty of the landscape pleases and challenges all levels. Greens #16 and #18 have been rebuilt. Foxwoods nearby.

	1	2	3	4	5	6	7	8	9
PAR	4	4	5	3	4	3	4	5	4
YARDS	366	347	486	152	352	158	394	520	355
	10	11	12	13	14	15	16	17	18
PAR	5	3	4	4	5	4	3	4	4
YARDS	468	164	440	338	525	309	166	297	425

Directions: I-95 to Exit 2. Bear right to stop sign, take right, ¾ mile on right. I-95 North to Exit 2. From North, left off exit to stop sign. Take a right, ¾ mile on right.

Foster Country Club   ✪✪   12 ▶

67 Johnson Road
Foster, RI (401) 397-7750
www.fostercountryclub.com

Tees	Holes	Yards	Par	USGA	Slope
BACK					
MIDDLE	18	6187	72	71.5	117
FRONT	18	5499	72	70.0	112

Club Pro: Brian Benson
Payment: Visa, MC
Tee Times: 7 days adv.
Fee 9 Holes: Weekday: $17   **Weekend:** $20
Fee 18 Holes: Weekday: $27   **Weekend:** $36
Twilight Rates: After 2pm   **Discounts:** Junior weekdays
Cart Rental: $14pp/18, $7pp/9   **Driving Range:** Practice nets
Lessons: Yes **Schools:** No   **Junior Golf:** No
Membership: Yes   **Architect/Yr Open:** Geoffrey Cornish/1962
Other: Clubhouse / Snack Bar / Restaurant / Bar-Lounge / 180-Seat Banquet Hall

"Friendly atmosphere, nice clubhouse, challenging layout, back nine a bit quirky." –GM

	1	2	3	4	5	6	7	8	9
PAR	4	4	3	5	4	4	3	5	4
YARDS	356	340	241	595	295	425	130	485	310
	10	11	12	13	14	15	16	17	18
PAR	4	4	5	4	5	4	4	3	3
YARDS	405	310	495	375	450	295	315	170	195

Directions: Take I-95 to Route 102 North to Route 14. Left on Route 14 to Moosup Valley Road (on right) to Johnson Road (on right). Follow to course.

Goddard State Park Golf Course NR

Ives Road
Warwick, RI (401) 884-9834
www.riparks.com

Club Pro:
Payment: Cash or Check
Tee Times: No
Fee 9 Holes: Weekday: $12
Fee 18 Holes: Weekday:
Twilight Rates: No
Cart Rental: $15pp/9
Lessons: No **Schools:** No
Membership: No

Tees	Holes	Yards	Par	USGA	Slope
BACK	9	3250	36	34.2	111
MIDDLE	9	3032	36	33.8	109
FRONT					

Weekend: $14
Weekend:
Discounts: Senior ½ price
Driving Range: No
Junior Golf: No
Architect/Yr Open: 1939

Other: Clubhouse / Snack Bar / Picnic Facilities / Beach / Showers

The course, located inside Goddard State Park, is open and very walkable. Horse paths and jogging trails are also available. 300 trees have been added to the course, resulting in more of a challenge.

	1	2	3	4	5	6	7	8	9
PAR	5	4	3	4	5	4	3	4	4
YARDS	503	377	180	292	500	301	168	390	321
PAR									
YARDS									

Directions: I-95 to Route 4 cutoff, take first exit (East Greenwich). Take Route 401 and follow signs to course.

Green Valley Country Club ✪✪½ 14

371 Union Street
Portsmouth, RI (401) 847-9543
www.greenvalleyccofri.com

Club Pro: Gary P. Dorsi, PGA
Payment: Visa, MC, Amex
Tee Times: 3 days adv.
Fee 9 Holes: Weekday:
Fee 18 Holes: Weekday: $38
Twilight Rates: After 3pm
Cart Rental: $16pp/18
Lessons: $35/half hour **Schools:** Yes
Membership: Yes, Junior
Other: Snack Bar / Clubhouse / Outings

Tees	Holes	Yards	Par	USGA	Slope
BACK	18	6830	71	72.1	125
MIDDLE	18	6721	71	71.6	122
FRONT	18	5459	71	69.5	120

Weekend:
Weekend: $48
Discounts: None
Driving Range: $3/bucket
Junior Golf: Yes
Architect/Yr Open: Manuel Raposa/1957
GPS:

Hosted USGA Qualifiers, RI Amateur, RI Open. May book large or small outings. Nice character with old stone walls. Ideal for tournaments and outings and an afternoon of golf.

	1	2	3	4	5	6	7	8	9
PAR	4	4	4	5	3	4	4	3	4
YARDS	361	454	386	541	175	392	354	201	424
	10	11	12	13	14	15	16	17	18
PAR	5	3	3	4	4	4	4	5	4
YARDS	605	220	125	327	440	334	394	540	368

Directions: I-195 to Route 24 South, follow Route 114 South, Raytheon Corp is on right. Take left on Union Street (2nd light after Raytheon Corp.).

RI

Harbor Lights Golf & Country Club ☺☺☺

150 Gray Street
Warwick, RI (401) 737-6353
www.harborlightsri.com

Tees	Holes	Yards	Par	USGA	Slope
BACK	9	2777	36	67.0	118
MIDDLE	9	2488	34	66.3	116
FRONT	9	2152	33	65.8	114

Club Pro: Al Vallante, PGA
Payment: Most Credit Cards
Tee Times: No
Fee 9 Holes: Weekday: $19   **Weekend:** $20
Fee 18 Holes: Weekday: $29   **Weekend:** $31
Twilight Rates: No   **Discounts:** Senior
Cart Rental: $14pp/18, $7pp/9   **Driving Range:** Yes, irons only
Lessons: Yes **Schools:** No   **Junior Golf:** Yes
Membership: Yes   **Architect/Yr Open:** Geoffrey Cornish
Other: Clubhouse / Snack Bar / Bar-Lounge   **GPS:**

The scenic and beautifully manicured Harbor Lights Golf & Country Club is the former Seaview Country Club — reclaimed, redesigned and reconditioned to a quality befitting its prime seaside location.

	1	2	3	4	5	6	7	8	9
PAR	4	4	3	5	3	3	4	4	4
YARDS	313	233	195	501	124	167	286	256	413
PAR									
YARDS									

Directions: From I-95, take Exit 10E onto Route 117 East. Follow Route 117 for 4 miles to Warwick Neck Ave (Sunoco station) on right. Turn onto Warwick Neck Ave for .6 miles to Meadow View Avenue on right. Turn onto Meadow View Avenue and follow the signs to Harbor Lights.

Jamestown Golf Course

245 Conanicus Ave
Jamestown, RI (401) 423-9930
www.jamestowngolf.com

Tees	Holes	Yards	Par	USGA	Slope
BACK	9	3048	36	69.7	110
MIDDLE	9	2751	36	69.7	110
FRONT	9	2421	38		

Club Pro:
Payment: All Types
Tee Times: No
Fee 9 Holes: Weekday: $17   **Weekend:** $19
Fee 18 Holes: Weekday: $27   **Weekend:** $29
Twilight Rates: No   **Discounts:** None
Cart Rental: $12pp/18, $7pp/9   **Driving Range:** No
Lessons: No **Schools:** No   **Junior Golf:** Yes
Membership: No   **Architect/Yr Open:** 1901
Other: Clubhouse / Snack Bar / Bar-Lounge   **GPS:**

Course is completely watered by irrigation. Open April - November.

	1	2	3	4	5	6	7	8	9
PAR	4	5	4	4	3	5	3	4	4
YARDS	270	484	279	375	114	379	141	368	328
PAR									
YARDS									

Directions: I-95 to Route 138 East. Go over Jamestown Bridge. Cross the island and follow signs to the Newport Bridge. When toll booths are in sight, take last exit before toll. Course is on right.

Laurel Lane Country Club ✪✪✪ 17 ►

309 Laurel Lane
West Kingston, RI (401) 783-3844
www.laurellanecountryclub.com

Club Pro: Pat O'Brien
Payment: Cash, Visa, MC, Amex
Tee Times: 7 days adv.
Fee 9 Holes: Weekday: $23
Fee 18 Holes: Weekday: $33
Twilight Rates: After 2pm
Cart Rental: $18pp/18, $10pp/9
Lessons: Yes **Schools:** Jr.
Membership: Yes
Other: Clubhouse / Snack Bar / Bar-Lounge

Tees	Holes	Yards	Par	USGA	Slope
BACK	18	6177	71	69.1	124
MIDDLE	18	6010	71	67.8	117
FRONT	18	4966	70	69.2	120

Weekend: $25
Weekend: $38
Discounts: Senior & Junior
Driving Range: Yes
Junior Golf: Yes
Architect/Yr Open: Holley, Sr., Thoren, Bota/1961
GPS:

COUPON

Fun course for all. Easy to walk. Excellent greens. Friendly staff. Fabulous practice facilities including driving range, 4 tier putting green, chipping area and bunkers. Check out the restaurant — great food!

	1	2	3	4	5	6	7	8	9
PAR	4	5	3	4	4	4	3	4	4
YARDS	410	470	177	362	347	236	207	363	372
	10	11	12	13	14	15	16	17	18
PAR	4	4	4	4	4	3	5	3	5
YARDS	390	306	319	340	384	150	475	162	540

Directions: I-95 to Exit 3A. Go approximately 6 miles east on Route 138. Right on Laurel Lane.

Lindhbrook Golf Course NR 18 ►

299 Woodville Alton Road
Hope Valley, RI (401) 539-8700

Club Pro: Bill Patnoad
Payment: Visa, MC, Amex
Tee Times: Yes
Fee 9 Holes: Weekday: $15
Fee 18 Holes: Weekday: $20
Twilight Rates: After 5:30pm
Cart Rental: $18pp/18, $12pp/9
Lessons: Yes **Schools:** No
Membership: Yes
Other: Snack Bar / Restaurant / Bar-Lounge

Tees	Holes	Yards	Par	USGA	Slope
BACK	18	3000	54		
MIDDLE	18	2869	54		
FRONT	18	2600	54		

Weekend: $15
Weekend: $25
Discounts: Senior & Junior
Driving Range: No
Junior Golf: Yes
Architect/Yr Open: 1954
GPS:

South County course.

	1	2	3	4	5	6	7	8	9
PAR	3	3	3	3	3	3	3	3	3
YARDS	132	146	171	172	150	168	158	175	125
	10	11	12	13	14	15	16	17	18
PAR	3	3	3	3	3	3	3	3	3
YARDS	139	143	127	180	181	192	143	183	184

Directions: I-95 to Exit 2. If Northbound, bear right; if Southbound, turn left. Course 800 yards from I-95 on right.

RI

Meadow Brook ✪✪✪✪ 19 ▶

163 Kingstown Road
Richmond, RI (401) 539-8491
www.meadowbrookgolfri.com

Tees	Holes	Yards	Par	USGA	Slope
BACK	18	7468	72	74.4	130
MIDDLE	18	6532	72	69.9	119
FRONT	18	5308	72	68.9	117

Club Pro: John Grimley, PGA
Payment: Visa, MC
Tee Times: 2 days adv.
Fee 9 Holes: Weekday:
Fee 18 Holes: Weekday: $60 (with cart)
Twilight Rates: Available
Cart Rental: Included
Lessons: Yes **Schools:** No
Membership: No
Other: Clubhouse / Restaurant / Bar-Lounge

Weekend:
Weekend: $70 (with cart) S/S
Discounts: Senior
Driving Range: No
Junior Golf: No
Architect/Yr Open: Rulewich & Fleury/2010
GPS:

Located 2 miles off of I-95 on Route 138. Meadow Brook is 30 minutes from Providence, the beaches and the casinos. Stretching over 7400 yards, Meadow Brook is the longest golf course in RI. Beautiful yet challenging and playable for golfers at all levels offering 5 sets of tees.

	1	2	3	4	5	6	7	8	9
PAR	4	5	4	3	4	3	4	5	4
YARDS	374	486	359	178	432	139	371	506	361
	10	11	12	13	14	15	16	17	18
PAR	3	4	5	4	4	5	4	3	4
YARDS	151	376	538	362	399	569	404	159	368

Directions: I-95 to Exit 3A in RI. Continue on Route 138 East. Course is 1 mile east of I-95.

Melody Hill Golf Course NR 20 ▶

55 Melody Hill Lane
Harmony, RI (401) 949-9851
www.melodyhillcc.com

Tees	Holes	Yards	Par	USGA	Slope
BACK	18	6004	71	68.4	109
MIDDLE	18	5801	71	67.5	108
FRONT	18	5363	71	70.4	113

Club Pro:
Payment: Cash Only
Tee Times: No
Fee 9 Holes: Weekday: $19
Fee 18 Holes: Weekday: $27
Twilight Rates: $18 after 4pm; $16 after 5pm
Cart Rental: $28/18, $14/9 per cart
Lessons: Yes **Schools:** No
Membership: Limited
Other: Clubhouse / Snack Bar / Bar-Lounge

Weekend: $20
Weekend: $31
Discounts: Senior $21pp/18, $17pp/9 (M-F)
Driving Range: No
Junior/Senior Golf: Senior Rates
Architect/Yr Open: Sam Mitchell/1967
GPS:

Lessons by certified teacher of golf. Twilight rates: 9 holes only $15 after 5pm weekdays; $17 after 4pm weekends. Seniors M-F 9 holes $17, 18 holes $21.

	1	2	3	4	5	6	7	8	9
PAR	4	4	4	3	4	3	4	5	4
YARDS	360	315	385	95	465	145	425	500	235
	10	11	12	13	14	15	16	17	18
PAR	5	4	5	3	4	3	4	4	4
YARDS	445	405	535	185	360	165	355	400	410

Directions: Route 44 West toward CT, take first left after fire station in Harmony Center onto Saw Mill Road.

Midville Country Club

100 Lombardi Lane
West Warwick, RI (401) 828-9215
www.midvillegolfclub.com

Club Pro:
Payment: Visa, MC, Disc
Tee Times: No

Tees	Holes	Yards	Par	USGA	Slope
BACK	9	2970	35	68.3	115
MIDDLE	9	2779	35	68.2	114
FRONT	9	2340	35		

Fee 9 Holes: Weekday: $25   **Weekend:** $26
Fee 18 Holes: Weekday: $37   **Weekend:** $41
Twilight Rates: No
Discounts: Senior & Junior (before 2pm wkdy, after 2pm wknd)
Cart Rental: $18pp/18, $9pp/9, pull cart: $2   **Driving Range:** No
Lessons: No **Schools:** No   **Junior Golf:** Yes
Membership: No   **Architect/Yr Open:** Carmine Lombardi/1962
Other: Clubhouse / Snack Bar / Bar-Lounge   **GPS:**

Scenic 9-hole layout. Well-conditioned public course. April - December.

	1	2	3	4	5	6	7	8	9
PAR	4	4	4	4	3	5	3	4	4
YARDS	335	395	335	345	145	523	145	290	335
PAR									
YARDS									

Directions: I-95 to Route 113 West exit. Go straight through 3 sets of lights. Cross bridge, bear right and then straight through the 4th light. Course is 1 mile on left.

Montaup Country Club

500 Anthony Road
Portsmouth, RI (401) 683-0955
www.montaupcc.com

Club Pro: Steve Diemoz
Payment: Cash, Visa, MC, Check
Tee Times: 3 days adv.

Tees	Holes	Yards	Par	USGA	Slope
BACK	18	6321	71	70.3	126
MIDDLE	18	5807	71	68.3	123
FRONT	18	5359	73	71.4	118

Fee 9 Holes: Weekday: **Weekend:**
Fee 18 Holes: Weekday: $47   **Weekend:** $47
Twilight Rates: After 3:30pm wknds only   **Discounts:** None
Cart Rental: $19pp/18   **Driving Range:** No
Lessons: Yes **Schools:** No   **Junior Golf:** Yes
Membership: No   **Architect/Yr Open:** 1923
Other: Clubhouse / Snack Bar / Restaurant / Bar-Lounge

Player Comments: "Always in excellent shape and great to walk." "Excellent greens, lots of room to hit away." Open April - December.

	1	2	3	4	5	6	7	8	9
PAR	4	4	3	4	5	4	5	3	4
YARDS	414	405	213	386	503	351	521	145	339
	10	11	12	13	14	15	16	17	18
PAR	3	4	3	5	3	4	5	4	4
YARDS	154	398	184	503	163	424	519	399	300

Directions: Exit 3 from Route 24 South, left on Anthony Road to entrance. Exit 4 from 24 North, left on Boyd Lane, right on Anthony Road to entrance.

RI

Newport National Golf Club ✪✪✪✪

324 Mitchell's Lane
Middletown, RI (401) 848-9690
www.newportnational.com

Club Pro: Andy Farrea
Payment: Cash, All Major Cards
Tee Times: 7 days adv.

Tees	Holes	Yards	Par	USGA	Slope
BACK	18	7244	72	74.4	138
MIDDLE	18	6553	72	71.9	130
FRONT	18	5217	71	68.8	119

Fee 9 Holes: Weekday:
Fee 18 Holes: Weekday: $65 w/cart
Twilight Rates: After 1pm
Cart Rental: Included
Lessons: Yes **Schools:** No
Membership: Yes
Other: Restaurant / Bar-Lounge

Weekend:
Weekend: $95 w/cart
Discounts: No
Driving Range: None
Junior Golf: Yes
Architect/Yr Open: Arthur Hill, Drew Rogers/2002
GPS:

Named the "Best Course that You Can Play" by *Golf Digest, Golf Week* and *Golf Magazine* for Rhode Island.
#1 slope and rated course in the State.

	1	2	3	4	5	6	7	8	9
PAR	5	4	3	3	4	4	4	5	4
YARDS	486	400	168	154	296	449	444	495	348
	10	11	12	13	14	15	16	17	18
PAR	4	5	4	3	5	4	3	4	4
YARDS	383	505	326	148	523	396	212	439	381

Directions: I-195 to MA Route 24 South or RI 138 or RI 114 South. Follow signs to Newport.
Take 138 South (East Main Road) through Portsmouth. Watch for Mitchell's Lane on the left.
Newport Airport? You went too far.

North Kingstown Munipal GC ✪✪✪

615 Callahan Road
North Kingstown, RI (401) 294-0684
www.nkgc.com

Club Pro: John Rainone, Head Pro
Payment: Cash, Visa, MC
Tee Times: 2 days adv.

Tees	Holes	Yards	Par	USGA	Slope
BACK	18	6161	70	69.3	123
MIDDLE	18	5848	70	67.8	121
FRONT	18	5227	70	69.5	115

Fee 9 Holes: Weekday: $23
Fee 18 Holes: Weekday: $31
Twilight Rates: $23 after 4pm (weekends only)
Discounts: Senior
Cart Rental: $32/18, $18/9 per cart
Lessons: Yes **Schools:** Yes
Membership: Yes
Other: Restaurant / Lounge / Clubhouse

Weekend: $23
Weekend: $39

Driving Range: $8/lg, $5/sm
Junior Golf: Yes
Architect/Yr Open: Walter Johnson/1943
GPS:

COUPON

Player Comments: "Just plain enjoyable. Redefines what a muncipal can be." Hosted 2006 US Open
Qualifier. Links-style overlooking Narragansett Bay. South County course.

	1	2	3	4	5	6	7	8	9
PAR	4	4	3	5	4	4	5	3	4
YARDS	369	411	185	499	375	353	545	197	283
	10	11	12	13	14	15	16	17	18
PAR	3	5	4	4	3	4	4	4	3
YARDS	171	559	333	403	194	413	398	315	158

Directions: I-95 South to Route 45. Exit 7A off Route 45 (403E). Follow approximately 4.5 miles.
Go left at 1st light. First right. Clubhouse on the right.

Pinecrest Golf Course ✪✪½ ▶ 25

25 Pinehurst Drive
Carolina, RI (401) 364-8600
www.pinecrestri.com

Tees	Holes	Yards	Par	USGA	Slope
BACK	9	2900	35	67.7	131
MIDDLE	9	2611	35	66.2	123
FRONT	9	2309	35	69.4	123

Club Pro: Joseph Scott
Payment: Visa, MC, Personal Cks, Cash
Tee Times: 4 day adv./Wed. for nonmembers
Fee 9 Holes: Weekday: $20   **Weekend:** $22
Fee 18 Holes: Weekday: $30   **Weekend:** $32
Twilight Rates: After 3pm   **Discounts:** Senior & Junior
Cart Rental: $13pp/18, $8pp/9   **Driving Range:** No
Lessons: No **Schools:** No   **Junior Golf:** No
Membership: Yes
Architect/Yr Open: Beakman-Wermy/Intergolf Design/2002
Other: Bar / Grille / Clubhouse

COUPON

"Short 9 holes with one par 5. Very playable for all levels of golfing ability. 2nd is the signature hole." –RW

	1	2	3	4	5	6	7	8	9
PAR	4	4	4	5	3	4	4	3	4
YARDS	320	385	348	540	129	382	337	145	314

PAR									
YARDS									

Directions: I-95 to Exit 3 to Route 138 East to Route 112. 2.4 miles to Pinehurst Drive on left.

RI

Richmond Country Club ✪✪✪ ▶ 26

74 Sandy Pond Road
Richmond, RI (401) 364-9200
www.richmondcountryclub.net

Tees	Holes	Yards	Par	USGA	Slope
BACK	18	6515	71	69.9	117
MIDDLE	18	5827	71	68.5	114
FRONT	18	4974	71	70.4	113

Club Pro: Jonathan Rapoza
Payment: Visa, MC
Tee Times: 3 days adv.
Fee 9 Holes: Weekday: $18 after 3pm   **Weekend:**
Fee 18 Holes: Weekday: $35   **Weekend:** $40
Twilight Rates: After 3pm   **Discounts:** Senior & Junior
Cart Rental: $15pp/18   **Driving Range:** Yes
Lessons: Yes **Schools:** No   **Junior Golf:** Yes
Membership: No   **Architect/Yr Open:** Cornish & Silva/1992
Other: Restaurant / Clubhouse / Bar-Lounge / Banquet Facilities

Player Comments: "Plush fairways. Pure greens. Aesthetically pleasant." South County course.
Look for new tee box locations for more challenging play.

	1	2	3	4	5	6	7	8	9
PAR	4	4	3	5	3	4	5	4	4
YARDS	318	353	204	504	165	428	450	277	285
	10	11	12	13	14	15	16	17	18
PAR	4	5	3	4	4	3	5	3	4
YARDS	320	431	184	408	368	176	474	154	328

Directions: I-95 to Exit 3B; follow 2 miles. Left at flashing light onto Mechanic Street. Go 2.5 miles,
turn right onto Sandy Pond Road.

Rolling Greens Golf Course

NR **27**▶

1625 Pen Rod Road
North Kingstown, RI (401) 294-9859
www.rollinggreensri.com

Tees	Holes	Yards	Par	USGA	Slope
BACK					
MIDDLE	9	3072	35		
FRONT					

Club Pro:
Payment: Cash, Credit Cards
Tee Times: No
Fee 9 Holes: Weekday: $18   **Weekend:** $20
Fee 18 Holes: Weekday: $24   **Weekend:** $26
Twilight Rates: No   **Discounts:** No
Cart Rental: $20pp/18, $12pp/9   **Driving Range:** No
Lessons: No **Schools:** No   **Junior Golf:** No
Membership: Yes   **Architect/Yr Open:** 1969
Other: Clubhouse / Snack Bar / Restaurant / Bar-Lounge

The course is hilly and has just 1 water hole. South County course.

	1	2	3	4	5	6	7	8	9
PAR	4	4	4	3	5	4	4	3	4
YARDS	339	353	383	147	550	325	315	220	440
PAR									
YARDS									

Directions: I-95 to Route 4, North Kingston. Get onto Route 102 West toward Exeter. Course is 1.25 miles on right.

Rose Hill Golf Club

★★ **28**▶

222 Rose Hill Road
Wakefield, RI (401) 788-1088
www.rosehillri.com

Tees	Holes	Yards	Par	USGA	Slope
BACK	9	1206	27		
MIDDLE	9	1206	27		
FRONT	9	981	27		

Club Pro:
Payment: Visa, MC
Tee Times: No
Fee 9 Holes: Weekday: $12   **Weekend:** $12
Fee 18 Holes: Weekday: $18   **Weekend:** $18
Twilight Rates: No   **Discounts:** Senior & Junior
Cart Rental: $10pp/9, $15pp/18, $3 pullcart   **Driving Range:** No
Lessons: Yes **Schools:** Sr. & Jr. **Junior Golf:** Yes
Membership: Yes   **Architect/Yr Open:** Beckman, Weremay/2001
Other: New Bistro / Restaurant / Pub / Clubhouse / League Play

COUPON

"Sophisticated design for a 9-holer that circles a pond situated in the middle of the course. Excellent greens." –RW Family-friendly environment. South County course.

	1	2	3	4	5	6	7	8	9
PAR	3	3	3	3	3	3	3	3	3
YARDS	144	140	74	101	143	168	129	178	129
PAR									
YARDS									

Directions: Route 1 to Route 138 West 2.5 miles, and turn left onto Rose Hill Road. Course is 9/10 mile on right.

I Want More Distance
NOW!!
ROCK SOLID SET-UP

First things first. We need to ensure that your set-up is rock solid, and this includes your thought process on the tee box.

- Chin up, not pinned.

- Arms hang down tension-free with shoulders in line with toes.

- The right bend from hip joints, not waist, creating athletic angles in my hip crease and knees.

- Shaft pointing to belt buckle ensuring I am the correct distance from ball.

- Pressure points in feet favoring the balls of my feet.

EXCERPT FROM GOLF AUTHOR CHRISTINA RICCI'S
SHINY NEW YELLOW BOOK!
www.golfsurvivalguide.com

YES

The L of my right elbow is still intact. My legs are driving the downswing with my hands and arms following.

Pressure point moves toward front toe.

once you reach hip height

My shoulder plane is still intact. Once I hit hip height, I release the L hard through impact.

Using the ground as leverage, I am driving into the ground with my front leg.

ANGLES EQUAL POWER

YES

My angles are intact and ready to unleash!

MAINTAIN THOSE ANGLES UNTIL LAUNCH TIME

EXPLODE!

My right arm crosses over my left. My left palm is facing toward the sky and my left arm is STILL connected to my upper chest.

RELEASE LET IT GO!

A GOOD RELEASE IS A RESULT OF DOING EVERYTHING ELSE RIGHT!

3

Finish for POWER!!

Aggressively getting to your finish is the secret to power, assuming you have loaded in the backswing.

YES

My right shoulder has completely rotated through the shot.

BELT FACING LEFT OF TARGET →

Back foot completely on its toe, indicating a successful weight transfer.

Pressure point on the outside of my front heel.

A Girl's On-Course Survival Guide to Golf Series
Jam-Packed Instructional From Tee to Green and In-Between

A BRAND NEW BOOK

CHRISTINA RICCI

More Pars = More Fun!

Triggs Memorial Golf Course ✪✪✪

1533 Chalkstone Avenue
Providence, RI (401) 521-8460
www.triggs.us

Club Pro: Mike Ryan, PGA
Payment: Visa, MC, Cash
Tee Times: 2 weeks adv.

Tees	Holes	Yards	Par	USGA	Slope
BACK	18	6522	72	72.8	128
MIDDLE	18	6302	72	71.7	125
FRONT	18	5392	72	73.1	123

Fee 9 Holes: Weekday: $23
Fee 18 Holes: Weekday: $38
Twilight Rates: No
Cart Rental: $18pp/18, $9pp/9
Lessons: No **Schools:** No
Membership: Yes
Other: Full Kitchen and Lounge

Weekend: $23
Weekend: $40
Discounts: Senior $23/18 weekday
Driving Range: No
Junior Golf: Yes
Architect/Yr Open: Donald Ross/1933
GPS:

Player Comments: "Solid layout. No easy holes, quick greens, very challenging. Course maintenance has improved." Classic Ross design.

	1	2	3	4	5	6	7	8	9
PAR	4	4	4	3	4	5	3	4	4
YARDS	379	411	445	184	316	437	185	332	391
	10	11	12	13	14	15	16	17	18
PAR	5	4	3	5	3	5	4	4	4
YARDS	502	340	195	447	140	496	302	401	399

Directions: I-95 to Exit 23. Go right at exit. Right on Douglas Avenue. First red light is Chalkstone, turn left. Go 2 miles. I-95 South take Exit 21. Right onto Atwell at light, right at Dean Street, at 5th light, take left onto Chalkstone. Go 1.5 miles.

West Warwick Country Club, The

335 Wakefield Street
West Warwick, RI
(401) 821-9789

Club Pro:
Payment: Most Major
Tee Times: No

Tees	Holes	Yards	Par	USGA	Slope
BACK					
MIDDLE	9	3015	35	67.6	120
FRONT					

Fee 9 Holes: Weekday: $25
Fee 18 Holes: Weekday: $39
Twilight Rates: No
Cart Rental: $16pp/18, $8pp/9
Lessons: No **Schools:** No
Membership: Yes
Other: Bar-Lounge / Snacks / Restaurant / Banquet Facilities

Weekend: $25
Weekend: $39
Discounts: None
Driving Range: No
Junior Golf: No
Architect/Yr Open: McGregor/1941

Road divides course: First 4 holes are hilly, back 5 are parallel and flat. Public play limited to weekends after 2:30pm.

	1	2	3	4	5	6	7	8	9
PAR	4	4	3	4	4	4	4	3	5
YARDS	419	338	140	390	360	363	333	162	510
PAR									
YARDS									

Directions: I-95 to Route 113 West for 1 mile. At intersection of Route 2, go straight through onto East Avenue for ½ mile. Turn right onto River Street for ¼ mile. River Street becomes Wakefield Street at light. Club is 1.5 miles up on top of hill.

Windmill Hill Golf Course

NR 31 ►

35 Schoolhouse Road
Warren, RI (401) 245-1463
www.windmillgolfri.com

Tees	Holes	Yards	Par	USGA	Slope
BACK	9	1432	27		
MIDDLE	9	1191	27		
FRONT	9	891	27		

Club Pro:
Payment: Most Major
Tee Times:
Fee 9 Holes: Weekday: $12
Fee 18 Holes: Weekday: $19
Twilight Rates: No
Cart Rental: $14/18, $7/9 per cart
Lessons: Yes **Schools:** No
Membership: Yes, $650

Weekend: $12
Weekend: $19
Discounts: Senior & Junior
Driving Range: No
Junior Golf: No
Architect/Yr Open: Beckman, Weremay/2000

COUPON

Other: Clubhouse / Showers / Restaurant / Bar-Lounge / Banquet Facilities / Decks

Pleasant challenge for all levels. Course makes you use all your clubs. Lush greens and fairways.

	1	2	3	4	5	6	7	8	9
PAR	3	3	3	3	3	3	3	3	3
YARDS	116	160	193	136	164	133	218	133	128
PAR									
YARDS									

Directions: I-195 to Exit 2 to Route 136 South. Follow 136 South for 2 miles and turn left onto Schoolhouse Road. Entrance is .3 miles on right.

Winnapaug Golf Course

✪✪ 32 ►

184 Shore Road
Westerly, RI (401) 596-1237
www.winnapaugcountryclub.com

Tees	Holes	Yards	Par	USGA	Slope
BACK	18	6361	72	70.6	124
MIDDLE	18	5944	72	68.6	119
FRONT	18	5183	72	69.2	118

Club Pro: Jeff Beaupre, PGA
Payment: Cash, Check, Charge
Tee Times: 1 week adv.
Fee 9 Holes: Weekday: $20
Fee 18 Holes: Weekday: $40
Twilight Rates: After 4pm
Cart Rental: $16pp/18, $9pp/9
Lessons: Yes **Schools:** Yes
Membership: Yes

Weekend:
Weekend: $60 w/cart & lunch (June)
Discounts: Senior & Junior
Driving Range: Practice range
Junior Golf: No
Architect/Yr Open: Donald Ross/1922

Other: Clubhouse / Restaurant / Bar-Lounge / Beverage Cart

Donald Ross design with tight, short fairways and demanding greens. Open year-round. South County course. New green on #1, 30 yards longer. Close to the Misquamicot Beaches.

	1	2	3	4	5	6	7	8	9
PAR	4	5	3	4	4	3	4	4	5
YARDS	319	484	156	402	270	106	344	322	508
	10	11	12	13	14	15	16	17	18
PAR	4	4	3	5	4	5	3	4	4
YARDS	395	348	141	472	383	451	140	376	302

Directions: I-95 to Exit 92, take right onto Route 2, follow to Route 78, follow signs for beaches. Turn left onto Route 1A, course is 1 mile on left.

Wood River Golf

78A Woodville Alton Road
Hope Valley, RI (401) 364-0700
www.woodrivergolf.com

Tees	Holes	Yards	Par	USGA	Slope
BACK					
MIDDLE	18	5273	69		
FRONT	18	4452	69		

Club Pro:
Payment: Cash, Checks, Credit Cards
Tee Times: No
Fee 9 Holes: Weekday: $14 (11 holes)
Fee 18 Holes: Weekday: $22, $30 all day
Twilight Rates: After 3pm
Cart Rental: $16 per cart, $10pp
Lessons: Schools:
Membership: No
Other: Pub and Restaurant / Clubhouse

Weekend: $14 (11 holes)
Weekend: $22
Discounts: None
Driving Range: No
Junior Golf: No
Architect/Yr Open: Weston Thompson/2000
GPS:

COUPON

Natural setting, links-style course. South county course. Improvements on 15th, 16th, 17th. Course more user-friendly. 20 minutes from local beaches and casino.

	1	2	3	4	5	6	7	8	9
PAR	5	3	4	3	5	4	3	4	4
YARDS	453	152	332	185	445	315	217	331	315
	10	11	12	13	14	15	16	17	18
PAR	3	4	4	4	4	4	4	4	3
YARDS	153	305	315	300	265	400	330	305	155

Directions: I-95 to Exit 2. Go 3.5 miles along Woodville Alton Road, course is on the left.

Woodland Greens Golf Club

655 Old Baptist Road
North Kingstown, RI (401) 294-2872
www.woodlandgc.com

Tees	Holes	Yards	Par	USGA	Slope
BACK					
MIDDLE	9	3023	35	69.2	126
FRONT	9	2872	35	68.3	124

Club Pro:
Payment: Visa, MC
Tee Times: No
Fee 9 Holes: Weekday: $21
Fee 18 Holes: Weekday: $28
Twilight Rates: No
Cart Rental: $32/18, $16/9 per cart
Lessons: No **Schools:** No
Membership: Yes
Other: Snack Bar / Bar-Lounge

Weekend: $23
Weekend: $31
Discounts: Senior M-F, 7am-1pm
Driving Range: No
Junior Golf: No
Architect/Yr Open: Geoffrey Cornish/1963
GPS:

Player Comments: "The course has tight fairways and fast greens." Open March - December. South County course.

	1	2	3	4	5	6	7	8	9
PAR	4	5	3	5	3	4	4	3	4
YARDS	360	413	198	505	152	330	297	203	414
PAR									
YARDS									

Directions: I-95 to Route 4 South. Take left at 2nd light onto Stony Lane. At 1st intersection take left onto Old Baptist Road. Course is ⅛ mile on left.

RI

Champlain Country Club	13
Copley Country Club	14
Country Club of Barre	15
Crown Point CC	16
Enosburg Falls CC	17
Equinox Golf Club	18
Essex Country Club	19
Green Mt. National GC	20
Hermitage Golf Club	21
Jay Peak Resort GC	22
John P. Larkin CC	23
Killington Golf Course	24
Kwiniaska Golf Club	25
Lake Morey CC	26
Lake St. Catherine CC	27
Links at Lang Farm	28
Montague Golf Club	39
Montpelier Elks CC	30
Mt. Anthony CC	31
Mount Snow Golf Club	32
Neshobe Golf Club	33
Newport CC	34
Northfield CC	35

Okemo Valley GC	36
Orleans Country Club	37
Proctor Pittsford CC	38
Prospect Bay CC	39
Ralph Myhre GC	40
Richford CC	41
Rocky Ridge GC	42
Rutland CC	43
Ryder Brook Golf Club	44
Sitzmark GC	45
St. Johnsbury CC	46
Stamford Valley CC	47
Stonehedge GC	48
Stowe Country Club	49
Stratton Mountain	50
Sugarbush Resort Golf Club	51
Tater Hill Golf Club	52
West Bolton Golf Club	53
White River Golf Club	54
Wilcox Cove GC	55
Williston Golf Club	56
Woodbury GC	57
Woodstock Inn	58

Alburg Golf Links	1
Apple Island Resort GC	2
Arrowhead GC	3
Bakersfield CC	4
Barton Golf Club	5
Basin Harbor Club	6
Bellows Falls CC	7
Blush Hill CC	8
Bradford Golf Course	9
Brattleboro CC	10
Catamount Golf Club	11
Cedar Knoll CC	12

KEY TO THE STAR RATINGS:
5✪ = Outstanding   4✪ = Excellent   3✪ = Very Good   2✪ = Good   1✪ = Average   **NR** = Not Rated

Alburg Golf Links   ✪✪   ▶ 1

230 Route 129
Alburg, VT (802) 796-4248
www.alburggolflinks.com

Club Pro: Mike Engberg, PGA
Payment: Visa, MC, Personal Checks, Cash
Tee Times: 7 days adv.
Fee 9 Holes: Weekday: $23
Fee 18 Holes: Weekday: $40
Twilight Rates: After 2pm
Cart Rental: $16pp/18, $11pp/9
Lessons: Yes **Schools:** Yes
Membership: Yes
Other: Clubhouse / Restaurant / Bar-Lounge / Club Rental

Tees	Holes	Yards	Par	USGA	Slope
BACK	18	6493	72	70.1	121
MIDDLE	18	5877	72	67.3	115
FRONT	18	5041	72	66.4	105

Weekend: $20
Weekend: $48
Discounts: Junior, ½ price w/adult
Driving Range: $7 Lg., $4 Sm.
Junior Golf: Yes
Architect/Yr Open: Dick Ellison/1967

COUPON

A good vacation course, challenging and very friendly.

	1	2	3	4	5	6	7	8	9
PAR	4	4	4	4	3	4	5	3	4
YARDS	310	378	385	290	130	396	460	140	370
	10	11	12	13	14	15	16	17	18
PAR	5	3	4	5	4	4	3	5	4
YARDS	475	167	405	472	296	286	140	487	340

Directions: Take I-89 to Exit 17; take Route 2 to Champlain Islands North to Alburg; take Route 129 to course.

Apple Island Resort Golf Course   NR   ▶ 2

VT

71 Route 2
South Hero, VT (802) 372-9600
www.appleislandresort.com/golf.html

Club Pro:
Payment: Cash, Checks
Tee Times: No
Fee 9 Holes: Weekday: $14.75
Fee 18 Holes: Weekday:
Twilight Rates: After 5:30pm
Cart Rental: $2/pull
Lessons: No **Schools:** No
Membership: Yes
Other: Resort

Tees	Holes	Yards	Par	USGA	Slope
BACK					
MIDDLE	9	1108	27		
FRONT					

Weekend: $16.75
Weekend:
Discounts: None
Driving Range: No
Junior Golf: No
Architect/Yr Open: Walter Barcomb/1977
GPS:

Course in great shape and all tees have been redone. No one under 5 years allowed. Open May 1 - October 20. Extended tee off boxes holes #3 & #5.

	1	2	3	4	5	6	7	8	9
PAR	3	3	3	3	3	3	3	3	3
YARDS	100	90	158	184	158	108	84	96	130
PAR									
YARDS									

Directions: Exit 17 off I-89. Go 6 miles, course on left. Must drive through campground to reach course.

Arrowhead Golf Course ✪✪ ▶3

350 Murray Avenue
Milton, VT (802) 893-0234
www.arrowheadvt.com

Tees	Holes	Yards	Par	USGA	Slope
BACK	9	1542	27	56.6	80
MIDDLE	9	1330	27	56.0	79
FRONT	9	1005	27	48.8	55

Club Pro:
Payment: Cash, Check, Credit
Tee Times: No
Fee 9 Holes: Weekday: $14   **Weekend:** $16
Fee 18 Holes: Weekday: $18   **Weekend:** $20
Twilight Rates: No   **Discounts:** None
Cart Rental: $10pp/18, $7pp/9   **Driving Range:** $7/lg., $4/sm. bucket
Lessons: No **Schools:** No   **Junior Golf:** No
Membership: Yes, $215   **Architect/Yr Open:** T.F. Goodwin/1997
Other: Clubhouse   **GPS:**

This 9-hole, par 3 golf course consists of gently rolling fairways, unique design characteristics, excellent greens, sand bunkers, water hazards, and natural hazards. 3rd hole is very challenging. New range mats.

	1	2	3	4	5	6	7	8	9
PAR	3	3	3	3	3	3	3	3	3
YARDS	165	148	195	90	119	195	136	104	178
PAR									
YARDS									

Directions: Exit 18 from I-89. Go south on Route 7 approximately ½ mile. Turn right onto Ballard Road for ½ mile, take left onto Old Stage Road for 1 mile, then right onto Murray Avenue for 1.6 miles. Course is on left.

Bakersfield Country Club NR ▶4

Boston Post Road
Bakersfield, VT (802) 933-5100

Tees	Holes	Yards	Par	USGA	Slope
BACK	18	6222	72		
MIDDLE	18	5881	72	69.0	115
FRONT	18	5006	72	68.7	108

Club Pro:
Payment: Visa, MC, Amex
Tee Times: Yes
Fee 9 Holes: Weekday: $18   **Weekend:** $18
Fee 18 Holes: Weekday: $23   **Weekend:** $26
Twilight Rates: After 4:15pm   **Discounts:** None
Cart Rental: $13pp/18, $8pp/9   **Driving Range:** No
Lessons: Inquire **Schools:** No   **Junior Golf:** No
Membership: Junior   **Architect/Yr Open:** John Watson/1987
Other: Snack Bar / Restaurant / Bar-Lounge   **GPS:**

	1	2	3	4	5	6	7	8	9
PAR	4	4	5	3	4	3	4	5	4
YARDS	273	357	424	128	445	155	350	460	375
	10	11	12	13	14	15	16	17	18
PAR	4	3	4	4	5	3	5	3	5
YARDS	360	155	345	290	468	150	392	155	599

Directions: Route 108 through Bakersfield. Take right onto Boston Post Road. Follow signs.

Barton Golf Club ✪✪ 5

548 Telfer Hill Road
Barton, VT (802) 525-1126
www.bartongolfclub.com

Club Pro: Bill King
Payment: Visa, MC, Disc
Tee Times: Yes
Fee 9 Holes: Weekday: $13
Fee 18 Holes: Weekday: $21
Twilight Rates: After 6pm
Cart Rental: $14pp/18, $7pp/9
Lessons: No **Schools:** No
Membership: Yes
Other: Light Fare Menu

Tees	Holes	Yards	Par	USGA	Slope
BACK	18	6000	70	66.8	114
MIDDLE	18	5304	70	65.3	104
FRONT	18	4500	69		

Weekend: $13
Weekend: $21
Discounts: None
Driving Range: No
Junior Golf: No
Architect/Yr Open: Brian King/1991
GPS:

COUPON

Scenic 18 holes in the heart of Vermont's Northeast Kingdom. New layout due to the replacement of 7 holes. Spectacular views.

	1	2	3	4	5	6	7	8	9
PAR	4	5	4	3	4	4	3	5	4
YARDS	256	465	303	120	304	396	160	440	365
	10	11	12	13	14	15	16	17	18
PAR	4	3	5	4	3	3	5	3	4
YARDS	268	130	450	385	140	150	502	135	335

Directions: I-91 to Exit 25. Take Route 16 into Barton. Go right on Water Street. Cross Route 5. Left on High Street. Club is 1 mile on right.

Basin Harbor Club ✪✪✪ 6   VT

4800 Basin Harbor Road
Vergennes, VT (802) 475-2309
www.basinharbor.com

Club Pro: Paul Meunier, PGA
Payment: Visa, MC
Tee Times: Anytime for current season
Fee 9 Holes: Weekday: $36
Fee 18 Holes: Weekday: $50
Twilight Rates: After 12pm
Cart Rental: $20pp/18, $13pp/9
Lessons: $40/half hour **Schools:** Yes
Membership: Yes
Other: Clubhouse / Snack Bar / Restaurant / Bar-Lounge / Hotel

Tees	Holes	Yards	Par	USGA	Slope
BACK	18	6567	72	71.6	126
MIDDLE	18	6243	72	70.0	123
FRONT	18	5053	72	68.3	111

Weekend: $36
Weekend: $50
Discounts: No
Driving Range: $6 sm./$10 lg.
Junior Golf: No
Architect/Yr Open: Alex Campbell/1927

Fairly flat, located on Lake Champlain. Collared shirt required. No cutoffs. Open May 1 - mid-October. 18-hole rate reduced after 1pm, free cart after 3. New women's tee boxes. Improved playability through bunker work, tree removal and tees. Resort guests have reduced rates.

	1	2	3	4	5	6	7	8	9
PAR	4	4	4	4	3	4	3	4	5
YARDS	350	360	395	308	100	345	156	435	498
	10	11	12	13	14	15	16	17	18
PAR	4	4	5	3	4	4	3	5	4
YARDS	391	379	495	180	344	418	172	509	410

Directions: Route 7 to Vergennes exit. Straight through town on Route 22A. Cross over bridge, take right at sign to Basin Harbor. 1 mile to Basin Harbor Road, take right, 6 miles to course.

Bellows Falls Country Club   ✪✪½

 7

Route 103
Bellows Falls, VT (802) 463-9809
www.bellowsfallscountryclub.com
Club Pro:
Payment: Visa, MC, Cash
Tee Times: No
Fee 9 Holes: Weekday: $18
Fee 18 Holes: Weekday: $30
Twilight Rates: After 5pm
Cart Rental: $30/18, $20/9 per cart
Lessons: No **Schools:** No
Membership: Yes
Other: Restaurant / Bar

Tees	Holes	Yards	Par	USGA	Slope
BACK					
MIDDLE	9	2892	35	65.8	117
FRONT	9	2569	35	65.8	110

Weekend: $22
Weekend: $33
Discounts: Senior/Junior
Driving Range: No
Junior Golf: No
Architect/Yr Open: 1923
GPS:

Open May 1 - November 1. Vermont Country Store, Bellows Falls and Chester Village nearby!
"Lots to like, but many blind shots. Above average greens." –GM

	1	2	3	4	5	6	7	8	9
PAR	4	5	3	3	4	4	4	3	5
YARDS	389	513	178	155	381	370	320	158	428
PAR									
YARDS									

Directions: I-91 to Exit 6. Take Route 103 North. Turn right onto Country Club Road. Across from Vermont Country Store.

Blush Hill Country Club   ✪✪

8

141 Lonesome Trail
Waterbury, VT (802) 244-8974
www.blushhillcountryclub.com
Club Pro:
Payment: Visa, MC, Disc
Tee Times: Recommended
Fee 9 Holes: Weekday: $20
Fee 18 Holes: Weekday: $30
Twilight Rates: No
Cart Rental: $29/18, $19/9 per cart
Lessons: No; **Schools:** No
Membership: Yes
Other: Clubhouse/Snack Bar /Bar

Tees	Holes	Yards	Par	USGA	Slope
BACK					
MIDDLE	9	2416	33	62.7	113
FRONT	9	2275	33	66.2	114

Weekend: $22 F/S/S
Weekend: $28 F/S/S
Discounts: None
Driving Range: No
Junior Golf: No
Architect/Yr Open: Andrew Freeland/1926

One of the most extraordinary scenic views in Vermont. Course kept in excellent shape. Open May 1 - October 15. Ben & Jerry's right around the corner.

	1	2	3	4	5	6	7	8	9
PAR	4	4	4	3	4	3	3	4	4
YARDS	377	350	206	171	266	146	157	377	302
PAR									
YARDS									

Directions: ½ mile off I-89 North, on Route 100. 1000 feet left on Blush Hill Road, ¾ mile beyond Best Western on Blush Hill Road. Turn left on Lonesome Trail.

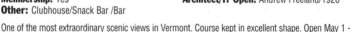

Bradford Golf Course ✪✪ ▶ 9

150 Memorial Field
Bradford, VT (802) 222-5207
www.bradfordgolfclubinc.com

Club Pro:
Payment: Cash, Visa, MC
Tee Times: No
Fee 9 Holes: Weekday: $16
Fee 18 Holes: Weekday: $21
Twilight Rates: $12+tax after 5pm
Cart Rental: $15pp/18, $10pp/9
Lessons: No **Schools:** No
Membership: Yes
Other: Snacks

Tees	Holes	Yards	Par	USGA	Slope
BACK					
MIDDLE	9	2155	32		
FRONT	9	2052	32		

Weekend: $16
Weekend: $24
Discounts: None
Driving Range: No
Junior Golf: No
Architect/Yr Open: 1927
GPS:

"Greens usually in fine shape." –JS Par 32, 18 sets of tees.

	1	2	3	4	5	6	7	8	9
PAR	3	4	3	3	4	3	5	4	3
YARDS	174	239	160	115	304	185	431	294	150
PAR									
YARDS									

Directions: From I-91, take Exit 16, turn right and go ¾ of a mile. Turn left, go 1 mile north. Turn right, go by Bradford Academy to bottom of hill.

Brattleboro Country Club ✪✪½ ▶ 10

Upper Dummerston Road
Brattleboro, VT (802) 257-7380
www.brattleborocountryclub.com

Club Pro: Eric Sandstrum, PGA
Payment: Visa, MC, Amex
Tee Times: 3 days adv.
Fee 9 Holes: Weekday: $24
Fee 18 Holes: Weekday: $30
Twilight Rates: No
Cart Rental: $19pp/18, $12pp/9
Lessons: Yes **Schools:** No
Membership: Yes
Other: Restaurant / Clubhouse / Bar-Lounge / Showers / Lodging Partner
GPS:

Tees	Holes	Yards	Par	USGA	Slope
BACK	18	6533	71	71.8	127
MIDDLE	18	6073	71	69.6	122
FRONT	18	5051	71	67.1	110

Weekend: $28
Weekend: $40
Discounts: No
Driving Range: Yes
Junior Golf: Yes
Architect/Yr Open: Wayne Stiles, Durkee/1914

COUPON

Wide fairways and fast greens! In great condition. Awesome foliage! Friendly staff. Hidden gem! First course in Vermont when travelling I-91 North. 5 minutes from New Hampshire. Many new hotels and restaurants in Brattleboro VT. "Best kept secret in Southern Vermont." –GG

	1	2	3	4	5	6	7	8	9
PAR	4	5	4	3	4	4	5	3	4
YARDS	405	504	359	155	397	243	455	155	363
	10	11	12	13	14	15	16	17	18
PAR	5	4	4	3	4	4	3	4	4
YARDS	492	378	376	172	346	386	152	346	389

Directions: I-91 North or South take Exit 2, go 1 mile to Cedar Street on left. Follow to bottom of hill. Left at stop sign. Left onto Upper Dummerston Road. Club 1 mile on left.

Catamount Golf Club

NR 11

1400 Mountain View Road
Williston, VT (802) 878-7227
www.catamountgolf.com

Tees	Holes	Yards	Par	USGA	Slope
BACK					
MIDDLE	9	2844	35	33.3	112
FRONT					

Club Pro: Lou Jarvis, PGA
Payment: Cash, Visa, MC
Tee Times:
Fee 9 Holes: Weekday: $18   **Weekend:** $18
Fee 18 Holes: Weekday: **Weekend:**
Twilight Rates: No   **Discounts:** No
Cart Rental: $8pp/9   **Driving Range:** $9/lg., $5/sm.
Lessons: Schools: Yes   **Junior Golf:** Yes
Membership: Yes   **Architect/Yr Open:** Marty Keene/1999
Other: Snack Bar   **GPS:**

COUPON

$130 discount card available for 10 9-hole rounds. Course landscaped to provide visual depiction of the route to play this links-style course.

	1	2	3	4	5	6	7	8	9
PAR	4	3	4	3	5	3	5	4	4
YARDS	346	156	357	170	490	165	470	330	360
PAR									
YARDS									

Directions: 3 miles north of Taft Corners.

Cedar Knoll Country Club

NR 12

13020 Route 116
Hinesburg, VT (802) 482-3186
www.cedarknollgolf.com

Tees	Holes	Yards	Par	USGA	Slope
BACK	27/18	6541	72	72.5	117
MIDDLE	27/18	6144	72	72.5	117
FRONT	27/18	5360	72	69.5	108

Club Pro: Barry Churchill, PGA
Payment: Visa, MC, Amex
Tee Times: Yes
Fee 9 Holes: Weekday: $20   **Weekend:** $20
Fee 18 Holes: Weekday: $33   **Weekend:** $33
Twilight Rates: After 5pm   **Discounts:** None
Cart Rental: $17pp/18, $10pp/9   **Driving Range:** $4/sm., $7/lg. bucket
Lessons: Yes **Schools:** Yes   **Junior Golf:** Yes
Membership: Yes   **Architect/Yr Open:** Raymond Ayer/1994
Other: Restaurant / Clubhouse / Bar-Lounge / Lockers / Showers / Snack Bar

Now 27 holes. Rolling hills. 250 acres allows for nice spacing of holes. Beautiful scenery. Cedar Knoll South 9-hole addition is also open. 9-hole rate, $20. Our practice facility includes a putting green, pitching green w/sand bunkers and a 270 yard driving range. Improve your game with PGA Teaching Professional, Barry Churchill.

	1	2	3	4	5	6	7	8	9
PAR	5	3	4	4	5	3	4	4	4
YARDS	500	156	315	358	505	170	392	313	438
	10	11	12	13	14	15	16	17	18
PAR	5	3	4	4	3	4	4	4	5
YARDS	494	169	298	333	156	291	341	315	536

Directions: I-89 to Exit 12; follow 5 miles to intersection of Routes 2A and 116. Take left and go 5 miles on 116. Course is on right.

Champlain Country Club

NR 13 ▶

587 St. Albans Road
Swanton, VT (802) 527-1187
www.champlaincountryclub.com

Club Pro: Michael Swim
Payment: MC, Visa, Disc
Tee Times: Weekends, Holidays
Fee 9 Holes: Weekday: $25
Fee 18 Holes: Weekday: $35
Twilight Rates:
Cart Rental: $15pp/18, $10pp/9
Lessons: $25/half hour **Schools:**
Membership: Yes
Other: Clubhouse / Lockers / Showers / Snack Bar / Restaurant / Bar-Lounge
GPS: Yes

Tees	Holes	Yards	Par	USGA	Slope
BACK	18	6237	70	69.9	123
MIDDLE	18	5959	70	68.8	121
FRONT	18	5366	70	70.4	117

Weekend: $30
Weekend: $40
Discounts:
Driving Range: Free balls
Junior Golf: Yes
Architect/Yr Open: Duer Irving Sewall/1915

COUPON

Overlooking Lake Champlain. Nice views. New tees.

	1	2	3	4	5	6	7	8	9
PAR	4	5	3	4	4	4	3	4	4
YARDS	359	472	152	377	353	347	135	350	342
	10	11	12	13	14	15	16	17	18
PAR	4	4	3	4	3	5	4	4	4
YARDS	303	444	142	370	167	526	328	415	315

Directions: I-89 to Exit 20; take Route 7 North ½ mile to course.

Copley Country Club

NR 14 ▶   VT

377 Copley Country Club Road
Morrisville, VT (802) 888-3013
www.copleycountryclub.com

Club Pro:
Payment: Visa, MC
Tee Times: Required
Fee 9 Holes: Weekday: $19
Fee 18 Holes: Weekday: $29.50
Twilight Rates: No
Cart Rental: $16pp/18, $10.50pp/9
Lessons: No **Schools:** No
Membership: Yes
Other: Clubhouse / Lockers / Snack Bar / Restaurant / Bar-Lounge

Tees	Holes	Yards	Par	USGA	Slope
BACK	9	2775	35	67.4	112
MIDDLE	9	2706	35	67.4	112
FRONT	9	2510	35	68.0	106

Weekend: $19
Weekend: $29.50
Discounts: None
Driving Range: No
Junior Golf: Yes
Architect/Yr Open: 1936

Ideal conditions. The course is level with a handful of tree-lined holes.

	1	2	3	4	5	6	7	8	9
PAR	4	3	4	4	3	5	4	4	4
YARDS	310	218	326	296	171	526	395	270	262
PAR									
YARDS									

Directions: I-89 to Waterbury exit, follow 18 miles to Morrisville.

Country Club of Barre ✪✪½ 15

Plainsfield Road
Barre, VT (802) 476-7658
www.ccofbarre.com

Tees	Holes	Yards	Par	USGA	Slope
BACK	18	6315	71	70.4	123
MIDDLE	18	5938	71	68.9	121
FRONT	18	5126	71	70.3	121

Club Pro: Roger King, PGA
Payment: Visa, MC, Amex
Tee Times: 5 days adv.
Fee 9 Holes: Weekday: $26   **Weekend:** $26
Fee 18 Holes: Weekday: $47   **Weekend:** $47
Twilight Rates: After 4pm on weekends   **Discounts:** None
Cart Rental: $23pp/18, $12pp/9   **Driving Range:** $3/lg.
Lessons: $35/40 min. **Schools:** No   **Junior Golf:** For members
Membership: Yes   **Architect/Yr Open:** Wayne Stiles/1924
Other: Clubhouse / Lockers / Showers / Snack Bar / Restaurant / Bar-Lounge

COUPON

Player Comments: "One of the hidden gems in Vermont." Semi-private, call for tee times.

	1	2	3	4	5	6	7	8	9
PAR	4	4	4	3	5	4	3	4	4
YARDS	368	383	285	190	455	339	142	370	368
	10	11	12	13	14	15	16	17	18
PAR	5	4	4	3	4	5	3	4	4
YARDS	492	372	314	170	431	439	125	343	352

Directions: I-89 to Exit 7. Follow Route 62 towards Barre (straight into 14 North). Take right onto Plainfield Brook Road, turn left onto Mitchell Road, turn right onto Mitchell Nursery Road. Club is 3 miles on right.

Crown Point Country Club ✪✪✪ 16

Weathersfield Center Road
Springfield, VT (802) 885-1010
www.crownpointcc.com

Tees	Holes	Yards	Par	USGA	Slope
BACK	18	6602	72	71.2	128
MIDDLE	18	6120	72	69.1	122
FRONT	18	5542	72	73.0	124

Club Pro: Todd Nalette, PGA/Dan Russell, PGA
Payment: Visa, MC, Cash
Tee Times: Recommended
Fee 9 Holes: Weekday: $20   **Weekend:** $23
Fee 18 Holes: Weekday: $35   **Weekend:** $50
Twilight Rates: After 2pm & 4pm   **Discounts:** Senior & Junior
Cart Rental: $20.75pp/18, $11.32pp/9   **Driving Range:** Yes
Lessons: Yes **Schools:** No   **Junior Golf:** Yes
Membership: Yes   **Architect/Yr Open:** William Mitchell/1953
Other: Clubhouse / Showers / Restaurant / Bar-Lounge

COUPON

Course noted for smooth fast greens. Friendly staff. Great views. Open April 15 - November 1 (weather permitting).

	1	2	3	4	5	6	7	8	9
PAR	4	5	4	4	3	4	5	4	3
YARDS	370	426	344	337	168	365	487	376	154
	10	11	12	13	14	15	16	17	18
PAR	4	5	4	3	4	5	4	4	3
YARDS	344	463	390	158	344	459	381	371	183

Directions: I-91 North to Exit 7; turn right and follow to center of Springfield. Turn right onto Valley Street. Course 3 miles on left.

Enosburg Falls Country Club   NR 17▶

53 Elm Street
Enosburg Falls, VT (802) 933-2296
www.efccvt.com

Tees	Holes	Yards	Par	USGA	Slope
BACK	18	5580	72	67.4	116
MIDDLE	18	5418	72	66.8	115
FRONT	18	4633	72	63.4	108

Club Pro: Rick Marckres, Head Pro
Payment: MC, Visa
Tee Times: Yes
Fee 9 Holes: Weekday: $19   **Weekend:** $19
Fee 18 Holes: Weekday: $30   **Weekend:** $30
Twilight Rates: After 3pm   **Discounts:** Junior
Cart Rental: $28/18, $15/9 per cart   **Driving Range:** Irons range
Lessons: Yes **Schools:** No   **Junior Golf:** Yes
Membership: Yes   **Architect/Yr Open:** 1963
Other: Restaurant / Clubhouse / Lockers / Showers

COUPON

Course has some great birdie opportunities. Variety of rates for special memberships. Upgrading course with new bunkers. Open May - October.

	1	2	3	4	5	6	7	8	9
PAR	4	5	4	4	4	3	4	5	3
YARDS	249	498	337	251	350	115	331	552	119
	10	11	12	13	14	15	16	17	18
PAR	4	3	4	5	5	3	4	4	4
YARDS	272	140	335	490	478	112	267	255	267

Directions: I-89 to St. Albans Exit to Route 105 North; follow to Enosberg Falls. Take left at junction of Routes 108 and 105 to course.

Equinox Golf Club   ✪✪✪½ 18▶   VT

108 Union Street
Manchester, VT (802) 362-7870
www.playequinox.com

Tees	Holes	Yards	Par	USGA	Slope
BACK	18	6423	71	70.8	129
MIDDLE	18	6069	71	69.2	125
FRONT	18	5082	71	69.0	122

Club Pro: Joan McDonald, LPGA
Payment: MC, Visa, Amex, Disc, Cash
Tee Times: 14 days adv.
Fee 9 Holes: Weekday: $59   **Weekend:** $79
Fee 18 Holes: Weekday: $79   **Weekend:** $119
Twilight Rates: After 3pm   **Discounts:** Junior
Cart Rental: Included   **Driving Range:** No
Lessons: $60/half hour **Schools:** No   **Junior Golf:** Yes
Membership: Yes   **Architect/Yr Open:** Walter Travis/1927
Other: Restaurant / Clubhouse / Snack Bar / Bar-Lounge / Hotel / Lockers / Showers

COUPON

Rated the #1 course you can play in Vermont by *Golfweek* and the 45th Best Golf Resort in North America by *Golf Digest*. Our course is an enjoyable par 71 with unforgettable views.

	1	2	3	4	5	6	7	8	9
PAR	4	4	4	3	4	4	5	4	4
YARDS	334	385	346	141	316	323	502	380	344
	10	11	12	13	14	15	16	17	18
PAR	4	4	4	4	3	5	3	4	4
YARDS	336	361	347	401	112	462	181	403	395

Directions: Exit 4 on Route 7 towards Manchester, left on 7A, left on Union Street.

Essex Country Club

332 Old Stage Road
Essex Junction, VT (802) 879-3232
www.essexccvt.com

Club Pro: Lou Jarvis, PGA
Mike Morelli, Assistant Pro
Payment: Visa, MC, Amex
Tee Times: Weekends
Fee 9 Holes: Weekday: $20
Fee 18 Holes: Weekday: $32
Twilight Rates: $20 after 4pm
Cart Rental:
Lessons: Yes **Schools:** No
Membership: Yes
Other:

Tees	Holes	Yards	Par	USGA	Slope
BACK	18	6475	72	70.0	117
MIDDLE	18	6315	72	70.0	117
FRONT	18	5500	72	69.1	112

Weekend: $20
Weekend: $32
Discounts: No
Driving Range: $5/sm., $6/med., $7/lg. bucket
Junior Golf: Yes
Architect/Yr Open: Joe Chastaney/1988
GPS:

Ongoing improvements. Monday, Tuesday and Wednesday specials. Upgraded irrigation. 14 of the 18 holes are fully irrigated. New putting green and practice range.

	1	2	3	4	5	6	7	8	9
PAR	4	3	4	4	5	4	5	4	3
YARDS	365	155	400	330	450	335	530	315	190
	10	11	12	13	14	15	16	17	18
PAR	5	4	4	3	4	5	3	4	4
YARDS	580	320	355	130	360	530	170	350	450

Directions: I-89 to Exit 12. Williston exit Route 2A to Essex 5 corner; then take Route 15 to Old Stage Road 3 miles north to course.

Green Mountain National GC ✪✪✪✪½

Barrows Towne Road (Route 100)
Killington, VT (802) 422-GOLF
www.gmngc.com

Club Pro: David Soucy, PGA
Payment: Visa, MC, Amex, Disc
Tee Times: 7 days adv.
Fee 9 Holes: Weekday: $46.78 w/cart
Fee 18 Holes: Weekday: $80.20 w/cart
Twilight Rates: $49 after 3pm weekday, $52 Sat/Sun
Discounts: Junior
Cart Rental: Included
Lessons: $60-80/hour **Schools:** Adult
Membership: Resident/Non-Resident passes
Other: Bar / Lounge / Snack Bar

Tees	Holes	Yards	Par	USGA	Slope
BACK	18	6589	71	72.1	138
MIDDLE	18	6164	71	70.2	133
FRONT	18	4740	71	68.9	118

Weekend: $49.78 w/cart
Weekend: $90.20 w/cart

COUPON

Driving Range: $7/lg., $4/sm.
Junior Golf: Yes
Architect/Yr Open: Gene Bates/1996
GPS: Yes

Player Comments: "Unbelievable in the fall. Incredibly challenging. Great layout, conditions and friendly personnel." Several stay-and-play partners.

	1	2	3	4	5	6	7	8	9
PAR	5	4	4	4	3	5	3	4	4
YARDS	494	387	381	406	152	492	145	348	419
	10	11	12	13	14	15	16	17	18
PAR	4	4	4	3	4	5	4	3	4
YARDS	396	350	375	157	326	437	359	169	371

Directions: I-91 to Exit 6. Turn left onto Route 103 North for about 30 minutes. Take right onto Route 100 North. Go by Killington Mountain Road. Course is 2 miles on left. Travel time from I-91 is about 1 hour.

Hermitage Golf Club   ✪✪✪✪   21 ▶

70 Spyglass Drive, P.O. Box 369
Wilmington, VT (802) 464-8301
www.hermitagegolfclub.com

Club Pro: John Cleanthes, PGA
Payment: Visa, MC, Amex, Disc
Tee Times: 14 days adv.

Tees	Holes	Yards	Par	USGA	Slope
BACK	18	6549	72	71.7	128
MIDDLE	18	6164	72	69.3	125
FRONT	18	5396	74	70.8	121

Fee 9 Holes: Weekday: $39 w/cart
Fee 18 Holes: Weekday: $55 w/cart
Twilight Rates: After 3pm
Cart Rental: Included
Lessons: Yes **Schools:** No
Membership: Yes
Weekend: $55 w/cart
Weekend: $85 w/cart
Discounts: Sr., Mon-Thu/Non-Hldy
Driving Range: $5/bucket irons only
Junior Golf: Yes
Architect/Yr Open: Desmond Muirhead/1972

COUPON

Other: Clubhouse / Restaurant / Bar-Lounge / Lodging Partner / Stay & Play packages available

Hermitage's manicured layout was created by acclaimed designer Desmond Muirhead, one of only two in New England. Hermitage meanders over a gently rolling landscape without the blind shots one expects in a mountain course. The only way you'll know you are in the mountains is by the stunning views of the surrounding mountains.

	1	2	3	4	5	6	7	8	9
PAR	4	4	5	3	4	4	3	5	4
YARDS	348	389	460	181	347	291	166	505	380
	10	11	12	13	14	15	16	17	18
PAR	4	5	4	3	5	4	3	4	4
YARDS	328	509	352	160	516	343	165	301	423

Directions: Exit 2 off I-91. Take Route 9 West to Wilmington. Take right at traffic light onto 100 North. Follow signs to golf course.

Jay Peak Resort Golf Course   ✪✪✪½   22 ▶   VT

4850 Route 242
Jay, VT (802) 988-2611
www.jaypeakresort.com

Club Pro: David Jankowski, PGA
Payment: Visa, MC, Amex, Disc, Checks
Tee Times: Yes

Tees	Holes	Yards	Par	USGA	Slope
BACK	18	6908	72	73.1	138
MIDDLE	18	6330	72	71.0	133
FRONT	18	5094	72	69.1	120

Fee 9 Holes: Weekday: $49 w/cart
Fee 18 Holes: Weekday: $79 w/cart
Twilight Rates: After 3pm
Cart Rental: Included
Lessons: Yes **Schools:** Yes
Membership: Yes
Other:
Weekend:
Weekend: $99 w/cart
Discounts: Senior & Junior
Driving Range: Yes
Junior Golf:
Architect/Yr Open: Graham Cooke/2006
GPS: Yes

COUPON

Front 9 wraps its way around Eastern edge of the resort. Back 9 course design by Graham Cooke. Outstanding championship course in the Northeast kingdom. Spectacular course is a must-play.

	1	2	3	4	5	6	7	8	9
PAR	4	3	4	5	3	4	5	4	4
YARDS	410	133	422	538	167	347	472	380	367
	10	11	12	13	14	15	16	17	18
PAR	4	5	3	5	3	4	5	3	4
YARDS	399	474	129	513	196	335	486	155	407

Directions: I-91 to Exit 26 (Orleans). Go north via Route 5 to Route 14 North. Then go south on Route 100. Take a right in center of Troy onto 101 North. Left onto Route 242. Follow to entrance on right.

John P. Larkin Country Club 23

Route 5
Windsor, VT (802) 674-6491
www.clublarkin.com

Tees	Holes	Yards	Par	USGA	Slope
BACK					
MIDDLE	9	2670	34	65.1	105
FRONT	9	2462	36	68.2	109

Club Pro:
Payment: Visa, MC
Tee Times: Wknds/M/T/Hldy
Fee 9 Holes: Weekday: $15   **Weekend:** $25
Fee 18 Holes: Weekday: $18   **Weekend:** $28
Twilight Rates: No   **Discounts:** None
Cart Rental: $25/18, $15/9 per cart   **Driving Range:** No
Lessons: Yes **Schools:** No   **Junior Golf:** Yes
Membership: Yes   **Architect/Yr Open:** 1921
Other: Restaurant / Clubhouse / Snack Bar / Bar-Lounge / Lockers / Showers

Course has views of Mt. Ascutney and Connecticut River. New irrigation. New Hampshire is out of bounds.

	1	2	3	4	5	6	7	8	9
PAR	4	3	4	4	4	3	3	5	4
YARDS	332	215	333	309	383	176	140	442	340
PAR									
YARDS									

Directions: I-91 to Exit 9, left on Route 5, course is 3.5 miles down.

Killington Golf Course ✪✪½ 24

227 E. Mountain Road
Killington, VT (802) 422-6700
www.killingtongolf.com

Tees	Holes	Yards	Par	USGA	Slope
BACK	18	6168	72	70.3	129
MIDDLE	18	5876	72	68.9	124
FRONT	18	4803	72	68.3	119

Club Pro: Dave Beckwith
Payment: Visa, MC, Amex, Disc
Tee Times: Recommended
Fee 9 Holes: Weekday: $30   **Weekend:** $35
Fee 18 Holes: Weekday: $50   **Weekend:** $60
Twilight Rates: After 3pm

COUPON

Discounts: Junior, appropriate attire, shirts no jeans
Cart Rental: $20pp/18, $12pp/9   **Driving Range:** $4/bucket
Lessons: $60/hour **Schools:** Jr. & Sr.   **Junior Golf:** Yes
Membership: Yes   **Architect/Yr Open:** Geoffrey Cornish/1983
Other: Hotel / Clubhouse / Showers / Snack Bar / Restaurant / Bar-Lounge / Lodging Partner / Appropriate Attire / Collared Shirts / No Jeans

Very scenic with dramatic elevation changes. The 6168 yard par 72 Geoffrey Cornish layout presents a refreshing round for any golfer no matter what skill level or handicap.

	1	2	3	4	5	6	7	8	9
PAR	4	5	3	4	5	3	5	4	4
YARDS	354	485	163	395	452	138	480	321	270
	10	11	12	13	14	15	16	17	18
PAR	4	5	4	4	3	4	4	3	4
YARDS	334	485	300	355	174	370	360	150	290

Directions: I-89 to US Route 4 West to the Killington Access Road. Follow to the ski area and follow the signs.

Kwiniaska Golf Club ✪✪ 25 ▶

5531 Spear Street
Shelburne, VT (802) 985-3672
www.kwiniaska.com

Tees	Holes	Yards	Par	USGA	Slope
BACK	18	6848	72	72.7	129
MIDDLE	18	6601	72	71.7	126
FRONT	18	5246	72	70.6	115

Club Pro: Michael Bailey, PGA
Payment: Visa, MC, Disc
Tee Times: 1 day adv.
Fee 9 Holes: Weekday: $25   **Weekend:** $25
Fee 18 Holes: Weekday: $38   **Weekend:** $38
Twilight Rates: $25 after 4pm   **Discounts:** No
Cart Rental: $17pp/18, $10pp/9   **Driving Range:** Yes
Lessons: Yes **Schools:** No   **Junior Golf:** Yes
Membership: Yes/limited   **Architect/Yr Open:** A. Bradford Caldwell/1965
Other: Restaurant / Clubhouse / Lockers / Showers

Course is framed with trees that are spectacular during foliage. Course plays tougher than it looks. 3rd longest course in the state.

	1	2	3	4	5	6	7	8	9
PAR	4	3	5	3	4	4	4	4	5
YARDS	425	186	467	181	446	375	407	374	541
	10	11	12	13	14	15	16	17	18
PAR	4	4	3	5	4	3	5	4	4
YARDS	367	341	169	495	399	193	490	328	417

Directions: I-89 to Exit 14 West. Follow signs to Spear Street, then 5 miles south.

Lake Morey Country Club ✪✪½ 26 ▶   VT

179 Club House Road
Fairlee, VT (802) 333-4800
www.lakemoreycc.com

Tees	Holes	Yards	Par	USGA	Slope
BACK	18	6024	70	69.4	120
MIDDLE	18	5807	70	68.4	118
FRONT	18	4942	70	68.0	115

Club Pro: Bill Ross Jr., PGA
Payment: Visa, MC, Disc, Amex
Tee Times: 4 days adv.
Fee 9 Holes: Weekday: $24   **Weekend:** $24
Fee 18 Holes: Weekday: $35   **Weekend:** $45
Twilight Rates: $23 after 3pm, $16 after 4pm   **Discounts:** Sr. M-T $27; Jr. M-T $25
Cart Rental: $18 pp/18, $11pp/9   **Driving Range:** $4/bucket
Lessons: Yes **Schools:** No   **Junior Golf:** Yes
Membership: Yes   **Architect/Yr Open:** 1915; Geoffrey Cornish/1989
Other: Clubhouse / Snack Bar / Restaurant / Bar-Lounge / Hotel / Resort Lake Activities

COUPON

Home of Vermont Open. Come play where the Pros play.

	1	2	3	4	5	6	7	8	9
PAR	3	5	4	4	4	3	3	4	4
YARDS	213	460	356	337	334	158	114	395	321
	10	11	12	13	14	15	16	17	18
PAR	4	4	5	5	4	3	4	3	4
YARDS	324	369	504	517	373	188	371	160	313

Directions: I-91 North to Exit 15, take left off ramp and follow signs. 25 minutes north of White River Junction.

Lake St. Catherine Country Club ✪✪½

Route 30
Poultney, VT (802) 287-9341
www.lsccc.net

Tees	Holes	Yards	Par	USGA	Slope
BACK	18	6204	72	69.0	125
MIDDLE	18	5840	72	67.3	118
FRONT	18	4899	72	62.0	107

Club Pro: Matt Hibbert
Payment: Visa, MC, Cash
Tee Times: 1 week adv.
Fee 9 Holes: Weekday: $19
Fee 18 Holes: Weekday: $29
Twilight Rates: After 3pm
Cart Rental: $15pp/18, $9pp/9
Lessons: $50/hour **Schools:** No
Membership: Yes
Weekend: $29
Weekend: $36
Discounts: Senior
Driving Range: Yes
Junior Golf: Yes
Architect/Yr Open: 1925
Other: Snack Bar / Bar-Lounge / Full-Service Restaurant

Open April - October. Player Comments: "15th and 16th holes most scenic in state." "Rolling hills, nice greens, playable for all levels." –GM

	1	2	3	4	5	6	7	8	9
PAR	4	4	3	4	4	4	5	3	5
YARDS	391	340	156	405	354	333	517	186	444
	10	11	12	13	14	15	16	17	18
PAR	5	4	4	4	3	4	3	4	5
YARDS	522	343	327	320	125	374	166	388	513

Directions: Directly on Route 30 South of Poultney, easily accessible from Route 4 to 30 South.

Links at Lang Farm ✪✪½

39 Essex Way
Essex Junction, VT (802) 878-0298
www.linksatlangfarm.com

Tees	Holes	Yards	Par	USGA	Slope
BACK	18	3809	60	59.8	102
MIDDLE	18	3444	60	58	96
FRONT	18	2884	60		

Club Pro: Steve Gonsalves, PGA
Payment: Visa, MC, Disc, Check, Cash
Tee Times: Yes
Fee 9 Holes: Weekday: $22
Fee 18 Holes: Weekday: $34
Twilight Rates: Yes
Cart Rental: $16pp/18, $8pp/9
Lessons: Yes **Schools:** Yes
Membership: Yes
Weekend: $22
Weekend: $34
Discounts: Senior
Driving Range: Yes
Junior Golf: Yes
Architect/Yr Open: Michael Asmundson/2002
GPS: Yes
Other: Inn / Lodging Partner / Stay and Play

Appealing to all levels of play. Exceptional conditions. Call ahead for times. Golf packages available with The Inn at Essex. New clubhouse.

	1	2	3	4	5	6	7	8	9
PAR	3	3	3	4	3	4	3	3	3
YARDS	158	167	155	295	124	307	133	180	156
	10	11	12	13	14	15	16	17	18
PAR	3	3	4	3	4	3	3	4	4
YARDS	156	147	273	126	258	102	152	231	324

Directions: I-89 to Exit 11. Follow Route 117, 6 miles to VT 289. Exit 10, turn left.

Montague Golf Club ✪✪

Randolph Avenue
Randolph, VT (802) 728-3806
www.montaguegolf.com

Club Pro: Paul Politano, PGA
Payment: Visa, MC, Amex
Tee Times: Yes
Fee 9 Holes: Weekday: $18
Fee 18 Holes: Weekday: $32
Twilight Rates: After 4:00pm
Cart Rental: $18pp/18, $9pp/9
Lessons: Yes, PGA **Schools:** No
Membership: Yes
Other: Clubhouse / Snack Bar / Putting Green
Area Attractions: 3 Stallion Inn

Tees	Holes	Yards	Par	USGA	Slope
BACK	18	6134	70	69.6	119
MIDDLE	18	5730	70	68.0	115
FRONT	18	4785	71	68.7	109

Weekend: $22
Weekend: $35
Discounts: Sr. (M), Jr. (w/adult)
Driving Range: Yes
Junior Golf: Yes
Architect/Yr Open: 1913/Geoffrey Cornish
GPS:

COUPON

New owners Sam & Jinny Sammis have improved the experience at Montague. 2 new holes, 8 new tee boxes, more planned!

	1	2	3	4	5	6	7	8	9
PAR	4	4	4	3	4	4	3	4	3
YARDS	317	375	328	168	425	420	157	330	120
	10	11	12	13	14	15	16	17	18
PAR	3	5	4	4	5	4	4	4	4
YARDS	214	540	305	402	472	375	379	389	398

Directions: I-89 North to Exit 4. Follow Route 66 into downtown Randolph on Route 12 South. Take left on Merchant Road. Go straight onto Randolph Avenue — end of road, take left.

Montpelier Elks Country Club NR   VT

203 Country Club Road
Montpelier, VT (802) 223-7457
www.montpelierelkscc.com

Club Pro:
Payment: Cash, Credit
Tee Times: Weekends, 1 day adv.
Fee 9 Holes: Weekday: $15
Fee 18 Holes: Weekday: $22
Twilight Rates: No
Cart Rental: $15pp/18, $11pp/9
Lessons: Private and Group **Schools:** No
Membership: Yes
Other: Clubhouse / Lockers / Showers / Snack Bar / Restaurant / Bar-Lounge

Tees	Holes	Yards	Par	USGA	Slope
BACK	9	2564	35	67.0	117
MIDDLE	9	2739	35	66.6	114
FRONT	9	2383	35	67.9	112

Weekend: $15
Weekend: $22
Discounts: None
Driving Range: No
Junior Golf: Yes
Architect/Yr Open: 1902

The course is relatively short but made challenging by the hilly terrain. Open April 1 - October 31.

	1	2	3	4	5	6	7	8	9
PAR	4	3	5	5	4	3	4	3	4
YARDS	358	155	422	459	226	149	325	191	279
PAR									
YARDS									

Directions: I-89 to Route 2 exit, follow signs for Montpelier.

Mt. Anthony Country Club   ✪✪✪½   31

180 Country Club Drive
Bennington, VT (802) 447-7079
www.mtanthonycc.com

Tees	Holes	Yards	Par	USGA	Slope
BACK	18	6200	71	75.0	125
MIDDLE	18	6000	71	69.2	125
FRONT	18	5200	71	67.7	106

Club Pro: Douglas A. Ruttle, PGA
Payment: Visa, MC, Cash
Tee Times: Yes
Fee 9 Holes: Weekday: $30
Fee 18 Holes: Weekday: $45
Twilight Rates: No
Cart Rental: $20pp/18, $10pp/9
Lessons: Call for rates **Schools:** Junior
Membership: Yes

Weekend: $35
Weekend: $55
Discounts: Junior
Driving Range: $7/bucket
Junior Golf: Yes
Architect/Yr Open: Jay Jerome/1897

Other: Snack Bar / Restaurant / Bar-Lounge / Lockers / Showers

Player Comments: "Good price. Scenic. Great services. Well-maintained." Open April - October.
Recently renovated to take advantage of the spectacular Green Mountain setting.

	1	2	3	4	5	6	7	8	9
PAR	4	3	5	3	5	4	4	4	4
YARDS	366	182	474	104	538	369	338	331	304
	10	**11**	**12**	**13**	**14**	**15**	**16**	**17**	**18**
PAR	4	4	4	3	3	4	5	4	4
YARDS	344	368	348	156	182	304	435	406	351

Directions: From Route 7 go to Bennington Center. Turn onto West Main Street (Route 9 West).
¼ mile after Paradise Motel take first right onto Convent Avenue. Follow to end and take left.
Course is down on the right.

Mount Snow Golf Club   ✪✪½   32

Country Club Road
Mount Snow, VT (802) 464-4254
www.mountsnow.com

Tees	Holes	Yards	Par	USGA	Slope
BACK	18	6943	72	73.7	129
MIDDLE	18	6539	72	71.9	125
FRONT	18	5384	72	70.4	117

Club Pro: Jay Morelli, PGA
Payment: Visa, MC, Amex, Disc
Tee Times: Yes
Fee 9 Holes: Weekday: $36 w/cart
Fee 18 Holes: Weekday: $44 w/cart
Twilight Rates: After 2pm
Cart Rental: Included
Lessons: $40/half hour **Schools:** Yes
Membership: Yes

Weekend:
Weekend: $75 w/cart
Discounts: Senior & Junior
Driving Range: Yes
Junior Golf: Yes
Architect/Yr Open: Geoffrey Cornish/1967

Other: Clubhouse / Snack Bar / Restaurant / Bar-Lounge / Hotel / Spa

Home of the Original Golf School, headed by Jay Morelli, MSGC offers breathtaking views and challenging
golf for all ability levels. Gold Tees for seniors in 2005. New ladies' tees. Rates subject to change.

	1	2	3	4	5	6	7	8	9
PAR	4	5	3	4	4	3	5	4	4
YARDS	372	593	160	407	432	150	480	400	396
	10	**11**	**12**	**13**	**14**	**15**	**16**	**17**	**18**
PAR	4	4	3	4	5	3	5	4	4
YARDS	394	364	143	354	479	187	542	323	163

Directions: I-91 to Exit 2 in Brattleboro to Route 9 West, 20 miles to Wilmington. Turn right at the
stop light onto Route 100 North. About 6 miles, take a left on Crosstown Road. At top of hill on left.

Neshobe Golf Club

✪✪✪   33 ▶

224 Town Farm Road
Brandon, VT (802) 247-3611
www.neshobe.com

Tees	Holes	Yards	Par	USGA	Slope
BACK	18	6349	72	71.6	125
MIDDLE	18	5865	72	68.7	122
FRONT	18	5179	73	64.9	117

Club Pro: Rodney Bicknell, PGA
Payment: MC, Visa, Disc, Checks, Cash
Tee Times: 7 days adv.
Fee 9 Holes: Weekday: $30 with cart
Fee 18 Holes: Weekday: $60 with cart
Twilight Rates: After 3pm
Cart Rental: $20pp/18, $14pp/9
Lessons: Yes **Schools:** No
Membership: Available

Weekend: $30 with cart
Weekend: $60 with cart
Discounts: Seniors/Junior
Driving Range: Yes
Junior Golf: Yes
Architect/Yr Open: Steve Durkee/1958/1996

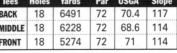

Other: Clubhouse / Lockers / Showers / Snack Bar / Restaurant / Bar-Lounge / Lodging Partner

Excellent conditions. Friendly staff. 12 new holes designed by Steve Durkee. #7 hole redesigned in 2012. A hidden gem!

	1	2	3	4	5	6	7	8	9
PAR	4	4	4	4	5	3	4	5	4
YARDS	309	317	339	389	508	140	384	458	272
	10	11	12	13	14	15	16	17	18
PAR	3/4	5	3	4	5	4	4	3	4
YARDS	165	491	140	343	522	357	243	117	344

Directions: Route 7 to Route 73 East. Follow for 1.5 miles East of Brandon Center.

Newport Country Club

✪✪½   34 ▶   VT

590 Mount Vernon Street
Newport, VT (802) 334-2391
www.newportscountryclub.com

Tees	Holes	Yards	Par	USGA	Slope
BACK	18	6491	72	70.4	117
MIDDLE	18	6228	72	68.6	114
FRONT	18	5274	72	71	114

Club Pro: Carl Fitz III, PGA
Payment: MC, Visa
Tee Times: 2 day adv.
Fee 9 Holes: Weekday: $20
Fee 18 Holes: Weekday: $36
Twilight Rates: No
Cart Rental: $18pp/18, $10pp/9
Lessons: $40/half hour **Schools:**
Membership: Yes

Weekend: $20
Weekend: $36
Discounts: Junior under 10 yrs/$5
Driving Range: $5/bucket
Junior Golf: Yes
Architect/Yr Open: Ralph Barton

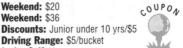

Other: Restaurant / Clubhouse / Bar-Lounge / Lockers / Showers / Snack Bar

Very friendly. Improvements continuing. Nicer greens.

	1	2	3	4	5	6	7	8	9
PAR	4	3	4	5	4	3	4	4	5
YARDS	354	172	356	484	326	150	397	335	469
	10	11	12	13	14	15	16	17	18
PAR	5	4	4	3	4	4	4	3	5
YARDS	479	374	387	144	375	395	314	142	464

Directions: I-91 to Exit 27. Head toward Newport about ½ mile. Take left and follow signs.

Northfield Country Club

NR 35 ▶

Route 12A
Northfield, VT (802) 485-4515
www.northfieldcountryclub.com

Tees	Holes	Yards	Par	USGA	Slope
BACK	18	5972	70	69.0	122
MIDDLE	18	5768	70	68.0	120
FRONT	18	5140	70	63.1	119

Club Pro: Joe Dingledine, PGA
Payment: Visa, MC, Cash, Checks
Tee Times: Required
Fee 9 Holes: Weekday: $15 M-Th   **Weekend:** $20 F/S/S
Fee 18 Holes: Weekday: $21 M-Th   **Weekend:** $28 F/S/S
Twilight Rates: No   **Discounts:** Junior and under free
Cart Rental: $15pp/18, $9pp/9   **Driving Range:** Netted practice area
Lessons: Private and Group **Schools:** No   **Junior Golf:** Yes
Membership: Yes   **Architect/Yr Open:** Les Heon/1927
Other: Restaurant / Bar / Clubhouse / Showers **GPS:**

Player Comments: "Old-fashioned, wonderful and friendly course." Known for 'The Volcano" hole #4.

	1	2	3	4	5	6	7	8	9
PAR	4	4	4	3	4	5	4	3	4
YARDS	348	314	276	148	377	532	336	183	367
	10	11	12	13	14	15	16	17	18
PAR	4	4	3	3	5	5	4	3	4
YARDS	340	352	175	148	465	532	325	183	367

Directions: I-89 to Exit 5, follow to bottom of hill. Go straight .75 mile to a T. Turn left on 12A and go 2.5 miles. Clubhouse is on right.

Okemo Valley Golf Club

✪✪✪✪ 36 ▶

89 Fox Lane
Ludlow, VT (802) 228-1396
www.okemo.com/golf

Tees	Holes	Yards	Par	USGA	Slope
BACK	18	6400	70	71.1	130
MIDDLE	18	6104	70	69.6	128
FRONT	18	5105	70	70.1	125

Club Pro: Jim Remy
Payment: Visa, MC, Amex
Tee Times: 7 days adv.
Fee 9 Holes: Weekday: $39   **Weekend:** $43
Fee 18 Holes: Weekday: $72   **Weekend:** $83
Twilight Rates: After 1:30pm weekdays;   **Discounts:** Junior
                  After 2:30pm weekends
Cart Rental: $22pp/18, $11pp/9   **Driving Range:** Yes
Lessons: $75/hour **Schools:** Adult   **Junior Golf:** Jr Rates
Membership: Waiting list   **Architect/Yr Open:** Steve Durkee/1999
Other: Full Restaurant / Clubhouse / Hotel / Inn / Lockers / Showers / Bar

COUPON

Vermont's only Heathland Course. "One of Vermont's best public courses. Great views of Okemo Mountain and valley. Many memorable holes. Excellent facilities." –GM

	1	2	3	4	5	6	7	8	9
PAR	4	5	4	3	4	3	5	3	4
YARDS	381	522	352	175	368	167	487	173	347
	10	11	12	13	14	15	16	17	18
PAR	4	5	4	4	3	4	4	3	4
YARDS	305	502	371	304	205	396	435	196	418

Directions: Just North of Ludlow about 1 mile on Route 103. Right onto Fox Lane (signs on highway).

Orleans Country Club

316 Country Club Lane
Orleans, VT (802) 754-2333
www.orleanscc.com

Tees	Holes	Yards	Par	USGA	Slope
BACK	18	6185	72	69.3	121
MIDDLE	18	5970	72	68.5	119
FRONT	18	5523	73	66.7	116

Club Pro: Joshua Olney
Payment: MC, Visa, Checks
Tee Times: 7 days adv.
Fee 9 Holes: Weekday: $18   **Weekend:** $19
Fee 18 Holes: Weekday: $36   **Weekend:** $38
Twilight Rates: After 3pm   **Discounts:** Under 12 free w/adult
Cart Rental: $19pp/18, $10pp/9   **Driving Range:** $8/lg, $4/sm bucket
Lessons: $40/half hour   **Schools:** Yes   **Junior Golf:** Yes
Membership: Yes   **Architect/Yr Open:** Alex Reid/1928
Other: Clubhouse / Restaurant / Snack Bar / Bar Lounge / Lockers / Showers / Lodging Partner
GPS: No

COUPON

Excellent course conditions, scenic mountain views. Course is relatively short at 6200 yards from blue tees, however the challenge starts on the greens.

	1	2	3	4	5	6	7	8	9
PAR	5	4	3	5	4	4	4	3	4
YARDS	442	319	152	439	365	356	300	180	355
	10	11	12	13	14	15	16	17	18
PAR	3	5	4	3	4	4	5	4	4
YARDS	200	479	359	134	426	292	495	285	392

Directions: From Interstate 91 make a left turn onto State Route 58. Remain on 58 for almost 3 miles, course on the right.

Proctor Pittsford Country Club

Cornhill Road
Pittsford, VT (802) 483-9379
www.proctor-pittsford.com

Tees	Holes	Yards	Par	USGA	Slope
BACK	18	6052	70	69.4	121
MIDDLE	18	5728	70	67.9	118
FRONT	18	5446	72	66.1	115

Club Pro:
Payment: MC, Visa, Disc
Tee Times: 2 days adv.
Fee 9 Holes: Weekday: $22   **Weekend:** $22 after 12pm
Fee 18 Holes: Weekday: $40   **Weekend:** $40
Twilight Rates: $22 after 4pm   **Discounts:** None
Cart Rental: $20pp/18, $10 pp/9   **Driving Range:** Yes
Lessons: Yes   **Schools:** No   **Junior Golf:** Yes
Membership: Yes   **Architect/Yr Open:** Henry Collin/1927
Other: Restaurant / Lounge   **GPS:** No

COUPON

Beautiful views, excellent greens and fairways, good test of golf. Open April 15 - October 31. Brand-new driving range. Full-service restaurant. Check out the marble clubhouse.

	1	2	3	4	5	6	7	8	9
PAR	4	4	4	5	4	4	3	4	3
YARDS	325	386	308	489	370	326	133	281	219
	10	11	12	13	14	15	16	17	18
PAR	4	3	5	4	4	4	4	3	4
YARDS	409	144	468	377	332	301	388	163	309

Directions: Take Route 7 for 4 miles north, take left after Nissan dealer. Go ½ mile, take right at "T," go 3 miles on Cornhill Road.

Prospect Bay Country Club NR 39 ▶

Prospect Point Road (Route 30)
Bomoseen, VT (802) 468-5581

Tees	Holes	Yards	Par	USGA	Slope
BACK	9	2635	35	65.2	115
MIDDLE	9	2557	35	64.6	114
FRONT	9	2294	35	65.4	114

Club Pro: Brian Kilpatick, Manager
Payment: MC, Visa
Tee Times: No
Fee 9 Holes: Weekday: $15, $23/ride   **Weekend:** $17, $26/ride
Fee 18 Holes: Weekday: $22, $30/ride   **Weekend:** $26, $36/ride
Twilight Rates: After 4pm weekdays   **Discounts:** None
Cart Rental: $13.50pp/18, $9pp/9   **Driving Range:** No
Lessons: No **Schools:** No   **Junior Golf:** Yes
Membership: Yes   **Architect/Yr Open:** 1953
Other: Clubhouse / Snack Bar   **GPS:**

The course is hilly and scenic. Great shape. Open April - November.

	1	2	3	4	5	6	7	8	9
PAR	5	3	4	4	4	4	4	4	3
YARDS	405	155	311	283	268	335	298	370	132
PAR									
YARDS									

Directions: Route 4 to Exit 4; follow Route 30 North for 2 miles to course entrance.

Ralph Myhre Golf Course ✪✪ 40 ▶

317 Golf Course Road
Middlebury, VT (802) 443-5125
www.middlebury.edu

Tees	Holes	Yards	Par	USGA	Slope
BACK	18	6379	71	70.8	124
MIDDLE	18	6014	71	69.2	68.9
FRONT	18	5337	71	66.9	120

Club Pro: Jim Dayton
Payment: Cash, Visa, MC
Tee Times: Recommended
Fee 9 Holes: Weekday: $20   **Weekend:** $20
Fee 18 Holes: Weekday: $39   **Weekend:** $39
Twilight Rates: After 4pm   **Discounts:** Students
Cart Rental: $20pp/18, $11pp/9   **Driving Range:** Yes
Lessons: Yes **Schools:** No   **Junior Golf:** Yes
Membership: Yes   **Architect/Yr Open:** Ralph Myhre/1920
Other: Clubhouse / Snack Bar / Showers   **GPS:** Yes

COUPON

Open fairways with moderate hills. Well-kept and tees sodded. Owned by Middlebury College.
Any student (any school) pays $15.

	1	2	3	4	5	6	7	8	9
PAR	5	4	4	3	4	4	3	4	4
YARDS	479	341	311	166	356	370	141	353	365
	10	**11**	**12**	**13**	**14**	**15**	**16**	**17**	**18**
PAR	4	5	3	4	3	4	5	4	4
YARDS	404	525	152	325	126	363	512	351	377

Directions: Route 7 to Route 30 South. Course is just beyond Middlebury College Field House.

Richford Country Club

249 Golf Course Road
Richford, VT (802) 848-3527
www.richfordcountryclub.weebly.com

Club Pro: John Sheridan
Payment: Visa, MC
Tee Times: No
Fee 9 Holes: Weekday: $14 M-Th
Fee 18 Holes: Weekday: $16 M-Th
Twilight Rates: Wed. after 3pm
Cart Rental: $12.50pp/18, $18.50pp/9
Lessons: No **Schools:** No
Membership: $350 (before Dec. 11)
Other: Clubhouse / Snack Bar / Bar-Lounge

Tees	Holes	Yards	Par	USGA	Slope
BACK					
MIDDLE	9	2908	36	68.2	116
FRONT	9	2326	36	72.0	118

Weekend: $18 F/S/S
Weekend: $22 F/S/S
Discounts: None
Driving Range: No
Junior Golf: Yes
Architect/Yr Open: 1915 (Redesigned 2009)

COUPON

We have added 6 new tees to add an even better look, and greater challenge. Excellent views of the Green Mountains. New clubhouse. "Vermont's most scenic golf course." Open April - October.

	1	2	3	4	5	6	7	8	9
PAR	4	5	3	4	5	3	3	4	4
YARDS	283	464	170	318	400	453	175	298	367
PAR									
YARDS									

Directions: I-89 to St. Albans exit. Follow Route 105 North to Richford (28 miles).

Rocky Ridge Golf Club

7470 Route 116
St. George, VT (802) 482-2191
www.rockyridge.com

Club Pro: Ed Coleman
Payment: Visa, MC, Disc, Check
Tee Times: 48 hours adv.
Fee 9 Holes: Weekday:
Fee 18 Holes: Weekday: $34
Twilight Rates: After 5pm
Cart Rental: $17pp/18
Lessons: No **Schools:**
Membership: Yes
Other: Clubhouse / Restaurant / Bar-Lounge

Tees	Holes	Yards	Par	USGA	Slope
BACK	18	6282	72	70.3	126
MIDDLE	18	6000	72	69.1	124
FRONT	18	5230	72	69.9	117

Weekend:
Weekend: $38
Discounts: No
Driving Range: Yes
Junior Golf: Yes
Architect/Yr Open: E. Farrington/1963

COUPON

A challenging and very scenic country setting for all skill levels. Online course review. Voted best Public Course in the Burlington area.

	1	2	3	4	5	6	7	8	9
PAR	4	5	3	5	4	4	4	3	4
YARDS	270	542	195	576	314	251	339	191	345
	10	**11**	**12**	**13**	**14**	**15**	**16**	**17**	**18**
PAR	4	4	4	4	3	4	5	3	5
YARDS	395	289	312	367	156	315	460	163	513

Directions: I-89 to Exit 12. Go 5 miles west. Course is at intersection of Routes 2A and 116.

Rutland Country Club ✪✪✪ ▶43

275 Grove Street
Rutland, VT (802) 773-3254
www.rutlandcountryclub.com

Tees	Holes	Yards	Par	USGA	Slope
BACK	18	6135	70	69.7	125
MIDDLE	18	5758	70	67.9	122
FRONT	18	5368	71	71.6	125

Club Pro: Greg Nelson, PGA
Payment: Visa, MC, Disc
Tee Times: 48 hours adv.
Fee 9 Holes: Weekday: **Weekend:**
Fee 18 Holes: Weekday: Call for rates **Weekend:** Call for rates
Twilight Rates: Call for rates **Discounts:** Junior
Cart Rental: Included **Driving Range:** No
Lessons: Yes **Schools:** No **Junior Golf:** Yes
Membership: Yes **Architect/Yr Open:** George Low/1902
Other: Clubhouse / Lockers / Showers / Snack Bar / Restaurant / Bar-Lounge

Player Comments: "Great greens and great values. Worth the money." Open May - October.
"One of the best older style public courses I've ever played" –GM

	1	2	3	4	5	6	7	8	9
PAR	4	4	3	5	3	4	4	4	4
YARDS	379	381	125	463	215	366	322	368	300
	10	11	12	13	14	15	16	17	18
PAR	4	4	3	5	4	3	4	4	4
YARDS	296	316	193	513	347	121	351	326	376

Directions: I -89 to Exit 1. Take Route 4 West to Rutland. Take right onto Grove Street and follow signs to course.

Ryder Brook Golf Club NR ▶44

3266 Laporte Road
Morrisville, VT (802) 888-3525
www.ryderbrookgc.com.com

Tees	Holes	Yards	Par	USGA	Slope
BACK	9	3037	36	68.6	118
MIDDLE	9	2847	36	67.8	115
FRONT	9	2517	36	74.0	113

Club Pro: Eileen Kask, PGA
Payment: Visa, MC
Tee Times: Yes
Fee 9 Holes: Weekday: $22 **Weekend:** $24
Fee 18 Holes: Weekday: $32 **Weekend:** $35
Twilight Rates: After 4pm **Discounts:** Senior/Junior
Cart Rental: $13.50pp/18, $9pp/9 **Driving Range:** Yes
Lessons: Yes **Schools:** Yes **Junior Golf:** Yes
Membership: Yes **Architect/Yr Open:** Geoffrey Cornish/1969
Other: Junior Camp **GPS:**

COUPON

Great course for golfers of all abilities. Play & stay at 1 location. Open May - October. Fairways and greens improvements! Montreal and Stow, Vermont close by.

	1	2	3	4	5	6	7	8	9
PAR	4	4	5	3	3	5	4	3	5
YARDS	351	315	466	158	148	574	410	157	458
PAR									
YARDS									

Directions: Exit 10 from I-89. North on Route 100. 5.5 miles north of Stowe Village. Left side of Route 100.

Sitzmark Golf Course

 NR 45 ▶

54 E. Dover Road
Wilmington, VT (802) 464-3384
www.sitzmarkbarandgrill.com

Club Pro:
Payment: All Major Credit Cards
Tee Times: No
Fee 9 Holes: Weekday: $18
Fee 18 Holes: Weekday: $25
Twilight Rates: After 5:00pm
Cart Rental: $5/pullcart; $15/motorized
Lessons: No **Schools:** No
Membership: No
Architect/Yr Open: Robert Miller & Charles Rotollo/1979
Other:

Tees	Holes	Yards	Par	USGA	Slope
BACK					
MIDDLE	18	2650	57		
FRONT					

Weekend: $18
Weekend: $25
Discounts: Senior $20/Junior $15
Driving Range: No
Junior Golf: No

An 18-hole par 3, plus 2 long shots. Generally considered an "iron course," it provides a challenge for the experienced golfer and an excellent introduction for the beginner. A fun, walkable course. Located in the heart of the beautiful Southern Vermont Valley. Wednesday special: play 18 for the price of 9.

	1	2	3	4	5	6	7	8	9
PAR	3	3	3	3	3	3	3	3	4
YARDS	190	90	115	130	155	90	115	130	255
	10	**11**	**12**	**13**	**14**	**15**	**16**	**17**	**18**
PAR	4	4	3	3	3	3	3	3	3
YARDS	350	285	105	120	120	90	105	90	115

Directions: Take I-91 to Exit 2 - Brattleboro. Get on Route 9 West towards Wilmington; right onto Route 100 North, then right onto E. Dover Road. Course is on the left.

St. Johnsbury Country Club

✪✪½ 46 ▶ **VT**

Route 5
St. Johnsbury, VT (802) 748-9894
www.golfstjcc.com

Club Pro: Bryce Chaffee, PGA
Payment: Cash, Visa, MC, Amex, Discover
Tee Times: 1 week adv.
Fee 9 Holes: Weekday: $16
Fee 18 Holes: Weekday: $32
Twilight Rates: After 4pm
Cart Rental: $17pp/18, $12pp/9
Lessons: 3 lessons/$125 **Schools:** No
Membership: Yes
Other: Clubhouse / Snack Bar / Renovated Restaurant / Bar-Lounge

Tees	Holes	Yards	Par	USGA	Slope
BACK	18	6373	70	70.4	130
MIDDLE	18	5860	70	68.6	125
FRONT	18	5480	70	71.3	120

Weekend: $19
Weekend: $38
Discounts: Junior
Driving Range: $5/med., $3/sm.
Junior Golf: Yes
Architect/Yr Open: Willie Park Jr./1923

Player Comments: "Great value." Front 9, wide open. Back 9, narrow and challenging. Lots of hills and blind shots. Not for the timid." Prices subject to change.

	1	2	3	4	5	6	7	8	9
PAR	4	4	3	4	3	5	3	5	4
YARDS	314	363	168	434	232	578	188	473	434
	10	**11**	**12**	**13**	**14**	**15**	**16**	**17**	**18**
PAR	5	4	3	4	4	3	5	3	4
YARDS	496	385	176	398	395	195	575	203	366

Directions: I-91 North to Exit 23 (US Route 5); follow 3 miles. From I-91 South to Exit 22 to Route 5; follow 4 miles.

Stamford Valley Country Club   NR   47 ▶

194 Phelene Lane (Route 9)
Stamford, VT (802) 694-9144
www.stamfordvalleygolf.com

Club Pro:
Payment: Cash, Visa, MC
Tee Times: Recommended
Fee 9 Holes: Weekday: $14
Fee 18 Holes: Weekday: $20
Twilight Rates: No
Cart Rental: $12pp/18, $7pp/9
Lessons: No **Schools:** No
Membership: Yes
Other: Full Restaurant

Tees	Holes	Yards	Par	USGA	Slope
BACK					
MIDDLE	9	2709	36	66.6	104
FRONT					

Weekend: $14
Weekend: $20
Discounts: None
Driving Range: No
Junior Golf: No
Architect/Yr Open: Stan & Leroy Lawrence/1964
GPS:

Great foliage and wonderful mountain views. Over 20 new bunkers and brand-new clubhouse with complete restaurant facility. A course for all ages.

	1	2	3	4	5	6	7	8	9
PAR	4	4	4	5	4	4	3	4	4
YARDS	232	288	342	392	330	320	215	355	235
PAR									
YARDS									

Directions: Route 8 North (out of North Adams), about 5 miles over Stamford line.

Stonehedge Golf Course   NR   48 ▶

216 Squire Road
North Clarendon, VT
(802) 773-2666
www.stonehedgegolf.com

Club Pro:
Payment: Visa, MC, Cash, Check
Tee Times: Yes
Fee 9 Holes: Weekday: $11.50
Fee 18 Holes: Weekday: $15.50
Twilight Rates: No
Cart Rental: $9.50pp/18, $6.50pp/9
Lessons: No **Schools:** No
Membership: No
Other: Snacks and Soft Drinks

Tees	Holes	Yards	Par	USGA	Slope
BACK					
MIDDLE	9	1107	27		
FRONT					

Weekend: $12.50
Weekend: $17.50
Discounts: Senior Wednesdays
Driving Range: No
Junior Golf: No
Architect/Yr Open: Robert Matson/1995
GPS:

Challenging par 3 with pretty views — excellent greens, water and sand traps — easy course to walk.

	1	2	3	4	5	6	7	8	9
PAR	3	3	3	3	3	3	3	3	3
YARDS	153	84	181	152	86	77	180	93	101
PAR									
YARDS									

Directions: Located 3 miles South of Rutland (no interstate nearby) at the junction of Routes 7 and 103.

Stowe Country Club

○○½ ▶ 49

5781 Mountain Road
Stowe, VT (802) 253-4893
www.stowe.com

Tees	Holes	Yards	Par	USGA	Slope
BACK	18	6213	72	69.3	117
MIDDLE	18	5851	72	67.5	114
FRONT	18	5365	74	68.5	112

Club Pro: Dan Lehmann, PGA
Payment: Visa, MC, Amex, Disc
Tee Times: Anytime
Fee 9 Holes: Weekday:
Fee 18 Holes: Weekday: $90-$105 w/cart
Twilight Rates: After 2pm
Cart Rental: Included
Lessons: Yes **Schools:** Golf School
Membership: Yes
Weekend:
Weekend: $90-$105 w/cart
Discounts: None
Driving Range: $5/lg bucket
Junior Golf: Yes
Architect/Yr Open: Walter Barcomb/1950
Other: Clubhouse / Lockers / Showers / Restaurant / Bar/ Hotel / Beverage Cart

Player Comments: "Beautiful course. Friendly staff." Excellent stay & play golf package. Open May -
mid-October. Fees vary with season and time of day.

	1	2	3	4	5	6	7	8	9
PAR	5	3	5	3	4	5	4	3	4
YARDS	482	152	450	153	367	472	381	135	370
	10	11	12	13	14	15	16	17	18
PAR	3	5	4	4	5	3	4	4	4
YARDS	170	445	371	327	447	158	352	341	279

Directions: I-89 to Exit 10. Follow Route 100 for 10 miles to blinking light in center of Stowe Village,
turn left onto Route 108. Turn right directly past Whiskers Restaurant onto Cape Cod Road. Course
straight ahead.

Stratton Mountain

○○○½ ▶ 50

VT

Rural Route 1
Stratton Mountain, VT
(802) 297-4118
www.stratton.com

Tees	Holes	Yards	Par	USGA	Slope
BACK	27/18	6526	72	71.2	125
MIDDLE	27/18	6044	72	69.4	122
FRONT	27/18	5155	74	69.8	123

Club Pro: Matthew McPhillips
Payment: Most Major Credit Cards
Tee Times: Anytime
Fee 9 Holes: Weekday: $49-$59 w/cart
Fee 18 Holes: Wkdy: $69-$79 (M-Th) w/cart
Twilight Rates: After 5pm
Cart Rental: Cart included
Lessons: $40/half hour **Schools:** Yes
Membership: Yes
Weekend: $69-$79 w/cart
Wknd: $89-$99 incl. cart F/S/S/H
Discounts: Junior
Driving Range: $7/lg., $4/sm.
Junior Golf: No
Architect/Yr Open: Geoffrey Cornish/1959

COUPON

Other: Clubhouse / Snack Bar / Restaurant / Bar-Lounge / Hotel

27-hole complex—Forest & Lake 9s below. Cornish design features. Rates vary by season.
Player Comments: "1st-class services really makes a golfer feel special."

	1	2	3	4	5	6	7	8	9
PAR	4	4	4	3	5	4	3	5	4
YARDS	372	387	305	129	467	295	140	504	379
	10	11	12	13	14	15	16	17	18
PAR	4	4	4	3	4	5	3	4	5
YARDS	353	395	328	164	269	466	193	390	508

Directions: Take I-91 to Brattleboro exit, follow Route 30 East for 30 miles to Bondville; look for
signs to Stratton Mountain.

Sugarbush Resort Golf Club ✪✪✪✪

 51

1091 Golf Course Road
Warren, VT (802) 583-6725
www.sugarbush.com

Tees	Holes	Yards	Par	USGA	Slope
BACK	18	6404	71	71.7	131
MIDDLE	18	5922	71	69.0	122
FRONT	18	4879	71	70.5	129

Club Pro: R.J. Austin
Payment: Visa, MC, Amex, Disc, Cash
Tee Times: Yes
Fee 9 Holes: Weekday: $60   **Weekend:** $65
Fee 18 Holes: Weekday: $90   **Weekend:** $100
Twilight Rates: After 2pm
Discounts: Junior free w/adult after 2pm; $30 w/o
Cart Rental: Included in fee   **Driving Range:** Yes
Lessons: Yes **Schools:** No   **Junior Golf:** Yes
Membership: Yes   **Architect/Yr Open:** Robert Trent Jones Sr./1962
Other: Restaurant / Clubhouse / Hotel / Bar-Lounge / Snack Bar / Showers / Lodging Partner
GPS: Yes

Challenging layout set in the Green Mountains. "Breathtaking views and dramatic elevation changes with a variety of blind shots and fun shots. A nice place to visit." –FP

	1	2	3	4	5	6	7	8	9
PAR	4	4	4	4	3	4	4	3	4
YARDS	345	380/506	409	361	170	373	434	184	353
	10	**11**	**12**	**13**	**14**	**15**	**16**	**17**	**18**
PAR	5	3	4	4	5	4	3	4	4
YARDS	516	155	385	358	359	161	334	334	326

Directions: I-89 North to Exit 10 - 100 South, Sugarbush Access Road. Left onto Golf Course Road. One mile on left.

Tater Hill Golf Club ✪✪✪

 52

6802 Popple Dungeon Road
North Windham, VT
(802) 875-2517
www.taterhillgolfclub.com

Tees	Holes	Yards	Par	USGA	Slope
BACK	18	6048	70	71.4	129
MIDDLE	18	5426	72	68.7	125
FRONT	18	4475	70	68.1	112

Club Pro: John Pawlak, PGA
Payment: Visa, MC, Amex
Tee Times: 5 days adv.
Fee 9 Holes: Weekday: $35   **Weekend:** $35
Fee 18 Holes: Weekday: $57   **Weekend:** $77 w/cart
Twilight Rates: After 4pm   **Discounts:** Junior
Cart Rental: $19pp/18, $10pp/9   **Driving Range:** $3/30 balls
Lessons: $40/half hour **Schools:** No   **Junior Golf:** Yes
Membership: Yes   **Architect/Yr Open:** Don Warner/1963
Other: Clubhouse / Bar-Lounge / Restaurant   **GPS:**

Reconstructed front 9 in 2005. "Very well maintained, greens are fantastic, terrific staff." "Better every year." –KL Sister course to Okemo.

	1	2	3	4	5	6	7	8	9
PAR	5	3	3	4	3	5	4	4	5
YARDS	473	133	193	352	160	470	397	305	450
	10	**11**	**12**	**13**	**14**	**15**	**16**	**17**	**18**
PAR	3	4	4	4	4	3	5	4	5
YARDS	168	388	414	373	324	148	462	295	530

Directions: I-91 to Exit 6; take left onto Route 103, turns into 11 West; 7 miles outside Chester look for signs to course.

West Bolton Golf Club ✪✪ 53 ►

5161A Stage Road, West Bolton
Jericho, VT (802) 434-4321
www.westboltongolfclub.com

Tees	Holes	Yards	Par	USGA	Slope
BACK					
MIDDLE	18	5761	72	66.8	115
FRONT	18	5165	72	72.5	111

Club Pro: Ken Stavisky
Payment: Visa, MC, Cash, Check
Tee Times: 1 week adv.
Fee 9 Holes: Weekday: $20
Fee 18 Holes: Weekday: $27
Twilight Rates: After 3pm
Cart Rental: $14pp/18, $7pp/9
Lessons: Yes **Schools:** Junior
Membership: Yes
Other: Clubhouse / Snack Bar

Weekend: $20
Weekend: $27
Discounts: Srs., Jrs., Ladies
Driving Range: No
Junior Golf: Yes
Architect/Yr Open: Ken Wheeler/1983
GPS:

Unique 18-hole course nestled in the Green Mountains. The fairway trees are small, but the mountains surrounding the course are grand.

	1	2	3	4	5	6	7	8	9
PAR	4	5	3	4	4	3	4	4	4
YARDS	303	481	149	248	353	191	329	359	295
	10	11	12	13	14	15	16	17	18
PAR	3	5	4	5	3	5	4	4	4
YARDS	128	430	392	451	180	458	273	323	418

Directions: I-89 to Exit 11 toward Richmond. Left at light (Four Corners). Go about 7 miles and take a right at the West Bolton Golf Course sign. Continue for 4 miles.

White River Golf Club NR 54 ►

3070 Route 100
Rochester, VT (802) 767-4653
www.whiterivergolf.com

Tees	Holes	Yards	Par	USGA	Slope
BACK	9	2657	34	65.6	115
MIDDLE	9	2345	34	64.6	112
FRONT	9	1988	34	60.2	104

Club Pro:
Payment: Cash, MC, Visa
Tee Times: Recommended
Fee 9 Holes: Weekday: $20
Fee 18 Holes: Weekday: $30
Twilight Rates: M/T/Th/F after 3:30pm
Cart Rental: $10pp/18
Lessons: Schools: Yes
Membership: Yes
Other: Clubhouse / Bar-Lounge / Snack Bar

Weekend: $21
Weekend: $31
Discounts: Junior
Driving Range: Yes
Junior Golf: Yes
Architect/Yr Open: Peter McGowan/1972
GPS:

COUPON

9-hole panoramic from every hole. Recent design changes have made a true test of skill for the experienced golfer while still appealing to the novice golfer. Open May - October. 10-play ticket available.

	1	2	3	4	5	6	7	8	9
PAR	3	5	4	3	3	4	4	4	4
YARDS	175	485	248	115	118	385	218	332	269
PAR									
YARDS									

Directions: I-89 to Route 107 West to Route 100 North. Course is 10 miles north on Route 100. Approximately halfway between Killington and Sugarbush.

Wilcox Cove Golf Course

NR ▶ **55**

3 Camp Vermont Court (Highway 314)
Grand Isle, VT (802) 372-8343
www.wilcoxcove.com

Club Pro:
Payment: Cash, Check
Tee Times: No
Fee 9 Holes: Weekday: $15
Fee 18 Holes: Weekday: $15
Twilight Rates: After 6pm
Cart Rental: $3/pull
Lessons: No **Schools:** No
Membership: Yes
Other: No

Tees	Holes	Yards	Par	USGA	Slope
BACK					
MIDDLE	9	1732	32		
FRONT					

Weekend: $18
Weekend: $18
Discounts: None
Driving Range: No
Junior Golf:
Architect/Yr Open: Michael Hurzdan/1947
GPS:

COUPON

An executive-type course on the West shore of Grand Isle, looking over Lake Champlain to the Adirondack Mountains of New York. A fairly level course. Twilight weekend rates.

	1	2	3	4	5	6	7	8	9
PAR	4	4	4	3	4	3	4	3	3
YARDS	240	210	254	120	245	190	185	193	95
PAR									
YARDS									

Directions: I-89 to Exit 17 (Route 2 North). Take Route 314 past Grand Isle ferry.

Williston Golf Club

✪✪ ▶ **56**

424 Golf Course Road
Williston, VT (802) 878-3747
www.willistongolfclub.com

Club Pro: Todd Trono, PGA
Payment: Visa, MC, Disc
Tee Times: Weekends and Holidays
Fee 9 Holes: Weekday:
Fee 18 Holes: Weekday: $32
Twilight Rates: After 4pm
Cart Rental: $36/18, $18/9 per cart
Lessons: No **Schools:** Yes
Membership: Yes
Other: Resturant / Clubhouse / Bar-Lounge

Tees	Holes	Yards	Par	USGA	Slope
BACK	18	6621	69	N/R	N/R
MIDDLE	18	5262	69	66.6	113
FRONT	18	4716	71	64	106

Weekend:
Weekend: $35
Discounts: None
Driving Range: Nearby
Junior Golf: Yes
Architect/Yr Open: Ben Murray/1927
GPS: Yes

COUPON

Player Comments: "Play it at least twice a season. Very well kept. Always friendly." Fully irrigated. Open May - November 1.

	1	2	3	4	5	6	7	8	9
PAR	4	4	4	4	4	3	4	4	5
YARDS	316	390	289	272	260	184	267	382	445
	10	11	12	13	14	15	16	17	18
PAR	4	3	3	4	4	3	3	4	5
YARDS	325	160	212	254	395	151	90	360	510

Directions: I-89 to Exit 11 or 12; Route 2 East to North Williston Road. Course is ½ mile on right. 7 miles east of Burlington, Vermont.

Woodbury Golf Course

NR 57

2120 East Hill Road
South Woodbury, VT (802) 456-7421
www.woodburygolf.com

Tees	Holes	Yards	Par	USGA	Slope
BACK					
MIDDLE	9	1264	27		
FRONT					

Club Pro: Darwin Thompson
Payment: Visa, MC, Checks
Tee Times: (802) 456-1250
Fee 9 Holes: Weekday: $11   **Weekend:** $12 (tax included)
Fee 18 Holes: Weekday: $16.50   **Weekend:** $18 (tax included)
Twilight Rates: No
Discounts: Juniors 12 and under - free w/paying adult
Cart Rental: $10/9 per cart   **Driving Range:** No
Lessons: No **Schools:** No   **Junior Golf:**
Membership: Yes   **Architect/Yr Open:** Thompson Family/2004

COUPON

Great for your short game or a quick round with the family.

	1	2	3	4	5	6	7	8	9
PAR	3	3	3	3	3	3	3	3	3
YARDS	120	145	128	185	147	118	125	129	167
PAR									
YARDS									

Directions: I-89 to Route 2 East. Take Route 14 North. Right onto East Hill Road in South Woodbury. Course is 2 miles on right.

Woodstock Inn & Resort

✪✪✪½ 58

14 The Green
Route 106 South, Woodstock, VT
(802) 457-6674
www.woodstockinn.com

Tees	Holes	Yards	Par	USGA	Slope
BACK	18	6052	70	69.7	123
MIDDLE	18	5619	70	68.0	117
FRONT	18	4924	71	69.0	113

Club Pro: Jim Gunnare
Payment: Cash, MC, Visa, Amex
Tee Times: Yes
Fee 9 Holes: Weekday: $59   **Weekend:** $69
Fee 18 Holes: Weekday: $89   **Weekend:** $109
Twilight Rates: After 3pm   **Discounts:** None
Cart Rental: $20pp/18   **Driving Range:** $8/lg, $5/sm bucket
Lessons: $50/half hour **Schools:** Jr. & Sr.   **Junior Golf:** Yes
Membership: Yes   **Architect/Yr Open:** William H. Tucker/1895
Other: Clubhouse / Lockers / Showers / Restaurant / Bar-Lounge / Hotel / Snack Bar

Renovated clubhouse restaurant, ballroom, dining room, and new deck. Hosting annual Northeast PGA seniors championship. Updated by Robert Trent Jones in 1962. Driving range with new tee boxes.

	1	2	3	4	5	6	7	8	9
PAR	5	3	4	4	3	5	3	4	4
YARDS	465	162	346	382	134	503	162	356	386
	10	11	12	13	14	15	16	17	18
PAR	5	3	4	3	4	3	5	4	4
YARDS	414	131	381	150	272	144	520	315	396

Directions: I-89 to Exit 1 (VT), Route 4 West to Woodstock - South on Route 106 (1 mile).

Aroostook Valley CC	1	Hidden Meadows GC	23	Northeast Harbor GC	45
Bangor Municipal GC	2	Hillcrest Golf Club	24	Northport Golf Club	46
Bar Harbor Golf Course	3	Houlton Community GC	25	Palmyra Golf Course	47
Barnes Brook Golf Course	4	Island Country Club	26	Penobscot Valley CC	48
Barren View	5	Jato Highlands Golf Course	27	Pine Hill Golf Club	49
Belgrade Lakes GC	6	Johnson W. Parks GC	28	Pine Ridge Golf Course	50
Blink Bonnie	7	Katahdin Country Club	29	Piscataquis CC	51
Bucksport Golf Club	8	Kebo Valley Golf Club	30	Portage Hill CC	52
Caribou Country Club	9	Kenduskeag Valley GC	31	Presque Isle CC	53
Castine Golf Club	10	Lakeview Golf Course	32	Rocky Knoll Country Club	54
Causeway Club	11	Lakewood Golf Course	33	Sawmill Woods Golf Course	55
Cedar Springs Golf Course	12	Limestone CC	34	Searsport Pines Golf Course	56
Clinton Golf Club	13	Long Lake Country Club	35	Squaw Mt. Village CC	57
Country View GC	14	Loons Cove Golf Course	36	St. Croix Country Club	58
Dexter Municipal GC	15	Lucerne-in-Maine GC	37	Streamside Golf Course	59
Evergreen Golf Club	16	Mars Hill Country Club	38	Sugarloaf Golf Club	60
Fort Kent Golf Club	17	Mingo Springs GC	39	Traditions Golf Club	61
Foxcroft Golf Club	18	Moose River GC	40	Va-Jo-Wa Golf Club	62
Great Cove Golf Course	19	Mt. Kineo Golf Course	41	Waterville Country Club	63
Grindstone Neck GC	20	Natanis GC (Arrowhead)	42	White Tail Golf Course	64
Hampden CC	21	Natanis GC (Tomahawk)	43	Wilson Lake CC	65
Hermon Meadow GC	22	Newport CC	44		

KEY TO THE STAR RATINGS:
5✪ = Outstanding 4✪ = Excellent 3✪ = Very Good 2✪ = Good 1✪ = Average **NR** = Not Rated

Aroostook Valley Country Club ✪✪✪½

235 Russell Road
Fort Fairfield, ME (207) 476-8083
www.avcc.ca

Club Pro: Steven Leitch, CPGA
Payment: Visa, MC
Tee Times: 7 days adv.
Fee 9 Holes: Weekday: $23
Fee 18 Holes: Weekday: $45
Twilight Rates: After 2pm
Cart Rental: $17pp/18, $8.50pp/9
Lessons: $25/half hour **Schools:** No
Membership: Yes
Other: Clubhouse / Snack Bar / Bar-Lounge / Lockers / Showers

Tees	Holes	Yards	Par	USGA	Slope
BACK	18	6304	72	69.6	117
MIDDLE	18	5957	72	68.4	113
FRONT	18	5373	72	74.1	119

Weekend: $23
Weekend: $45
Discounts: Junior $20
Driving Range: $5/bucket
Junior Golf: Yes
Architect/Yr Open: Howard K. Watson/1927

COUPON

Very beautiful course; difficult inclines on back 9 make it challenging. White silica sand in bunkers. "Great conditions and beautiful holes make this a must-play." –DW

	1	2	3	4	5	6	7	8	9
PAR	4	4	5	3	5	4	4	3	4
YARDS	375	327	478	132	440	308	334	139	365
	10	11	12	13	14	15	16	17	18
PAR	4	4	5	3	5	3	4	3	5
YARDS	382	322	489	189	510	156	383	134	494

Directions: I-95 to last exit; take left onto Route 1 to Fort Fairfield, cross bridge. Take first right. Follow Russell Road to course.

Bangor Municipal Golf Course ✪✪½   2

278 Webster Avenue
Bangor, ME (207) 941-0232
www.bangorgc.com

Club Pro: Brian Enman
Payment: Cash, Visa, MC, Disc, Check
Tee Times: Weekends, Holidays
Fee 9 Holes: Weekday: $15
Fee 18 Holes: Weekday: $30
Twilight Rates: $18 after 4pm
Cart Rental: $14pp/18, $7pp/9
Lessons: $45/45 min. **Schools:** Yes
Membership: Yes
Other: Restaurant / Clubhouse / Bar-Lounge

Tees	Holes	Yards	Par	USGA	Slope
BACK	18	6335	71	69.2	115
MIDDLE	18	5833	71	67.9	112
FRONT	18	5173	71	69.1	111

Weekend: $15
Weekend: $30
Discounts: Senior, $18 wkdys before 11am
Driving Range: $4/bucket
Junior Golf: Yes
Architect/Yr Open: Geoffrey Cornish/1964
GPS:

27 holes. Hosted 1978 National Public Links Championship. Very playable golf course for all levels of play.

	1	2	3	4	5	6	7	8	9
PAR	4	4	3	5	4	3	4	4	4
YARDS	334	385	165	526	348	199	393	413	398
	10	11	12	13	14	15	16	17	18
PAR	4	3	4	4	4	5	3	4	5
YARDS	401	207	430	318	400	445	159	359	455

Directions: I-95 to Exit 183 (Hammond Street). Turn right and then immediate right onto Norway Road. Go to stop sign and turn right — ½ mile on left.

Bar Harbor Golf Course

✪✪½   ▶ 3

51 Jordan River Road, Route 204
Trenton, ME (207) 667-7505
www.barharborgolfcourse.com

Tees	Holes	Yards	Par	USGA	Slope
BACK	18	6680	71	71.1	128
MIDDLE	18	6450	71	70.3	127
FRONT	18	5428	73	70.5	125

Club Pro: Charles Crowley, GM
Payment: Visa, MC
Tee Times: No
Fee 9 Holes: Weekday: $25   **Weekend:** $25
Fee 18 Holes: Weekday: $40   **Weekend:** $40
Twilight Rates: No   **Discounts:** None
Cart Rental: $15pp/18, $8pp/9   **Driving Range:** No
Lessons: No **Schools:** No   **Junior Golf:** No
Membership: Yes   **Architect/Yr Open:** Philip Wogan/1967
Other: Clubhouse / Snack Bar / Bar-Lounge   **GPS:** Yes

COUPON

Links-style tract was designed by Phil Wogan. Located adjacent to the ocean, it is challenging and picturesque. A lengthy 18th hole which plays around and over tidle inlets. The course is mostly open and exposed to the wind.

	1	2	3	4	5	6	7	8	9
PAR	4	4	5	3	4	4	4	3	4
YARDS	427	388	520	156	402	408	368	172	343
	10	11	12	13	14	15	16	17	18
PAR	4	3	4	5	4	4	4	3	5
YARDS	428	155	295	589	374	318	405	158	544

Directions: Route 3 toward Bar Harbor. Course is located at intersection of Route 3 and Route 204 in Trenton.

Barnes Brook Golf Course

✪✪   ▶ 4

1886 Main Road (Route 2)
West Enfield, ME (207) 732-3006
www.barnesbrookgolfandski.com

Tees	Holes	Yards	Par	USGA	Slope
BACK	9	3100	36	68.4	127
MIDDLE	9	2897	36	67.0	119
FRONT	9	2625	36	63.8	109

Club Pro: Michael Clendenning
Payment: Cash, Visa, MC, Disc, Amex
Tee Times: No
Fee 9 Holes: Weekday: $14   **Weekend:** $14
Fee 18 Holes: Weekday: $20   **Weekend:** $20
Twilight Rates: No   **Discounts:** Junior and Senior
Cart Rental: $12/18, $9/9 per cart   **Driving Range:** Yes
Lessons: Yes **Schools:**   **Junior Golf:** Yes
Membership: Yes   **Architect/Yr Open:** Henry & James Ploude/1964
Other: Full Swing Indoor Golf Facility / Cross Country Ski Center

COUPON

Recently rebuilt all bunkers and overseeded fairways. Family friendly, Home of the Maine Junior Golf Club. Relatively easy to walk. Attractions include those of Lincoln Lakes area. Under new ownership.

	1	2	3	4	5	6	7	8	9
PAR	5	3	4	4	4	4	3	4	4
YARDS	490	172	288	238	355	450	156	366	382
PAR									
YARDS									

Directions: I-95 to Exit 217, go right. Go ¾ of a mile to stop sign. Take a right. Go ¾ of a mile to stop sign. Take left on Route 2. Go 4 miles, course is located off Route 2 on right.

Barren View Golf Course ✪✪ ▶ 5

1354 Route 1
Jonesboro, ME (207) 434-6531
www.barrenview.com

Tees	Holes	Yards	Par	USGA	Slope
BACK	9	2741	34	64.9	112
MIDDLE	9	2613	34	32.5	112
FRONT	9	2321	34	64.9	112

Club Pro:
Payment:
Tee Times:
Fee 9 Holes: Weekday: $15   **Weekend:** $15
Fee 18 Holes: Weekday: $25   **Weekend:** $25
Twilight Rates: **Discounts:** Junior 12 and under - $10
Cart Rental: $14pp/18, $8pp/9   **Driving Range:** $4/bucket
Lessons: Yes **Schools:**   **Junior Golf:**
Membership: Yes   **Architect/Yr:** Brad Prout & Lenny Espling/2003
Other: **GPS:**

Links-style course for all levels. "The course features expansive views of blueberry barrens. A hidden gem." –DW

	1	2	3	4	5	6	7	8	9
PAR	4	3	5	3	3	4	4	4	4
YARDS	369	129	406	201	143	280	292	361	430

PAR									
YARDS									

Directions: I-95 North to I-395 East to Route 1A. Exit toward Bar Harbor/Ellsworth. Take Route 1 out of Ellsworth toward Machias. Course is on right.

Belgrade Lakes Golf Club ✪✪✪✪ ▶ 6

46 Clubhouse Drive
Belgrade Lakes, ME (207) 495-GOLF
www.belgradelakesgolf.com

Tees	Holes	Yards	Par	USGA	Slope
BACK	18	6723	71	72.2	135
MIDDLE	18	6285	71	69.9	131
FRONT	18	5168	71	64.1	126

Club Pro:
Payment: Visa, MC, Amex
Tee Times:
Fee 9 Holes: Weekday: $80   **Weekend:** $80
Fee 18 Holes: Weekday: $135 (July/August)   **Weekend:** $135 (July/August)
Twilight Rates: No   **Discounts:** None
Cart Rental: $25pp/18   **Driving Range:** Hitting net
Lessons: No **Schools:** No   **Junior Golf:** Yes
Membership: No   **Architect/Yr Open:** Clive Clark/1997
Other: Snack Bar   **GPS:** Yes

Player Comments: "Every hole different and spectacularly beautiful." Improvements: enlarged and lengthened several tees. Walking encouraged. Caddies available for a fee plus tip. *Golf Magazine* 'Top 100 Courses You Can Play.'

	1	2	3	4	5	6	7	8	9
PAR	4	3	5	4	3	5	4	3	4
YARDS	424	156	450	424	161	485	384	186	376
	10	**11**	**12**	**13**	**14**	**15**	**16**	**17**	**18**
PAR	4	4	5	3	4	4	5	3	4
YARDS	346	395	568	203	344	311	530	171	371

Directions: I-95 to Exit 112B. Turn right onto Route 27. Go for 12 miles to town of Belgrade Lakes. Turn left at the Sunset Grille onto West Road. Course is ¼ mile on left.

Blink Bonnie Golf Links

✪✪½

185 East Side Road
Sorrento, ME (207) 422-3930

Club Pro:
Payment: Cash or Check
Tee Times:
Fee 9 Holes: Weekday: $20 all day
Fee 18 Holes: Weekday: $20 all day
Twilight Rates: No
Cart Rental: $2/pull
Lessons: No **Schools:**
Membership: Yes
Other:

Tees	Holes	Yards	Par	USGA	Slope
BACK					
MIDDLE	9	2520	36	65	112
FRONT					

Weekend: $30 all day
Weekend: $30 all day
Discounts: None
Driving Range: No
Junior Golf:
Architect/Yr Open:
GPS:

Player Comments: "Undiscovered gem. Breathtaking views, right on the ocean." Sorrento Village Improvement Association Yacht Club members only Friday morning until noon. Great for a quick 9.

	1	2	3	4	5	6	7	8	9
PAR	4	4	3	5	5	4	3	4	4
YARDS	350	270	180	510	490	310	120	290	330
PAR									
YARDS									

Directions: 48 miles from Bangor. Route Alternate 1 to Ellsworth (23 miles). Stay on Route 1 to Hancock. Then in Sullivan, go right on Route 185 (East Side Road) and proceed 2 miles. Course is on left.

Bucksport Golf Club

✪✪½

397 State Route 46
Bucksport, ME (207) 469-7612
www.bucksportgolfclub.com

Club Pro: Wayne Hand, PGA
Payment: Visa, MC
Tee Times: No
Fee 9 Holes: Weekday: $20
Fee 18 Holes: Weekday: $30
Twilight Rates: No
Cart Rental: $70pp/18, $12pp/9
Lessons: Yes **Schools:** No
Membership: Yes
Other: Bar-Lounge / Snack Bar / Lockers / Showers
GPS: Yes

Tees	Holes	Yards	Par	USGA	Slope
BACK	9	3890	37	72.5	
MIDDLE	9	3373	37	72.5	136
FRONT	9	5972	74	72.2	128

Weekend: $20
Weekend: $30
Discounts: Junior
Driving Range: $5/lg., $3.50/sm.
Junior Golf: Yes
Architect/Yr Open: Phil Wogan/1967

COUPON

9 holes with 2 sets of tees — 6780 yards, par 74, when you play both. Natural state of land emphasized in design. Golf specials: $70/18 for 2 people with cart; $50/9 for 2 people with cart.

	1	2	3	4	5	6	7	8	9
PAR	4	5	3	4	5	3	4	4	5
YARDS	330	500	147	407	504	163	408	354	560
PAR									
YARDS									

Directions: From Augusta: Route 3 to Belfast. Route 1 North to Bucksport. From Bangor: take Route 1A to Route 46. Course is 3 miles from Downtown Bucksport.

Caribou Country Club

⭐½ 9

723 Sweden Street
Caribou, ME (207) 493-3933
www.caribougolf.com

Club Pro: Jeff Jose
Payment: Visa, MC, Amex, Disc
Tee Times: No
Fee 9 Holes: Weekday: $15
Fee 18 Holes: Weekday: $22
Twilight Rates: No
Cart Rental: $22pp/18, $15pp/9
Lessons: Yes **Schools:** No
Membership: Yes

Tees	Holes	Yards	Par	USGA	Slope
BACK	9	3231	36	35.1	119
MIDDLE	9	3160	36	69.0	124
FRONT	9	3167	36	34.9	117

Weekend: $15
Weekend: $22
Discounts: Junior memberships
Driving Range: $7/lg, $3/sm bucket
Junior Golf: Yes
Architect/Yr Open: Geoffrey Cornish/1970

COUPON

Other: Restaurant / Clubhouse / Bar-Lounge / Snack Bar / Lockers / Showers

"Separate tee boxes carefully constructed to give the feel of an 18 hole course." –MH
The course has a beautiful log cabin clubhouse. Open May 1 - October 15.

	1	2	3	4	5	6	7	8	9
PAR	4	4	3	4	4	4	3	5	5
YARDS	340	330	215	408	360	330	170	530	484
	10	11	12	13	14	15	16	17	18
PAR	4	4	3	5	4	4	3	5	4
YARDS	360	345	195	515	411	340	150	550	365

Directions: Route 161 North; follow 1.5 miles outside Caribou; course is on right side.

Castine Golf Club

⭐⭐ 10

200 Battle Avenue
Castine, ME (207) 326-8844
www.castinegolfclub.com

Club Pro: Noah Tapley
Payment: Visa, MC, Cash
Tee Times: No
Fee 9 Holes: Weekday: $25
Fee 18 Holes: Weekday: $40
Twilight Rates:
Cart Rental: $15pp/18, $7.50pp/9
Lessons: Yes **Schools:** No
Membership: Yes
Other: Lockers / Lodging Partner

Tees	Holes	Yards	Par	USGA	Slope
BACK					
MIDDLE	9	3002	35	69.0	122
FRONT	9	2638	36	71.5	127

Weekend: $25
Weekend: $40
Discounts: Junior, call
Driving Range: Yes
Junior Golf: Yes
Architect/Yr Open: Willie Park Jr./1921
GPS: Yes

COUPON

The Castine Golf Club is a challenging and beautifully maintained 9 hole par 35. Scottish golf course designer, Willie Park Jr., now a Hall of Fame Designer, laid out the current nine holes in 1921, which offers stunning views of Castine Harbor and Penobscot Bay. Currently, the only Willie Park course in the state.

	1	2	3	4	5	6	7	8	9
PAR	4	3	4	3	4	4	5	4	4
YARDS	405	175	400	152	378	356	464	312	358
PAR									
YARDS									

Directions: Routes 1 & 3 through Bucksport. Turn right onto Route 175 to Route 166. Course is on right.

Causeway Club

⊛⊛½ 11 ▶

10 Fernald Point Road
S.W. Harbor, ME (207) 244-3780
www.thecausewayclub.org

Club Pro:
Payment: Visa, MC
Tee Times: No
Fee 9 Holes: Weekday: $35
Fee 18 Holes: Weekday: $45
Twilight Rates: After 4pm
Cart Rental: $25/18, $18/9 per cart
Lessons: No **Schools:** No
Membership: Yes
Other: Clubhouse / Lockers / Snacks

Tees	Holes	Yards	Par	USGA	Slope
BACK					
MIDDLE	9	2302	32	60.9	95
FRONT	9	2085	32	63.9	102

Weekend: $35
Weekend: $45
Discounts: Junior
Driving Range: No
Junior Golf: Yes
Architect/Yr Open: Alonso Yates/1923
GPS: Yes

On S.W. Harbor with scenic views. Closed to public after 6:30pm. Near Acadia National Park. New practice facility. 9-hole executive course with 2 sets of tees. Two 9s equal 4718 yards, par 65.

	1	2	3	4	5	6	7	8	9
PAR	4	4	4	4	4	3	3	3	3
YARDS	390	270	298	278	390	140	228	175	133
PAR									
YARDS									

Directions: I-95 to ALT Route 1 to Ellsworth. Follow Route 3 to Mt. Desert Island. Take Route 102 to Southwest Harbor.

Cedar Springs Golf Course

⊛½ 12 ▶

63 Bog Road
Albion, ME (207) 437-2073
www.cedarspringsgc.com

Club Pro: Tim Theriault
Payment: Cash, Checks
Tee Times: No
Fee 9 Holes: Weekday: $15
Fee 18 Holes: Weekday: $22
Twilight Rates: No
Cart Rental: $24pp/18, $12pp/9
Lessons: $20/30 min. **Schools:** No
Membership: Yes
Other: Restaurant / Clubhouse / Bar-Lounge / Snack Bar / Function Room

Tees	Holes	Yards	Par	USGA	Slope
BACK	9	2915	35		
MIDDLE	9	2700	35	65.6	109
FRONT	9	2355	55		

Weekend: $15
Weekend: $22
Discounts: None
Driving Range: No
Junior Golf: No
Architect/Yr Open: Tim Theriault/1997

COUPON

Cedar Springs is a well-maintained 9 hole picturesque golf course nestled in a country setting which offers a challenging 2700 yard layout. With their friendly staff and reasonable prices you will want to stay and enjoy lunch or a cool beverage after your round.

	1	2	3	4	5	6	7	8	9
PAR	4	4	3	4	4	3	5	4	4
YARDS	300	240	110	305	240	165	600	440	300
PAR									
YARDS									

Directions: Take I-95 to Exit 127 (Waterville/Oakland). Turn right onto Kennedy Memorial Drive (Route 137). Follow Route 137 through Winslow and China to Albion. In Albion turn left onto Bog Road. Cedar Springs is first right on Bog Road.

Clinton Golf Club

✪✪✪½ ▶13

510 Hill Road
Clinton, ME (207) 426-8795
www.clintongolfcourse.com

Club Pro:
Payment: Most Major Credit Cards
Tee Times: Call ahead
Fee 9 Holes: Weekday: $25
Fee 18 Holes: Weekday: $50
Twilight Rates: No
Cart Rental: $20pp/18, $10pp/9
Lessons: No **Schools:** No
Membership: No
Other: Snack Bar

Tees	Holes	Yards	Par	USGA	Slope
BACK	9	3240	36	71.2	140
MIDDLE	9	3002	36	68.8	138
FRONT	9	2348	36		

Weekend: $25
Weekend: $50
Discounts: None
Driving Range: No
Junior Golf: No
Architect/Yr Open: Steve Brown/2001
GPS:

Family-owned, -built, and -run. Limited access. Tee times every half hour. 9 holes with 2 sets of tees. "Very well kept, great way to spend a day." –GD

	1	2	3	4	5	6	7	8	9
PAR	4	4	4	3	5	4	3	5	4
YARDS	392	374	334	168	514	359	182	506	411
PAR									
YARDS									

Directions: I-95 to Exit 138 (Hinckley Road) to 100 North. Follow 100 to Railroad Street. Go left onto Railroad, and then left onto Hill Road.

Country View Golf Course

✪✪ ▶14

178 Moose Head Trail Highway
Brooks, ME (207) 722-3161

Club Pro:
Payment: Most Major Credit Cards
Tee Times: No
Fee 9 Holes: Weekday: $17
Fee 18 Holes: Weekday: $25
Twilight Rates: No
Cart Rental: $13pp/18, $8pp/9
Lessons: No **Schools:** No
Membership: Yes
Other: Snack Bar

Tees	Holes	Yards	Par	USGA	Slope
BACK	9	3000	36		115
MIDDLE	9	2885	36		115
FRONT	9	2480	36		105

Weekend: $17
Weekend: $25
Discounts: None
Driving Range: Yes
Junior Golf: No
Architect/Yr: Carl, Ralph & Steve Brown/1964
GPS:

COUPON

Very scenic and always dry. Very hilly course with tricky greens. "Challenging for good players but playable for all ability levels. Keep the ball below the hole on the green." –MH

	1	2	3	4	5	6	7	8	9
PAR	4	4	5	3	4	5	4	4	3
YARDS	330	335	450	125	345	480	340	335	145
PAR									
YARDS									

Directions: I-95 (in Fairfield) to Route 139 all the way to Brooks. Turn left to Route 7 North 1.5 miles.

N ME

Dexter Municipal Golf Course ✪✪½

35 Sunrise Avenue
Dexter, ME (207) 924-6477
www.dextermaine.org/golf

Club Pro:
Payment: Visa, MC, Disc
Tee Times: No
Fee 9 Holes: Weekday: $9
Fee 18 Holes: Weekday: $15
Twilight Rates: None
Cart Rental: $12pp/18, $6pp/9
Lessons: No **Schools:** Yes
Membership: Yes
Other: Clubhouse / Restaurant

Weekend: $9
Weekend: $15
Discounts: Junior
Driving Range: Yes
Junior Golf: Yes
Architect/Yr Open: Bill Nadeau/1968
GPS:

Tees	Holes	Yards	Par	USGA	Slope
BACK					
MIDDLE	9	2784	35	65.6	116
FRONT	9	2708	35	65.6	124

Not too long, but full of challenges. Lots of hills and ponds — fun course to play. Open April 15 - October 15.

	1	2	3	4	5	6	7	8	9
PAR	4	4	4	3	4	4	4	3	5
YARDS	275	285	338	155	376	275	377	183	444
	10	11	12	13	14	15	16	17	18
PAR	4	4	4	3	5	4	4	3	4
YARDS	305	295	343	161	426	300	390	188	376

Directions: I-95 to Exit 157 (Newport exit) follow Route 7 North to Dexter (14 miles). Take left on Liberty Street (across from Rite Aid). Take a left at the second stop sign. Course is second driveway on right.

Evergreen Golf Club ✪½

522 Dallas Hill Road
Rangeley, ME (207) 240-5248
www.evergreengolfrangeley.net

Club Pro: George Buck
Payment: Visa, MC, Amex, Disc, Checks
Tee Times: Yes
Fee 9 Holes: Weekday: $27
Fee 18 Holes: Weekday: $37
Twilight Rates: After 4pm
Cart Rental: $18pp/18, $10pp/9
Lessons: Yes **Schools:** Yes
Membership: Yes
Other: Clubhouse / Snack Bar / Pro Shop / Putting Course
GPS: Yes

Tees	Holes	Yards	Par	USGA	Slope
BACK	9	3324	35	72.9	139
MIDDLE	9	3040	35	70.9	129
FRONT	9	2155	35	60.3	112

Weekend: $27
Weekend: $37
Discounts: None
Driving Range: Yes
Junior Golf: Yes
Architect/Yr Open: George Buck, Jr./2001

COUPON

This is a championship quality course, 5 tees on each hole, spectacular views. Everyone who plays it, loves it.

	1	2	3	4	5	6	7	8	9
PAR	4	4	3	4	4	4	4	3	5
YARDS	422	361	178	345	391	442	464	196	524
PAR									
YARDS									

Directions: From I-95 Auburn-Lewiston exit – take Route 4 to Rangley.

Fort Kent Golf Club
⭐⭐½ ▶ **17**

304 Saint John Road
Fort Kent, ME (207) 834-3149
www.fortkentgolfclub.org

Club Pro: Kelly O'Leary, PGA
Payment: Visa, MC
Tee Times: No
Fee 9 Holes: Weekday: $20
Fee 18 Holes: Weekday: $35
Twilight Rates: No
Cart Rental: $25pp/18, $16pp/9 per cart
Lessons: $35/lesson **Schools:** No
Membership: Yes
Other: Restaurant / Clubhouse / Bar-Lounge / Lockers / Showers
GPS: Yes

Tees	Holes	Yards	Par	USGA	Slope
BACK					
MIDDLE	9	3122	35	69.0	111
FRONT	9	2681	36	69.0	111

Weekend: $20
Weekend: $35
Discounts:
Driving Range: Yes
Junior Golf: Yes
Architect/Yr Open: Ben Gray/1966

COUPON

The course, located a chip shot from the Canadian border, sports many challenges: bunkers, water hazards, and hills. Expanded water on hole #9.

	1	2	3	4	5	6	7	8	9
PAR	4	4	3	4	3	4	4	4	5
YARDS	406	302	160	322	151	390	412	437	542
PAR									
YARDS									

Directions: Route 161 to Fort Kent; follow 3 miles to course.

Foxcroft Golf Club
⭐⭐ ▶ **18**

84 Foxcroft Center Road
Dover Foxcroft, ME (207) 564-8887
www.foxcroftgolfclub.com

Club Pro:
Payment: Personal Checks, Cash
Tee Times: No
Fee 9 Holes: Weekday: $15
Fee 18 Holes: Weekday: $24
Twilight Rates: After 4pm
Cart Rental: $15pp/18, $10pp/9
Lessons: Yes **Schools:** No
Membership:
Other: Snack Bar/ Clubhouse

Tees	Holes	Yards	Par	USGA	Slope
BACK	9	3136	36	66.1	109
MIDDLE	9	2968	36	66.1	107
FRONT	9	2753	37	67.0	101

Weekend: $15
Weekend: $24
Discounts: None
Driving Range: No
Junior Golf: Yes
Architect/Yr Open: Renaldo Reynolds/1963
GPS:

COUPON

N
ME

Recently lengthened first tee. New White tees on #7 and #9. "Challenging course with fast greens. Very player-friendly for women and seniors." –MH

	1	2	3	4	5	6	7	8	9
PAR	5	4	4	3	4	4	3	4	5
YARDS	474	430	380	102	328	267	168	381	488
PAR									
YARDS									

Directions: I-95 to Exit 39 (Newport exit). Follow Route 7 into Dover-Foxcroft. Turn left. Go right at traffic light. Take 2nd right, Route 16. Take Route 16 from the post office 1.3 miles to Foxcroft Center Road. Sign is at corner of Milo Road.

Great Cove Golf Course ✪ ▶ 19

387 Great Cove Road
Roque Bluffs, ME (207) 434-7200
www.greatcovegolf.com

Tees	Holes	Yards	Par	USGA	Slope
BACK					
MIDDLE	9	1709	30	59.1	100
FRONT					

Club Pro:
Payment: Cash, Personal Checks
Tee Times: No
Fee 9 Holes: Weekday: $9   **Weekend:** $9
Fee 18 Holes: Weekday: $18   **Weekend:** $18
Twilight Rates: No   **Discounts:** None
Cart Rental: $10/9 per cart   **Driving Range:** $6/lg., $4/sm.
Lessons: No **Schools:** No   **Junior Golf:** Yes
Membership: Yes   **Architect/Yr Open:** Paul Browne/1977
Other: Clubhouse / Snack Bar   **GPS:**

3 short par 3's, 3 long par 3's, and 3 short par 4's. Great views of Englishman Bay.

	1	2	3	4	5	6	7	8	9
PAR	4	3	4	3	4	3	3	3	3
YARDS	304	185	245	193	228	103	137	177	137
PAR									
YARDS									

Directions: 3 miles off Route 1 from Jonesboro. Located on Great Cove Road.

Grindstone Neck Golf Course ✪✪✪ ▶ 20

Grindstone Avenue
Winter Harbor, ME (207) 963-7760
www.grindstonegolf.com

Tees	Holes	Yards	Par	USGA	Slope
BACK					
MIDDLE	9	3095	36		
FRONT	9	2550	36		

Club Pro: Kevin Conley
Payment: Visa, MC
Tee Times: No
Fee 9 Holes: Weekday: $24   **Weekend:** $28
Fee 18 Holes: Weekday: $36   **Weekend:** $45
Twilight Rates: After 4:30pm   **Discounts:** College & Juniors
Cart Rental: $25/18, $15/9 per cart, $4/pull **Driving Range:** No
Lessons: No **Schools:** No   **Junior Golf:** No
Membership: Yes
Architect/Yr: Alex Findlay/1895; Charlie Clark/1925
Other: No   **GPS:**

Player Comments: "Could not be more beautiful." Located on Frenchman's Bay. Enjoy cool sea breezes, spectacular ocean views.

	1	2	3	4	5	6	7	8	9
PAR	4	4	4	3	4	4	5	4	4
YARDS	345	340	317	138	413	335	457	343	407
PAR									
YARDS									

Directions: Route 1 to Route 186. Route 186 to Main Street. Right on Main for 1 mile to Grindstone Avenue.

Hampden Country Club ✪½ ▶ 21

25 Thomas Road
Hampden, ME (207) 862-9999
www.hampdengolf.net

Tees	Holes	Yards	Par	USGA	Slope
BACK	9	2930	36	64.9	104
MIDDLE	9	2759	36	64.9	108
FRONT	9	2550	36	69.6	118

Club Pro:
Payment: Cash, Check, Credit Card
Tee Times: Not Required
Fee 9 Holes: Weekday: $10
Fee 18 Holes: Weekday: $19
Twilight Rates: No
Cart Rental: $14pp/18, $8pp/9
Lessons: No **Schools:** No
Membership: Yes
Other: Snack Bar

Weekend: $10
Weekend: $19
Discounts: None
Driving Range: No
Junior Golf: No
Architect/Yr Open: Hamm Robbins/1967
GPS:

COUPON

The course is fairly wide open, friendly for beginners and seniors. Considered an easy walker. Tuesday is Ladies' Day – $15 all day. Thursday is Senior Citizens and Veterans Day – $15 all day.

	1	2	3	4	5	6	7	8	9
PAR	4	3	4	4	4	3	5	4	5
YARDS	320	170	330	295	257	170	462	310	420
PAR									
YARDS									

Directions: I-95 to Exit 174, follow Route 69 East for 1.5 miles. Take Route 9 East for 2 miles; course is on right.

Hermon Meadow Golf Club ✪✪ ▶ 22

281 Billings Road
Bangor, ME (207) 848-3741
www.hermonmeadow.com

Tees	Holes	Yards	Par	USGA	Slope
BACK	18	6329	72	69.4	117
MIDDLE	18	5895	72	67.7	113
FRONT	18	5395	72	70.9	120

Club Pro: Thea Davis
Payment: Most Major Credit Cards
Tee Times: No
Fee 9 Holes: Weekday: $15
Fee 18 Holes: Weekday: $27 all day
Twilight Rates: After 3pm
Cart Rental: $15pp/18, $8.50pp/9
Lessons: Yes **Schools:** Jr.
Membership: $600
Other: Clubhouse / Snack Bar / Bar-Lounge

Weekend: $15
Weekend: $27 all day
Discounts: Junior
Driving Range: $4/bucket
Junior Golf: Yes
Architect/Yr Open:
GPS:

COUPON

The greens are small and fast; back 9 is heavily wooded. Driving range has largest bent grass tees in Maine. Call for daily specials.

	1	2	3	4	5	6	7	8	9
PAR	4	4	3	5	4	5	4	3	4
YARDS	350	385	130	460	270	545	350	165	350
	10	11	12	13	14	15	16	17	18
PAR	4	4	3	5	4	5	3	4	4
YARDS	265	310	160	430	320	510	135	370	390

Directions: Take Union Street 4 miles past airport in Bangor, take left on Billings Road, course is 2 miles on left.

Hidden Meadows Golf Course ✪✪½ ▶ 23

240 West Old Town Road
Old Town, ME (207) 827-4779
www.hiddenmeadowsgolf.com

Club Pro: Joe Perdue, PGA
Payment: Cash, Visa, MC, Disc, Checks
Tee Times: No
Fee 9 Holes: Weekday: $12
Fee 18 Holes: Weekday: $18
Twilight Rates: No
Discounts: Senior & Junior 9/$10, 18/$15
Cart Rental: $12/18, $8/9 per cart
Lessons: Yes **Schools:** Yes
Membership: Yes
Other: Open April to November

Tees	Holes	Yards	Par	USGA	Slope
BACK					
MIDDLE	9	3144	35	66.5	112
FRONT	9	2481	35	66.4	109

Weekend: $14
Weekend: $21

Driving Range: Yes
Junior Golf: Yes
Architect/Yr Open: Jeffrey P. Dufour/1995
GPS:

COUPON

New Owner Joe Predue, PGA Professional. New tees #1, #3, #6, #7. New driving range. Full service discount Pro Shop includes: Caddy, Mizuno, TaylorMade, Titlest, Callaway and Cobra.

	1	2	3	4	5	6	7	8	9
PAR	4	4	4	3	5	4	4	3	4
YARDS	389	323	399	148	547	415	394	167	332
PAR									
YARDS									

Directions: I-95 to Exit 197. West on Route 43 toward Hudson. Golf course is ¾ mile from interstate on left.

Hillcrest Golf Club ✪½ ▶ 24

59 Grove Street
Millinocket, ME (207) 723-8410
www.hillcrestgolfme.com

Club Pro:
Payment: Visa, MC
Tee Times: No
Fee 9 Holes: Weekday: $13
Fee 18 Holes: Weekday: $17
Twilight Rates: No
Cart Rental: $20pp/18, $10pp/9
Lessons: Yes **Schools:** No
Membership: Yes
Other: Clubhouse / Snack Bar / Bar-Lounge

Tees	Holes	Yards	Par	USGA	Slope
BACK					
MIDDLE	9	2477	33	63.2	104
FRONT					

Weekend: $15
Weekend: $19
Discounts: None
Driving Range: No
Junior Golf: Yes
Architect/Yr Open: Larry Striley/1930
GPS:

Player Comments: "Sits at the Foot of Mt. Katahdin. Very nice short course, very tight with narrow, tree-lined fairways." Friendly Staff. Open April - October.

	1	2	3	4	5	6	7	8	9
PAR	4	3	4	4	4	4	3	3	4
YARDS	359	152	364	287	265	401	221	153	275
PAR									
YARDS									

Directions: I-95 to Medway Exit 244, left off ramp onto Route 157. Follow 12 miles to Millinocket. Past McDonald's to bottom of hill. Follow signs at right.

Houlton Community Golf Course ✪✪ 25 ▶

Nickerson Lake Road
Houlton, ME (207) 532-2662
www.houltongolf.com

Club Pro:
Payment: Cash, Check, Credit Cards
Tee Times: Yes
Fee 9 Holes: Weekday: $15
Fee 18 Holes: Weekday: $25
Twilight Rates: No
Cart Rental: $16pp/9 $32pp/18
Lessons: yes **Schools:** No
Membership: Yes
Other: Clubhouse / Snack Bar / Bar-Lounge

Tees	Holes	Yards	Par	USGA	Slope
BACK					
MIDDLE	9	2993	36	68.9	117
FRONT	9	2705	38	73.6	109

Weekend: $15
Weekend: $25
Discounts: Senior & Junior
Driving Range: Yes
Junior Golf: Yes
Architect/Yr Open: 1921
GPS:

COUPON

The course is adjacent to beautiful Nickerson Lake. Hilly, but other than a scenic view of the lake, has few water hazards. 2 sets of tees means a change of par on some holes on 2nd round. Open May - October.

	1	2	3	4	5	6	7	8	9
PAR	4	5	3	4	4	5	4	3	4
YARDS	310	455	134	246	403	405	340	170	356
PAR									
YARDS									

Directions: I-95 to Houlton Exit 305 (last U.S. exit on I-95 North), follow signs to course.

Island Country Club ✪✪ 26 ▶

442 Sunset Drive
Deer Isle, ME (207) 348-2379
www.islandcountryclub.net

Club Pro: Shaun Webb
Payment: Visa, MC
Tee Times: No
Fee 9 Holes: Weekday: $30
Fee 18 Holes: Weekday: $40
Twilight Rates: No
Cart Rental: $24pp/18, $12pp/9
Lessons: Yes **Schools:** No
Membership: Yes
Other: Clubhouse / Snack Bar

Tees	Holes	Yards	Par	USGA	Slope
BACK					
MIDDLE	9	2376	34	62.1	109
FRONT					

Weekend: $30
Weekend: $40
Discounts: Junior
Driving Range: No
Junior Golf: Yes
Architect/Yr Open: Stiles & Van Kleek/1918
GPS:

Hilly, fast greens. Contoured fairways, fully irrigated. Alcohol served on premises. Lunch 11-2 Tuesday-Sunday. Beaches, boating, tennis, fine dining, art galleries and shopping close by.

	1	2	3	4	5	6	7	8	9
PAR	4	4	3	3	4	3	4	5	4
YARDS	315	261	156	113	380	100	268	459	324
PAR									
YARDS									

Directions: Route 15 to Deer Isle, then Route 15A to Sunset. Club is about 3 miles on the left.

Jato Highlands Golf Course ✪✪✪

 27

175 Town Farm Road
Lincoln, ME (207) 794-2433
www.jatohighlands.com

Club Pro: Jaymis Dugamn
Payment: Visa, MC, Cash, Check
Tee Times: Yes

Tees	Holes	Yards	Par	USGA	Slope
BACK	18	5715	72	68	123
MIDDLE	18	5491	71	67	121
FRONT	18	4916	72	64.1	108

Fee 9 Holes: Weekday: $20   **Weekend:** $20
Fee 18 Holes: Weekday: $30   **Weekend:** $30
Twilight Rates: After 3pm
Discounts: Junior/$15, Seniors 80 and up/free
Cart Rental: $15pp/18, $10pp/9   **Driving Range:** Yes
Lessons: Yes **Schools:** Yes   **Junior Golf:** Yes
Membership: Yes   **Architect/Yr Open:** Tom Gardner/1999
Other: Restaurant / Clubhouse / Bar-Lounge   **GPS:**

COUPON

Player Comments: "A hidden gem. Well maintained. A demanding challenge from any tees." "Plays up and down the Highlands. Great course." –DW

	1	2	3	4	5	6	7	8	9
PAR	4	4	3	5	4	4	4	3	5
YARDS	314	322	172	421	258	309	282	122	409
	10	11	12	13	14	15	16	17	18
PAR	3	5	5	4	3	5	3	4	4
YARDS	186	424	465	367	164	432	144	298	406

Directions: I-95 to Lincoln exit. Left on Route 2, 6 miles on Town Farm Road on right.

Johnson W. Parks Golf Course ✪✪½

28

382 Hartland Avenue
Pittsfield, ME (207) 487-5545
www.jwparksgolf.com

Club Pro: Michael Dugas, PGA
Payment: Visa, MC, Personal Checks
Tee Times: No

Tees	Holes	Yards	Par	USGA	Slope
BACK	9	2927	35	34.1	120
MIDDLE	9	2678	35	35.1	120
FRONT	9	2554	35	35.0	120

Fee 9 Holes: Weekday: $14   **Weekend:** $16
Fee 18 Holes: Weekday: $18   **Weekend:** $22
Twilight Rates: After 5pm   **Discounts:** Junior, 1/2 price
Cart Rental: $14pp/18, $7pp/9   **Driving Range:** Yes
Lessons: $25/half hour **Schools:** No   **Junior Golf:** Yes
Membership: Yes   **Architect/Yr Open:** John Dana/1964
Other: Clubhouse / Sports Bar   **GPS:**

COUPON

Tall pines, narrow fairways and a series of streams add to the challenge at one of central Maine's most popular courses. Fully irrigated. Open April 25 - October 31. Twilight rates after 3pm and 5pm include cart.

	1	2	3	4	5	6	7	8	9
PAR	4	4	5	3	4	4	4	3	4
YARDS	375	405	531	227	308	268	322	160	331
PAR									
YARDS									

Directions: I-95 to Pittsfield Exit 150, go east off ramp. Take a left onto Route 152. ½ mile on the left.

Katahdin Country Club

80 Park Street
Milo, ME (207) 943-8734

Tees	Holes	Yards	Par	USGA	Slope
BACK					
MIDDLE	9	2968	36	65.8	103
FRONT					

Club Pro:
Payment: Cash Only
Tee Times: No
Fee 9 Holes: Weekday: $14 all day
Fee 18 Holes: Weekday: $14 all day
Twilight Rates: No
Cart Rental: $22pp/18, $11pp/9
Lessons: No **Schools:**
Membership: Yes
Other: Clubhouse / Snack Bar

Weekend: $14 all day
Weekend: $14 all day
Discounts: None
Driving Range: No
Junior Golf: Yes
Architect/Yr Open: Larry Striley/1931
GPS:

Wide-open fairways, short-cut rough and no water hazards. Largest sand trap around. Open April 15 - November.

	1	2	3	4	5	6	7	8	9
PAR	4	3	4	4	3	5	5	4	4
YARDS	327	150	322	257	180	485	519	447	281
PAR									
YARDS									

Directions: I-95 North to LaGrange-Milo exit, follow signs to course.

Kebo Valley Golf Club

136 Eagle Lake Road
Bar Harbor, ME (207) 288-3000
www.kebovalleyclub.com

Tees	Holes	Yards	Par	USGA	Slope
BACK	18	6131	70	69.0	124
MIDDLE	18	5933	70	69.0	122
FRONT	18	5440	72	72	121

Club Pro: Peiter K. DeVos, PGA
Jay Blackwell, PGA
Payment: Cash, Visa, MC, Amex
Tee Times: 6 days adv.
Fee 9 Holes: Weekday: Call - seasonal
Fee 18 Holes: Weekday: Call - seasonal
Twilight Rates: After 2:30pm
Cart Rental: $25pp/18, $15pp/9
Lessons: Yes **Schools:** No
Membership: Yes
Other: Restaurant / Bar-Lounge / Lockers

Weekend: Call - seasonal
Weekend: Call - seasonal
Discounts: None
Driving Range: No
Junior Golf: Yes
Architect/Yr Open: H.C. Leeds/1891
GPS: Yes

COUPON

8th-oldest club in the country. Majestic views of Acadia National Park. 17th hole restored to its original beauty. Clubhouse overlooks the golf course.

	1	2	3	4	5	6	7	8	9
PAR	4	4	4	3	5	3	4	4	3
YARDS	388	438	336	143	500	165	322	413	194
	10	11	12	13	14	15	16	17	18
PAR	4	4	4	4	5	3	4	4	4
YARDS	338	400	283	390	530	146	258	349	340

Directions: I-95 to Bangor, 395 to Route 1A, Route 1A to Route 3, Route 3 to Route 233. Look for signs to course.

N
ME

Kenduskeag Golf & Country Club ✪

31

947 Grant Road
Kenduskeag, ME (207) 884-7330
www.kenduskeaggolf.com

Club Pro:
Payment: Cash, Check, Credit Card
Tee Times: No
Fee 9 Holes: Weekday: $12
Fee 18 Holes: Weekday: $18
Twilight Rates: No
Cart Rental: $12pp/18, $8pp/9
Lessons: No **Schools:** No
Membership: Yes
Other: Clubhouse / Snack Bar

Weekend: $13
Weekend: $18
Discounts: Senior & Junior
Driving Range: No
Junior Golf: No
Architect/Yr Open: Robert Girvan, Sr./1958
GPS:

Tees	Holes	Yards	Par	USGA	Slope
BACK					
MIDDLE	9	2777	36		
FRONT					

COUPON

An easy but pretty course. Rolling, wooded and stream scenery. Appropriate dress. Open May 1 - October 31. New clubhouse.

	1	2	3	4	5	6	7	8	9
PAR	4	4	4	4	4	3	5	4	4
YARDS	320	343	246	400	285	143	465	265	310
PAR									
YARDS									

Directions: I-95 to Exit 185. Right to Route 15 North (Broadway), 12 miles to course. Left onto Grant Road.

Lakeview Golf Course ✪½

32

21 Reynolds Lane
Burnham, ME (207) 948-5414
www.lakeviewgolfcoursemaine.com

Club Pro:
Payment: Visa, MC
Tee Times: No
Fee 9 Holes: Weekday: $12
Fee 18 Holes: Weekday: $18
Twilight Rates: No
Cart Rental: $25pp/18, $13pp/9
Lessons: No **Schools:** No
Membership: Yes
Other: Cafe / Clubhouse / Lockers

Weekend: $15
Weekend: $20
Discounts: Junior
Driving Range: No
Junior Golf: No
Architect/Yr Open: Ronello Reynolds Sr./1927
GPS:

Tees	Holes	Yards	Par	USGA	Slope
BACK	9	3016	36	68.0	107
MIDDLE	9	2950	36	65.9	107
FRONT	9	2698	36	69.9	114

COUPON

Beautiful 9-hole course nestled on the shores of scenic Lake Winnecook. Friendly staff and great food. An excellent walking course with level fairways. Highly recommended for senior citizens. All-day passes available — $25 during the week and $30 on weekends.

	1	2	3	4	5	6	7	8	9
PAR	4	4	3	3	4	5	5	4	4
YARDS	381	298	120	159	328	503	485	351	325
PAR									
YARDS									

Directions: I-95 to Fairfield exit. Take Route 139 from Fairfield to Burnham West. Take Prairie Road off 139, clubhouse is on right.

Lakewood Golf Course ✪✪ 33

Route 201
Madison, ME (207) 474-5955
www.lakewoodgolfmaine.com

Tees	Holes	Yards	Par	USGA	Slope
BACK	18	6106	72	69.1	119
MIDDLE	18	5732	72	67.1	116
FRONT	18	4728	72	62.9	112

Club Pro:
Payment: Visa, MC, Disc, Checks
Tee Times: Yes
Fee 9 Holes: Weekday: $20
Fee 18 Holes: Weekday: $30
Twilight Rates: After 4pm
Cart Rental: $32/18, $20/9 per cart
Lessons: Yes **Schools:** No
Membership: Yes
Other: Snack Bar / Bar-Lounge / Hall Rental

Weekend: $20
Weekend: $30
Discounts: Spring and Fall
Driving Range: No
Junior Golf: Yes
Architect/Yr: Alex Chisolm/1925; Phil Wogan/1995
GPS:

COUPON

New Front Tee's #2, #4 and #8. Beautiful views overlooking Sugarloaf and the lake. Classic layout, built in 1926. Practice, chipping, and putting areas. #12 is a par 6. Open April - November. Spring and Fall Rates.

	1	2	3	4	5	6	7	8	9
PAR	4	4	3	5	4	3	4	4	5
YARDS	365	435	160	471	285	141	325	410	510
	10	11	12	13	14	15	16	17	18
PAR	3	4	6	4	4	4	4	4	3
YARDS	130	350	660	410	370	350	360	394	152

Directions: Route 201, go 6 miles past Showhegan toward Bingham.

Limestone Country Club ✪✪½ 34

487 West Gate Road
Limestone, ME (207) 328-7277
www.limestonecountryclub.com

Tees	Holes	Yards	Par	USGA	Slope
BACK					
MIDDLE	9	3355	36	70.4	114
FRONT	9	2870	36	71.4	116

Club Pro:
Payment: Visa, MC
Tee Times: No
Fee 9 Holes: Weekday: $14
Fee 18 Holes: Weekday: $22
Twilight Rates: No
Cart Rental: $22/18, $14/9 per cart
Lessons: No **Schools:** No
Membership: Yes
Other: Clubhouse / Bar / Lounge / Snack Bar / Restaurant

Weekend: $14
Weekend: $22
Discounts: Senior & Junior
Driving Range: No
Junior Golf: No
Architect/Yr Open: William Mitchell/1961

COUPON

N
ME

Course is sited to capture the wind. Fairways lined with evergreens and hardwoods. Elevated greens at different angles. Long- and short-term accomodations are available. Golf packages. New carts.

	1	2	3	4	5	6	7	8	9
PAR	4	5	3	4	4	3	4	5	4
YARDS	415	525	160	370	355	225	390	515	400
PAR									
YARDS									

Directions: I-95 North to Holton, then Route 1 North to Caribou. From Caribou take Route 89 East to Loring/Limestone. Take a left on West Gate Road for 2.5 miles and club is located on the right.

Long Lake Country Club ✪½ ▶ 35

744 Lake Shore Road
St. David, ME (207) 895-6957
www.longlakegolfcourse.com

Tees	Holes	Yards	Par	USGA	Slope
BACK	9	3000	36		
MIDDLE	9	2805	35		
FRONT	9	2610	36		

Club Pro: Al Hebert
Payment: Credit Card, Check, Cash
Tee Times: No
Fee 9 Holes: Weekday: $15   **Weekend:** $12
Fee 18 Holes: Weekday: $25   **Weekend:** $20
Twilight Rates: No
Discounts: Junior 12 and under $7.50/9 holes
Cart Rental: $25pp/18, $15pp/9   **Driving Range:** Yes
Lessons: Yes **Schools:** No   **Junior Golf:** No
Membership: Yes   **Architect/Yr Open:** Ben Gray/1961
Other: Bar-Lounge / Restaurant / Indoor Simulator

COUPON

6 New Tee Boxes. Scenic views — abundant wildlife — bring a camera!

	1	2	3	4	5	6	7	8	9
PAR	4	4	4	4	3	4	5	4	3
YARDS	265	345	395	335	160	385	475	290	155
PAR									
YARDS									

Directions: I-95 North to Houlton - Route 1, to Beaulieu Road, Madawaska to Lakeshore Road.

Loons Cove Golf Course ✪½ ▶ 36

Route 201
Skowhegan, ME (207) 474-9550
www.loonscovegolfcourse.com

Tees	Holes	Yards	Par	USGA	Slope
BACK					
MIDDLE	9	1214	27		
FRONT					

Club Pro: No
Payment: Cash or Check
Tee Times: No
Fee 9 Holes: Weekday: $8   **Weekend:** $8
Fee 18 Holes: Weekday: $12   **Weekend:** $12
Twilight Rates: No   **Discounts:** For members
Cart Rental: $18/18, $10/9 per cart   **Driving Range:** Yes
Lessons: Yes **Schools:** No   **Junior Golf:** Yes
Membership: Yes   **Architect/Yr Open:**
Other: Snacks / Beverages / Lunch Counter   **GPS:**

Host of the Special Olympics Skills Program.

	1	2	3	4	5	6	7	8	9
PAR	3	3	3	3	3	3	3	3	3
YARDS	142	162	125	160	110	125	128	115	147
PAR									
YARDS									

Directions: I-95 to Route 201. 6 miles to Skowhegan.

Lucerne-in-Maine Golf Course ✪✪ ▶ 37

16 Sunset Road
Dedham, ME (207) 843-6282
www.lucernegolf.com

Tees	Holes	Yards	Par	USGA	Slope
BACK	9	3205	36	70.6	119
MIDDLE	9	2845	36	67.4	119
FRONT	9	2650	36	69.5	116

Club Pro: David Gubler, Owner
Payment: Cash, Check, Visa, MC
Tee Times: 7 days adv.
Fee 9 Holes: Weekday: $15   **Weekend:** $15
Fee 18 Holes: Weekday: $25   **Weekend:** $25
Twilight Rates: No   **Discounts:** None
Cart Rental: $15pp/18, $8pp/9   **Driving Range:** No
Lessons: Yes **Schools: No**   **Junior Golf:** Yes
Membership: Yes   **Architect/Yr Open:** Donald Ross/1926
Other: Snack Bar / Lodging Available at Lucerne Inn

COUPON

Donald Ross course features tree-lined fairways, ample landing areas and small greens guarded by pot bunkers. Recently put back original bunkers that had been removed. New putting green.

	1	2	3	4	5	6	7	8	9
PAR	5	3	4	4	4	3	4	5	4
YARDS	450	155	235	360	305	150	340	485	365
PAR									
YARDS									

Directions: I-95 to Exit 182A (Route I-395) to 1A towards Ellsworth. Course is 8 miles on left, halfway between Bangor and Ellsworth on Route 1.

Mars Hill Country Club ✪✪✪ ▶ 38

75 Country Club Road
Mars Hill, ME (207) 425-4802
www.golfmhcc.com

Tees	Holes	Yards	Par	USGA	Slope
BACK	18	6043	72		
MIDDLE	18	5742	72	68.7	125
FRONT	18	5159	72		

Club Pro: Ronald Perry
Payment: Visa, MC
Tee Times: No
Fee 9 Holes: Weekday: $14   **Weekend:** $14
Fee 18 Holes: Weekday: $28   **Weekend:** $28
Twilight Rates: No   **Discounts:** None
Cart Rental: $16pp/18, $8pp/9   **Driving Range:** $3/lg bucket
Lessons: Yes **Schools:** No   **Junior Golf:** Yes
Membership: Yes   **Architect/Yr Open:** A. McQuade/1991
Other: Clubhouse / Full Snack Bar / Beer   **GPS:** Yes

COUPON

6th hole par 3, with a 162-foot vertical drop, is amazing. Moose, deer, and/or bear seen on course almost daily. Near New England's largest wind farm. "One of the best courses north of Bangor featuring dramatic elevation changes and great scenery." –DW

	1	2	3	4	5	6	7	8	9
PAR	4	5	4	5	4	3	4	3	4
YARDS	350	481	257	470	326	145	313	130	300
	10	**11**	**12**	**13**	**14**	**15**	**16**	**17**	**18**
PAR	4	4	5	3	4	3	4	5	4
YARDS	398	380	470	163	363	125	309	447	315

Directions: I-95 to Route US1 to Mars Hill. Then north ½ mile on Route 1A. Turn right onto Boynton Road, then left onto Country Club Road.

Mingo Springs Golf Course ✪✪½ ▶39

43 Country Club Road
Rangeley, ME (207) 864-5021
www.mingosprings.com

Club Pro:
Payment: Visa, MC, Disc, Cash
Tee Times: Yes

Tees	Holes	Yards	Par	USGA	Slope
BACK	18	6322	71	68.4	123
MIDDLE	18	6014	71	65.5	114
FRONT	18	5158	71	67.4	110

Fee 9 Holes: Weekday: $33 M-Th   **Weekend:** $33F/S/S
Fee 18 Holes: Weekday: $43 M-Th   **Weekend:** $43 F/S/S
Twilight Rates: After 3pm (excl. Tues. & Sat.)   **Discounts:**
Cart Rental: $22pp/18, $14pp/9   **Driving Range:** Irons only
Lessons: Yes **Schools:** No   **Junior Golf:** Yes
Membership: Yes   **Architect/Yr Open:** Phil Wogan/1925
Other: Snack Bar / Bar-Lounge   **GPS:**

New green on #16, new tee on #16 and new tee on #13. Noted for being a challenging old-fashioned course, yet family and beginner-friendly. Scenic views of Rangeley Mountains.

	1	2	3	4	5	6	7	8	9
PAR	4	4	4	3	4	4	3	4	5
YARDS	350	375	378	173	360	391	177	318	470
	10	11	12	13	14	15	16	17	18
PAR	3	5	3	4	4	4	4	4	4
YARDS	152	522	133	400	360	277	419	363	396

Directions: I-95 to Exit 12 (Auburn). Pick up Route 4. Go through Farmington to Rangeley Village. 2 miles toward Oquossoc, left on Mingo Loop Road. Follow signs to course.

Moose River Golf Course ✪½ ▶40

701 Main Street (Route 201)
Moose River, ME (207) 668-5331
www.jackman.com

Club Pro: Wade Turmel
Payment: Cash Only
Tee Times: No

Tees	Holes	Yards	Par	USGA	Slope
BACK					
MIDDLE	9	1976	31		
FRONT					

Fee 9 Holes: Weekday: $14   **Weekend:** $14
Fee 18 Holes: Weekday: $22   **Weekend:** $22
Twilight Rates: No   **Discounts:** None
Cart Rental: $18/18, $13/9 per cart   **Driving Range:** No
Lessons: No **Schools:** No   **Junior Golf:** No
Membership: Yes   **Architect/Yr Open:**
Other: **GPS:** 1935

Open May 15 - October 15. Rate subject to change. Interesting 9-hole course. Very fun to play. Greens are in good condition compared to past years. Great place for family and friends to get together. The interesting 205 par 4, 3rd hole bends right around an ancient cemetery in the middle of the fairway.

	1	2	3	4	5	6	7	8	9
PAR	3	3	4	4	4	3	3	3	4
YARDS	204	168	213	248	259	168	171	169	376
PAR									
YARDS									

Directions: I-95 to Fairfield exit, follow Route 201 North about 85 miles to Moose River.

Mt. Kineo Golf Course ✪✪✪

Trailhead Road
Kineo Island Township, ME
(207) 534-9012
www.mooseheadlakegolf.com

Club Pro:
Payment: Visa, MC, Amex, Disc, Checks
Tee Times: No
Fee 9 Holes: Weekday: $20
Fee 18 Holes: Weekday: $35
Twilight Rates: No
Cart Rental: $12.50pp/18, $6.50pp/9
Lessons: No **Schools:** No
Membership: Yes
Other: Clubhouse / Snack Bar

Weekend: $20
Weekend: $35
Discounts: Junior
Driving Range: No
Junior Golf: No
Architect/Yr Open: 1893

Tees	Holes	Yards	Par	USGA	Slope
BACK					
MIDDLE	18	6030	71	68.5	113
FRONT	18	4996	71	68.5	113

COUPON

A challenging island course nestled under beautiful Mount Kineo in Moosehead Lake. Small greens and narrow fairways ensure a satisfying round in a stunning setting. Our signature fourth hole, 141 yds. over water, is worth the trip!

	1	2	3	4	5	6	7	8	9
PAR	5	4	4	3	4	5	3	4	4
YARDS	484	420	234	134	331	467	141	425	388
	10	**11**	**12**	**13**	**14**	**15**	**16**	**17**	**18**
PAR	4	4	3	3	4	5	3	5	4
YARDS	448	420	197	149	331	467	141	450	403

Directions: From I-95 take Newport exit to Route 7; follow 7 North until Dexter. Take 23 North to Guilford. At Guilford, take Route 6/15 all the way to Rockwood. In Rockwood follow sign to "Kineo Docks". At the docks you will take the Kineo shuttle ferry boat to our island course.

Natanis Golf Course (Arrowhead) ✪✪✪

Webber Pond Road
Vassalboro, ME (207) 622-3561
www.natanisgc.com

Club Pro: Richard Browne, PGA
Payment: Visa, MC, Cash
Tee Times: 1 week adv.
Fee 9 Holes: Weekday: $21
Fee 18 Holes: Weekday: $36
Twilight Rates: After 4pm
Cart Rental: $15pp/18, $9pp/9
Lessons: $35/half hour **Schools:** No
Membership: Yes
Other: Clubhouse / Lockers / Snack Bar

Weekend: $21
Weekend: $36
Discounts: None
Driving Range: $4.50/lg., $3.50/sm. bucket
Junior Golf: Yes
Architect/Yr Open: Phil Wogan/1974
GPS:

Tees	Holes	Yards	Par	USGA	Slope
BACK	18	6338	72	70.0	117
MIDDLE	18	5847	72	67.8	116
FRONT	18	5019	72	68.7	117

Player Comments: "36 holes of top-notch golf. Challenging." Improved cart paths. State of Maine Museum and Fieldstone Gardens nearby. Distance below is from back tees. Come play both courses.

	1	2	3	4	5	6	7	8	9
PAR	5	4	4	5	3	4	3	4	4
YARDS	500	400	350	461	200	255	190	365	240
	10	**11**	**12**	**13**	**14**	**15**	**16**	**17**	**18**
PAR	3	4	3	4	4	5	4	5	4
YARDS	185	380	165	403	424	530	441	439	410

Directions: I-95 to Augusta/Winthrop exit onto Route 201 to Webber Pond Road. Follow signs.

Natanis Golf Course (Tomahawk) ✪✪✪½

Webber Pond Road
Vassalboro, ME (207) 622-3561
www.natanisgc.com

Tees	Holes	Yards	Par	USGA	Slope
BACK	18	6607	72	70.6	132
MIDDLE	18	6060	72	67.3	123
FRONT	18	5034	72	63.8	104

Club Pro: Richard Browne, PGA
Payment: Visa, MC, Cash
Tee Times: 1 week adv.
Fee 9 Holes: Weekday:
Fee 18 Holes: Weekday: $46
Twilight Rates: After 3pm
Cart Rental: $15pp/18
Lessons: $35/half hour **Schools:** No
Membership: Yes
Other: Clubhouse / Lockers / Snack Bar

Weekend:
Weekend: $46
Discounts: None
Driving Range: $4.50/lg., $3.50/sm. bucket
Junior Golf: Yes
Architect/Yr Open: Dan Maples/2002
GPS:

The tougher of this pair, the Dan Maples design has more length and more challenges. Distance below is from middle tees.

	1	2	3	4	5	6	7	8	9
PAR	5	4	5	3	4	4	3	4	4
YARDS	490	342	526	124	358	362	121	354	359
	10	11	12	13	14	15	16	17	18
PAR	3	4	4	3	5	5	4	4	4
YARDS	130	320	373	163	481	503	311	365	378

Directions: I-95 to Augusta/Winthrop exit onto Route 201 to Webber Pond Road. Follow signs.

Newport Country Club ✪½

170 Golf Course Road
Newport, ME (207) 368-5600

Tees	Holes	Yards	Par	USGA	Slope
BACK					
MIDDLE	9	2520	35		
FRONT					

Club Pro: Jeff Peabody, PGA
Payment: Cash Only
Tee Times: Yes
Fee 9 Holes: Weekday: $12
Fee 18 Holes: Weekday: $18
Twilight Rates: No
Cart Rental: $10pp/9
Lessons: Yes **Schools:** Yes
Membership: Yes
Other: Clubhouse / Snack Bar

Weekend: $12
Weekend: $18
Discounts: Senior & Junior
Driving Range: Yes
Junior Golf: Yes
Architect/Yr Open: 1951
GPS:

Built on the crest of a hill near apple orchards. "Great views of Lake Sebasticode. Good course for beginners and seniors." –DW

	1	2	3	4	5	6	7	8	9
PAR	3	3	5	4	4	5	4	3	4
YARDS	155	135	430	380	255	450	290	190	235
PAR									
YARDS									

Directions: I-95 to Exit 157 to Route 7 to right turn on Golf Course Road in Newport.

Northeast Harbor Golf Club ✪✪✪½   ▶ 45

15 Golf Club Road
N.E. Harbor, ME (207) 276-5335
www.nehgc.com

Tees	Holes	Yards	Par	USGA	Slope
BACK	18	5504	69	66.7	128
MIDDLE	18	5324	69	65.9	124
FRONT	18	4558	71	66.9	124

Club Pro: Rob Gardner, PGA
Payment: Visa, MC, Amex, Disc
Tee Times: No
Fee 9 Holes: Weekday: $25   **Weekend:** $25
Fee 18 Holes: Weekday: $45   **Weekend:** $45
Twilight Rates: No   **Discounts:** None
Cart Rental: $24pp/18, $12pp/9   **Driving Range:** Members only
Lessons: Private, Group, Jr. Clinic   **Schools:** Yes   **Junior Golf:** Yes
Membership: Yes   **Architect/Yr Open:** J.G. Thorpe/1895
Other: Clubhouse/ Lockers   **GPS:**

Located on Mt. Desert Island. Close to Acadia National Park. Open to the public May - June and September - October. Members only July and August. "An absolutely outstanding Maine golf course. 13 superb wooded holes and 5 traditional links style holes. Major elevation changes, very small greens and unmatched beauty." –DW

	1	2	3	4	5	6	7	8	9
PAR	4	4	3	4	4	3	4	3	5
YARDS	325	320	149	425	305	127	284	155	457
	10	11	12	13	14	15	16	17	18
PAR	5	4	3	4	3	4	4	4	4
YARDS	495	310	175	337	187	415	281	338	239

Directions: I-95 to Bangor exit (Route 1A), follow to Ellsworth, take Route 3 to Mt. Desert Island. Right at light at head of island on Route 198. Left at next light (still 198), right on Sargent Drive. NEHGC on left.

Northport Golf Club   ✪✪✪   ▶ 46

581 Bluff Road
Northport, ME (207) 338-2270
www.golfnorthport.com

Tees	Holes	Yards	Par	USGA	Slope
BACK					
MIDDLE	9	3047	36	34.2	112
FRONT	9	2747	37	35.7	113

Club Pro: Peter Hodgkins, PGA
Payment: Visa, MC, Amex, Disc, Cash, Check
Tee Times: Holidays
Fee 9 Holes: Weekday: $20   **Weekend:** $20
Fee 18 Holes: Weekday: $32   **Weekend:** $32
Twilight Rates: After 3pm, Sun/Mon/Thu   **Discounts:** Spring/Fall
Cart Rental: $15pp/18, $9pp/9   **Driving Range:** Yes
Lessons: $45/half hour   **Schools:** No   **Junior Golf:** Yes
Membership: Yes   **Architect/Yr Open:** William Jennings/1916
Other: Clubhouse / Snack Bar / Wifi   **GPS:** Sky Caddy Ready

COUPON

Whole course now fully irrigated. New tee on #2, and new practice green. Built in 1916 — rare velvet bentgrass fairways and greens.

	1	2	3	4	5	6	7	8	9
PAR	4	4	3	4	5	4	5	4	3
YARDS	290	377	157	310	483	412	530	338	150
PAR									
YARDS									

Directions: I-95 to Augusta. Exit onto Route 3 East to Belfast/Bar Harbor. Stay on Route 3 to Route 1 South 2 miles. Left at Dos Amigos restaurant.

N
ME

Palmyra Golf Course

47

✪✪

147 Lang Hill Road
Palmyra, ME (207) 938-4947
www.palmyra-me.com

Club Pro:
Payment: Visa, MC, Amex, Disc
Tee Times: Recommended

Tees	Holes	Yards	Par	USGA	Slope
BACK	18	6617	72	70.1	120
MIDDLE	18	6367	72	69.0	118
FRONT	18	5464	72	69.0	118

Fee 9 Holes: Weekday: $15   **Weekend:** $15
Fee 18 Holes: Weekday: $25   **Weekend:** $25
Twilight Rates: After 6pm   **Discounts:** Junior
Cart Rental: $12pp/18, $6pp/9   **Driving Range:** $3.50/45 balls
Lessons: Yes **Schools:** No   **Junior Golf:** Yes
Membership: Yes   **Architect/Yr Open:** Richard Cayer/1956
Other: Snack Bar / Campground with 100 Sites

Course noted for excellent value. Course awarded for programs advancing junior golf.

	1	2	3	4	5	6	7	8	9
PAR	4	4	5	3	4	4	4	3	5
YARDS	430	281	575	153	400	407	400	129	476
	10	**11**	**12**	**13**	**14**	**15**	**16**	**17**	**18**
PAR	4	3	4	4	5	4	4	3	5
YARDS	386	150	350	387	487	373	304	198	481

Directions: I-95 to Exit 157 (Newport). Route 2 West, approximately 5 miles. Right at white church. Course is on top of hill.

Penobscot Valley CC

48

✪✪✪½

366 Main Street
Orono, ME (207) 866-2423
www.penobscotvalleycc.com

Club Pro: Chad Hopkins
Payment: Most Major Credit Cards
Tee Times: Up to 1 week in adv.

Tees	Holes	Yards	Par	USGA	Slope
BACK	18	6536	72	71.3	130
MIDDLE	18	6320	72	70.4	127
FRONT	18	5311	73	70.9	120

Fee 9 Holes: Weekday: $25   **Weekend:** $25
Fee 18 Holes: Weekday: $39   **Weekend:** $39
Twilight Rates: No   **Discounts:** None
Cart Rental: $15pp/18, $7pp/9   **Driving Range:** $5/bag
Lessons: $35/half hour; $60/hour **Schools:** Yes **Junior Golf:** Yes
Membership: Yes   **Architect/Yr Open:** Donald Ross/1924
Other: Clubhouse / Lockers / Showers / Snack Bar / Restaurant / Bar-Lounge / Function Facilities

This "Central Maine Masterpiece" underwent a comprehensive restoration in 2008. Challenging, fun and thouroughly old school, this Donald Ross 18-hole track is host to many prestigious events. Stay and Play packages are available through Hollywood Slots at 877-779-7771.

	1	2	3	4	5	6	7	8	9
PAR	4	4	5	3	4	3	5	4	4
YARDS	392	399	512	144	346	158	446	350	367
	10	**11**	**12**	**13**	**14**	**15**	**16**	**17**	**18**
PAR	5	4	4	4	3	5	3	4	4
YARDS	493	382	378	411	144	458	193	321	426

Directions: I-95 to Exit 189. Right to dead end. Right ¼ mile to club.

Pine Hill Golf Club

11 Pine Hill Drive
Brewer, ME (207) 989-3824

Tees	Holes	Yards	Par	USGA	Slope
BACK	9	2979	36	66	100
MIDDLE	9	2749	36	66	100
FRONT	9	2580	36	67	99

Club Pro: Mark W. Hall, PGA
Payment: Visa, MC
Tee Times: No
Fee 9 Holes: Weekday: $13
Fee 18 Holes: Weekday: $15.50 all day
Twilight Rates: No
Cart Rental: $21/18, $13/9 per cart
Lessons: Yes **Schools:** No
Membership: Yes
Other: Clubhouse / Snack Bar

Weekend: $13.50
Weekend: $15.50 all day
Discounts: Ladies Monday
Driving Range: $3.50/med.
Junior Golf: No
Architect/Yr Open: Charlie Emery/1962
GPS:

Mostly level. Very scenic. A great course for ladies and seniors. No rough! Open April - October. "Second set of tees makes it interesting." –MH

	1	2	3	4	5	6	7	8	9
PAR	4	4	4	4	3	5	4	5	3
YARDS	292	333	326	339	166	498	320	495	210
PAR									
YARDS									

Directions: I-395 to South Main Street/Brewer exit, follow signs to course.

Pine Ridge Golf Course

97 West River Road
Waterville, ME (207) 873-0474

Tees	Holes	Yards	Par	USGA	Slope
BACK					
MIDDLE	9	2570	27		
FRONT					

Club Pro:
Payment: Cash or Check
Tee Times: No
Fee 9 Holes: Weekday: $11
Fee 18 Holes: Weekday:
Twilight Rates: No
Cart Rental: $5/pull
Lessons: No **Schools:** No
Membership: Yes
Other: Restaurant / Bar-Lounge

Weekend: $13
Weekend:
Discounts: Sr. & Jr. memberships
Driving Range: No
Junior Golf: No
Architect/Yr Open: Burt Anderson/1955
GPS:

Well-built and -maintained par 3. Great for beginners, seniors and people with little time.

	1	2	3	4	5	6	7	8	9
PAR	3	3	3	3	3	3	3	3	3
YARDS	160	135	110	125	220	100	125	175	135
PAR									
YARDS									

Directions: I-95 (Maine Turnpike) to Waterville exit. Follow signs for Thomas College.

**N
ME**

Piscataquis Country Club ✪✪ 51 ▶

17 Country Club Lane (Route 15)
Guilford, ME (207) 876-3203
www.piscataquisgolfcourse.com

Club Pro:
Payment: Visa, MC, Check
Tee Times: No
Fee 9 Holes: Weekday: $12
Fee 18 Holes: Weekday: $20
Twilight Rates: $10 after 4pm
Cart Rental: $20pp/18, $10pp/9
Lessons: Schools: No
Membership: Yes
Other: Clubhouse / Kitchen

Tees	Holes	Yards	Par	USGA	Slope
BACK	9	2844	36	66.0	115
MIDDLE	9	2582	36	64.3	106
FRONT	9	2417	36	69.7	123

Weekend: $12
Weekend: $20
Discounts: Junior
Driving Range: No
Junior Golf: Yes
Architect/Yr Open: 1926
GPS:

Number 5 is now a par 5, all uphill. All-day rates for juniors. Prices subject to change.

	1	2	3	4	5	6	7	8	9
PAR	4	4	4	4	5	3	4	4	4
YARDS	352	324	251	290	470	164	268	348	377
PAR									
YARDS									

Directions: I-95 to Newport exit, Route 7 to Route 23 North, to Route 15. Course is 1/10 mile from the intersection.

Portage Hills Country Club ✪✪ 52 ▶

Route 11
Portage, ME (207) 435-8221
www.portagehillscc.com

Club Pro:
Payment: Most Major Credit Cards
Tee Times: No
Fee 9 Holes: Weekday: $15
Fee 18 Holes: Weekday: $25
Twilight Rates: No
Cart Rental: $12pp/cart
Lessons: No Schools:
Membership: Yes
Other: Clubhouse / Snack Bar / Bar-Lounge

Tees	Holes	Yards	Par	USGA	Slope
BACK					
MIDDLE	9	3109	36	69.5	110
FRONT	9	2796	37	71.5	113

Weekend: $15
Weekend: $25
Discounts: None
Driving Range: No
Junior Golf: No
Architect/Yr Open: Ben Gray/1971
GPS:

The course is well-maintained, hilly and scenic. Open from mid-May to mid-September. Rates subject to change.

	1	2	3	4	5	6	7	8	9
PAR	4	4	4	4	5	3	4	5	3
YARDS	432	323	321	343	478	128	388	504	165
PAR									
YARDS									

Directions: I-95, to Sherman exit, Route 11. Follow Route 11 North for approximately 65 miles to the course.

Presque Isle Country Club ✪✪½ ▸53

35 Parkhurst Siding Road (Route 205)
Presque Isle, ME (207) 764-0430
www.picountryclub.com

Club Pro: Barry Madore
Payment: Cash, Visa, MC, Amex, Disc
Tee Times: No
Fee 9 Holes: Weekday: $20
Fee 18 Holes: Weekday: $40
Twilight Rates: After 3pm, $44 w/cart
Cart Rental: $16pp/18, $9pp/9
Lessons: $25/35 min. **Schools:** No
Membership: Yes
Architect/Yr Open: Front 9 - Ben Gray/1959; Back 9 - Rick Hobbs, Geoffrey Cornish/1987
Other: Clubhouse / Lockers / Showers / Restaurant / Bar Lounge

Tees	Holes	Yards	Par	USGA	Slope
BACK	18	6751	72	70.8	118
MIDDLE	18	6217	72	69.2	113
FRONT	18	5387	72	72.2	122

Weekend: $20
Weekend: $40
Discounts: None
Driving Range: $8/lg., $3.50/sm.
Junior Golf: Yes

COUPON

Player Comments: "Friendly and challenging." A very picturesque golf course. Home of the Spudland Open amateur golf tournament.

	1	2	3	4	5	6	7	8	9
PAR	4	4	4	3	4	4	5	3	5
YARDS	322	400	367	155	410	394	473	146	465
	10	11	12	13	14	15	16	17	18
PAR	4	4	5	4	4	5	3	3	4
YARDS	376	334	510	364	387	476	105	191	342

Directions: From Presque Isle, take Route 167 to Route 205. You can't miss it, but if you do, call course for directions.

Rocky Knoll Country Club ✪✪ ▸54

94 River Road
Orrington, ME (207) 989-0109
www.rockyknollcc.com

Club Pro: Mark W. Hall, PGA
Payment: Visa, MC, Amex, Disc, Checks
Tee Times: 7 days adv.
Fee 9 Holes: Weekday: $15
Fee 18 Holes: Weekday: $25
Twilight Rates: No
Cart Rental: $30/18, $15/9 per cart
Lessons: Yes **Schools:** Yes
Membership: Yes
Other: Restaurant / Clubhouse

Tees	Holes	Yards	Par	USGA	Slope
BACK	18	6062	72	69.0	109
MIDDLE	18	5835	72	67.7	107
FRONT	18	4965	72	64.8	106

Weekend: $15
Weekend: $25
Discounts: Sr./Wed, Jr./Fri
Driving Range: Yes
Junior Golf: Yes
Architect/Yr: Robert Phillips/2000
GPS: Yes

COUPON

N ME

2nd Nine opened July 2009, very challenging with large greens. Front Nine wide open with postage stamp greens. Good food. Getting better all the time.

	1	2	3	4	5	6	7	8	9
PAR	5	4	4	5	3	4	3	4	4
YARDS	470	350	399	444	151	401	154	291	342
	10	11	12	13	14	15	16	17	18
PAR	5	4	3	4	4	4	4	3	5
YARDS	510	301	146	420	300	290	302	125	439

Directions: I-395 Bangor Brewer Exit off 1-95. South Main Street Exit Route 15. As you drive away from town, Course is 1 mile on left, clearly visible.

Sawmill Woods Golf Course   ✪✪   55 ▶

800 Airline Road
Clifton, ME (207) 735-8771
www.sawmillwoodsgolf.com

Tees	Holes	Yards	Par	USGA	Slope
BACK	9	2874	36		124
MIDDLE	9	2679	36		121
FRONT	9	2236	36		

Club Pro:
Payment: Cash, Checks
Tee Times: No
Fee 9 Holes: Weekday: $12   **Weekend:** $12
Fee 18 Holes: Weekday: $17   **Weekend:** $17
Twilight Rates: No   **Discounts:** None
Cart Rental: $15pp/18, $10pp/9   **Driving Range:** Yes
Lessons: Yes **Schools:** No   **Junior Golf:** No
Membership: Yes   **Architect/Yr Open:** Hargarl Moore/2007
Other: Clubhouse / Snack Bar / Pro Shop / Putting Course

Sawmill Woods is a par 36 nine-hole course cut through the Maine forest and following the natural contours of the land. Large, undulating greens and tight fairways are enhanced by extensive landscaping, creating a challenging and beautiful rounds of play.

	1	2	3	4	5	6	7	8	9
PAR	4	3	5	4	3	4	5	4	4
YARDS	280	93	384	375	111	375	401	362	274
PAR									
YARDS									

Directions: From I-95 take I-395 exit at Bangor towards Downeast Maine; take Exit 6-A/Route 1A towards Ellesworth/Bar Harbor. Travel 5 miles to light, at Route 46 junction take left to Route 9 (5 miles); take right on Route 9 to course, 5 miles on left.

Searsport Pines Golf Course   ✪✪   56 ▶

240 Mt. Ephraim Road
Searsport, ME (207) 548-2854
www.searsportpines.com

Tees	Holes	Yards	Par	USGA	Slope
BACK					
MIDDLE	9	2695	36	65.9	122
FRONT	9	2366	35/36	68.7	116

Club Pro:
Payment: Cash, Visa, MC, Check
Tee Times: Not required
Fee 9 Holes: Weekday: $20   **Weekend:** $20
Fee 18 Holes: Weekday: $30   **Weekend:** $30
Twilight Rates: No   **Discounts:** Senior & Junior
Cart Rental: $15pp/18, $10pp/9   **Driving Range:** Yes
Lessons: No **Schools:** No   **Junior Golf:** Yes
Membership: Yes   **Architect/Yr Open:** Bert Witten/1997
Other: Food Concession / Beer / Wine / Club Rentals / Practice Area

COUPON

Plush greens, manicured fairways, meticulously maintained and fully irrigated. Friendly staff and scenic atmosphere. Easy-walking and enjoyable for all levels of players. Numerous antique shops, Penobscot Marine Museum, restaurants, lodging nearby. 10 minutes from Belfast. Tuesday greens fee discounts: $15/9 holes, $25/18 holes.

	1	2	3	4	5	6	7	8	9
PAR	4	4	4	4	5	3	4	5	3
YARDS	285	353	313	316	390	150	295	464	129
PAR									
YARDS									

Directions: Route 1 to Searsport Center. Turn left at Tozier's Market in Searsport onto Mt. Ephraim Road. Course is 2 miles on left.

Squaw Mt. Village Country Club ✪½ 57

Route 15
Greenville Junction, ME
(207) 695-3609

Club Pro:
Payment: Cash Only
Tee Times: No
Fee 9 Holes: Weekday: $15
Fee 18 Holes: Weekday: $25
Twilight Rates: No
Cart Rental: $20pp/18, $12pp/9
Lessons: No **Schools:** No
Membership: Yes
Other:

Tees	Holes	Yards	Par	USGA	Slope
BACK					
MIDDLE	9	2341	34	70	113
FRONT					

Weekend: $15
Weekend: $25
Discounts: Junior
Driving Range: No
Junior Golf: Yes
Architect/Yr Open: 1922
GPS:

Discount on membership for juniors, seniors, and families. Short 9 hole course providing views of Big Squaw Mountain and Moosehead Lake. Having its origin in the 1800's, it still has some of the vintage touches.

	1	2	3	4	5	6	7	8	9
PAR	4	3	5	4	4	3	4	3	4
YARDS	359	121	458	288	267	109	317	119	303
PAR									
YARDS									

Directions: I-95 South to Exit 217. Follow Route 6 toward Dover. Stay on 6 to Greenville. Or I-95 South, Exit 185 Bangor, stay on Route 15 North to Greenville. At blinking light in Greenville, go left on Route 15. Course is 3.2 miles on right.

St. Croix Country Club ✪✪ 58

River Road
Calais, ME (207) 454-8875
www.stcroixcc.com

Club Pro: Mike Ellis, PGA
Payment: Visa, MC
Tee Times: No
Fee 9 Holes: Weekday: $14
Fee 18 Holes: Weekday: $22
Twilight Rates: No
Cart Rental: $16pp/18, $10pp/9
Lessons: $30/half hour **Schools:** No
Membership: Yes
Other: Clubhouse / Showers / Bar-Lounge

Tees	Holes	Yards	Par	USGA	Slope
BACK					
MIDDLE	9	2797	35	65.2	107
FRONT	9	2647	36	64.8	119

Weekend: $14
Weekend: $22
Discounts: Senior
Driving Range: No
Junior Golf: Yes
Architect/Yr Open: 1927
GPS:

Easternmost golf course in U.S.A. Watch eagles train their young, eagle's nest on hole #7 on river. Call ahead for league or tournament times. Open May 1 - October 31.

	1	2	3	4	5	6	7	8	9
PAR	3	5	4	4	5	3	4	3	4
YARDS	162	495	319	405	495	126	295	188	312
PAR									
YARDS									

Directions: Head east on Route 1. Course is 2 miles outside of Calais.

N
ME

Streamside Golf Course   ✪½   **59**

551 Stream Road
Winterport, ME (207) 223-9009
www.golfstreamside.com

Tees	Holes	Yards	Par	USGA	Slope
BACK	9	2915	35		
MIDDLE	9	2700	35	65.6	109
FRONT	9	2355	55		

Club Pro:
Payment: Visa, MC, Checks
Tee Times: No
Fee 9 Holes: Weekday: $12   **Weekend:** $15
Fee 18 Holes: Weekday: $18   **Weekend:** $22
Twilight Rates: No   **Discounts:** Senior and Junior (65+/-15)
Cart Rental: $22pp/18, $15pp/9   **Driving Range:** No
Lessons: No   **Schools:** No   **Junior Golf:** No
Membership: Yes   **Architect/Yr Open:** Galen Wellman/1998
Other: Clubhouse / Snack Bar / Putting Course

Situated along the Marsh Stream, this challenging 9 hole layout will be enjoyable to players of all abilities.

	1	2	3	4	5	6	7	8	9
PAR	4	4	3	4	4	3	5	4	4
YARDS	300	240	110	305	240	165	600	440	300
PAR									
YARDS									

Directions: Exit 174 off I-95, go east on Route 69 until it joins Route 139. Turn right on Route 139. Go 4 miles — course is on the right.

Sugarloaf Golf Club   ✪✪✪✪   **60**

5092 Access Road (Route 27)
Carrabassett Valley, ME
(207) 237-2000
www.sugarloaf.com

Tees	Holes	Yards	Par	USGA	Slope
BACK	18	6457	72	72.4	143
MIDDLE	18	5946	72	71.6	138
FRONT	18	5289	72	72.5	131

Club Pro: Abby Spector
Payment: Cash or Credit Card
Tee Times: 14 days adv.
Fee 9 Holes: Weekday: $60   **Weekend:** $70
Fee 18 Holes: Weekday: $100 w/cart   **Weekend:** $120 w/cart
Twilight Rates: After 3pm   **Discounts:** Junior 50%
Cart Rental: $20pp/18, $10pp/9   **Driving Range:** Yes
Lessons: $50/half hour   **Schools:** Jr. & Sr.   **Junior Golf:** Yes
Membership: Yes   **Architect/Yr Open:** Robert Trent Jones Jr./1985
Other: Snack Bar / Restaurant / Bar-Lounge / Health Club / Hotel

COUPON

Player Comments: "Breathtaking resort course." "Challenging and picturesque." Discounted rates for guests.

	1	2	3	4	5	6	7	8	9
PAR	4	5	3	5	4	4	4	3	4
YARDS	372	510	168	466	358	337	331	153	363
	10	11	12	13	14	15	16	17	18
PAR	4	3	5	4	4	3	5	4	4
YARDS	255	166	495	359	333	132	458	339	351

Directions: Route 27. Located 36 miles north of Farmington on Route 27 at Sugarloaf Mountain Ski Resort.

Traditions Golf Club

✪✪¹/₂

1 Main Road
Holden, ME (207) 989-9909
www.traditionsgc.com

Tees	Holes	Yards	Par	USGA	Slope
BACK	9	2461	35	63.6	101
MIDDLE	9	2261	35	62.8	97
FRONT	9	1667	33	63.6	101

Club Pro: Colin Gillies
Payment: Visa, MC, Amex
Tee Times: No
Fee 9 Holes: Weekday: $13   **Weekend:** $13
Fee 18 Holes: Weekday: $20   **Weekend:** $20
Twilight Rates: No
Discounts: Junior/$10
Cart Rental: $10pp/18, $7pp/9   **Driving Range:** Yes
Lessons: Yes **Schools:** Yes   **Junior Golf:** Yes
Membership: Yes   **Architect/Yr:** Robert Spasks & Wendell Russell/1997
Other: Restaurant / Lounge / Night-Lit Driving Range

COUPON

New Ownership. Plays par 35 in scenic wooded Maine. Greens are regulation size. A challenge for all levels. Easy walker. Also try our mini-golf and mini-putt.

	1	2	3	4	5	6	7	8	9
PAR	4	4	4	4	4	5	3	3	4
YARDS	289	238	315	355	244	490	118	135	317
PAR									
YARDS									

Directions: I-95 to I-395 to Holden. Exit Route 1A in Holden. Approx. 2 miles south, first property after Holden line, course is on right.

Va-Jo-Wa Golf Club

✪✪

142 Walker Settlement Road
Island Falls, ME (207) 463-2128
www.vajowa.com

Tees	Holes	Yards	Par	USGA	Slope
BACK	18	6250	72	70.4	123
MIDDLE	18	5838	72	68.5	119
FRONT	18	4970	72	69.6	115

Club Pro: Warren Walker, Mgr.
Payment: MC, Visa, Disc
Tee Times:
Fee 9 Holes: Weekday: $20   **Weekend:** $20
Fee 18 Holes: Weekday: $30   **Weekend:** $30
Twilight Rates: **Discounts:** Junior
Cart Rental: $18pp/18, $12pp/9   **Driving Range:** Yes
Lessons: $40/half hour by appt. **Schools:** No **Junior Golf:** July
Membership: Yes   **Architect/Yr Open:** Vaughn Walker/1964
Other: Clubhouse / Snack Bar / Restaurant / Bar-Lounge / Condos / Bag Storage

COUPON

Only 18-hole course in 80-mile radius. Noted for scenic value and quality layout. Open May 1 - October 31. 16th hole and most of the back 9, great scenery including view of Mt. Katahdin.

	1	2	3	4	5	6	7	8	9
PAR	4	4	4	3	4	3	5	4	5
YARDS	308	445	283	207	378	116	517	354	531
	10	11	12	13	14	15	16	17	18
PAR	4	3	4	4	4	5	3	4	5
YARDS	315	138	381	458	387	478	161	371	524

Directions: I-95 to Exit 276; follow Route 2 East 3 miles; look for signs to Va-Jo-Wa.

N
ME

Waterville Country Club   ✪✪✪½   ▶63

Route 137
Oakland, ME (207) 465-9861
www.watervillecountryclub.com

Tees	Holes	Yards	Par	USGA	Slope
BACK	18	6427	70	70.1	123
MIDDLE	18	6108	70	68.6	118
FRONT	18	5381	70	71.3	119

Club Pro: Don Roberts, PGA
Payment: Cash, Visa, MC
Tee Times: Yes
Fee 9 Holes: Weekday: No   **Weekend:** No
Fee 18 Holes: Weekday: $65   **Weekend:** $65
Twilight Rates: No   **Discounts:** None
Cart Rental: $15pp/18   **Driving Range:** $3/bucket
Lessons: $35/half hour   **Schools:** No   **Junior Golf:** Yes
Membership: Yes   **Architect/Yr Open:** Cornish/1916; Orrin Smith
Other: Snack Bar / Restaurant / Bar-Lounge   **GPS:** Yes

Excellent for all golfers. Semi-private. "Great views, great layout." –FP

	1	2	3	4	5	6	7	8	9
PAR	4	3	5	4	4	3	4	4	5
YARDS	350	140	455	378	430	170	300	385	505
	10	**11**	**12**	**13**	**14**	**15**	**16**	**17**	**18**
PAR	4	4	4	3	4	4	3	4	4
YARDS	435	410	370	200	355	330	185	370	340

Directions: I-95 North to Exit 127 to Route 137 West to Oakland. Waterville Country Club is 1.5 miles on left.

Whitetail Golf Course   ✪½   ▶64

373 School Road
Charleston, ME (207) 285-7730
www.whitetailgolfmaine.com

Tees	Holes	Yards	Par	USGA	Slope
BACK	9	2814	34	66.1	114
MIDDLE	9	2637	34	66.1	114
FRONT	9	2358	34	66.6	106

Club Pro: Ken Martin
Payment: Cash or Check
Tee Times: No
Fee 9 Holes: Weekday: $13/walk; $20/cart   **Weekend:** $18/walk, $25 w/cart
Fee 18 Holes: Weekday: $18/walk; $25/cart   **Weekend:** $22/walk, $35 w/cart
Twilight Rates: No   **Discounts:** None
Cart Rental: Included in rates above   **Driving Range:** No
Lessons: No   **Schools:** No   **Junior Golf:**
Membership: Yes   **Architect/Yr Open:** Scott Duthie/1997
Other: Clubhouse / 18 Hole Putting Course
GPS:

COUPON

Scenic, country setting. with rolling hills and 40 different tees, making it challenging and fun for all abilities.

	1	2	3	4	5	6	7	8	9
PAR	5	3	3	4	3	4	5	4	4
YARDS	494	136	176	235	150	329	390	370	357
PAR									
YARDS									

Directions: I-95 to Bangor, exit North on Route 15. Go approximately 30 miles. Course is at the corner of Route 15 and School Road in Charleston. Turn right.

Wilson Lake Country Club ✪✪✪

65 ▶

320 Weld Road
Wilton, ME (207) 645-2016
www.wilsonlakecc.com

Club Pro: Joshua Best
Payment: Visa, MC
Tee Times: 1 day adv.
Fee 9 Holes: Weekday: $20
Fee 18 Holes: Weekday: $30
Twilight Rates: 4pm weekdays
Cart Rental: $15pp/18, $8pp/9
Lessons: Yes **Schools:** No
Membership: Yes
Other: Clubhouse / Bar-Lounge / Snack Bar

Tees	Holes	Yards	Par	USGA	Slope
BACK	9	3162	35	68.4	120
MIDDLE	9	3040	35	68.0	120
FRONT	9	2804	37	72.2	126

Weekend: $20
Weekend: $30
Discounts: Lung Card
Driving Range: No
Junior Golf: Yes
Architect/Yr Open: Wayne Stiles/1932

COUPON

Considered by many to be "the best nine in Maine" in picturesque Wilton. Although the routing includes five parallel holes, the uphill and downhill nature of their path from the clubhouse to the lower points of the property demand second shots of varying lengths. Noted for having some of the best greens in the state.

	1	2	3	4	5	6	7	8	9
PAR	4	3	5	4	4	4	3	4	4
YARDS	402	153	501	420	366	377	140	329	352
PAR									
YARDS									

Directions: Route 4 to Route 2 to Route 156 into Wilton. Course is on Weld Road in Wilton.

N
ME

Apple Valley GC	1	Lake Kezar CC	22	Rockland Golf Club	43
Bath Golf Club	2	Lebanon Pines GC	23	Sable Oaks Golf Club	44
Bethel Inn & CC	3	The Ledges Golf Club	24	Salmon Falls GC	45
Biddeford & Saco CC	4	The Links at Outlook	25	Samoset Resort GC	46
Boothbay Harbor CC	5	Maple Lane Inn and GC	26	Sandy River GC	47
Bridgton Highlands CC	6	Martindale CC	27	Sanford Country Club	48
Brunswick Golf Club	7	The Meadows Golf Club	28	Sebasco Harbor Resort GC	49
Cape Arundel Golf Club	8	Mere Creek	29	Sheepscot Links	50
Cape Neddick CC	9	Merriland Farm Par 3 GC	30	South Portland Muni.	51
Cobbossee Colony GC	10	Naples Golf and CC	31	Spring Meadows GC	52
Country Fareways	11	Nonesuch River GC	32	Springbrook GC	53
Deep Brook Golf Course	12	Norway Country Club	33	Sunday River Golf Club	54
Dunegrass Golf Club	13	Oakdale Country Club	34	Toddy Brook Golf Course	55
Dutch Elm Golf Course	14	Old Marsh Country Club	35	Turner Highland GC	56
Fairlawn Golf Club	15	Paris Hill Country Club	36	Twin Falls Golf Club	57
Fox Ridge Golf Club	16	Point Sebago Golf Club	37	Val Halla Golf Course	58
Freeport Country Club	17	Poland Spring CC	38	Wawenock CC	59
Frye Island Golf Course	18	Prospect Hill GC	39	Webhannet Golf Club	60
Goose River GC	19	Province Lake Golf Club	40	Western View Golf Club	61
Gorham Country Club	20	Rivermeadow GC	41	Willowdale Golf Club	62
Highland Green Golf Club	21	Riverside Muni. GC	42		

KEY TO THE STAR RATINGS:
5✪ = Outstanding   4✪ = Excellent   3✪ = Very Good   2✪ = Good   1✪ = Average   **NR** = Not Rated

Apple Valley Golf Course ✪✪

316 Pinewoods Road
Lewiston, ME (207) 784-9773

Tees	Holes	Yards	Par	USGA	Slope
BACK					
MIDDLE	9	2473	35	63.9	104
FRONT					

Club Pro:
Payment: Cash, Credit
Tee Times: Not required
Fee 9 Holes: Weekday: $15
Fee 18 Holes: Weekday: $20
Twilight Rates: After 3pm
Cart Rental: $14pp/18, $7pp/9
Lessons: No **Schools:** No
Membership: Yes
Other: Clubhouse / Snack Bar

Weekend: $15
Weekend: $20
Discounts: Junior
Driving Range: No
Junior Golf:
Architect/Yr Open: Arthur David Chapman/1962
GPS:

Open April 15 - November 15. New Apple Valley Estates golf residential community being built.

	1	2	3	4	5	6	7	8	9
PAR	4	4	3	5	3	4	4	4	4
YARDS	235	256	147	445	108	333	299	300	350
PAR									
YARDS									

Directions: Maine Turnpike to Exit 80 (Route 196 East) for 4 miles. Right onto Dyer Road. Left onto Pinewoods Road. Course is 2 miles on left.

Bath Golf Club ✪✪✪ 2

387 Whiskeag Road
Bath, ME (207) 442-8411
www.harrisgolfonline.com

Tees	Holes	Yards	Par	USGA	Slope
BACK	18	6301	70	70.8	130
MIDDLE	18	5840	70	68.3	129
FRONT	18	4708	70	67.9	108

Club Pro: Joe Cahoon
Payment: Cash, Credit Cards
Tee Times: Yes
Fee 9 Holes: Weekday: $25
Fee 18 Holes: Weekday: $40
Twilight Rates: No
Cart Rental: $13pp/18, $8pp/9
Lessons: Yes **Schools:** No
Membership: Yes
Other: Clubhouse / Restaurant / Lounge / Lockers

Weekend: $25
Weekend: $40
Discounts: No
Driving Range: No
Junior Golf: Yes
Architect/Yr Open: Wayne Stiles/1932
GPS: Yes

Fairways are tight and tree-lined. Paved cart paths. 8th hole is an outstanding par 4. Series of lessons offered. "Excellent course conditions. Friendly staff. Nice layout." –FP

	1	2	3	4	5	6	7	8	9
PAR	4	4	5	4	4	3	4	4	3
YARDS	338	375	500	370	325	160	420	425	178
	10	**11**	**12**	**13**	**14**	**15**	**16**	**17**	**18**
PAR	4	4	4	3	4	4	3	5	4
YARDS	258	326	275	115	352	356	163	525	352

Directions: I-295 to Route 1 North. From 1 North take New Meadows Road exit. Go right at stop sign. Go 1¼ miles to next stop sign. Go straight through onto Ridge Road for 1¼ miles to 18th tee. Go right.

S
ME

Bethel Inn & Country Club ✪✪

3

21 Broad Street
Bethel, ME (207) 824-6276
www.bethelinn.com

Club Pro: Chris Bourasso, PGA
Payment: MC, Visa, Amex, Cash
Tee Times: 2 days adv.

Tees	Holes	Yards	Par	USGA	Slope
BACK	18	6663	72	71.0	128
MIDDLE	18	6017	72	67.9	122
FRONT	18	5280	72	71.5	129

Fee 9 Holes: Weekday: $27
Fee 18 Holes: Weekday: $50
Twilight Rates: No
Cart Rental: $18pp/18, $13pp/9
Lessons: $50/half hour **Schools:** Yes
Membership: Yes
Other: Clubhouse / Showers / Snack Bar / Restaurant / Bar / Lodging

Weekend: $27
Weekend: $50 walk
Discounts: No
Driving Range: $5/lg. bucket
Junior Golf: Yes
Architect/Yr Open: Geoffrey Cornish/1913

COUPON

The Guaranteed Performance School of Golf at this Cornish-designed course highlights the summer season. New draining and watering. "Great views. We were treated very well."

	1	2	3	4	5	6	7	8	9
PAR	4	4	3	4	5	3	4	5	4
YARDS	340	262	130	370	492	141	361	500	292
	10	11	12	13	14	15	16	17	18
PAR	4	5	3	4	4	4	3	5	4
YARDS	325	546	167	294	397	400	151	506	343

Directions: Maine Turnpike to Exit 63 Gray. Take Route 26 North to Bethel. Route 26 becomes Main Street in Bethel. Follow Main Street to the top. Course is on left behind Main Inn.

Biddeford & Saco Country Club ✪✪✪

4

101 Old Orchard Road
Saco, ME (207) 282-5883
www.biddefordsacocountryclub.com

Club Pro: Tim Angis, PGA
Payment: All Major
Tee Times: 3 days adv., June-Sept.

Tees	Holes	Yards	Par	USGA	Slope
BACK	18	6333	71	69.6	130
MIDDLE	18	5918	71	68.6	123
FRONT	18	5319	72	71.4	117

Fee 9 Holes: Weekday:
Fee 18 Holes: Weekday: $40
Twilight Rates: No
Cart Rental: $18pp/18, $9pp/9
Lessons: Call for details **Schools:** No
Membership: Yes
Other: Restaurant / Snack Bar / Bar-Lounge / Lockers / Showers

Weekend:
Weekend: $50
Discounts: No
Driving Range: $4/bucket
Junior Golf: Yes
Architect/Yr Open: Donald Ross/1922

User friendly but still a challenge, wonderful playing condition in a pretty and peaceful atmosphere. "New practice facility, the best around. Nice greens." –MH

	1	2	3	4	5	6	7	8	9
PAR	4	3	5	4	4	4	4	3	4
YARDS	344	186	501	322	400	339	336	164	424
	10	11	12	13	14	15	16	17	18
PAR	3	4	5	4	4	3	4	5	4
YARDS	146	443	466	354	314	129	326	411	313

Directions: I-95 to Exit 36 Maine Turnpike. Straight to Rotary. Take right on Old Orchard Road, course is ½ mile on left.

Boothbay Harbor Country Club ✪✪✪½   5

33 Country Club Lane
Boothbay, ME (207) 633-3673
www.boothbayharborcc.com

Tees	Holes	Yards	Par	USGA	Slope
BACK	18	6356	71	68.9	133
MIDDLE	18	6084	71	66.5	122
FRONT	18	4770	71	67.1	120

Club Pro: Greg Sandell
Payment: Visa, MC, Amex
Tee Times: 3 days adv.
Fee 9 Holes: Weekday/Weekend: $40 (June 15-Sept. 30)
Fee 18 Holes: Weekday/Weekend: $77 before 1pm, $57 after 1pm (June 1-Sept. 30)
Twilight Rates: After 3pm
Discounts: $52pp/18, $30pp/9 (before June 15 and after Sept. 30)
Cart Rental: $18pp/18, $11pp/9   **Driving Range:** Yes
Lessons: Yes   **Schools:** No   **Junior Golf:** Yes
Membership: Yes   **Architect/Yr:** Stiles & Van Kleek/1921
Other: Restaurant / Clubhouse / Bar-Lounge / Art Gallery

Beautiful coastal gem. Rolling fairways w/fast undulating greens. Four sets of tees provide a challenge for every golfer. "Great getaway area. One of the most fun courses you'll ever play!" –FP

	1	2	3	4	5	6	7	8	9
PAR	4	3	4	4	4	5	3	4	5
YARDS	342	182	340	291	349	525	184	375	446
	10	11	12	13	14	15	16	17	18
PAR	4	4	4	4	4	3	4	3	5
YARDS	310	333	400	342	330	133	337	127	512

Directions: Via I-95, take Exit 48 onto Route 302. In Bridgton, turn right off Main Street at sign onto Highland Road and travel 1½ miles to course. From New Hampshire, follow Route 302 from Conway area to Bridgton. On Main Street, turn left at sign onto Highland Road.

Bridgton Highlands Country Club ✪✪✪   6

379 Highland Road
Bridgton, ME (207) 647-3491
www.bridgtonhighlands.com

Tees	Holes	Yards	Par	USGA	Slope
BACK	18	6224	72	70.4	128
MIDDLE	18	5810	72	69.0	123
FRONT	18	5300	74	66.5	117

Club Manager: Jim Mains
Payment: Cash, Check, Visa, MC, Disc
Tee Times: by phone or online
Fee 9 Holes: Weekday: $18 - $20   **Weekend:** $18 - $20
Fee 18 Holes: Weekday: $25 - $30   **Weekend:** $30 - $36
Twilight Rates: After 3pm   **Discounts:** Junior
Cart Rental: $17pp/18, $9pp/9   **Driving Range:** Yes
Lessons: Available   **Schools:** No   **Junior Golf:** Yes
Membership: Yes (see website)   **Architect/Yr Open:** A.W. Tillinghast/1927
Other: Snack Bar / Full Bar / 4 Tennis Courts & Tennis Program

18 holes of challenging and enjoyable golf in the scenic Lakes Region of western Maine with views of Pleasant Mountain/Shawnee Peak and the White Mountains of New Hampshire, including Mount Washington. "Very nice layout with a variety of thinking holes." –FP

	1	2	3	4	5	6	7	8	9
PAR	4	3	4	5	4	4	5	3	4
YARDS	434	152	377	437	333	313	413	148	328
	10	11	12	13	14	15	16	17	18
PAR	3	4	4	3	4	5	4	4	5
YARDS	153	324	383	152	350	442	282	296	493

Directions: I-95 to Exit 48 onto Route 302 West. In Bridgton, turn right off Main Street onto Highland Road. Travel 1.5 miles to course. From NH: follow Route 302 fron Conway to Bridgton. On Main Street turn left onto Highland Road.

S
ME

Brunswick Golf Club

165 River Road
Brunswick, ME (207) 725-8224
www.brunswickgolfclub.com

Club Pro: A. J. Kavanaugh, Dir. of Golf
Payment: Visa, MC, Disc
Tee Times: Anytime

Tees	Holes	Yards	Par	USGA	Slope
BACK	18	6609	72	69.9	126
MIDDLE	18	6251	72	70	123
FRONT	18	5772	74	71.6	123

Fee 9 Holes: Weekday: $25
Fee 18 Holes: Weekday: $40
Twilight Rates: After 4pm
Cart Rental: $15pp/18, $10pp/9
Lessons: $65/hour **Schools:** No
Membership: Yes
Weekend: $25
Weekend: $50
Discounts: Junior
Driving Range: Yes
Junior Golf: Yes

COUPON

Architect/Yr Open: Front: Cornish/1960; Back: Stiles & Van Cleek/1920
Other: Clubhouse / Deck / Snack Bar / Bar-Lounge / Lockers

A real classic layout, a must-play. "Easiest, challenging course to walk in New England." –FP

	1	2	3	4	5	6	7	8	9
PAR	4	5	5	3	3	4	4	4	5
YARDS	355	547	485	179	110	440	332	364	494
	10	11	12	13	14	15	16	17	18
PAR	4	3	4	4	4	3	5	4	4
YARDS	353	172	297	363	430	145	490	300	395

Directions: I-295 to Exit 28, Brunswick; at 2nd light take left onto River Road. Follow 1 mile to course on left.

Cape Arundel Golf Club

19 River Road
Kennebunkport, ME (207) 967-3494
www.capearundelgolfclub.com

Club Pro: Ken Raynor
Payment: Visa, MC, Amex
Tee Times: 3 days adv.

Tees	Holes	Yards	Par	USGA	Slope
BACK	18	5881	69	67.1	118
MIDDLE	18	5310	69	63.7	100
FRONT	18	5026	70	69.7	119

Fee 9 Holes: Weekday: $55
Fee 18 Holes: Weekday: $75
Twilight Rates: $35 after 4pm
Cart Rental: $20pp/18, $12pp/9
Lessons: Yes **Schools:** No
Membership:
Other: Clubhouse / Lockers
Weekend: $55
Weekend: $75
Discounts: Voucher books available
Driving Range: No
Junior Golf: No
Architect/Yr Open: Walter Travis/1921
GPS:

Home course of President Bush's family. Members only 11am - 2:30pm daily. Twilight rates are not available during July and August.

	1	2	3	4	5	6	7	8	9
PAR	4	4	3	4	4	3	4	4	5
YARDS	375	311	154	398	350	118	381	370	480
	10	11	12	13	14	15	16	17	18
PAR	4	4	4	3	4	4	3	4	4
YARDS	345	320	409	165	387	322	220	365	394

Directions: From South I-95 to Wells Exit 19. Left to Route 1.2 miles to right on Route 9 to Kennebunkport. From North I-95 Exit 32.

Cape Neddick Country Club ✪✪✪

650 Shore Road
Cape Neddick, ME (207) 361-2011
www.capeneddickgolf.com

Club Pro: Dustin Hunter
Payment: Visa, MC
Tee Times: 7 days adv.

Tees	Holes	Yards	Par	USGA	Slope
BACK	18	6066	70	69.3	119
MIDDLE	18	5698	70	67.5	116
FRONT	18	4904	71	69.1	121

Fee 9 Holes: Weekday: $35 M-Th   **Weekend:** $38
Fee 18 Holes: Weekday: $56 M-Th   **Weekend:** $63
Twilight Rates: $39 (with cart) after 3pm   **Discounts:** None
Cart Rental: $18pp/18, $10pp/9   **Driving Range:** Yes
Lessons: $30/half hour **Schools:** Yes   **Junior Golf:** Yes
Membership: Yes   **Architect/Yr:** Donald Ross/1920; Brian Silva/1999
Other: Restaurant / Clubhouse / Lockers / Bar-Lounge / Driving Range

COUPON

Player Comments: "Challenging; back 9 tougher than first 9. Fun for all skills." "Good summer vacation course. Nice ocean setting." Semi-private. Just 1 hour North of Boston. Best-conditioned course in Southern Maine! Accepts Players Pass and Lung Card.

	1	2	3	4	5	6	7	8	9
PAR	4	3	5	4	4	3	4	3	4
YARDS	340	168	577	302	305	122	300	151	326
	10	**11**	**12**	**13**	**14**	**15**	**16**	**17**	**18**
PAR	4	3	5	4	3	5	4	4	4
YARDS	432	153	518	384	170	540	324	268	318

Directions: From the South: I-95 to Exit 7 (York); go east .5 mile to U.S. 1. Go north for 3.4 miles to River Road. East on River Road for 1 mile to Shore Road. Club is 2.8 miles north on Shore Road.

Cobbossee Colony Golf Course ✪✪

885 Cobbossee Road
Monmouth, ME (207) 268-4182
www.golfcobbossee.com

Club Pro:
Payment: Cash, Check, Visa, MC
Tee Times: No

Tees	Holes	Yards	Par	USGA	Slope
BACK					
MIDDLE	9	2390	34	61.3	95
FRONT					

Fee 9 Holes: Weekday: $13   **Weekend:** $14
Fee 18 Holes: Weekday: $18   **Weekend:** $19
Twilight Rates: After 5pm   **Discounts:** Lung Card/Jr. Golf Card
Cart Rental: $20/18, $14/9 per cart   **Driving Range:** Yes
Lessons: Yes **Schools:** No   **Junior Golf:** No
Membership: Yes   **Architect/Yr Open:** Lee & Royal Cottrell/1922
Other: Snack Bar / Clubhouse   **GPS:**

COUPON

It's an easy walk, and fun. Practice green.

**S
ME**

	1	2	3	4	5	6	7	8	9
PAR	5	3	4	4	3	4	3	4	4
YARDS	450	140	246	312	216	331	108	293	294
PAR									
YARDS									

Directions: From Brunswick area, Exit 51 off I-295 Gardiner - Litchfield. Go approximately 6 miles west on Route 126. Right onto Hallowell Road for 1.5 miles. Left onto Hardscrabble Road. Course is about 1.5 miles on both sides of the road.

Country Fareways

●● **11** ▶

1549 Augusta Road
Bowdoin, ME (207) 666-5603
www.countryfareways.com

Tees	Holes	Yards	Par	USGA	Slope
BACK					
MIDDLE	10	1248	30		121
FRONT	10	1131	30		120

Club Pro:
Payment: Visa, MC, Disc, Cash, Checks
Tee Times: No
Fee 10 Holes: Weekday: $13   **Weekend:** $13
Fee 18 Holes: Weekday: $17   **Weekend:** $17
Twilight Rates: No   **Discounts:** Seniors/Juniors/Military/Veterans
Cart Rental: $17pp/18, $13pp/9   **Driving Range:** No
Lessons: No **Schools:** No   **Junior Golf:** Yes, Jrs. free w/paying adult
Membership: No   **Architect/Yr Open:** Dennis Gallant/1996
Other: 10-Play Package - Buy 9 Rounds, Play 10th Free

Well-groomed and beautifully landscaped. Great place to practice your short game. Beginner friendly but challenging. Some of the best greens in the area. Number 8 tee box in progress. New course record set August 25, 2013: "29" by owner Dennis Gallant.

	1	2	3	4	5	6	7	8	9
PAR	3	3	3	3	3	3	3	3	3
YARDS	132	108	148	119	104	134	96	132	100
PAR									
YARDS									

Directions: Route I-295 to Exit 37. From north ramp turn right. From south ramp turn left. Turn right on Route 125 and go to the stop sign. Turn right on Route 201. Course is 1 mile on right.

Deep Brook Golf Course

●●½ **12** ▶

36 New County Road
Saco, ME (207) 283-3500
www.deepbrookgolfcourse.com

Tees	Holes	Yards	Par	USGA	Slope
BACK	9	3076	36	70.0	129
MIDDLE	9	2831	36	67.8	127
FRONT	9	2312	36	67.6	111

Club Pro:
Payment: Cash or Credit Cards
Tee Times: 1 day adv.
Fee 9 Holes: Weekday: $18   **Weekend:** $20
Fee 18 Holes: Weekday: $28   **Weekend:** $30
Twilight Rates: After 4pm   **Discounts:** Senior & Junior
Cart Rental: $12pp/18, $7pp/9   **Driving Range:** No
Lessons: Yes **Schools:**   **Junior Golf:**
Membership: **Architect/Yr Open:** William Bradley Booth/2001
Other: Clubhouse / Snack Bar   **GPS:**

COUPON

Challenging course, geographicaly accessible for daily play. Tee lengths change on back 9. Open April - Snow. "A work in progress. Nice finishing hole." –RW

	1	2	3	4	5	6	7	8	9
PAR	4	4	3	4	5	3	5	4	4
YARDS	389	399	150	287	566	119	472	352	342
PAR									
YARDS									

Directions: Exit 5 from Maine Turnpike. Left at traffic light onto Industrial Park Road to first light; take left at light. Next light go right, then first left onto Garfield Street to end at light onto Route 5. Course is 1 mile on left.

Dunegrass Golf Club ✪✪✪✪ ▶13

200 Wild Dunes Way
Old Orchard Beach, ME
(207) 934-4513
www.dunegrass.com

Club Pro: Jim Fairbanks, PGA
Payment: Cash, Visa, MC, Amex
Tee Times: 7 days adv.
Fee 9 Holes: Weekday: $30
Fee 18 Holes: Weekday: $57 ($50 12-3pm)
Twilight Rates: After 3pm
Cart Rental: $18pp/18, $11pp/9
Lessons: Yes **Schools:** No
Membership: Yes, semi-private

Tees	Holes	Yards	Par	USGA	Slope
BACK	18	6644	72	71.6	134
MIDDLE	18	6266	72	68.8	125
FRONT	18	4920	72	68.0	113

Weekend: $30
Weekend: $57 ($50 12-3pm)
Discounts: See website
Driving Range: Yes
Junior Golf: Yes
Architect/Yr Open: Dan Maples/1999

Other: New Clubhouse / Restaurant / Lockers-Showers / Bar-Lounge / Hotel / Inn

Player Comments: "Great staff, fine conditions." "Visit once and you'll return. Super layout." –GD
Vacation packages available. $25/walking, $39/riding after 3pm. All you can play - $30 w/cart after 5pm.

	1	2	3	4	5	6	7	8	9
PAR	5	3	4	4	4	4	5	3	4
YARDS	539	140	387	301	368	348	526	163	333
	10	**11**	**12**	**13**	**14**	**15**	**16**	**17**	**18**
PAR	4	3	5	3	4	5	4	3	5
YARDS	376	168	500	175	395	443	410	170	524

Directions: I-95 to Exit 36 at I-195 to Exit 2B (Route 1 North). Travel about .1 mile on Route 1 to Ross Road on right. Take Ross Road for about 2 miles. See Wild Dunes Way and golf course on right.

Dutch Elm Golf Course ✪✪ ▶14

5 Brimstone Road
Arundel, ME (207) 282-9850
www.dutchelmgolf.com

Club Pro: Norm Hevey
Payment: Cash, Visa, MC
Tee Times: Yes
Fee 9 Holes: Weekday: $25
Fee 18 Holes: Weekday: $35
Twilight Rates: After 3pm
Cart Rental: $16pp/18, $10pp/9
Lessons: $25/half hour **Schools:** No
Membership: Yes
Other: Bar-Lounge / Snack Bar

Tees	Holes	Yards	Par	USGA	Slope
BACK	18	6314	72	69.7	122
MIDDLE	18	5934	72	68.3	118
FRONT	18	5304	72	70.9	120

Weekend: $30
Weekend: $40
Discounts: Senior & Junior
Driving Range: Yes
Junior Golf: No
Architect/Yr Open: Lucien Bourque/1965
GPS:

Greens roll very true. Water comes into play on many holes. Very well maintained.

	1	2	3	4	5	6	7	8	9
PAR	4	5	4	4	4	5	3	3	4
YARDS	300	494	276	347	326	493	202	182	357
	10	**11**	**12**	**13**	**14**	**15**	**16**	**17**	**18**
PAR	4	3	3	5	5	4	4	4	4
YARDS	356	156	150	440	486	411	300	342	357

Directions: Off Maine Turnpike, take Exit 32 (Biddeford). Turn right on Route 111, go 1 mile to Valero Gas Station. Bear left, go 1 mile to stop sign. Turn right, course is on left.

S
ME

Fairlawn Golf & Country Club ✪✪½ 15

434 Empire Road
Poland, ME (207) 998-4277
www.fairlawngolf.com

Club Pro: David Bartasuis, PGA
Payment: Visa, MC, Check, Cash
Tee Times: No
Fee 9 Holes: Weekday:
Fee 18 Holes: Weekday: $28
Twilight Rates: After 4pm
Cart Rental: $14/18, $7/9 per cart
Lessons: No **Schools:** No
Membership: Yes
Architect/Yr Open: Chick Adams & Frank Bartasuis/1963
Other: Clubhouse / Lockers / Snack Bar / Bar-Lounge

Weekend:
Weekend: $30
Discounts: None
Driving Range: Yes
Junior Golf: No

Tees	Holes	Yards	Par	USGA	Slope
BACK	18	6300	72	68.9	117
MIDDLE	18	5833	72	67.5	110
FRONT	18	5158	72	69.9	111

Open May 1 - until it snows. Condos on course available for rent. "Family owned, operated and designed course. Very popular due to the friendly atmosphere and reasonable fee. Very walkable." –DW

	1	2	3	4	5	6	7	8	9
PAR	4	3	5	4	4	4	5	3	4
YARDS	323	205	544	409	364	357	497	182	317
	10	11	12	13	14	15	16	17	18
PAR	4	3	5	3	4	4	5	4	4
YARDS	394	133	491	154	358	363	535	341	333

Directions: From Maine Turnpike, Exit 75, take right off exit; take first right (Kittyhawk). Go to end of road and take left (Lewiston Junction Road). At first stop sign take right. Course on left. From West: take Route 26 South to Route 122. Take right onto Route 122 and follow signs.

Fox Ridge Golf Club ✪✪✪✪ 16

550 Penley Corner Road
Auburn, ME (207) 777-GOLF (4653)
www.foxridgegolfclub.com

Club Pro: Bob Darling Jr.
Payment: Visa, MC
Tee Times: 10 days adv.
Fee 9 Holes: Weekday: $26
Fee 18 Holes: Weekday: $39
Twilight Rates: After 3pm
Cart Rental: $17pp/18, $10pp/9
Lessons: $40/half hour **Schools:** Yes
Membership: Yes
Other: Restaurant / Clubhouse / Bar-Lounge

Weekend: $28
Weekend: $48
Discounts: Junior
Driving Range: Yes
Junior Golf:
Architect/Yr Open: Carol Myshrall/2001
GPS:

Tees	Holes	Yards	Par	USGA	Slope
BACK	18	6814	72	73.4	133
MIDDLE	18	6297	72	70.7	131
FRONT	18	4959	72	69.8	125

COUPON

Golf Digest 4½ star rating out of 5 stars a course. Where you use every club in your bag. Island green.

	1	2	3	4	5	6	7	8	9
PAR	4	4	3	5	3	4	4	4	5
YARDS	322	387	167	529	191	349	360	300	489
	10	11	12	13	14	15	16	17	18
PAR	4	5	4	3	4	4	3	5	4
YARDS	383	551	378	113	322	344	203	518	391

Directions: Maine Turnpike to Exit 75. Left on Washington Avenue, right on Danville Corner Road, left on Danville Road, right on Hammond Corner Road.

Freeport Country Club

17

2 Old County Road
Freeport, ME (207) 865-0711
www.harrisgolfonline.com

Club Pro: Chad Hopkins, PGA
Payment: Visa, MC, Amex, Disc
Tee Times: Yes
Fee 9 Holes: Weekday: $15
Fee 18 Holes: Weekday: $25
Twilight Rates: No
Cart Rental: $15pp/18, $8pp/9
Lessons: Yes **Schools:** Yes
Membership: Yes, $425
Other: Clubhouse / Snack Bar

Tees	Holes	Yards	Par	USGA	Slope
BACK					
MIDDLE	9	2955	36	69.0	116
FRONT	9	2405	36	67.1	109

Weekend: $15
Weekend: $25
Discounts: None
Driving Range: Yes
Junior Golf: Yes
Architect/Yr Open: 1965
GPS:

Located just minutes from the world famous L.L. Bean, situated with easy striking distance of Portland, Lewiston/Auburn, and Brunswick. Brand new practice facility with target greens, natural surface teeing areas, lesson tees, putting greens, and a practice bunker.

	1	2	3	4	5	6	7	8	9
PAR	4	4	4	4	5	3	4	3	5
YARDS	378	390	370	250	453	197	306	148	463
PAR									
YARDS									

Directions: I-295 North to Exit 17, right on U.S.1 for 2 miles, left over the overpass, then 1st right to club.

Frye Island Golf Course

18

115 Cape Road Extension
Raymond, ME (207) 655-3551
www.fryeisland.com

Club Pro:
Payment: Cash, Credit Cards
Tee Times: Weekends
Fee 9 Holes: Weekday: $20
Fee 18 Holes: Weekday: $20
Twilight Rates: After 5pm
Cart Rental: $13pp/18, $8pp/9
Lessons: Yes **Schools:** No
Membership: Yes
Other: Snack Bar / Lounge

Tees	Holes	Yards	Par	USGA	Slope
BACK	9	3139	36	70.0	123
MIDDLE	9	3023	36	69.4	121
FRONT	9	2651	36	72.4	126

Weekend: $30
Weekend: $30
Discounts: Junior
Driving Range: No
Junior Golf: No
Architect/Yr Open: Geoffrey Cornish/1972
GPS:

This 9-hole course is narrow with water holes and tree-lined fairways. Open May 1 - November 1. "Great getaway course." FP

	1	2	3	4	5	6	7	8	9
PAR	4	5	4	3	4	4	5	3	4
YARDS	378	481	391	160	358	293	456	155	351
PAR									
YARDS									

Directions: Take Exit 48 (Westbrook) to Route 302 (2 miles) to Raymond Cape Road. Follow 20 miles to Frye Island Ferry Landing for 5 miles.

**S
ME**

Goose River Golf Club

50 Park Street
Rockport, ME (207) 236-8488
www.gooserivergolf.com

Tees	Holes	Yards	Par	USGA	Slope
BACK					
MIDDLE	9	3072	35	68.0	118
FRONT	9	2608	36	69.7	117

Club Pro: Jim Blanchett, Dir. of Golf
Payment: Cash, MC, Visa
Tee Times: Yes
Fee 9 Holes: Weekday: $25   **Weekend:** $25
Fee 18 Holes: Weekday: $35   **Weekend:** $35
Twilight Rates: After 3pm   **Discounts:** Junior
Cart Rental: $15pp/18, $10pp/9   **Driving Range:**
Lessons: Yes **Schools:** No   **Junior Golf:** Yes
Membership: Yes   **Architect/Yr Open:** Al Zikorus/1965
Other: Snack Bar   **GPS:** Yes

COUPON

9 holes, 2 sets of tees. Area known for sailing, kayaking, and hiking. Attractions include: Camden Hills, 2 museums, Rockport and Camden harbors.

	1	2	3	4	5	6	7	8	9
PAR	5	4	4	4	5	3	4	3	3
YARDS	550	336	367	336	472	163	335	189	306
PAR									
YARDS									

Directions: North on I-95, north on Route 1. Follow Route 1 into Camden and follow signs.

Gorham Country Club

68 McLellan Road
Gorham, ME (207) 839-3490
www.gorhamcountryclub.com

Tees	Holes	Yards	Par	USGA	Slope
BACK	18	6555	71	68.6	116
MIDDLE	18	6334	71	67.4	115
FRONT	18	5426	72	69.9	117

Club Pro: Rick Altham, PGA
Payment: Cash, Check, Credit
Tee Times: Weekends/Holidays
Fee 9 Holes: Weekday: $20   **Weekend:** $22
Fee 18 Holes: Weekday: $30   **Weekend:** $32
Twilight Rates: After 3pm   **Discounts:** Senior & Junior
Cart Rental: $16pp/18, $11pp/9   **Driving Range:** Yes
Lessons: Yes **Schools:** No   **Junior Golf:** Yes
Membership: Yes   **Architect/Yr Open:** Jim MacDonald/1961
Other: Lockers / Showers / Snack Bar / Restaurant

An 18-hole layout located on a game preserve. A beautiful and challenging course for all abilities.

	1	2	3	4	5	6	7	8	9
PAR	4	4	4	3	4	3	4	4	5
YARDS	324	344	369	160	406	141	391	378	488
	10	11	12	13	14	15	16	17	18
PAR	5	4	4	3	4	3	4	4	5
YARDS	561	427	365	155	424	168	358	375	500

Directions: I-95 to Exit 45. Follow Route 114 to Gorham. Take right onto McLellan Road.

Highland Green Golf Club ✪✪✪ ▶21

114 Village Drive
Topsham, ME (207) 725-8066
www.highlandgreengolf.com

Club Pro: Dick Harris, PGA
Payment: Most Major Credit Cards
Tee Times: Yes

Tees	Holes	Yards	Par	USGA	Slope
BACK	9	2910	35	67.7	134
MIDDLE	9	2679	35	65.6	122
FRONT	9	2071	35		

Fee 9 Holes: Weekday: $30 (cart included) **Weekend:** $30 (cart included)
Fee 18 Holes: Weekday: $45 (cart included) **Weekend:** $45 (cart included)
Twilight Rates: Yes   **Discounts:** None
Cart Rental: $18pp/18, $8pp/9   **Driving Range:**
Lessons: Yes **Schools:** No   **Junior Golf:** Yes
Membership: Yes   **Architect/Yr Open:** Jim Dodson/2001
Other: Snack Bar / Bar Lounge   **GPS:**

COUPON

A traditional (links) style course located in the heart of Maine's beautiful Mid-Coast region. Featuring contoured greens and fairways and surrounded by the beautiful Cathance River Nature Preserve. Well worth stopping for a round on a drive up the coast.

	1	2	3	4	5	6	7	8	9
PAR	4	4	5	4	4	3	4	4	3
YARDS	314	343	486	260	337	188	370	415	197
PAR									
YARDS									

Directions: 1 minute from I-95 and Route 1, on the Coastal Connector in Topsham, Maine.

Lake Kezar Country Club ✪✪✪ ▶22

578 Main Street
Lovell, ME (207) 925-2462
www.lakekezargolf.com

Club Pro:
Payment: Visa, MC
Tee Times: 7 days adv. members

Tees	Holes	Yards	Par	USGA	Slope
BACK	18	6010	72	63.3	117
MIDDLE	18	5600	72	65.7	111
FRONT	18	5105	72	68.8	114

Fee 9 Holes: Weekday: $21 (M-Th)   **Weekend:** $24 (F/S/S/H)
Fee 18 Holes: Weekday: $30 (M-Th)   **Weekend:** $34 (F/S/S/H)
Twilight Rates: After 4pm   **Discounts:** Juniors
Cart Rental: $12pp/18, $7pp/9   **Driving Range:** Practice Cage
Lessons: Yes **Schools:** Yes   **Junior Golf:** Yes
Membership: Yes   **Architect/Yr Open:** Donald Ross/1923
Other: Snack Bar / Bar-Lounge, Beverage Cart **GPS:** Yes

COUPON

Very scenic, pine trees, mountains, meandering brook, quiet. Clubhouse was 1-room schoolhouse. Facebook page, #1 value in NE, for the last 2 years. 6000 yards in 2013, new huge putting green. 5 new beautiful flower gardens. New 4th tee box, expanded pro shop, newly-renovated screen porch. "Great, friendly staff. Well worth the trip. You will come back." –FP

	1	2	3	4	5	6	7	8	9
PAR	4	4	4	4	3	4	3	5	4
YARDS	292	305	299	339	136	383	201	498	272
	10	**11**	**12**	**13**	**14**	**15**	**16**	**17**	**18**
PAR	5	4	3	4	5	4	3	4	5
YARDS	450	278	123	334	481	326	153	282	526

Directions: West on Route 302 from Gray exit on I-95. Right on Knights Hill Road across from Shawnee Peak. Follow signs on Route 5 North.

S
ME

Lebanon Pines Golf Course New ▶ 23

119 Center Road
Lebanon, ME (207) 457-2380

Club Pro:
Payment: Visa, MC, Cash
Tee Times: No
Fee 9 Holes: Weekday: $23
Fee 18 Holes: Weekday: $33, $30/cash
Twilight Rates:
Cart Rental: $20/9 per cart
Lessons: No **Schools:** No
Membership: Yes
Other:

Tees	Holes	Yards	Par	USGA	Slope
BACK					
MIDDLE	9	1489	31		
FRONT	9	1378	31		

Weekend: $23
Weekend: $33, $30/cash
Discounts: None
Driving Range: No
Junior Golf: No
Architect/Yr Open: Rene Doiron/2013

Great new course designed by the owner.

	1	2	3	4	5	6	7	8	9
PAR	4	4	4	5	3	4	5	3	4
YARDS	405	313	344	542	148	391	493	196	333
	10	11	12	13	14	15	16	17	18
PAR	4	3	5	4	3	4	4	4	5
YARDS	388	179	470	356	131	315	377	429	547

Directions: I-95 to Exit 4 (Route 16/US-4). Take Exit 16 towards Rochester/Sanford. Keep right at the fork and follow 202-E. Left on West Lebanon Road. First right onto Upper Guinea Road and right onto Center Road. Course is on right.

Ledges Golf Club, The ✪✪✪✪ ▶ 24

One Ledges Drive
York, ME (207) 351-3000
www.ledgesgolf.com

Club Pro: Matt Blasik
Payment: Visa, MC, Amex
Tee Times: 7 days adv.
Fee 9 Holes: Weekday: $40
Fee 18 Holes: Weekday: $75
Twilight Rates: After 2pm
Cart Rental: $17pp/18, $10pp/9
Lessons: Yes **Schools:** Yes
Membership: Yes
Other: Bar-Lounge / Restaurant / Clubhouse / Lockers / Showers / Lodging Partner

Tees	Holes	Yards	Par	USGA	Slope
BACK	18	6981	72	74.0	137
MIDDLE	18	6357	72	71.2	131
FRONT	18	5960	72	69.2	130

Weekend: $40
Weekend: $75
Discounts: None
Driving Range: Yes
Junior Golf: Yes
Architect/Yr Open: William Bradley Booth/1998

COUPON

"None better in Southern Maine. A must-play annual visit." –TM "I drive up from Boston every year for this one." –GD

	1	2	3	4	5	6	7	8	9
PAR	4	4	4	5	3	4	5	3	4
YARDS	405	313	344	542	148	391	493	196	333
	10	11	12	13	14	15	16	17	18
PAR	4	3	5	4	3	4	4	4	5
YARDS	388	179	470	356	131	315	377	429	547

Directions: I-95 to Exit 7. Go on Route 1 South for ¾ of a mile. Turn right on Route 91. Ledges is 5 miles up on right.

The Links at Outlook ✪✪✪✪ 25 ▶

Route 4
South Berwick, ME (207) 384-4653
www.outlookgolf.com

Tees	Holes	Yards	Par	USGA	Slope
BACK	18	6423	71	70.2	125
MIDDLE	18	6004	71	68.3	121
FRONT	18	5492	71	66.0	111

Club Pro: Dave Paskowski
Payment: Cash, Visa, MC, Disc, Cash
Tee Times: 7 days adv.
Fee 9 Holes: Weekday: $30 (M-Thur)   **Weekend:** $30 after 1pm
Fee 18 Holes: Weekday: $58 (M-Thur)   **Weekend:** $58 (F/S/S)
Twilight Rates: After 2pm   **Discounts:** Sr. & Jr. Mon-Th
Cart Rental: $17pp/18, $10pp/9
Driving Range: Yes, grass tees w/target greens
Lessons: Yes **Schools:** Junior Golf School   **Junior Golf:** Yes
Membership: Yes   **Architect/Yr Open:** Brian Silva/2000; Redesign 2010
Other: The Medalist Golf School & The Grille Room / Hole by Hole Video

COUPON

Player Comments: "Excellent fairways. Great conditions overall" –FP
Most of the course has a links-like, wide-open feel. Southern Maine beaches nearby. New Outlook Tavern.

	1	2	3	4	5	6	7	8	9
PAR	5	4	3	5	4	4	4	3	4
YARDS	503	416	183	475	328	361	347	199	333
	10	11	12	13	14	15	16	17	18
PAR	4	3	4	4	3	4	4	5	4
YARDS	348	164	299	361	142	373	354	484	334

Directions: From Boston: I-95 North to Exit 3, South Berwick. Right on Route 236. Follow 11 miles to end and take right. After ¼ mile, take right onto Route 4. Course is 1 mile up on right.
From Portland: I-95 South to Exit 19, Wells/Sanford. Take right past toll booths. Take next left onto Route 9. Follow Route 4 into South Berwick. Course on left.

Maple Lane Golf Club ✪✪ 26 ▶

295 Maple Lane
Livermore, ME (207) 897-3770
www.maplelane.me

Tees	Holes	Yards	Par	USGA	Slope
BACK	9	3019	35	65	118
MIDDLE	9	2797	35	62.8	114
FRONT	9	2665	35	65.8	118

Club Pro: Rick Carlton
Payment: Visa, MC
Tee Times: Yes
Fee 9 Holes: Weekday: $12   **Weekend:** $12
Fee 18 Holes: Weekday: $20   **Weekend:** $20
Twilight Rates: After 4pm   **Discounts:** Senior
Cart Rental: $15pp/18, $8pp/9   **Driving Range:** No
Lessons: Yes **Schools:** Jr. & Sr.   **Junior Golf:** Yes
Membership: Yes   **Architect/Yr Open:** Arthur Chapman/1976
Other: Snack Bar/ Dining Room & Patio / Hotel **GPS:**

COUPON

Stay-and-play packages start at $70 per couple per night. "Recently redesigned resulting in improved conditions. Interesting, fun course." –DW

	1	2	3	4	5	6	7	8	9
PAR	4	5	3	4	5	4	4	3	3
YARDS	356	347	555	370	155	170	348	540	168
PAR									
YARDS									

Directions: I-95 to Auburn Exit 75. Take Route 4 to Livermore/Livermore Falls town line. Take a right before bridge onto River Road. (From Augusta, take Route 17 South to 133 North.)

Martindale Country Club ✪✪✪ ½

527 Beech Hill Road
Auburn, ME (207) 782-1107
www.martindalecc.com

Club Pro: Nick Glicos, PGA
Payment: Visa, MC, Amex Disc, Cash
Tee Times: 7 days adv.

Tees	Holes	Yards	Par	USGA	Slope
BACK	18	6538	71	71.7	131
MIDDLE	18	6267	71	70.4	128
FRONT	18	5351	71	66.2	124

Fee 9 Holes: Weekday: $28
Fee 18 Holes: Weekday: $40
Twilight Rates: After 3pm
Cart Rental: $18pp/18, $10pp/9
Lessons: $60/hour **Schools:** Jr. & Sr.
Membership: Yes

Weekend: $30
Weekend: $45
Discounts: Senior, Junior
Driving Range: Yes
Junior Golf: Yes
Architect/Yr Open: Alex & Fred Chisholm/1921

Other: Restaurant / Lockers / Showers / Snack Bar / Bar-Lounge / Function Room

Championship golf course with superb course conditions at a great value. Some of the best greens in Maine. A must play for golfers at all levels.

	1	2	3	4	5	6	7	8	9
PAR	4	4	4	3	4	4	4	5	3
YARDS	325	358	402	173	330	359	364	555	232
	10	11	12	13	14	15	16	17	18
PAR	4	3	5	4	4	4	4	3	5
YARDS	388	152	591	374	325	360	395	160	424

Directions: I-95 to Auburn Exit 75. Take left off Exit. 2nd left is Beech Hill Road. Travel approximately 2 miles to the course.

The Meadows Golf Club ✪✪ 28

495 Huntington Hill Road
Litchfield, ME (207) 268-3000
www.themeadowsgolfclub.com

Club Pro:
Payment: Visa, MC, Check, Cash
Tee Times:

Tees	Holes	Yards	Par	USGA	Slope
BACK	18	5814	68	66.8	117
MIDDLE	18	5316	68	64.5	110
FRONT	18	4487	68	66.0	107

Fee 9 Holes: Weekday: $16
Fee 18 Holes: Weekday: $28
Twilight Rates: After 4pm
Cart Rental: $16pp/18, $11pp/9
Lessons: No **Schools:** No
Membership: Yes

Weekend: $16
Weekend: $28
Discounts: Sr. & Jr. and Military
Driving Range: No
Junior Golf: No
Architect/Yr Open: William Bradley Booth/1998

Other: Restaurant / Clubhouse / Bar-Lounge / Pro Shop / Putting Course

Scenic countryside course. Tree lined, dogleg fairways and undulating greens. New modern clubhouse with spacious bar and grill.

	1	2	3	4	5	6	7	8	9
PAR	4	4	3	5	3	4	3	4	4
YARDS	350	333	155	497	190	367	161	303	362
	10	11	12	13	14	15	16	17	18
PAR	5	3	4	4	4	3	4	3	4
YARDS	502	162	362	315	344	138	294	140	341

Directions: I-95 to Exit 86. Turn left on Route 9, right on Route 126, then right on Route 197. Go 14.6 miles to Huntington Hill Road. Turn left, course is 1.5 miles on the left.

Mere Creek Golf Course ✪✪

41 Merriconeag Road
Brunswick, ME (207) 721-9995
www.merecreekgolf.com

Club Pro: Kevin Joseph, PGA
Payment: Visa, MC, Disc, Cash
Tee Times: 7 days adv.

Tees	Holes	Yards	Par	USGA	Slope
BACK	9	3265	37	69.9	124
MIDDLE	9	3013	35	69.9	124
FRONT	9	2511	36	69.0	117

Fee 9 Holes: Weekday: $15
Fee 18 Holes: Weekday: $25
Twilight Rates: No
Cart Rental: $15pp/18, $8pp/9
Lessons: Yes **Schools:** Yes
Membership: Yes
Other: Clubhouse / Snack Bar

Weekend: $15
Weekend: $25
Discounts: No
Driving Range: Yes
Junior Golf: Yes
Architect/Yr Open: 1958
GPS:

COUPON

Managed by Harris Golf. Located at Brunswick Landing featuring new businesses and the Brunswick Executive Airport. Fun and enjoyable for all levels of players.

	1	2	3	4	5	6	7	8	9
PAR	5	4	4	3	4	4	4	3	4
YARDS	495	316	375	147	330	432	353	145	420
PAR									
YARDS									

Directions: I-295 to Exit 28, Brunswick. Follow Pleasant Street to end and turn right on Maine Street, left on Bath Road, right on Route 123. Go 2.4 miles and turn left into Brunswick Landing.

Merriland Farm Par 3 Golf ✪✪✪

545 Coles Hill Road
Wells, ME (207) 646-0508
www.merrilandfarm.com

Club Pro:
Payment: Cash, Visa, MC
Tee Times: No

Tees	Holes	Yards	Par	USGA	Slope
BACK					
MIDDLE	9	838	27		
FRONT					

Fee 9 Holes: Weekday: $14
Fee 18 Holes: Weekday: $22
Twilight Rates: No
Cart Rental: No
Lessons: Yes **Schools:** No
Membership: Yes
Other: Cafe Serving Breakfast & Lunch / Raspberry, Blueberry Baked Specialties

Weekend: $14
Weekend: $22
Discounts: None
Driving Range: Yes
Junior Golf: Yes
Architect/Yr Open: James Morrison/1992

COUPON

Player Comments: "A par 3 that lets you and the family enjoy the outing. Pleasant staff. Great muffins."

	1	2	3	4	5	6	7	8	9
PAR	3	3	3	3	3	3	3	3	3
YARDS	83	96	119	111	67	86	63	109	104
PAR									
YARDS									

Directions: I-95 to Exit 19 (Wells). Left onto Route 109, left onto Route 1 about 1.5 miles to Coles Hill Road on left. 1.5 miles up Coles Hill Road to course on right.

S
ME

Naples Golf and Country Club ✪✪½ 31 ►

Route 114
Naples, ME (207) 693-6424
www.naplesgolfcourse.com

Tees	Holes	Yards	Par	USGA	Slope
BACK	18	6039	72	71.9	126
MIDDLE	18	5617	72	67.8	121
FRONT	18	5498	72	N/A	N/A

Club Pro: Bob Caron II, PGA
Payment: Visa, MC
Tee Times: Required
Fee 9 Holes: Weekday: $20   Weekend: $20
Fee 18 Holes: Weekday: $31   Weekend: $31
Twilight Rates: After 11am & 3pm   Discounts: None
Cart Rental: $16pp/18, $8pp/9   Driving Range: Yes
Lessons: $35/hour Schools: No   Junior Golf: Yes
Membership: Yes   Architect/Yr Open: 1921
Other: Full Restaurant / Clubhouse / Bar-Lounge

COUPON

"Challenging for any level player. Friendly atmosphere. Beautiful setting." Located in the heart of the Sebago Lake Region. Area attractions center around Lake Region.

	1	2	3	4	5	6	7	8	9
PAR	5	4	4	4	4	4	4	4	3
YARDS	465	305	345	405	340	340	375	340	130
	10	11	12	13	14	15	16	17	18
PAR	4	3	4	4	5	4	3	4	5
YARDS	280	125	320	325	400	280	155	262	425

Directions: Exit 48 from Maine Turnpike. Turn right on Riverside Street. 3 miles to Route 302. Left on Route 302 for 30 miles to Naples. Take left on Route 114 in Naples Village. Course is 1 mile on left.

Nonesuch River Golf Club ✪✪✪½ 32 ►

304 Gorham Road
Scarborough, ME (207) 883-0007
www.nonesuchgolf.com

Tees	Holes	Yards	Par	USGA	Slope
BACK	18	6324	70	69.0	120
MIDDLE	18	6003	70	67.3	114
FRONT	18	5611	70	63.4	115

Club Pro: Jeff Hilton, Head Pro
Payment: Visa, MC, Amex, Disc
Tee Times: 7 days adv.
Fee 9 Holes: Weekday: $25   Weekend: $25
Fee 18 Holes: Weekday: $32-$36   Weekend: $36 - $40
Twilight Rates: $25 after 3pm walking   Discounts: None
Cart Rental: $18pp/18, $12pp/9   Driving Range: Yes
Lessons: Yes Schools: Yes   Junior Golf: Yes
Membership: Yes   Architect/Yr Open: Tom Walker/1996
Other: Clubhouse / Bar-Lounge / Restaurant / Lodging Partner

COUPON

Unique layout with a great mix of par 4's that wind through a lush forest with ponds and the Nonesuch River. Among the top 100 courses you can play in New England. Private club conditions at an affordable rate. "Fun, friendly and affordable."

	1	2	3	4	5	6	7	8	9
PAR	4	3	5	3	4	3	4	4	4
YARDS	389	180	539	214	362	173	348	413	431
	10	11	12	13	14	15	16	17	18
PAR	5	4	4	4	4	3	5	3	4
YARDS	492	375	365	397	381	160	496	174	435

Directions: Maine Turnpike to Exit 42. Turn left out of toll. Turn left at 2nd set of lights onto Route 114. Course is .5 miles on left.

Norway Country Club

✪✪½ **33** ►

310 Waterford Road
Norway, ME (207) 743-9840
www.norwaycountryclub.com

Club Pro: Dave Mazzeo, PGA
Payment: Most Major Credit Cards
Tee Times: No
Fee 9 Holes: Weekday: $18
Fee 18 Holes: Weekday: $26
Twilight Rates: After 4pm
Cart Rental: $13/pp/18, $7/pp/9
Lessons: $45/half hour **Schools:** Clinics
Membership: Yes
Other: Restaurant / Clubhouse / Snack Bar / Bar-Lounge

Tees	Holes	Yards	Par	USGA	Slope
BACK					
MIDDLE	9	2909	35	66.8	114
FRONT					

Weekend: $18
Weekend: $26
Discounts: Seniors
Driving Range: $5/bucket
Junior Golf: Yes
Architect/Yr Open: George Dunn/1929

Greens in excellent condition. "Most scenic-9 hole course in Maine." –DM

	1	2	3	4	5	6	7	8	9
PAR	4	3	4	4	4	3	5	4	4
YARDS	375	187	327	300	430	167	450	420	253
PAR									
YARDS									

Directions: I-95 North to Exit 63. Take Route 26 to Norway. Follow Main Street/Route 118, 3 miles to the course.

Oakdale Country Club

✪✪ **34** ►

13 Country Club Road
Mexico, ME (207) 364-3951
www.oakdalecc.com

Club Pro: Carol Mitchell
Payment: Visa, MC, Disc
Tee Times: No
Fee 9 Holes: Weekday: $17
Fee 18 Holes: Weekday: $22
Twilight Rates: After 5pm
Cart Rental: $15pp/18, $8pp/9
Lessons: Yes **Schools:** No
Membership: Yes
Other: Clubhouse / Snack Bar / Cocktails

Tees	Holes	Yards	Par	USGA	Slope
BACK					
MIDDLE	18	6133	72	68.4	121
FRONT	18	5486	74	73.6	125

Weekend: $17
Weekend: $22
Discounts: None
Driving Range: No
Junior Golf: Yes
Architect/Yr Open: 1923
GPS:

ᶜᴼᵁᴾᴼᴺ COUPON

Course is noted for playability. Hilly fairways and challenging greens.

	1	2	3	4	5	6	7	8	9
PAR	4	5	4	3	4	4	4	4	4
YARDS	327	471	339	149	415	383	289	224	362
	10	11	12	13	14	15	16	17	18
PAR	4	5	4	3	5	4	4	3	4
YARDS	332	456	350	135	420	365	341	206	392

Directions: I-95 to Exit 75, Route 4 North to Route 108 toward Rumford. Then to Route 2 West to course.

S ME

Old Marsh Country Club ✪✪✪✪

675 Littlefield Road
Wells, ME (207) 251-4653
www.oldmarshcountryclub.com
Club Pro: Richard Harris, PGA
Payment: Visa, MC, Amex, Disc, Check, Cash
Tee Times: 7 days adv.

Tees	Holes	Yards	Par	USGA	Slope
BACK	18	6523	70	71.7	135
MIDDLE	18	6012	70	68.9	130
FRONT	18	4847	70	68.7	116

Fee 9 Holes: Weekday: $50
Fee 18 Holes: Weekday: $69
Twilight Rates: After 4pm
Cart Rental: Included
Lessons: Yes **Schools:** Yes
Membership: Yes
Weekend: $50
Weekend: $89
Discounts: None
Driving Range: Yes, offsite
Junior Golf: Yes
Architect/Yr Open: Brian Silva/2008

Other: Restaurant / Clubhouse / Bar-Lounge / Lockers / Showers

Player Comments: A new course that is fully mature. A creative masterpiece that is pleasantly deceptive that you most certainly want to play again. A perfect mix of strategic and penal holes with each green unique to any other. Greens roll true, fast but fair. Brian Silva's best design. A must play!

	1	2	3	4	5	6	7	8	9
PAR	4	4	5	4	4	3	4	3	4
YARDS	349	347	485	358	384	169	381	174	421
	10	11	12	13	14	15	16	17	18
PAR	4	4	4	5	4	3	4	3	4
YARDS	311	335	348	511	256	151	427	187	418

Directions: I-95 to Exit 19 Wells/Sanford. Turn right on Route 109, go 3 miles and turn left on Route 9, go 1.6 miles and turn left on Route 9B and then left on Clubhouse Road.

Paris Hill Country Club ✪½

455 Paris Hill Road
Paris, ME (207) 743-2371
www.parishillcc.com
Club Pro: Chris Johnson
Payment: Cash, Visa, MC
Tee Times: No

Tees	Holes	Yards	Par	USGA	Slope
BACK					
MIDDLE	9	2305	33	62.1	102
FRONT					

Fee 9 Holes: Weekday: $15
Fee 18 Holes: Weekday: $20
Twilight Rates: After 4pm, $10 for as many holes as you can play
Cart Rental: $15pp/18, $10pp/9
Lessons: Yes **Schools:** Yes
Membership: Yes
Weekend: $15
Weekend: $20

Driving Range: No
Junior Golf:
Architect/Yr Open: 1899

Other: Clubhouse / Luncheonette / Bar / Dining Room

Overlooks beautiful Oxford Hills and mountains. Open May - October. Great family-play golf course.

	1	2	3	4	5	6	7	8	9
PAR	4	4	4	3	4	3	4	3	4
YARDS	350	260	231	194	352	125	309	129	355
PAR									
YARDS									

Directions: I-95 to Exit 63 (Gray). Take Route 26 to South Paris.

Point Sebago Golf Club ✪✪✪½

261 Point Sebago Road (Route 302)
Casco, ME (207) 655-2747
www.pointsebago.com

Tees	Holes	Yards	Par	USGA	Slope
BACK	18	7002	72	73.7	135
MIDDLE	18	6474	72	71.3	130
FRONT	18	5645	72	67.5	122

Club Pro: Michael Cloutier
Payment: Visa, MC, Disc, Check, Cash
Tee Times: 7 days adv.
Fee 9 Holes: Weekday: $35
Fee 18 Holes: Weekday: $59
Twilight Rates: After 3pm
Cart Rental: Mandatory
Lessons: Yes **Schools:** No
Membership: Yes
Architect/Yr Open: Philip Wogan & George Sargent/1996
Other: Resort / Restaurant / Snack Bar

Weekend: $39 F/S/S
Weekend: $69 F/S/S
Discounts: Junior
Driving Range: Yes
Junior Golf: Yes

"Upscale layout with a nice variety of holes. Long distance between holes cut deep in the woods. Back tees and fast greens will challenge all players. Nice granite distance markers, and well-marked fairways help." –FP

	1	2	3	4	5	6	7	8	9
PAR	5	3	4	4	4	4	5	3	4
YARDS	502	154	388	375	335	383	549	181	418
	10	11	12	13	14	15	16	17	18
PAR	4	5	4	4	3	4	4	3	5
YARDS	390	533	380	370	163	302	361	183	507

Directions: Turn off Maine Turnpike at Exit 48 and follow signs to Route 302 West for approximately 22.5 miles. Look for Chute's Cafe in Casco. Take second left. Follow signs.

Poland Spring Country Club ✪✪✪ 38

543 Main Street (Route 26)
Poland Spring, ME (207) 998-6002
www.polandspringresort.com

Tees	Holes	Yards	Par	USGA	Slope
BACK	18	6178	71	69.5	127
MIDDLE	18	5931	71	68.1	126
FRONT	18	5133	73	69.0	117

Club Pro: Allan Menne, PGA
Payment: Cash or Credit Card
Tee Times: Up to 1 year adv.
Fee 9 Holes: Weekday:
Fee 18 Holes: Weekday: $35
Twilight Rates: After 3pm
Cart Rental: $17pp/18
Lessons: Yes **Schools:** Yes
Membership: Yes
Other: Clubhouse / Lockers / Showers / Pool / Snack Bar / Restaurant / Bar-Lounge / Hotel

Weekend:
Weekend: $40
Discounts: None
Driving Range: Yes
Junior Golf: No
Architect/Yr Open: Fenn/Ross/1895

Oldest 18-hole resort course in U.S. (1893) designed by Donald Ross. Open May 1 - November 1.
"Great value. Great views. Wide landing areas. Will definitely go back." –EP

	1	2	3	4	5	6	7	8	9
PAR	4	4	4	4	4	3	4	3	4
YARDS	337	306	388	410	305	132	378	184	322
	10	11	12	13	14	15	16	17	18
PAR	4	5	4	3	4	4	5	4	4
YARDS	293	446	292	169	399	404	531	292	329

Directions: Maine Turnpike Exit 63. Take Route 26 North 10 miles. Course is on right.

S
ME

Prospect Hill Golf Course ✪✪ 39 ►

694 South Main Street
Auburn, ME (207) 782-9220
www.prospecthillgolfcourse.com

Club Pro:
Payment: Visa, MC, Disc
Tee Times: Optional
Fee 9 Holes: Weekday: $17
Fee 18 Holes: Weekday: $25
Twilight Rates: After 4pm
Cart Rental: $15pp/18, $8pp/9
Lessons: No **Schools:** Yes
Membership: Yes
Other: Snack Bar / Bar-Lounge / Function Hall

Tees	Holes	Yards	Par	USGA	Slope
BACK					
MIDDLE	18	5846	71	69.9	110
FRONT	18	5227	71	69.9	111

Weekend: $17
Weekend: $25
Discounts: None
Driving Range: No
Junior Golf: Yes
Architect/Yr Open: 1957
GPS:

The front 9 are wide open with a few small creeks, while the back 9 have 4 ponds and tree-lined fairways. Spikeless course. Collared shirts required. New ownership, new function hall.

	1	2	3	4	5	6	7	8	9
PAR	5	4	3	4	3	4	4	4	4
YARDS	460	350	210	230	225	395	370	260	290
	10	11	12	13	14	15	16	17	18
PAR	4	4	5	4	4	3	4	4	4
YARDS	412	290	510	276	357	138	366	311	396

Directions: I-95 to Exit 75, left off ramp, look for signs.

Province Lake Golf Club ✪✪ 40 ►

18 Mountain Road
Parsonfield, ME
(800) 325-4434 (207) 793-4040
www.provincelakegolf.com

Club Pro: Patrick E. DeAngelo
Payment: Visa, MC
Tee Times: 7 days adv.
Fee 9 Holes: Weekday: $24; $19 after 1pm
Fee 18 Holes: Weekday: $39; $29 after 1pm
Twilight Rates: After 3pm
Cart Rental: $16pp/18, $11pp/9
Lessons: Yes **Schools:** Yes
Membership: Yes
Other: Clubhouse / Snack Bar / Restaurant / Bar-Lounge / Function Room / Patio / 2 Decks / Childcare

Tees	Holes	Yards	Par	USGA	Slope
BACK	18	6277	71	70.6	130
MIDDLE	18	5904	71	69.4	125
FRONT	18	4935	71	64.1	112

COUPON

Weekend: $45; $30 after 3pm
Weekend: $52; $39 after 3pm
Discounts: Junior/Senior
Driving Range: Yes
Junior Golf: No
Architect/Yr Open: Lawrence Van Etten/1918

Playable for all. New beginners' tees — 2000 yards. Constantly improving course. Definitely family-friendly — $4/hr babysitter on site. 3rd year in a row named the number 1 golf course for women in New England by *Golf Magazine* July 2007.

	1	2	3	4	5	6	7	8	9
PAR	4	5	3	4	3	5	4	4	4
YARDS	378	438	201	378	144	525	369	376	309
	10	11	12	13	14	15	16	17	18
PAR	4	3	4	4	3	5	4	4	4
YARDS	338	146	295	337	142	483	383	331	331

Directions: I-95 to Route 16 (Spaulding Turnpike) to Route 153 North. Course is 15 miles north. Or access Route 153 South from Route 25.

Rivermeadow Golf Club ✪½ ▶ 41

216 Lincoln Street
Westbrook, ME (207) 854-1625
www.rivermeadowgolf.com

Club Pro:
Payment: Visa, MC, Amex
Tee Times: 7 days adv.

Tees	Holes	Yards	Par	USGA	Slope
BACK	9	2915	35	67.0	112
MIDDLE	9	2759	35	67.0	112
FRONT	9	2605	36	67.0	112

Fee 9 Holes: Weekday: $16
Fee 18 Holes: Weekday: $24
Twilight Rates: No
Cart Rental: $12pp/18, $8pp/9
Lessons: No **Schools:** Yes
Membership: Yes
Weekend: $16
Weekend: $24
Discounts: None
Driving Range: Yes
Junior Golf: Yes
Architect/Yr Open: Rufus Jordan/1958
Other: Grill Room and Bar / Clubhouse / Snack Bar / Restaurant

Open April - November 15th. Easy walking course.

	1	2	3	4	5	6	7	8	9
PAR	4	4	4	3	4	4	4	3	5
YARDS	371	411	248	139	350	350	295	150	445

PAR
YARDS

Directions: Maine Turnpike (Route 95), Exit 48 to Route 25 West into Westbrook (approximately 2 miles). Right turn onto Bridge Street (approximately ¼ mile). Left onto Lincoln Street to course.

Riverside Municipal Golf Course ✪✪ ▶ 42

1158 Riverside Street
Portland, ME (207) 797-3524
www.portlandmaine.gov

Club Pro: Ron Bibeau, PGA
Payment: Visa, MC, Cash
Tee Times: Required

Tees	Holes	Yards	Par	USGA	Slope
BACK	18	6370	72	69.2	115
MIDDLE	18	6052	72	67.5	112
FRONT	18	5630	73	70.7	112

Fee 9 Holes: Weekday: $22
Fee 18 Holes: Weekday: $30
Twilight Rates: No
Cart Rental: $16pp/18, $10pp/9
Lessons: $45/half hour **Schools:** No
Membership: Yes
Weekend: $23
Weekend: $35
Discounts: Senior & Junior weekdays
Driving Range: $8/bucket
Junior Golf: Yes
Architect/Yr: Stiles & Van Kleek/1932
Other: Clubhouse / Lockers / Showers / Snack Bar / Restaurant / Bar-Lounge

S
ME

27 holes available. South course is an additional 9-hole regulation course with 3102 yards. Wide fairways, medium-speed greens, only a little hilly. Open ASAP; close on first snow. "Best shape ever!" –RB

	1	2	3	4	5	6	7	8	9
PAR	5	4	3	5	4	3	4	4	4
YARDS	450	365	202	488	322	197	314	324	396
	10	**11**	**12**	**13**	**14**	**15**	**16**	**17**	**18**
PAR	5	4	4	3	4	4	4	4	4
YARDS	540	384	414	167	346	338	334	374	382

Directions: Maine Turnpike to Exit 48. Follow signs to course.

Rockland Golf Club

✪✪✪ ▶ 43

Old County Road
Rockland, ME (207) 594-9322
www.rocklandgolf.com

Club Pro: Keenan Flanagan, PGA
Payment: Most Major Credit Cards
Tee Times: 3 days adv.
Fee 9 Holes: Weekday: $25
Fee 18 Holes: Weekday: $50
Twilight Rates: No
Cart Rental: $20pp/18, $10pp/9
Lessons: $35/half hour **Schools:** No
Membership: Yes
Other: Clubhouse / Bar-Lounge / Snack Bar / Showers

Tees	Holes	Yards	Par	USGA	Slope
BACK	18	5041	70	69.2	118
MIDDLE	18	5773	70	68.1	116
FRONT	18	5023	71	64.6	112

Weekend:
Weekend:
Discounts: Junior
Driving Range: No
Junior Golf: Yes
Architect/Yr Open: Roger Sorrent/1930

COUPON

Player Comments: "Courteous, friendly staff." New irrigation system and new tee markers. Views of ocean and Rockland Harbor. Series of 5 1-hour lessons for $240. Punch and Play card. Opens early Spring.

	1	2	3	4	5	6	7	8	9
PAR	5	4	4	4	3	4	5	4	3
YARDS	521	378	268	359	136	303	485	398	215
	10	**11**	**12**	**13**	**14**	**15**	**16**	**17**	**18**
PAR	3	3	4	4	4	5	4	4	3
YARDS	176	210	282	425	357	582	341	232	163

Directions: I-95 to Coastal Route 1 through Thomaston. Left onto old Country Road to course 3.5 miles on left.

Sable Oaks Golf Club

✪✪✪½ ▶ 44

505 Country Club Drive
South Portland, ME (207) 775-6257
www.sableoaks.com

Club Pro: Roger E. Densmore III, PGA
Payment: Visa, MC, Disc, Amex
Tee Times: Recommended/7 days adv.
Fee 9 Holes: Weekday: $30
Fee 18 Holes: Weekday: $40
Twilight Rates: After 4pm
Cart Rental: $15pp/18, $10pp/9
Lessons: $70/hour **Schools:** No
Membership: Yes
Other: Snack Bar / Bar-Lounge / Function Hall / Showers / Locker Room / Lodging

Tees	Holes	Yards	Par	USGA	Slope
BACK	18	6359	70	71.6	130
MIDDLE	18	5545	70	68.2	120
FRONT	18	4786	72	69.1	129

Weekend: $35
Weekend: $45
Discounts: Junior
Driving Range: No
Junior Golf: Yes
Architect/Yr Open: Cornish & Silva/1989

COUPON

You'll be treated to some challenging yet enjoyable golf, surrounded by woods and ponds, with soft fairways and gently rolling manicured greens. *Travel Golf Magazine* calls Sable Oaks "One of the most imaginative courses in the state." Sister course to Samoset Resort. Off-season rates, inquire.

	1	2	3	4	5	6	7	8	9
PAR	4	5	4	4	5	3	4	3	4
YARDS	389	460	419	398	442	170	319	138	394
	10	**11**	**12**	**13**	**14**	**15**	**16**	**17**	**18**
PAR	4	3	4	3	5	4	4	3	4
YARDS	378	159	437	171	443	384	383	164	408

Directions: I-95 to Exit 45 (Maine Mall, Jet Port). Take 1st exit off Exit 45. Go right at light. At 4th light, go left on Running Hill Road. Take the second right onto Country Club Drive.

Salmon Falls Golf Course ✪½ ▶ 45

52 Golf Course Lane
Hollis, ME (207) 929-5233
www.salmonfalls-resort.com

Club Pro:
Payment: Visa, MC, Amex, Disc
Tee Times: Weekends and Holidays

Tees	Holes	Yards	Par	USGA	Slope
BACK	9	2965	36	67.7	113
MIDDLE	9	2883	36	67.7	113
FRONT	9	2550	36	69.5	112

Fee 9 Holes: Weekday: $17
Fee 18 Holes: Weekday: $23
Twilight Rates: After 5pm
Cart Rental: $9pp/18, $7pp/9
Lessons: No **Schools:** No
Membership: Yes
Other: Clubhouse / Snack Bar

Weekend: $17
Weekend: $23
Discounts: Seasonal
Driving Range: No
Junior Golf: No
Architect/Yr Open: Robert Trent Jones Sr./1966
GPS:

COUPON

Suggest beginners come after 1pm on weekends. Open March through November. Noted for beauty of Maine. Improved cart paths and sand traps. Great course, great price, great people.

	1	2	3	4	5	6	7	8	9
PAR	4	4	3	5	5	3	4	4	4
YARDS	365	250	190	500	455	165	303	251	404
	10	11	12	13	14	15	16	17	18
PAR	4	4	3	5	5	3	4	4	4
YARDS	380	245	235	510	460	165	310	265	395

Directions: I-95 to Exit 36 (Saco), follow Route 112 North. Follow signs to course.

Samoset Resort Golf Club ✪✪✪✪ ▶ 46

220 Warrenton Street
Rockport, ME (207) 594-1431
www.samosetresort.com

Club Pro: Gary Soule, PGA
Payment: All Major Cards
Tee Times: 2 days adv.

Tees	Holes	Yards	Par	USGA	Slope
BACK	18	6617	70	70.7	130
MIDDLE	18	5615	70	68.9	124
FRONT	18	5145	72	71.2	125

Fee 9 Holes: Weekday: $70
Fee 18 Holes: Weekday: $130
Twilight Rates: After 2pm
Cart Rental: Included
Lessons: $70/half hour **Schools:** Yes
Membership: Yes
Other: Clubhouse / Snack Bar / Restaurant / Bar-Lounge / Hotel / Lockers / Showers

Weekend: $130
Weekend: $130
Discounts: Junior
Driving Range: $7/bag
Junior Golf: Yes
Architect/Yr Open: Bob Elder/1902

COUPON

S
ME

Noted for spectacular ocean views and excellent playing conditions.

	1	2	3	4	5	6	7	8	9
PAR	4	4	3	5	3	4	3	4	4
YARDS	360	388	190	481	165	380	176	330	312
	10	11	12	13	14	15	16	17	18
PAR	4	3	5	3	5	4	4	4	5
YARDS	338	120	494	190	500	355	375	400	478

Directions: I-95 to I-295 to Exit 28 to Brunswick Coastal Route 1 North, through Rockland. Turn right onto Warrenton Street.

Sandy River Golf Course ✪½ ▶ 47

154 George Thomas Road
Chesterville, ME (207) 778-2492
www.sandyrivergolfcourse.com

Club Pro: Scott Hoisington, PGA
Payment: Cash
Tee Times: None
Fee 9 Holes: Weekday: $12
Fee 18 Holes: Weekday: $18
Twilight Rates:
Cart Rental: $2/pull cart
Lessons: Yes **Schools:** Yes
Membership: Yes
Other: Snack Bar

Tees	Holes	Yards	Par	USGA	Slope
BACK					
MIDDLE	9	1828	32		
FRONT	9	1762	32		

Weekend: $12
Weekend: $18
Discounts: Junior & Senior
Driving Range: Yes
Junior Golf: Yes
Architect/Yr Open: 1968

Short but challenging and charming 9 hole course. Family-oriented.

	1	2	3	4	5	6	7	8	9
PAR	3	3	3	3	4	4	4	4	4
YARDS	105	216	152	150	234	258	143	250	320
PAR									
YARDS									

Directions: I-95 to Route 27 North to US-2/ME-27 to ME-41/ME-156. Course is ½ mile on left.

Sanford Country Club ✪✪½ ▶ 48

Route 4
Sanford, ME (207) 324-5462
www.sanfordcountryclub.com

Club Pro: Jon Ellis, PGA
Payment: Cash, Visa, MC
Tee Times: Yes
Fee 9 Holes: Weekday: $31
Fee 18 Holes: Weekday: $41
Twilight Rates: After 3pm
Cart Rental: $24pp/18, $12pp/9
Lessons: Yes **Schools:** Jr.
Membership: Yes
Architect/Yr Open: Alex Chisolm & Marvin Armstrong/1932
Other: Restaurant / Clubhouse / Bar-Lounge / Snack Bar

Tees	Holes	Yards	Par	USGA	Slope
BACK	18	6726	72	73.2	128
MIDDLE	18	6217	72	70.5	122
FRONT	18	5320	74	66.5	114

Weekend: $38
Weekend: $48
Discounts: None
Driving Range: Yes
Junior Golf: Yes
GPS: Yes

COUPON

Course has outstanding reviews. Stay-and-play packages available. Call pro shop for specials. Home of the 2005 Maine Amateur and qualifying site of the 2006 U.S. Amateur.
"Nice layout, with 4 sets of tees." –FP

	1	2	3	4	5	6	7	8	9
PAR	4	4	3	5	5	4	4	3	4
YARDS	417	308	185	440	488	429	326	130	423
	10	11	12	13	14	15	16	17	18
PAR	4	4	5	3	4	4	3	4	5
YARDS	342	313	488	100	323	373	186	389	557

Directions: I-95 to Exit 2, head north on Route 109 for approximately 10 miles to Route 4 Intersection. Take left off 109 to Route 4 South for 2.5 miles. Located on left.

Sebasco Harbor Resort Golf Club ✪✪½   49 ▶

29 Kenyon Road
Sebasco Estates, ME (207) 389-9060
www.sebasco.com

Tees	Holes	Yards	Par	USGA	Slope
BACK	9	3046	36	70.6	123
MIDDLE	9	2794	36	67.0	119
FRONT	9	2364	36	68.2	127

Club Pro: Dennis Estes
Payment: Visa, MC, Amex, Disc
Tee Times: Yes
Fee 9 Holes: Weekday: $40   **Weekend:** $40
Fee 18 Holes: Weekday: $60   **Weekend:** $60
Twilight Rates: No   **Discounts:** None
Cart Rental: $15pp/18, $10pp/9   **Driving Range:** Practice course
Lessons: $50/hour, $30/half hour   **Schools:** Clinics   **Junior Golf:** No
Membership: Yes   **Architect/Yr Open:** Alex Chisolm/1926
Other: Full Restaurant / Clubhouse / Hotel / Inn / Lockers / Showers / Bar-Lounge
GPS: Yes

Newly renovated course. 9 hole gem carved along Maine's mid-coast. Beautiful ocean and forest views including our signature par 3 2nd hole over the cove. New 3-hole practice course. Discounted rates for guests and boaters.

	1	2	3	4	5	6	7	8	9
PAR	4	3	5	4	4	3	4	4	5
YARDS	370	140	467	309	339	179	387	316	480
PAR									
YARDS									

Directions: South of Bath on Route 209 for 10 miles. Turn right onto Route 217. Follow the Sebasco signs. Course ¼ mile on left.

Sheepscot Links Golf Club   ✪½   50 ▶

822 Townhouse Road
Whitefield, ME (207) 549-7060
www.sheepscotlinks.com

Tees	Holes	Yards	Par	USGA	Slope
BACK	9	2834	35	68.4	115
MIDDLE	9	2538	35	66.6	115
FRONT	9	2233	35		

Club Pro:
Payment: Check, Visa, MC
Tee Times: 7 days adv.
Fee 9 Holes: Weekday: $15   **Weekend:** $15
Fee 18 Holes: Weekday: $24   **Weekend:** $24
Twilight Rates: No   **Discounts:** Sr. & Jr
Cart Rental: $15pp/18, $9pp/9   **Driving Range:**
Lessons: No   **Schools:** No   **Junior Golf:** Yes
Membership: Yes   **Architect/Yr:** 2001
Other: Clubhouse / Snack Bar / Putting Course

Located on the Sheepscot River in a rural setting. The Links offer a good variety of water, sand, dog legs, elevated tees, and elevated greens. Often described as the best kept golf secret in Central Maine.

S
ME

	1	2	3	4	5	6	7	8	9
PAR	4	3	4	4	4	4	5	3	4
YARDS	354	149	286	292	351	309	514	141	282
PAR									
YARDS									

Directions: Traveling north on 295, take the first Gardiner exit, turn right on 201. Follow 201 across the Kennebec River Bridge. Turn right on Route 27, left on 194, then left on Townhouse Road. 30 minutes from the highway to the Links!

South Portland Municipal GC ✪½

155 Wescott Road
South Portland, ME (207) 775-0005

Tees	Holes	Yards	Par	USGA	Slope
BACK					
MIDDLE	9	2071	32	59.0	92
FRONT					

Club Pro:
Payment: Cash/Check Only
Tee Times: No
Fee 9 Holes: Weekday: $12   **Weekend:** $13
Fee 18 Holes: Weekday: **Weekend:**
Twilight Rates: No   **Discounts:** None
Cart Rental: $2/pull   **Driving Range:** No
Lessons: Group lessons **Schools:** No   **Junior Golf:** No
Membership: Yes, residents   **Architect/Yr Open:** Larry Rowe/1931
Other: Snack Bar   **GPS:**

Well-maintained, polite staff. Carts are not required. Pay once, play for 3 rounds. Clinics offered by recreation center.

	1	2	3	4	5	6	7	8	9
PAR	4	3	4	3	4	3	3	4	4
YARDS	340	140	238	132	372	167	122	285	275
PAR									
YARDS									

Directions: I-95 to Exit 3 (Westbrook Street). Go east on Westbrook Street (about 3/10 of a mile). Take a left onto Wescott Street. The clubhouse is on the left under Bradts Memorial Library.

Spring Meadows Golf Course ✪✪✪½ 52

59 Lewiston Road
Gray, ME (207) 657-2586
www.springmeadowsgolf.com

Tees	Holes	Yards	Par	USGA	Slope
BACK	18	6656	71	72.1	126
MIDDLE	18	6065	71	69.2	124
FRONT	18	4706	71	67.9	109

Club Pro: Ben Morey, PGA
Payment: Most Major
Tee Times: Up to 7 days
Fee 9 Holes: Weekday: $23   **Weekend:** $26
Fee 18 Holes: Weekday: $36   **Weekend:** $43
Twilight Rates: After 3pm   **Discounts:** None
Cart Rental: $16pp/18, $8pp/9   **Driving Range:** Yes
Lessons: $60/hour **Schools:** Junior   **Junior Golf:** No
Membership: Yes   **Architect/Yr Open:** William Bradley Booth/1999
Other: Refurbished Barn with Banquet Facilities Seating 220 / Player's Lounge
GPS: Yes

COUPON

Great conditions from tee to green. Well layed out with water on many holes. Great elevated look to the flags on holes #6 and #7. "Fun to play." –FP

	1	2	3	4	5	6	7	8	9
PAR	4	4	5	3	4	3	4	4	4
YARDS	405	337	555	162	351	146	300	387	363
	10	11	12	13	14	15	16	17	18
PAR	5	4	4	3	4	5	3	4	4
YARDS	522	357	315	127	327	509	116	420	336

Directions: Course is 1 mile from Exit 63 off Maine Turnpike, on Route 4/100/202 Northbound.

Springbrook Golf Course ✪✪½ ▶ 53

Route 202
Leeds, ME (207) 946-5900
www.springbrookgolfclub.com

Tees	Holes	Yards	Par	USGA	Slope
BACK	18	6408	71	68.1	119
MIDDLE	18	6163	71	64.7	111
FRONT	18	4989	74	61.4	96

Club Pro: Ed Balboni, PGA
Payment: Visa, MC
Tee Times: Weekends, Holidays
Fee 9 Holes: Weekday: $15
Fee 18 Holes: Weekday: $28 all day
Twilight Rates: After 4pm
Cart Rental: $16pp/18, $8pp/9
Lessons: $45/45 min. **Schools:** No
Membership: Yes
Other: Clubhouse / Lockers / Showers / Snack Bar / Bar-Lounge / Discount Game Cards

Weekend: $15 after 2pm
Weekend: $28 all day
Discounts: Juniors, Seniors, Ladies
Driving Range: $2.50/sm., $4.50/lg. bucket
Junior Golf: Yes
Architect/Yr Open: Arnold Biondi/1966

Sig. Hole: #15 is a 219-yard, uphill par 3. Very difficult hole. Rolling hills and roughly reminiscent of a Scottish-style course.

	1	2	3	4	5	6	7	8	9
PAR	4	3	4	4	4	4	5	3	4
YARDS	415	160	410	350	335	385	520	168	340
	10	11	12	13	14	15	16	17	18
PAR	4	4	5	3	4	3	5	4	4
YARDS	420	290	460	180	350	206	480	325	365

Directions: Maine Turnpike to Lewiston exit to Route 202 East. Course is 10 miles outside of Lewiston-Auburn.

Sunday River Golf Club ✪✪✪✪½ ▶ 54

18 Championship Drive
Newry, ME (207) 824-4653
www.sundayrivergolf.com

Tees	Holes	Yards	Par	USGA	Slope
BACK	18	7130	72	75.3	150
MIDDLE	18	6558	72	72.3	139
FRONT	18	5006	72	65.0	120

Club Pro: Peter (Stroke) Flint, PGA
Payment: Visa, MC, Amex, Disc
Tee Times: 7 days adv.
Fee 9 Holes: Weekday: $60 w/cart
Fee 18 Holes: Weekday: $95 w/cart
Twilight Rates: After 3pm
Cart Rental: "2 for 1" nine holes only
Lessons: Yes **Schools:** Yes
Membership: Yes
Other: Wilderness Lodge Clubhouse / Restaurant / Full Banquet at Resort

Weekend: $60 w/cart
Weekend: $95 w/cart
Discounts: Yes
Driving Range: Yes
Junior Golf:
Architect/Yr Open: Robert Trent Jones Jr./2004

COUPON

Opened late 2004. Robert Trent Jones Jr. design. Each hole has 4 tee boxes. Yardage below is from the Blue tees. Sunday River's wide fairways, dynamic green settings, pristine playing conditions, and jaw-dropping alpine views combine to form *Golf Week's* #1 course in Maine and one of *Golf* magazine's (Top 100 You Can Play) in the U.S.

	1	2	3	4	5	6	7	8	9
PAR	5	4	4	3	4	3	5	4	4
YARDS	499	384	332	175	425	178	440	410	339
	10	11	12	13	14	15	16	17	18
PAR	4	5	4	4	3	5	3	4	4
YARDS	385	565	412	316	185	483	142	474	414

Directions: Take Route 1 North to I-95 North to Maine Turnpike (I-495). Take Maine Turnpike (I-495) to Exit 11 (Gray). Take Route 26 North to Bethel. Follow Route 2 East for 2.6 miles. Take left onto Sunday River Road which becomes Monkey Brook Road. Go 2.5 miles and turn right on Championship Drive.

S
ME

Toddy Brook Golf Course ✪✪✪½ 55 ▶

925 Sligo Road
North Yarmouth, ME (207) 829-5100
www.toddybrookgolf.com

Tees	Holes	Yards	Par	USGA	Slope
BACK	18	5886	71	68.9	126
MIDDLE	18	5173	71	65.4	115
FRONT	18	4409	71	67.6	113

Club Pro: Gregg Baker, PGA
Payment: Visa, MC, Amex, Disc
Tee Times: 7 day adv.
Fee 9 Holes: Weekday: $25
Fee 18 Holes: Weekday: $35
Twilight Rates: After 3pm
Cart Rental: $15pp/18, $10pp/9
Lessons: Yes **Schools:** Yes
Membership: Variety
Weekend: $25
Weekend: $40
Discounts: Junior
Driving Range: Yes
Junior Golf:
Architect/Yr Open: Robert Anderson/2002
Other: Restaurant / Clubhouse / Lockers / Showers / Bar-Lounge/Banquet Facility

COUPON

Beautiful layout with challenging tees. Each hole has unique design with plenty of sand & water to test your skills. New back 9 with beautiful views. Layout ends with a daunting island green. Back tees below.

	1	2	3	4	5	6	7	8	9
PAR	4	4	4	3	5	3	4	4	5
YARDS	307	357	366	151	453	184	350	314	506
	10	11	12	13	14	15	16	17	18
PAR	4	3	4	5	4	4	3	5	3
YARDS	363	158	369	466	371	380	133	546	124

Directions: I-95 to Yarmouth exit. Follow Route 1 to Route 115 exit. Take 115 West about ¼ mile to Sligo Road on right. Go approx. 3⅛ miles. Course is on right.

Turner Highlands Golf Course ✪✪✪ 56 ▶

10 B Highland Avenue
Turner, ME (207) 224-7060
www.turnerhighlands.com

Tees	Holes	Yards	Par	USGA	Slope
BACK					
MIDDLE	18	6033	71	68.6	115
FRONT	18	4705	71	67.5	113

Club Pro:
Payment: Visa, MC, Amex, Disc
Tee Times: Yes
Fee 9 Holes: Weekday: $16
Fee 18 Holes: Weekday: $28
Twilight Rates: After 2 pm
Cart Rental: $16pp/18, $9pp/9
Lessons: Yes **Schools:** No
Membership: No
Weekend: $24
Weekend: $42
Discounts: M-Th before 12pm: $16
Driving Range: Yes
Junior Golf: Yes, $11 wknds after 4pm
Architect/Yr Open: Steve Leavitt/1993
Other: Lockers / Showers / Snack Bar / Restaurant.

COUPON

Player Comments: "A well-maintained local popular favorite, good value, great day trip." –FP
Now 18 holes. A scenic golf course situated high on a hill.

	1	2	3	4	5	6	7	8	9
PAR	4	5	4	3	4	5	4	3	4
YARDS	280	442	282	149	365	452	372	204	376
	10	11	12	13	14	15	16	17	18
PAR	3	4	4	4	5	3	5	4	3
YARDS	135	365	370	430	592	125	500	387	182

Directions: I-95 to Exit 75 toward Auburn. Get onto Route 4 North. Turn right onto Route 117. Stay on Route 117 for 8.5 miles. Course is on the right.

Twin Falls Golf Club

364 Spring Street
Westbrook, ME (207) 854-5397
www.twinfallsgolfclub.com

Tees	Holes	Yards	Par	USGA	Slope
BACK					
MIDDLE	9	5242	68	61.3	90
FRONT					

Club Pro:
Payment: Cash, Credit, Debit
Tee Times: No
Fee 9 Holes: Weekday: Walk/$15; ride/$20   **Weekend:** Walk/$15; ride/$20
Fee 18 Holes: Weekday: Walk/$20; ride/$30   **Weekend:** Walk/$20; ride/$30
Twilight Rates: After 5pm   **Discounts:** None
Cart Rental: **Driving Range:** No
Lessons: No **Schools:** No   **Junior Golf:** No
Membership: Yes   **Architect/Yr Open:** Albert Young/1972
Other: Clubhouse / Snack Bar   **GPS:**

"Fine public course for beginners. Keep your drive on #1 to the left of center as the brook hidden from view will come into play." –AP

	1	2	3	4	5	6	7	8	9
PAR	4	3	3	4	4	4	4	4	4
YARDS	334	152	110	343	351	260	275	330	298
	10	11	12	13	14	15	16	17	18
PAR	4	3	3	4	4	4	4	4	4
YARDS	334	152	110	343	351	260	275	330	298

Directions: I-95 to Exit 45, follow Maine Mall Road to Spring Street to course.

Val Halla Golf Course

Val Halla Road
Cumberland, ME (207) 829-2225
www.valhallagolf.com

Tees	Holes	Yards	Par	USGA	Slope
BACK	18	6567	72	71.1	126
MIDDLE	18	6201	72	69.3	122
FRONT	18	5437	72	71.4	120

Club Pro: Cory Mansfield, PGA
Payment: Visa, MC
Tee Times: Yes
Fee 9 Holes: Weekday: $22   **Weekend:** $24
Fee 18 Holes: Weekday: $30   **Weekend:** $35
Twilight Rates: After 4pm   **Discounts:** Senior & Junior
Cart Rental: $12.50pp/18, $7.50pp/9 **Driving Range:** $4/bucket
Lessons: $40/half hour **Schools:** No **Junior Golf:** Yes
Membership: Yes   **Architect/Yr Open:** Phil Wogan/1965
Other: Snack Bar / Lounge   **GPS:**

Consistently rated 1 of Maine's best public courses. Bent grass, good shape, wooded, hilly, scenic, brooks and streams, excellent layout. Open April 15 - November 1.

	1	2	3	4	5	6	7	8	9
PAR	4	3	5	4	4	4	4	3	5
YARDS	350	142	553	383	394	340	369	175	484
	10	11	12	13	14	15	16	17	18
PAR	4	4	3	5	5	4	4	3	4
YARDS	376	347	148	465	440	388	294	155	398

Directions: From Portland take 295 North to Exit 10. Follow Route 9 to Cumberland Center. The course is off Greely Road on Val Halla Road.

S
ME

Wawenock Country Club

✪✪½ **59** ▶

Route 129
Walpole, ME (207) 563-3938
www.wawenockgolfclub.com

Club Pro: Lon Wanser
Payment: Cash, Check, Visa, MC, Amex, Disc
Tee Times: July - August
Fee 9 Holes: Weekday: $20
Fee 18 Holes: Weekday: $30
Twilight Rates: After 5pm
Cart Rental: $14pp/18, $11pp/9
Lessons: Yes **Schools:** No
Membership: Yes
Other: Clubhouse / Bar-Lounge / Snack Bar / Showers

Tees	Holes	Yards	Par	USGA	Slope
BACK					
MIDDLE	9	3009	35	68.8	122
FRONT	9	2727	36	73.5	119

Weekend: $20
Weekend: $30
Discounts: Junior
Driving Range: Yes
Junior Golf: No
Architect/Yr: Wayne Stiles & John Van Kleek/1928

COUPON

Fairly open course with small greens and hills, but challenging. Shoulder season rates. Open May - October. The only golf course on beautiful Pemaquid Peninsula. "The 8th hole is one of the best short par 3's in Maine." –DW

	1	2	3	4	5	6	7	8	9
PAR	4	4	3	5	4	4	4	3	4
YARDS	329	398	233	477	415	296	357	134	370
PAR									
YARDS									

Directions: Route 1 to Route 129; follow for 7 miles. 5 miles from town of Damariscotta, Maine.

Webhannet Golf Club

✪✪✪½ **60** ▶

26 Golf Club Drive
Kennebunk, ME (207) 967-2061
www.webhannetgolfclub.com

Club Pro: Kirk Kimball
Payment:
Tee Times: Yes
Fee 9 Holes: Weekday: $35
Fee 18 Holes: Weekday: $65
Twilight Rates: No
Cart Rental: $18pp/18, $9pp/9
Lessons: Yes **Schools:** No
Membership: No
Other: Clubhouse

Tees	Holes	Yards	Par	USGA	Slope
BACK					
MIDDLE	18	6088	71	68.6	114
FRONT	18	5828	71	67.2	113

Weekend: $35
Weekend: $65
Discounts: No
Driving Range: Yes
Junior Golf: No
Architect/Yr Open: Skip Wogan/1901

COUPON

The 1901 Skip Wogan design has the traditional small undulating greens which makes this very challenging to the low handicapper. We have some of the best maintained condition golf course in the state. –FP

	1	2	3	4	5	6	7	8	9
PAR	4	4	3	5	3	4	4	5	3
YARDS	367	320	225	515	170	295	370	428	200
	10	11	12	13	14	15	16	17	18
PAR	4	3	4	4	5	3	4	5	4
YARDS	390	142	390	370	470	155	280	421	320

Directions: ME Tpke., Exit 25, Kennebunk. Left on Rte. 35 to Kennebunk. At light, turn left on Rte. 1 for about 100 yards. Turn right on Route 35/9A. Continue through 2 lights to beach. Follow along beach to playground on the left. Go right on Ridge Lane. Go through stop sign then bear right at fork to clubhouse.

Western View Golf Club

⚙½ **61** ▶

130 Bolton Hill Road
Augusta, ME (207) 622-5309

Tees	Holes	Yards	Par	USGA	Slope
BACK	18	5357	70	64.0	100
MIDDLE	18	4632	70	61.7	95
FRONT	18	4559	71	66.0	117

Club Pro: Peter Matthews, PGA
Payment: Visa, MC, Amex, Disc
Tee Times: No
Fee 9 Holes: Weekday: $15
Fee 18 Holes: Weekday: $25
Twilight Rates: No
Cart Rental: $15pp/18, $8pp/9
Lessons: Yes **Schools:** No
Membership: Yes

Weekend: $15
Weekend: $25
Discounts: Junior membership
Driving Range: Yes
Junior Golf: Yes
Architect/Yr Open: Archie Humphrey/1927

COUPON

Other: Snack Bar / Clubhouse / Lounge / Restaurant / Range / Lodging Partner, Holiday Inn

Scenic and sporty 9 hole course — short but challenging with nice greens.

	1	2	3	4	5	6	7	8	9
PAR	4	3	4	3	5	4	4	4	4
YARDS	305	170	258	195	445	315	285	385	375
	10	11	12	13	14	15	16	17	18
PAR	4	3	4	3	5	4	4	4	4
YARDS	315	180	268	150	462	330	248	391	380

Directions: I-95, then Exit 113, 5½ miles to Bolton Hill Road on right. Go ½ mile on Bolton Hill Road.

Willowdale Golf Club

⚙⚙ **62** ▶

52 Willowdale Road
Scarborough, ME (207) 883-9351
www.willowdalegolf.com

Tees	Holes	Yards	Par	USGA	Slope
BACK					
MIDDLE	18	5881	70	67.7	115
FRONT	18	5049	70	68.9	116

Club Pro: Pam Lewis, Manager
Payment: Visa, Amex, MC, Disc, Checks
Tee Times: 5 days adv. for weekends
Fee 9 Holes: Weekday: $18
Fee 18 Holes: Weekday: $29
Twilight Rates: After 4pm
Cart Rental: $14pp/18, $7pp/9
Lessons: **Schools:** No
Membership: Yes
Other: Clubhouse / Snack Bar / Showers

Weekend: $20
Weekend: $31
Discounts: Junior memberships
Driving Range: No
Junior Golf: No
Architect/Yr Open: Eugene Wogan/1930
GPS:

**S
ME**

Sig. Hole: #5 is a beautiful, 195-yard par 3. Water on 1 side, tree-lined on the other. Difficult shot for a par 3. Twilight rates offered 7 days a week. Pitching and putting green available.

	1	2	3	4	5	6	7	8	9
PAR	4	5	4	4	3	4	3	4	4
YARDS	357	487	386	349	197	367	163	342	325
	10	11	12	13	14	15	16	17	18
PAR	4	3	4	4	4	3	4	4	5
YARDS	393	185	367	382	280	150	374	288	489

Directions: Exit 36 off Maine Turnpike. US 95 to Route 1. Turn left onto Route 1 North. First light, turn right ¼ mile.

Airways Golf Course	1	Harrisville GC	18	Skungamaug River GC	35
Birch Plain Golf Course	2	Hotchkiss School GC	19	Stanley Golf Club	36
Blackledge CC - Anderson's	3	Keney Golf Club	20	Tallwood Country Club	37
Blackledge CC - Gilead	4	Lake of Isles GC & Resort	21	Timberlin Golf Club	38
Blue Fox Run	5	Long Hill Country Club	22	Topstone Golf Course	39
Brooklyn CC	6	Manchester CC	23	Tower Ridge GC	40
Buena Vista GC	7	Minnechaug GC	24	Tunxis Plan. CC (Green)	41
Canaan Country Club	8	Norwich Golf Course	25	Tunxis Plan. CC (White)	42
Cedar Knob GC	9	Pequot Golf Club	26	Tunxis Plan. GC (Red)	43
Cedar Ridge GC	10	Quarryview Golf Course	27	Twin Hills CC	44
Connecticut National GC	11	Raceway Golf Club	28	Villa Hills Par 3	45
Copper Hill GC	12	River Ridge Golf Course	29	Westwoods Golf Course	46
Elmridge Golf Course	13	Rockledge CC	30	Willimantic CC	47
Fairview Farm GC	14	Rolling Greens GC	31	Willow Brook Golf Course	48
Gillette Ridge Golf Club	15	Rolling Meadows CC	32	Wintonbury Hills GC	49
Goodwin Golf Course	16	Shennecosset GC	33	Woodstock Golf Course	50
Grassmere CC	17	Simsbury Farms GC	34	Crestview CC (Agawam, MA)	51

KEY TO THE STAR RATINGS:
5✪ = Outstanding **4✪** = Excellent **3✪** = Very Good **2✪** = Good **1✪** = Average **NR** = Not Rated

Airways Golf Course

1070 South Grand Street
West Suffield, CT (860) 668-4973
www.airwaysgolf.com

Tees	Holes	Yards	Par	USGA	Slope
BACK	18	5914	71	66.0	106
MIDDLE	18	5528	71	65.0	103
FRONT	18	5134	72	65.0	103

Club Pro:
Payment: Visa, MC, Cash
Tee Times: 1 week adv.
Fee 9 Holes: Weekday: $13
Fee 18 Holes: Weekday: $21
Twilight Rates: No
Cart Rental: $11pp/18, $5.50pp/9
Lessons: No **Schools:** No
Membership: No
Other: Clubhouse / Snack Bar

Weekend: $14
Weekend: $24
Discounts: Senior
Driving Range: No
Junior Golf: No
Architect/Yr Open: Geoffrey Cornish/1973
GPS:

Noted for great value. Easy to walk, beautiful course.

	1	2	3	4	5	6	7	8	9
PAR	4	4	4	5	4	4	3	4	4
YARDS	336	351	351	487	301	302	147	320	273
	10	11	12	13	14	15	16	17	18
PAR	3	5	4	3	4	3	5	4	4
YARDS	127	451	369	133	346	132	451	388	263

Directions: I-91 to Exit 40 (Route 20 West). At 4th light turn right, course is 2 miles on the right. Check website.

Birch Plain GC & Driving Range

119 High Rock Road
Groton, CT (860) 445-9918
www.birchplaingolf.com

Tees	Holes	Yards	Par	USGA	Slope
BACK					
MIDDLE	18	2666	54		
FRONT					

Club Pro: Jeff Beaupre, PGA
Payment: Visa, MC, Disc
Tee Times: No
Fee 9 Holes: Weekday: $22
Fee 18 Holes: Weekday: $22
Twilight Rates: After 5:30pm
Discounts: Senior/60+, Junior/-18, Military - active only
Cart Rental: $12pp/18, $4/pull cart
Lessons: Yes **Schools:** No
Membership: Yes
Other: Snacks

Weekend: $26
Weekend: $26

Driving Range: $8/lg., $7/sm. bucket
Junior Golf: Yes
Architect/Yr Open: Armando Baldelli/1969
GPS:

A pleasant par 3. Good for beginners. Easy walking flat & open. Close to beaches, Mystic Seaport, Aquarium and casinos. Sand traps re-engineered in 2010.

	1	2	3	4	5	6	7	8	9
PAR	3	3	3	3	3	3	3	3	3
YARDS	107	170	148	228	206	124	113	137	129
	10	11	12	13	14	15	16	17	18
PAR	3	3	3	3	3	3	3	3	3
YARDS	105	187	108	147	136	164	150	155	156

Directions: I-95 to Route 349 (Clarence Sharp Highway). At second light, take left. At next light, take right. Follow signs for Groton/New London Airport. Course is on right.

**NE
CT**

Blackledge CC - Anderson's Glen ✪✪½

180 West Street
Hebron, CT (860) 228-0250
www.blackledgecc.com

Club Pro: K. J. Higgins, PGA & C. Morris
Payment: Visa, MC
Tee Times: 1 week adv.

Tees	Holes	Yards	Par	USGA	Slope
BACK	18	6787	72	72.0	128
MIDDLE	18	6137	72	68.9	122
FRONT	18	5458	72	71.7	123

Fee 9 Holes: Weekday: $18 walk, $26 ride **Weekend:** $21 walk, $28 ride
Fee 18 Holes: Weekday: $36 walk, $49 ride **Weekend:** $41 walk, $55 ride
Twilight Rates: After 5:30pm weekdays, after 1pm and 3pm on F/S/S
Discounts: Senior & Junior
Cart Rental: $24pp/18, $12pp/9
Lessons: $35/half hour **Schools:** No
Membership: Yes
Other: Clubhouse / Snack Bar / Restaurant / Bar-Lounge

Driving Range: No
Junior Golf: No
Architect/Yr Open: Geoffrey Cornish/1964

Good walking course that tests every shot in your game. Fairways are in great shape. Greens are on the fast side. Open March - December. Please visit website.

	1	2	3	4	5	6	7	8	9
PAR	4	4	4	5	4	3	4	3	5
YARDS	375	365	389	480	350	153	318	170	485
	10	11	12	13	14	15	16	17	18
PAR	4	4	5	3	4	4	3	5	4
YARDS	316	408	465	142	383	369	179	425	365

Directions: Route 2 East to Exit 8. Left off ramp, go 9 miles. Take a right onto West Street. Course is on the right.

Blackledge CC - Gilead Highlands ✪✪½

171 West Street
Hebron, CT (860) 228-0250
www.blackledgecc.com

Club Pro: Kevin J. Higgins, PGA
Payment: Visa, MC
Tee Times: 1 week adv.

Tees	Holes	Yards	Par	USGA	Slope
BACK	18	6129	72	69.8	121
MIDDLE	18	5714	72	68.0	116
FRONT	18	4951	72		

Fee 9 Holes: Weekday: $18 walk, $26 ride **Weekend:** $21 walk, $28 ride
Fee 18 Holes: Weekday: $36 walk, $49 ride **Weekend:** $41 walk, $55 ride
Twilight Rates: After 5:30pm weekdays; after 1pm and 3pm on F/S/S
Discounts: Senior & Junior
Cart Rental: $24pp/18, $12pp/9
Lessons: $35/half hour **Schools:** No
Membership: Yes
Other: Clubhouse / Snack Bar / Restaurant / Bar-Lounge

Driving Range: No
Junior Golf: No
Architect/Yr Open: Mark Mungeam/1974

Player Comments: "Best course conditions ever." New improved website, please visit. Open March - December.

	1	2	3	4	5	6	7	8	9
PAR	4	3	5	4	4	4	5	3	4
YARDS	369	133	436	275	359	325	455	142	366
	10	11	12	13	14	15	16	17	18
PAR	5	3	5	3	4	4	4	4	4
YARDS	464	142	454	148	358	346	301	320	327

Directions: Route 2 East to Exit 8. Left off ramp, go 9 miles. Take a right onto West Street. Course is on the right.

Blue Fox Run

😊😊 5 ▶

65 Nod Road
Avon, CT (860) 678-1679
www.bluefoxent.com

Tees	Holes	Yards	Par	USGA	Slope
BACK	18	6779	71	72.0	125
MIDDLE	18	6116	71	69.2	121
FRONT	18	5232	72	70.2	124

Club Pro: Sean Smedick, PGA
Payment: Visa, MC, Amex
Tee Times: Yes
Fee 9 Holes: Weekday: $20 M-Th   **Weekend:** $22 F/S/S/H
Fee 18 Holes: Weekday: $34 M-Th   **Weekend:** $44 F/S/S/H
Twilight Rates: After 5:30pm weekdays   **Discounts:** Senior & Junior
Cart Rental: $15pp/18, $9pp/9   **Driving Range:** $5 token
Lessons: $50/half hour, $100/hour **Schools:** Yes **Junior Golf:** Yes
Membership: No   **Architect/Yr Open:** Joe Brunoli/1974
Other: Restaurant / Bar-Lounge / Banquet Facilities **GPS:** Yes

Prices subject to change without notice.

Player Comments: "Course is in good shape. Very pretty in fall." Open March 1 - December 15.

	1	2	3	4	5	6	7	8	9
PAR	4	4	3	4	5	4	3	5	3
YARDS	335	305	148	334	486	374	202	512	170
	10	11	12	13	14	15	16	17	18
PAR	4	4	5	4	5	3	4	3	4
YARDS	388	392	512	414	513	136	365	150	380

Directions: I-84 Exit 39 to Route 4, Farmington Center. Turn right onto Waterville Road (Route 10 North). Go 5 miles, cross over Route 44 intersection to Nod Road. Club is ½ mile on left.

Brooklyn Country Club

NR 6 ▶

170 South Street
Brooklyn, CT (860) 779-9333
www.brooklyngolfcourse.com

Tees	Holes	Yards	Par	USGA	Slope
BACK					
MIDDLE	9	2783	35		
FRONT	9	2659	35		

Club Pro:
Payment: Visa, MC
Tee Times: Weekends
Fee 9 Holes: Weekday: $12   **Weekend:** $12
Fee 18 Holes: Weekday: $24   **Weekend:** $24
Twilight Rates: After 5pm   **Discounts:** Senior & Junior
Cart Rental: $6pp/9   **Driving Range:** Yes
Lessons: Yes **Schools:** No   **Junior Golf:** Yes
Membership: Yes   **Architect/Yr Open:** 1960
Other: Clubhouse / Snack Bar / Bar-Lounge   **GPS:**

This course is now a municipal golf course and improvements are being made to its overall appearance. Driving range is lighted for evening use.

	1	2	3	4	5	6	7	8	9
PAR	4	4	4	4	5	3	4	3	4
YARDS	385	350	340	410	460	130	420	135	250
PAR									
YARDS									

**NE
CT**

Directions: I-395 to Route 6 West exit; take left onto Allen Hill Road. Take first left onto South Street, course is ½ mile on left.

Buena Vista Golf Course

NR 7

Buena Vista Road
West Hartford, CT (860) 521-7359
www.west-hartford.com

Club Pro: Richard Crow, PGA
Payment: Cash or Check
Tee Times: No
Fee 9 Holes: Weekday: $13
Fee 18 Holes: Weekday: $22.25
Twilight Rates: No
Cart Rental: $12pp/9
Lessons: No **Schools:** No
Membership: West Hartford residents only
Other: Putting Green

Tees	Holes	Yards	Par	USGA	Slope
BACK					
MIDDLE	9	1977	31		
FRONT	9	1653	30		

Weekend: $14
Weekend: $23.75
Discounts: Sr. & Jr., W. Hartford residents only
Driving Range: No
Junior Golf: No
Architect/Yr Open: 1960
GPS:

A good mix of holes. Great for all levels of golfers. Open April-December. Additional tee boxes to accommodate a greater number of golfing abilities.

	1	2	3	4	5	6	7	8	9
PAR	4	4	4	3	3	3	3	3	4
YARDS	263	344	295	171	130	98	223	214	239
PAR									
YARDS									

Directions: I-84 to Exit 43 (Park Road); left off ramp; go through 3 lights, take left onto Buena Vista Road. Course is on left. Parking lot shared with Cornerstone Pool.

Canaan Country Club

NR 8

74 High Street (Route 7)
Canaan, CT (860) 824-7683
www.canaancountryclub.com

Club Pro:
Payment: Most Major Credit Cards
Tee Times: No
Fee 9 Holes: Weekday: $16
Fee 18 Holes: Weekday: $21
Twilight Rates: No
Cart Rental: $17p/18, $9.50pp/9
Lessons: No **Schools:** No
Membership: Yes
Other: Snack Bar / Restaurant / Function Rooms

Tees	Holes	Yards	Par	USGA	Slope
BACK	9	2941	35	66.8	114
MIDDLE	9	2835	35	66.8	114
FRONT	9	2412	36	67	107

Weekend: $21
Weekend: $30
Discounts: Senior & Junior
Driving Range: No
Junior Golf: Yes
Architect/Yr Open: 1931
GPS:

The course is mostly flat with a few rolling hills. Considered a good walking course. New pro shop and irrigation systems. Set in beautiful Blackberry River Valley. New 5th hole par 3 replaced old 7th. All holes are now irrigated.

	1	2	3	4	5	6	7	8	9
PAR	4	5	3	5	3	4	4	3	4
YARDS	317	490	184	450	132	356	371	180	355
PAR									
YARDS									

Directions: Route 8 North to Winsted, West on Route 44 to town of Canaan. South ½ mile on Route 7.

Cedar Knob Golf Course ✪✪✪ 9

466 Billings Road
Somers, CT (860) 749-3550
www.cedarknobgolfcourse.com

Club Pro: Jeffrey Swanson
Payment: Most Major Credit Cards
Tee Times: 7 days adv.
Fee 9 Holes: Weekday: $20
Fee 18 Holes: Weekday: $35
Twilight Rates: No
Cart Rental: $15pp/18, $7.50pp/9
Lessons: $40/45 min. **Schools:** No
Membership: No

Tees	Holes	Yards	Par	USGA	Slope
BACK	18	6734	72	72.4	126
MIDDLE	18	6298	72	70.5	122
FRONT	18	5784	74	73.9	129

Weekend: $23
Weekend: $38
Discounts: Sr. & Jr. weekdays
Driving Range: Yes, must use own balls
Junior Golf: Yes
Architect/Yr Open: Geoffrey Cornish/1963

Other: Clubhouse / Snack Bar / Restaurant / Bar-Lounge

Dress code. Open year round (weather permitting). Call about specials. "Cut nicely into a great, wooded area. A fun and fair challenge." –FP

	1	2	3	4	5	6	7	8	9
PAR	4	3	5	4	3	4	5	4	4
YARDS	384	154	482	397	209	319	478	327	328
	10	11	12	13	14	15	16	17	18
PAR	5	4	4	4	3	4	3	5	4
YARDS	490	370	410	350	170	350	210	470	400

Directions: I-91 to Exit 47 (East toward Somers). Right onto Route 83; right on Billings Road. Course is ½ mile on left.

Cedar Ridge Golf Course NR 10

34 Drabik Road
East Lyme, CT (860) 691-4568
www.cedarridgegolf.com

Club Pro: Chris Madeiros
Payment: Cash, Visa, MC
Tee Times: 7 days adv.
Fee 9 Holes: Weekday: $15
Fee 18 Holes: Weekday: $22
Twilight Rates: After 4pm
Cart Rental: $12pp/18, $6pp/9
Lessons: Yes **Schools:** No
Membership: Ticket Packets
Other: Snacks Only

Tees	Holes	Yards	Par	USGA	Slope
BACK					
MIDDLE	18	3025	54		
FRONT					

Weekend: $20
Weekend: $28
Discounts: Sr & Jr, weekday only
Driving Range: No
Junior Golf: Yes
Architect/Yr Open: Chester Jenkins/1962
GPS:

COUPON

Beginners will enjoy the relaxed atmosphere and shorter length of the course, while experienced players will appreciate the test of shot-making skills demanded by the Par 3 layout.

	1	2	3	4	5	6	7	8	9
PAR	3	3	3	3	3	3	3	3	3
YARDS	157	160	177	103	191	160	122	150	166
	10	11	12	13	14	15	16	17	18
PAR	3	3	3	3	3	3	3	3	3
YARDS	155	130	250	145	196	218	215	203	127

Directions: I-95 to Exit 74, left on Route 161 North. 1 mile to Drabik Road on left.

Connecticut National Golf Club ✪✪✪ 11 ►

136 Chase Road
Putnam, CT (860) 928-7748
www.ctnationalgolf.com

Tees	Holes	Yards	Par	USGA	Slope
BACK	18	6935	71	72.9	133
MIDDLE	18	6321	71	70.5	128
FRONT	18	5002	71	69.2	119

Club Pro: Jim West, Dir. of Golf
Payment: Visa, MC, Amex, Disc , Checks
Tee Times: 7 days adv.
Fee 9 Holes: Weekday: $25
Fee 18 Holes: Weekday: $31
Twilight Rates: After 1pm
Cart Rental: $15pp/18, $9pp/9
Lessons: $55/hour **Schools:** Yes
Membership: Yes

Weekend:
Weekend: $43
Discounts: Senior & Junior wkdys
Driving Range: Yes
Junior Golf: Yes
Architect/Yr Open: Mark Mungeam/2009

COUPON

Other: Clubhouse / Restaurant / Bar Lounge / Showers / Snack Bar / Function Room

Extensive redesign completed in 2009. Course has been taken upscale and lengthened to over 6900 yards from the black tees. "More beautiful and friendly than ever from the forward tees. A tremendous value." –FP

	1	2	3	4	5	6	7	8	9
PAR	5	4	4	3	4	5	3	4	3
YARDS	461	387	389	207	327	560	171	333	151
	10	11	12	13	14	15	16	17	18
PAR	4	3	5	4	4	3	4	4	5
YARDS	375	182	505	333	399	193	427	369	552

Directions: I-395 to Exit 97, east on Route 44. 3½ miles to public course, sign on right. Right onto East Putnam Road. At 2nd stop sign, take a right (Chase Road). Course is 1 mile on right.

Copper Hill Golf Club NR 12 ►

20 Copper Hill Road
East Granby, CT (860) 653-6191
www.copperhillgolf.com

Tees	Holes	Yards	Par	USGA	Slope
BACK					
MIDDLE	18	6004	72	68.6	116
FRONT	18	5090	72	68.1	124

Club Pro: Paul Banks, PGA
Payment: Visa, MC, Amex
Tee Times: 7 days adv.
Fee 9 Holes: Weekday: $15
Fee 18 Holes: Weekday: $21
Twilight Rates: After 6pm
Cart Rental: $12pp/18, $8pp/9
Lessons: Yes **Schools:** Yes
Membership: Yes, semi-private

Weekend: $16
Weekend: $23
Discounts: Senior & Junior
Driving Range: Across street
Junior Golf: Yes
Architect/Yr Open: Allen Bissette/1956

COUPON

Other: Clubhouse / Snack Bar / Restaurant / Bar-Lounge

Improvements include full irrigation. New greens superintendent. All grass 4-tiered driving range. Frequent Player card available.

	1	2	3	4	5	6	7	8	9
PAR	4	4	3	5	4	3	4	5	4
YARDS	331	313	163	437	241	164	308	426	376
	10	11	12	13	14	15	16	17	18
PAR	4	4	3	5	4	3	4	5	4
YARDS	336	356	176	473	261	178	361	459	402

Directions: I-91 to Exit 40 (Bradley Field exit). Follow Route 20 West to Newgate Road (6 lights). Turn right on Newgate Road. Go past old Newgate prison to stop sign. Turn left to course.

Elmridge Golf Course

⊕⊕⊕½ ▶ 13

229 Elmridge Road
Pawcatuck, CT (860) 599-2248
www.elmridgegolf.com

Tees	Holes	Yards	Par	USGA	Slope
BACK	27/18	6347	71	70.8	115
MIDDLE	27/18	6014	71	69.3	112
FRONT	27/18	5430	71	69.0	109

Club Pro: Thomas Jones
Payment: Visa, MC, Amex
Tee Times: Call Monday for weekends
  Call Friday for weekdays
Fee 9 Holes: Weekday: $24   **Weekend:** $28
Fee 18 Holes: Weekday: $37 (M-Th)   **Weekend:** $45 (F/S/S)
Twilight Rates: After 5pm   **Discounts:** Sr, Jr, Mltry/wkdys only
Cart Rental: $18pp/18, $12pp/9   **Driving Range:** Yes
Lessons: $40/45 min. **Schools:** No   **Junior Golf:** Yes
Membership: Yes   **Architect/Yr Open:** Joe & Charlie Rustici/1964
Other: Clubhouse / Snack Bar / Restaurant / Bar-Lounge/ Outings

COUPON

Elmridge Golf Course is located just minutes from both casinos, Misquamicut Beach and Mystic Aquarium. 27 holes means tee times are always available.

	1	2	3	4	5	6	7	8	9
PAR	4	4	4	5	4	3	4	3	4
YARDS	366	335	360	462	149	324	167	385	268
	10	11	12	13	14	15	16	17	18
PAR	4	5	4	3	5	3	5	3	4
YARDS	365	485	342	149	576	340	365	206	370

Directions: I-95 to Exit 92. Route 2 East to Elmridge Road. Course is 1 mile on left.

Fairview Farm Golf Course

⊕⊕½ ▶ 14

300 Hill Road
Harwinton, CT (860) 689-1000
www.fairviewfarmgolfcourse.com

Tees	Holes	Yards	Par	USGA	Slope
BACK	18	6539	72	71.7	128
MIDDLE	18	6149	72	69.8	122
FRONT	18	4780	72	67.6	118

Club Pro: Bob Sparks, PGA
Payment: Visa, MC, Amex
Tee Times: 7 days adv.
Fee 9 Holes: Weekday: $21   **Weekend:** $33
Fee 18 Holes: Weekday: $40   **Weekend:** $64
Twilight Rates: No   **Discounts:** None
Cart Rental: $18pp/18, $9pp/9 (included wknds) **Driving Range:** Yes
Lessons: $90/hour **Schools:** Yes   **Junior Golf:** Yes
Membership: No   **Architect/Yr Open:** Bob Ferrarotti/2000
Other: Clubhouse / Restaurant / Bar-Lounge / Snacks
GPS: Yes

Player Comments: "Well kept. Well laid out." Challenging scenic layout. Fabulous views with scenic par 3s. Upscale public course. "First-class design." –RW

	1	2	3	4	5	6	7	8	9
PAR	4	4	5	3	4	5	3	4	4
YARDS	380	355	500	160	330	450	155	350	375
	10	11	12	13	14	15	16	17	18
PAR	3	4	3	4	4	4	5	4	5
YARDS	187	350	175	340	320	385	545	307	510

Directions: Route 8, Exit 42. Head east on Route 118, 2 miles right on Route 222. Club is ½ mile on left.

Gillette Ridge Golf Club ✪✪½ ▶ 15

1360 Hall Boulevard
Bloomfield, CT (860) 726-1430
www.gilletteridgegolf.com

Club Pro: Pat Aquaro, PGA
Payment: Most Major Credit Cards
Tee Times: 7 days adv.
Fee 9 Holes: Weekday:
Fee 18 Holes: Weekday: $50 w/cart
Twilight Rates: Yes
Cart Rental: Included
Lessons: Yes **Schools:**
Membership: Yes

Tees	Holes	Yards	Par	USGA	Slope
BACK	18	7191	72	74.8	135
MIDDLE	18	6703	72	72.2	133
FRONT	18	6133	72	67.2	117

Weekend:
Weekend: $65 w/cart
Discounts: None
Driving Range: $5/bucket
Junior Golf:
Architect/Yr Open: Arnold Palmer/2004
Other: Clubhouse / Bar-Lounge / Showers / Lockers

Opened July 2004. "Fairways are generous but approach to green narrows. This is a course that keeps coming at you. Many carries, especially to the green. Bring your aerial game. Great fun." –JD

	1	2	3	4	5	6	7	8	9
PAR	4	5	4	3	4	4	5	3	4
YARDS	379	418	380	162	283	336	555	157	389
	10	11	12	13	14	15	16	17	18
PAR	4	3	5	4	4	3	4	5	4
YARDS	377	155	528	242	326	156	383	502	405

Directions: I-91 to Exit 39B West. 218 West for approximately 6 miles. Route 218 becomes Cottage Grove Road.

Goodwin Golf Course ✪✪ ▶ 16

1130 Maple Avenue
Hartford, CT (860) 956-3601
www.goodwinparkgolf.com

Club Pro: Mark Castelhano, GM
Payment: Visa, MC, Discover, Check
Tee Times: 7 days adv.
Fee 9 Holes: Weekday: $15.50
Fee 18 Holes: Weekday: $23.50
Twilight Rates: After 5pm
Cart Rental: $13.50pp/18, $8.75pp/9
Lessons: $65/hour **Schools:** Yes
Membership: Yes
Other: Banquet Facility / Snack Bar

Tees	Holes	Yards	Par	USGA	Slope
BACK	18	5953	70	68.0	116
MIDDLE	18	5605	70	66.6	110
FRONT	18	5069	70	69.6	109

Weekend: $17
Weekend: $26.50
Discounts: Senior & Junior
Driving Range: Yes
Junior Golf: Yes
Architect/Yr Open: Everett Pyle/1930
GPS:

COUPON

New clubhouse renovations, full menu, bar, new banquet facilities. Renovated bunkers and cart paths. Good contrast between open and tight holes.

	1	2	3	4	5	6	7	8	9
PAR	5	4	4	4	4	4	3	3	4
YARDS	486	315	367	322	370	286	127	155	332
	10	11	12	13	14	15	16	17	18
PAR	4	3	5	4	4	3	4	4	4
YARDS	334	213	471	361	312	138	336	352	361

Directions: I-91 to Exit 28. Take Route 15, 5 South to Exit 85 (Route 99), follow ramp to first light. Right on Joran to right on Maple.

Grassmere Country Club ✪✪ 17

130 Town Farm Road
Enfield, CT (860) 749-7740
www.grassmerecountryclub.com

Tees	Holes	Yards	Par	USGA	Slope
BACK	9	3031	35	70.0	121
MIDDLE	9	2870	35	68.2	118
FRONT	9	2727	35	66.8	115

Club Pro:
Payment: Cash, Check, Credit Cards
Tee Times: Anytime
Fee 9 Holes: Weekday: $18
Fee 18 Holes: Weekday: $23
Twilight Rates: No
Cart Rental: $13pp/18, $8pp/9
Lessons: No **Schools:** No
Membership: Yes
Other: Clubhouse / Snack Bar / Banquet Facility

Weekend: $19
Weekend: $28
Discounts: Sr. & Jr. M-F until 3pm, Sat 12-close
Driving Range: No
Junior Golf: Yes
Architect/Yr Open: 1976
GPS:

Emphasis on nice landscaping aound the holes. Open March 15 - December 31. Noted for friendly staff and beautifully manicured course. Always in beautiful shape. New design on some of the tees.

	1	2	3	4	5	6	7	8	9
PAR	4	4	4	4	3	5	4	4	3
YARDS	360	390	405	415	160	475	320	360	180
PAR									
YARDS									

Directions: Route I-91 to Exit 45, right onto Route 140 East. Merge with Route 191 East. Stay on 191 for 5.8 miles. Left on Town Farm Road. Course is on left.

Harrisville Golf Course NR 18

125 Harrisville Road
Woodstock, CT (860) 928-6098
www.harrisvillegolfcourse.com

Tees	Holes	Yards	Par	USGA	Slope
BACK	9	2915	36	67.4	118
MIDDLE	9	2725	36	65.0	109
FRONT	9	2415	35	66.4	115

Club Pro: Michael Sosik
Payment: Cash, Check, Credit
Tee Times: Weekend mornings
Fee 9 Holes: Weekday: $14
Fee 18 Holes: Weekday: $20
Twilight Rates: No
Cart Rental: $14pp/18, $7pp/9
Lessons: No **Schools:** No
Membership: Yes
Other: Snack Bar

Weekend: $16
Weekend: $22
Discounts: Senior & Junior
Driving Range: No
Junior Golf:
Architect/Yr Open: Aimee Salvas/1929
GPS: No

COUPON

Best value in golf. Enjoyable round. Friendly staff!

	1	2	3	4	5	6	7	8	9
PAR	4	3	5	4	4	5	4	4	3
YARDS	290	170	500	265	410	420	295	235	200
PAR									
YARDS									

**NE
CT**

Directions: I-395 to Exit 97. Take right onto Route 171 West. Take left at Public Golf Course sign (Citizens Bank). Follow signs (next 2 rights).

Hotchkiss School Golf Course ✪✪ 19 ▶

Route 112
Lakeville, CT (860) 435-4400
www.hotchkiss.org
Club Pro: James Kennedy, PGA
Payment: Cash Only
Tee Times: No

Tees	Holes	Yards	Par	USGA	Slope
BACK					
MIDDLE	9	3043	35	68.8	117
FRONT					

Fee 9 Holes: Weekday: $14
Fee 18 Holes: Weekday: $20
Twilight Rates: No
Cart Rental: $30/18, $15/9 per cart
Lessons: Yes **Schools:** Yes
Membership: Yes
Other: Snack Bar

Weekend: $15
Weekend: $25
Discounts: None
Driving Range: No
Junior Golf: No
Architect/Yr: Seth Raynor & Charles Banks/1911
GPS:

COUPON

Good variety, mildly challenging.

	1	2	3	4	5	6	7	8	9
PAR	4	3	4	4	3	4	5	3	5
YARDS	420	192	401	370	128	347	500	165	520
PAR									
YARDS									

Directions: Route 7 to Route 112 West to course, or Route 44 to Route 112 East.

Keney Golf Club ✪✪ 20 ▶

280 Tower Avenue
Hartford, CT (860) 525-3656
www.keneyparkgolf.com
Club Pro:
Payment: Visa, MC, Disc
Tee Times: 7 days adv.

Tees	Holes	Yards	Par	USGA	Slope
BACK	18	6014	70	68.1	115
MIDDLE	18	5739	70	66.8	113
FRONT	18	4967	70	68.9	116

Fee 9 Holes: Weekday: $15.50
Fee 18 Holes: Weekday: $23.50
Twilight Rates: After 5pm
Cart Rental: $13.50pp/18, $8.75pp/9
Lessons: Yes **Schools:** Yes
Membership: Yes
Other: Clubhouse / Lockers / Snack Bar

Weekend: $17
Weekend: $26.50
Discounts: Senior & Junior
Driving Range: No
Junior Golf: Yes
Architect/Yr Open: Devereaux Emmet/1927

COUPON

Player Comments: "Tight course. Good challenge" "A sleeper." True links-style. The clubhouse is reminiscent of the grand architectural style of the late 20s. Resident rate. Early-bird rates. Open year round.

	1	2	3	4	5	6	7	8	9
PAR	4	5	3	4	4	3	4	4	4
YARDS	315	487	109	328	396	134	363	381	377
	10	11	12	13	14	15	16	17	18
PAR	5	3	4	3	5	4	4	4	3
YARDS	526	190	261	162	446	366	374	364	160

Directions: I-91 to Exit 34. Left at ramp, right at light. Course is 5 minutes north of downtown Hartford.

Lake of Isles GC and Resort ✪✪✪½ 21 ▶

One Lake of Isles Road
North Stonington, CT (888) 475-3746
www.lakeofisles.com

Tees	Holes	Yards	Par	USGA	Slope
BACK	18	7252	72	76.6	146
MIDDLE	18	6304	72	71.5	135
FRONT	18	4937	72	68.9	127

Club Pro: Robbie Leming, Dir. of Golf
Payment: Visa, MC, Amex
Tee Times: 30 days adv.
Fee 9 Holes: Weekday: **Weekend:**
Fee 18 Holes: Weekday: $155 - $195   **Weekend:** $195
Twilight Rates: No   **Discounts:** Junior
Cart Rental: Included   **Driving Range:** Yes
Lessons: $110/hour, $60/half hour **Schools:** Yes **Junior Golf:** Yes
Membership: Yes   **Architect/Yr Open:** Rees Jones/2005
Other: Restaurant / Clubhouse / Bar & Lounge / Indoor Outdoor Practice Facility / Luxury Villas

Located around a 90-acre lake, Rees Jones design. Multiple tee locations offer a varied test for all levels. "Many carries; visually splendid. Expecting this to become one of New England's best." –JD

	1	2	3	4	5	6	7	8	9
PAR	5	3	4	4	5	4	3	4	4
YARDS	550	164	308	398	457	395	182	325	389
	10	11	12	13	14	15	16	17	18
PAR	4	3	5	4	4	5	3	4	4
YARDS	399	154	469	345	399	496	166	342	366

Directions: I-95 North to Exit 92 in CT. Turn left on Route 2 West. Lake of Isles is 8 miles on Route 2 West. Directly across the street from Foxwoods Resort.

Long Hill Country Club ✪✪ 22 ▶

130 Long Hill Street
East Hartford, CT (860) 528-5082
www.longhillcc.com

Tees	Holes	Yards	Par	USGA	Slope
BACK	18	6186	71	69.1	124
MIDDLE	18	6076	71	68.6	124
FRONT	18	5072	72	68.9	113

Club Pro: Kevin Tierney, PGA
Payment: Visa, MC, Disc
Tee Times: Weekends, 1 week adv.
Fee 9 Holes: Weekday: $17   **Weekend:** $22
Fee 18 Holes: Weekday: $23   **Weekend:** $29
Twilight Rates: After 6pm   **Discounts:** Sr. & Jr. weekdays
Cart Rental: $14pp/18, $8pp/9 **Driving Range:** No
Lessons: $40/half hour **Schools:** No **Junior Golf:** Yes
Membership: No
Architect/Yr Open: Devereaux Emmet and Alfred Tull/1927
Other: Restaurant   **GPS:**

COUPON

Dress code: no tank tops or cutoffs. Pond recently added to #13; recent drainage work and sand trap renovations.

	1	2	3	4	5	6	7	8	9
PAR	4	4	4	3	5	4	4	3	4
YARDS	305	397	322	123	508	415	308	127	385
	10	11	12	13	14	15	16	17	18
PAR	5	3	4	4	4	3	4	4	5
YARDS	512	188	308	330	356	150	457	384	500

Directions: I-84 to Exit 60, onto Burnside Avenue toward East Hartford. Enter East Hartford, take a right at second traffic light onto Long Hill Street. Proceed through 3 stop signs, course on right.

Manchester Country Club ✪✪½ 23 ▶

305 South Main Street
Manchester, CT (860) 646-0226
www.mancc.com

Club Pro: John Cook, PGA
Payment: MC, Visa
Tee Times: 7 days adv.

Tees	Holes	Yards	Par	USGA	Slope
BACK	18	6285	72	70.8	125
MIDDLE	18	6167	72	69.7	123
FRONT	18	5610	73	72.0	120

Fee 9 Holes: Wkdy: $23 non-res./$21 res.
Fee 18 Holes: Wkdy: $41 non-res./$38 res.
Twilight Rates: No
Cart Rental: $16pp/18, $8pp/9
Lessons: Call for rates **Schools:** No
Membership: Yes
Other: Clubhouse / Lockers / Showers / Snack Bar / Restaurant / Bar-Lounge

Weekend: $25 non-res./$23 res.
Weekend: $43 non-res./$41 res.
Discounts: Senior & Junior
Driving Range: Yes
Junior Golf: Yes
Architect/Yr Open: Devereux Emmet/1917

COUPON

Old-style golf course. Variety of elevation changes. Open April - December. Dress code.

	1	2	3	4	5	6	7	8	9
PAR	4	4	5	5	3	4	4	3	4
YARDS	308	333	507	500	144	406	331	143	348
	10	11	12	13	14	15	16	17	18
PAR	4	4	3	4	5	5	4	4	3
YARDS	294	340	135	335	520	510	397	362	182

Directions: I-84 to Route 384 East (Exit 3). Take left 1000 yards up onto South Main Street. Course is on the left.

Minnechaug Golf Course NR 24 ▶

16 Fairway Crossing
Glastonbury, CT (860) 643-9914
www.minnechauggolf.com

Club Pro: Peter Seaman, PGA
Payment: Cash or Credit
Tee Times: 1 week adv.

Tees	Holes	Yards	Par	USGA	Slope
BACK	9	2654	35	67.4	112
MIDDLE	9	2527	35	66.5	110
FRONT	9	2186	35	62.7	102

Fee 9 Holes: Weekday: $16
Fee 18 Holes: Weekday: $25
Twilight Rates: No
Cart Rental: $13pp/18, $7pp/9
Lessons: Yes **Schools:** Yes
Membership: No
Other: Restaurant / Beer / Snacks

Weekend: $17
Weekend: $27
Discounts: Senior, Junior, Resident
Driving Range: No
Junior Golf: Yes
Architect/Yr Open: Geoffrey Cornish/1959
GPS:

Reduced rates for residents, juniors and seniors, open year round.

	1	2	3	4	5	6	7	8	9
PAR	4	4	5	4	5	3	4	3	3
YARDS	311	307	464	327	437	161	269	116	135
PAR									
YARDS									

Directions: I-84 to Route 384 East, Exit 3. Left off exit on Route 83. Follow for 3 miles. Course on right.

Norwich Golf Course ✪✪ ▶ 25

New London Turnpike
Norwich, CT (860) 889-6973
www.norwichgolf.com

Club Pro: John Paesani, PGA
Payment: Visa, MC
Tee Times: 3 days adv.
Fee 9 Holes: Weekday:
Fee 18 Holes: Weekday: $40 (rates may change)
Twilight Rates: After 5pm
Cart Rental: $18pp/wknd, $16pp/wkdy
Lessons: $50/half hour **Schools:**
Membership: Yes
Other: Clubhouse / Lockers / Showers / Restaurant / Bar-Lounge

Weekend:
Weekend: $48 (rates may change)
Discounts: None
Driving Range: No
Junior Golf: Yes
Architect/Yr Open: Donald Ross/1926

Tees	Holes	Yards	Par	USGA	Slope
BACK	18	6183	71	69.5	129
MIDDLE	18	5877	72	68.1	126
FRONT	18	5104	71	70.2	118

Short but tricky course: overly aggressive play could lead to disaster. Designed by Donald Ross. Open April - November. Residents' rate. New bridges. Visit website for full listing of rates.

	1	2	3	4	5	6	7	8	9
PAR	4	4	4	4	5	4	4	4	3
YARDS	303	276	366	410	487	330	370	300	170
	10	**11**	**12**	**13**	**14**	**15**	**16**	**17**	**18**
PAR	4	4	5	3	5	4	4	4	3
YARDS	355	388	503	105	545	170	330	303	166

Directions: I-95 to I-395 North to Exit 80 East. Take right off ramp (West Main Street), follow to 5th light. Take right onto New London Turnpike. Course is ½ mile down on right.

Pequot Golf Club ✪✪ ▶ 26

127 Wheeler Road
Stonington, CT (860) 535-1898
www.pequotgolf.com

Club Pro: Joe Brucas, PGA
Payment: Visa, MC, Amex, Disc, Checks, Cash
Tee Times: 7 days adv.
Fee 9 Holes: Weekday: $20
Fee 18 Holes: Weekday: $30
Twilight Rates: After 1pm, wknds only
Cart Rental: $16pp/18, $11pp/9
Lessons: Yes **Schools:** No
Membership: Yes
Other: Restaurant / Clubhouse / Bar-Lounge

Weekend: $21
Weekend: $35
Discounts: Sr. & Jr., wkdys only
Driving Range: Yes
Junior Golf: Yes
Architect/Yr Open: Wendell Ross/1959
GPS:

COUPON

Tees	Holes	Yards	Par	USGA	Slope
BACK					
MIDDLE	18	5903	70	68.5	121
FRONT	18	5248	71	69.7	113

Player Comments: "Beautiful course." Open March 1 - December 15. Historic Mystic Seaport and casinos nearby.

	1	2	3	4	5	6	7	8	9
PAR	4	4	4	4	4	3	4	4	3
YARDS	353	329	358	287	328	179	379	376	209
	10	**11**	**12**	**13**	**14**	**15**	**16**	**17**	**18**
PAR	4	4	3	5	4	4	4	3	5
YARDS	276	361	149	469	417	336	339	193	565

Directions: I-95 to Exit 91. Left off 95 South, right off 95 North. Go 1 mile. Take right onto Wheeler Road.

Quarryview Golf Course

NR **27** ►

30 Allyndale Road
East Canaan, CT (860) 824-4252
www.quarryviewgolf.com

Tees	Holes	Yards	Par	USGA	Slope
BACK	9	1626	31		
MIDDLE	9	1576	31	59.0	93
FRONT	9	1532	31	58.0	89

Club Pro:
Payment: Visa, MC
Tee Times: No
Fee 9 Holes: Weekday: $11
Fee 18 Holes: Weekday: $17
Twilight Rates: No
Cart Rental: $10pp/18, $6pp/9
Lessons: Schools:
Membership: Yes
Other: Snack Bar

Weekend: $14
Weekend: $20
Discounts: None
Driving Range: Yes, grass
Junior Golf: Yes
Architect/Yr Open: Leonard Allyn/2002
GPS:

9 hole executive course, families welcome, with a full-service practice range. A work in progress. Also has a driving range.

	1	2	3	4	5	6	7	8	9
PAR	3	3	3	3	3	3	5	4	4
YARDS	95	188	150	125	120	128	385	200	220
PAR									
YARDS									

Directions: Route 44 in East Canaan to Allyndale Road.

Raceway Golf Club

⊙⊙ **28** ►

Route 31
Thompson, CT (860) 923-9591
www.racewaygolf.com

Tees	Holes	Yards	Par	USGA	Slope
BACK	18	6663	72	71.1	119
MIDDLE	18	6154	72	68.9	111
FRONT	18	5403	72	71.3	117

Club Pro: David Hall, PGA
Payment: Visa, MC, Disc
Tee Times: M-F 7 days, S/S 4 days
Fee 9 Holes: Weekday:
Fee 18 Holes: Weekday: $37 w/cart & lunch
Twilight Rates: After 5:30pm
Cart Rental: Included
Lessons: Yes **Schools:**
Membership:
Other: Clubhouse / Lockers/ Snack Bar / Restaurant / Bar-Lounge

Weekend:
Weekend: $44 w/cart
Discounts: None
Driving Range: 40 mats, grass $6
Junior Golf: Yes
Architect/Yr Open: Don Hoenig/1947

Signature hole #4, downhill with water covering the front edge of the green. Many undulating greens. "An enjoyable course to play." –FP

	1	2	3	4	5	6	7	8	9
PAR	4	4	4	3	5	5	4	4	3
YARDS	277	387	304	152	536	486	350	402	174
	10	11	12	13	14	15	16	17	18
PAR	5	4	4	5	3	4	4	3	4
YARDS	492	382	342	425	146	353	347	166	289

Directions: I-395 to Exit 99; go into Thompson Center, left at blinking light onto Route 193. Follow signs to Thompson Speedway which will lead to the course.

River Ridge Golf Course ✪✪✪

259 Poreston Road
Jewitt City, CT (860) 376-3268
www.riverridgegolf.com

Club Pro: Brian Morrow, PGA
Payment: Visa, MC
Tee Times: 10 days
Fee 9 Holes: Weekday: $20
Fee 18 Holes: Weekday: $35
Twilight Rates: After 1pm
Cart Rental: $16pp/18, $9pp/9
Lessons: Yes **Schools:** No
Membership: Yes
Other: Full Restaurant / Bar-Lounge

Tees	Holes	Yards	Par	USGA	Slope
BACK	18	6871	72	73.0	129
MIDDLE	18	6474	72	71.0	127
FRONT	18	5393	72	70.4	119

Weekend: $20
Weekend: $42
Discounts: Junior
Driving Range: No
Junior Golf: No
Architect/Yr Open: Joseph & Charlie Rustici/1999

Complete bunker renovations. Challenging course cut through trees with significant elevation changes. 24-hour automated tee time system. "Nice tee boxes, fairways, and greens." –FP

	1	2	3	4	5	6	7	8	9
PAR	4	4	5	3	5	3	4	4	5
YARDS	390	391	510	180	530	156	350	354	560
	10	11	12	13	14	15	16	17	18
PAR	4	3	4	4	4	5	4	3	4
YARDS	401	122	420	326	350	530	340	185	379

Directions: I-395 to Exit 85 to Route 164 South. 7/10 mile on right.

Rockledge Country Club ✪✪✪½

289 South Main Street
West Hartford, CT (860) 521-3156
www.golfrockledge.com

Club Pro: Richard F. Crowe, PGA
Payment: Visa, MC, Cash
Tee Times: 7 days adv. (860) 521-6284
Fee 9 Holes: Weekday: $17.25
Fee 18 Holes: Weekday: $33
Twilight Rates: Yes, depends on sunset
Cart Rental: $14pp/18, $8pp/9
Lessons: $40/half hour **Schools:** No
Membership: Yes
Other: Clubhouse / Lockers / Showers / Snack Bar / Restaurant / Bar-Lounge

Tees	Holes	Yards	Par	USGA	Slope
BACK	18	6436	72	71.1	129
MIDDLE	18	6069	72	69.3	125
FRONT	18	5434	72	72.7	129

Weekend: $18.75
Weekend: $37
Discounts: Senior & Junior
Driving Range: $9/lg, $6.50/med, $3.75/sm
Junior Golf: Yes
Architect/Yr Open: Al Zikorus/1940

Player Comments: "Challenging layout. Always in great condition." Open April - December. Resident fees and tee times. Lottery for weekends.

	1	2	3	4	5	6	7	8	9
PAR	4	4	4	4	3	5	4	3	5
YARDS	334	286	394	395	177	450	299	181	448
	10	11	12	13	14	15	16	17	18
PAR	4	4	5	3	5	4	3	4	4
YARDS	404	302	465	136	515	357	152	381	393

Directions: I-84 to Exit 41. From West take a right off the exit, from East take a left off the exit. Course is ¼ mile on left.

NE CT

Rolling Greens Golf Club NR 31

600 Cold Spring Road
Rocky Hill, CT (860) 257-9775
www.ctrollinggreens.com

Tees	Holes	Yards	Par	USGA	Slope
BACK					
MIDDLE	9	3131	35	70.1	130
FRONT	9	2614	36	71.7	130

Club Pro: Gary Deep, PGA
Payment: Visa, MC
Tee Times: No
Fee 9 Holes: Weekday: $17   **Weekend:** $17
Fee 18 Holes: Weekday: $34   **Weekend:** $34
Twilight Rates: After 5:30pm   **Discounts:** Senior & Junior
Cart Rental: $16pp/18, $10pp/9   **Driving Range:** No
Lessons: $60 **Schools:** No   **Junior Golf:** No
Membership: Yes   **Architect/Yr Open:** Geoffrey Cornish/1973
Other: Clubhouse / Lockers / Showers / Restaurant / Bar-Lounge

Challenging! Shotmaker's course. Great shape. Dress code (no tank tops, T-shirts, or cutoff jeans). Open March - November.

	1	2	3	4	5	6	7	8	9
PAR	4	5	3	4	4	4	4	3	4
YARDS	360	553	191	315	379	440	373	180	340
PAR									
YARDS									

Directions: I-91 to Exit 23. Signs to Rolling Greens. Approximately 1 mile from exit.

Rolling Meadows Country Club ✪✪ 32

77 Sadds Mill Road
Ellington, CT (860) 870-5328
www.rollingmeadowscountryclub.com

Tees	Holes	Yards	Par	USGA	Slope
BACK	18	6818	72	72.5	128
MIDDLE	18	6269	72	70	123
FRONT	18	5331	72	70.4	122

Club Pro: Mark Castellano, Dir. of Golf
Payment: Visa, MC, Disc
Tee Times: 1 week adv.
Fee 9 Holes: Weekday: $22   **Weekend:** $24
Fee 18 Holes: Weekday: $36   **Weekend:** $39
Twilight Rates: After 2 pm   **Discounts:** Sr. & Jr. M-Th
Cart Rental: $16pp/18, $8 pp/9   **Driving Range:** Yes
Lessons: No **Schools:** Yes   **Junior Golf:** Yes
Membership: Yes   **Architect/Yr Open:** Al Zirokus/1997
Other: Restaurant / Bar / Beverage Cart   **GPS:**

COUPON

Player Comments: " Getting better every year." Weekday specials available - call pro shop for details. Special: 7am-1pm, Monday - Friday - $41 with cart, $38 military or senior.

	1	2	3	4	5	6	7	8	9
PAR	5	4	3	5	4	4	4	3	4
YARDS	488	316	166	491	390	366	335	186	346
	10	11	12	13	14	15	16	17	18
PAR	4	5	4	3	5	4	4	3	4
YARDS	383	473	366	163	490	433	345	190	342

Directions: I-91 to Route 140 or I-84 to 83 to Route 140 (across from Brookside Park, Ellington).

Shennecosset Golf Club ✪✪✪ ▶ 33

Plant Street
Groton, CT (860) 445-0262
www.shennygolf.com

Tees	Holes	Yards	Par	USGA	Slope
BACK	18	6562	71	71.5	122
MIDDLE	18	6088	71	69.1	121
FRONT	18	5671	74	72.4	122

Club Pro: Todd Goodhue, PGA
Payment: Visa, MC
Tee Times: 3 days adv.
Fee 9 Holes: Weekday: **Weekend:**
Fee 18 Holes: Weekday: $42   **Weekend:** $47
Twilight Rates: After 12pm   **Discounts:** Junior
Cart Rental: $18pp/18   **Driving Range:** No
Lessons: Yes **Schools:** No   **Junior Golf:** Yes
Membership: Yes   **Architect/Yr Open:** Donald Ross
Other: Clubhouse / Snack Bar / Restaurant / Bar-Lounge

Player Comments: "Great old course. Newer holes along the river are terrific." Fully irrigated. Donald Ross-designed seaside course. Open year round. Mohegan Sun and Foxwoods Casino nearby.

	1	2	3	4	5	6	7	8	9
PAR	4	4	4	3	5	4	4	5	3
YARDS	350	368	361	195	488	145	433	367	418
	10	**11**	**12**	**13**	**14**	**15**	**16**	**17**	**18**
PAR	4	4	3	4	4	3	4	4	5
YARDS	400	160	460	542	323	116	343	362	311

Directions: I-95 to Exit 87 (Clarence Sharp Highway); take right at second light. Take left at next light, proceed past Pfizer; course is on left side.

Simsbury Farms Golf Club ✪✪ ▶ 34

100 Old Farms Road
West Simsbury, CT (860) 658-6246
www.simsburyfarms.com

Tees	Holes	Yards	Par	USGA	Slope
BACK	18	6509	72	71.0	122
MIDDLE	18	6119	72	69.0	119
FRONT	18	5400	72	70.8	122

Club Pro: John Verrengia, PGA
Payment: Cash, Check, Most Major
Tee Times: 3 days wknds, 7 days wkdays
Fee 9 Holes: Weekday: $20   **Weekend:** $23
Fee 18 Holes: Weekday: $34   **Weekend:** $38
Twilight Rates: After 6pm   **Discounts:** Senior & Junior
Cart Rental: $16pp/18, $10pp/9   **Driving Range: Yes**
Lessons: $50/45 min. **Schools:** No   **Junior Golf:** Yes
Membership: Yes (non-resident available)   **Architect/Yr Open:** Geoffrey Cornish/1972
Other: Restaurant / Clubhouse   **GPS:** Yes

COUPON

Good challenge with a decent mix of holes. A nice hilly course. All bunkers re-done in 2012. Continued drainage improvements. Open April - November.

	1	2	3	4	5	6	7	8	9
PAR	4	4	4	3	5	4	5	4	3
YARDS	341	381	361	135	487	361	535	279	178
	10	**11**	**12**	**13**	**14**	**15**	**16**	**17**	**18**
PAR	4	4	5	3	5	4	3	4	4
YARDS	346	335	533	169	465	325	200	302	386

Directions: Route 185 North to end. Take left on to 10 North. At 2nd light take left onto Stratton Brook Road. Through 2 traffic lights, course is ¾ mile on the right.

**NE
CT**

Skungamaug River Golf Club ✪✪ ▸ 35

104 Folly Lane
Coventry, CT (860) 742-9348
www.skungamauggolf.com

Club Pro: Rick Nelson, PGA
Payment: Visa, MC, Amex, Disc
Tee Times: M-F 7 days adv., S/S 6 days adv.
Fee 9 Holes: Weekday: $18
Fee 18 Holes: Weekday: $35
Twilight Rates: After 6pm
Cart Rental: $15pp/18, $8pp/9
Lessons: $50/half hour **Schools:** No
Membership: Yes
Other: See website for specials

Tees	Holes	Yards	Par	USGA	Slope
BACK	18	5785	70	69.4	120
MIDDLE	18	5624	70	68.6	118
FRONT	18	4838	71	69.3	119

Weekend: $19
Weekend: $37
Discounts: Senior
Driving Range: $5/lg, $3/sm bucket
Junior Golf: Yes
Architect/Yr Open: Chet Jenkins/1962
GPS:

COUPON

River runs along right side, large tree divides upper and lower levels of hole #15. No cutoffs or tank tops. Open April - December.

	1	2	3	4	5	6	7	8	9
PAR	4	3	4	5	3	4	5	3	4
YARDS	339	154	291	438	139	332	461	158	351
	10	**11**	**12**	**13**	**14**	**15**	**16**	**17**	**18**
PAR	4	3	4	4	4	4	4	3	5
YARDS	376	171	363	371	395	290	323	189	483

Directions: I-84 to Exit 68. South on Route 195, ¼ mile to light. Turn right onto Goose Lane, follow yellow, triangular arrows on telephone poles. 3 miles to club.

Stanley Golf Club ✪✪✪½ ▸ 36

245 Hartford Road
New Britain, CT (860) 827-8570
www.stanleygolf.com

Club Pro: Kyle Hedstrom, PGA
Payment: Most Major Credit Cards
Tee Times: Wknds, 3 days adv. (860-827-1362)
Fee 9 Holes: Weekday: $18.25
Fee 18 Holes: Weekday: $30.50
Twilight Rates: No
Cart Rental: $29/18, $18/9 per cart
Lessons: Yes **Schools:** No
Membership: Season Pass
Other: Clubhouse / Lockers / Showers / Restaurant / Bar-Lounge / Snack / Outings
GPS: Yes

Tees	Holes	Yards	Par	USGA	Slope
BACK	27/18	6452	72	70.8	115
MIDDLE	27/18	6107	72	69.1	114
FRONT	27/18	5434	73	71.3	115

Weekend: $19.75
Weekend: $33
Discounts: Senior & Junior
Driving Range: $9.50/lg, $7/med
Junior Golf: Yes
Architect/Yr Open: Robert Ross/1930

27 holes. White to Red score card below. Improvements include 4 redesigned holes. New driving range. Resident rates. New carts with GPS, new practice area and 9 Blue Green.

	1	2	3	4	5	6	7	8	9
PAR	5	4	3	4	4	4	3	4	5
YARDS	492	430	150	352	365	320	105	387	460
	10	**11**	**12**	**13**	**14**	**15**	**16**	**17**	**18**
PAR	4	3	5	4	4	4	3	4	5
YARDS	338	201	461	357	325	376	160	363	465

Directions: I-84 to Exit 39A, then right onto Route 9 South to Exit 30. Take right at end of ramp. Course is ½ mile on left.

Tallwood Country Club ✪✪½ 37

91 North Street (Route 85)
Hebron, CT (860) 646-1151
www.tallwoodcountryclub.com

Tees	Holes	Yards	Par	USGA	Slope
BACK	18	6374	72	70.1	122
MIDDLE	18	6126	72	69.3	121
FRONT	18	5424	72	70.0	126

Club Pro: John Nowobilski, PGA
Payment: Visa, MC, Disc
Tee Times: M-F 7 days, S/S 5 days
Fee 9 Holes: Weekday: $18.50   **Weekend:** $19.50
Fee 18 Holes: Weekday: $36   **Weekend:** $39
Twilight Rates: After 4pm   **Discounts:** Senior & Junior
Cart Rental: $14pp/18, $7pp/9   **Driving Range:** Yes
Lessons: Yes Schools: Yes   **Junior Golf:** No
Membership: Yes   **Architect/Yr Open:** Mike Ovian/1970
Other: Clubhouse / Snack Bar / Practice Facilties **GPS:**

Great practice faciltiy with practice bunkers, chipping area, driving range with grass tees and mats and two putting greens. Annual host of CTPGA, CSGA events. Open March - December.

	1	2	3	4	5	6	7	8	9
PAR	5	4	3	5	4	3	4	4	3
YARDS	528	287	176	483	400	158	341	359	167
	10	11	12	13	14	15	16	17	18
PAR	4	5	4	4	3	4	5	4	4
YARDS	296	500	361	346	157	364	460	377	366

Directions: I-84 East to I-384. Exit 5 off I-384, right off exit puts you on Route 85 South. Course is on right.

Timberlin Golf Club ✪✪✪ 38

330 Southington Road
Berlin, CT (860) 828-3228
www.timberlingolf.com

Tees	Holes	Yards	Par	USGA	Slope
BACK	18	6733	72	72.0	127
MIDDLE	18	6342	72	70.2	126
FRONT	18	5472	72	72.0	125

Club Pro: Marc S. Bayram, PGA
Payment: Cash or Credit
Tee Times: 7 days/wkdys, 3 days/wknd
Fee 9 Holes: Weekday: $22.75   **Weekend:** $24.75
Fee 18 Holes: Weekday: $36.50   **Weekend:** $40.50
Twilight Rates: After 4pm   **Discounts:** Senior & Junior
Cart Rental: $17pp/18, $9.75 pp/9   **Driving Range:** Yes
Lessons: Yes **Schools:** Yes   **Junior Golf:** Yes
Membership: Yes   **Architect/Yr Open:** Al Zikorus/1970
Other: Clubhouse / Showers / Snack Bar   **GPS:**

COUPON

Player Comments: "Friendly staff." "Challenging course in great shape." "Good value." Conservative layout with well-placed traps. Open April - November. Bunker and irrigation improvements complete. Berlin resident rates available.

	1	2	3	4	5	6	7	8	9
PAR	5	4	4	3	4	5	3	4	4
YARDS	550	340	360	170	360	526	150	342	377
	10	11	12	13	14	15	16	17	18
PAR	5	4	3	5	4	4	3	4	4
YARDS	492	361	160	477	362	400	163	359	393

Directions: Located off Route 71 which runs between I-691 and Route 372. Course is on Route 364, .6 mile from Route 71. Left onto Southington Avenue.

NE
CT

Topstone Golf Course   ✪✪✪¹⁄₂   ▶ 39

516 Griffin Road
South Windsor, CT (860) 648-4653
www.topstonegc.com

Tees	Holes	Yards	Par	USGA	Slope
BACK	18	6546	72	70.9	124
MIDDLE	18	6113	72	69.0	119
FRONT	18	5077	72	67.9	111

Club Pro: Casey Morris
Payment: Visa, MC, Amex, Disc
Tee Times: 14 days
Fee 9 Holes: Weekday: $21   **Weekend:** $23
Fee 18 Holes: Weekday: $41   **Weekend:** $44
Twilight Rates: After 12pm   **Discounts:** Senior & Junior
Cart Rental: $13pp/18, $7pp/9   **Driving Range:** No
Lessons: $40/half hour   **Schools:** No   **Junior Golf:** Yes
Membership: Yes   **Architect/Yr Open:** Al Zikorus, Joe Kelley/1997
Other: Bar / Restaurant / Clubhouse   **GPS:**

Player Comments: "A good value for your golfing dollars." "Shows a great deal of maturity. Back 9 has more distinctive holes." "Well-kept course. Great greens." Challenging for all abilities with 5 sets of tees.

	1	2	3	4	5	6	7	8	9
PAR	4	5	4	3	5	4	4	3	4
YARDS	360	491	309	170	505	389	392	145	285
	10	11	12	13	14	15	16	17	18
PAR	5	4	3	4	4	3	5	4	4
YARDS	490	380	169	354	399	140	460	332	343

Directions: Take I-291 from either Routes 84 or 91. Take Exit 4 (Route 5). Go north on Route 5 for 4 miles, turn right onto Route 194 for .5 mile. Left onto Rye Street for 1.5 miles, Turn right onto Griffin Street for 1.25 miles.

Tower Ridge   ✪✪✪¹⁄₂   ▶ 40

140 Nod Road
Simsbury, CT (860) 658-9767
www.towerridge.com

Tees	Holes	Yards	Par	USGA	Slope
BACK	18	6443	71	71.5	132
MIDDLE	18	6124	71	70.0	129
FRONT	18	5164	72	76.3	133

Club Pro: James Becker
Payment: Most Major Credit Cards
Tee Times: 7 days per week
Fee 9 Holes: Weekday: $27   **Weekend:** $35
Fee 18 Holes: Weekday: $45   **Weekend:** $59
Twilight Rates: After 1pm wknd, after 3pm wkdys   **Discounts:** Senior
Cart Rental: Included   **Driving Range:** Yes
Lessons: $80/hour   **Schools:** Yes   **Junior Golf:** Yes
Membership: Yes   **Architect/Yr Open:** Geoffrey Cornish/1959
Other: Restaurant / Tennis Center & Swim Club for Members

COUPON

Former private now accepting public play. Partially flat, partially hilly. Several nice views from elevated tees. A challenging course for any level of player. Spectacular view of Simsbury mountain range and Hueblein Tower. Plays along the Farmington River.

	1	2	3	4	5	6	7	8	9
PAR	4	4	3	4	4	4	4	4	4
YARDS	367	383	141	369	377	341	416	230	335
	10	11	12	13	14	15	16	17	18
PAR	5	4	3	4	5	4	3	4	4
YARDS	449	429	179	397	480	389	164	314	364

Directions: I-84 to exit Route 4 Farmington. At 2nd light, right on Route 10 North. Cross Route 44. Club is on right.

Tunxis Plantation CC (Green) ✪✪✪

87 Town Farm Road
Farmington, CT (860) 677-1367
www.tunxisgolf.com

Club Pro: Lou Pandolfi, PGA
Payment: Visa, MC, Amex, Disc
Tee Times: 1 week adv.
Fee 9 Holes: Weekday: $22
Fee 18 Holes: Weekday: $37
Twilight Rates: No
Cart Rental: $16.50pp/18, $9pp/9
Lessons: $40/half hour **Schools:** No
Membership: Season Pass $1,995

Tees	Holes	Yards	Par	USGA	Slope
BACK	18	6446	70	70.9	125
MIDDLE	18	6027	70	69.0	121
FRONT	18	4883	70	71.0	115

Weekend: $23.50
Weekend: $45
Discounts: Senior and Junior
Driving Range: $4/bucket
Junior Golf: Yes
Architect/Yr Open: Al Zakoris/1962

Other: Restaurant / Clubhouse / Bar-Lounge / Lockers / Snack Bar / Showers

Very well run for such a complex. Fine staff. Wide-open fairways make for a forgiving layout. Great course for intermediate players. Open April 1 - November 20.

	1	2	3	4	5	6	7	8	9
PAR	4	5	4	4	3	4	4	3	4
YARDS	363	511	354	369	188	434	345	166	335
	10	11	12	13	14	15	16	17	18
PAR	4	4	3	4	4	4	4	5	3
YARDS	348	365	165	373	342	291	397	496	185

Directions: I-84 to Exit 39 (Route 4); first right over Farmington River.

Tunxis Plantation CC (Red) ✪✪✪

87 Town Farm Road
Farmington, CT (860) 677-1367
www.tunxisgolf.com

Club Pro: Lou Pandolfi, PGA
Payment: Visa, MC, Amex, Disc
Tee Times: Yes, call in advance
Fee 9 Holes: Weekday: $22
Fee 18 Holes: Weekday: $37
Twilight Rates: No
Cart Rental: $16.50pp/18, $9pp/9
Lessons: $40/half hour **Schools:** No
Membership: Season Pass $1,995

Tees	Holes	Yards	Par	USGA	Slope
BACK	9	3219	35	35.1	125
MIDDLE	9	2999	35	34.1	121
FRONT	9	2872	35	35.8	117

Weekend: $23.50
Weekend: $45
Discounts: Senior and Junior
Driving Range: $4/bucket
Junior Golf: Yes
Architect/Yr Open: Al Zikorus/1962

Other: Restaurant / Clubhouse / Bar-Lounge / Lockers / Snack Bar / Showers

9-hole course in excellent condition located in Farmington Valley, next to Farmington River. Open April 1 - November 20.

	1	2	3	4	5	6	7	8	9
PAR	4	4	3	4	5	4	4	3	4
YARDS	348	395	141	322	483	396	366	177	371
PAR									
YARDS									

NE CT

Directions: I-84 to Exit 39 (Route 4); first right over Farmington River.

Tunxis Plantation CC (White) ✪✪✪ 43

87 Town Farm Road
Farmington, CT (860) 677-1367
www.tunxisgolf.com

Tees	Holes	Yards	Par	USGA	Slope
BACK	18	6638	72	71.3	124
MIDDLE	18	6241	72	69.4	120
FRONT	18	5744	72	71.5	116

Club Pro: Lou Pandolfi, PGA
Payment: Visa, MC, Amex, Discover
Tee Times: Call in advance
Fee 9 Holes: Weekday: $22
Fee 18 Holes: Weekday: $37
Twilight Rates: No
Cart Rental: $16.50pp/18, $9pp/9
Lessons: $40/half hour **Schools:** No
Membership: Season Pass: $1,995
Weekend: $23.50
Weekend: $45
Discounts: Senior and Junior
Driving Range: $4/bucket
Junior Golf: Yes
Architect/Yr Open: Al Zikorus/1962
Other: Restaurant / Clubhouse / Bar-Lounge / Lockers / Snack Bar / Showers

Great course for intermediate players. Play from the Blue tees for a real challenge. Lake comes into play on several holes. Open April 1 - November 20. "Florida-style golf: water and sand provide challenges. Holes 5 & 13 really tough." –AR

	1	2	3	4	5	6	7	8	9
PAR	5	4	4	3	5	4	4	3	4
YARDS	526	407	343	153	476	366	358	147	332
	10	11	12	13	14	15	16	17	18
PAR	4	5	4	5	3	4	3	4	4
YARDS	334	508	358	515	176	413	154	357	318

Directions: I-84 to Exit 39 (Route 4); first right over Farmington River.

Twin Hills Country Club NR 44

199 Bread and Milk Street
Coventry, CT (860) 742-9705
www.twinhillscountryclub.com

Tees	Holes	Yards	Par	USGA	Slope
BACK	18	6365	71	69.3	121
MIDDLE	18	5992	71	68.0	117
FRONT	18	5249	71	69.5	116

Club Pro: Eric DeStefano, PGA
Payment: Visa, MC
Tee Times: 7 days F/S/S/H
Fee 9 Holes: Weekday: $19
Fee 18 Holes: Weekday: $34
Twilight Rates: No
Cart Rental: $15pp/18, $8pp/9
Lessons: Yes **Schools:** No
Membership: No
Other: Clubhouse / Snack Bar / Beer & Soda
Weekend: $20
Weekend: $39
Discounts: Senior & Junior
Driving Range: No
Junior Golf: Yes
Architect/Yr Open: George McDermott/1971
GPS:

COUPON

A rustic, but interesting, layout. Number 3 is a fun par 5 with risk/reward chance for a birdie. Open March - December.

	1	2	3	4	5	6	7	8	9
PAR	4	4	5	3	5	4	4	3	4
YARDS	380	284	530	144	502	348	446	152	357
	10	11	12	13	14	15	16	17	18
PAR	4	4	4	3	4	5	3	4	4
YARDS	320	336	311	204	374	494	144	361	267

Directions: Route 84E Exit 67 to Route 31 South; follow 5 miles. Course is on the right.

Villa Hills Par 3

NR   45 ▶

497 Middle Turnpike
Storrs, CT (860) 429-6421

Tees	Holes	Yards	Par	USGA	Slope
BACK					
MIDDLE	9	1158	27		
FRONT					

Club Pro: Bernie Broder, Owner
Payment: Cash, Visa, MC
Tee Times:
Fee 9 Holes: Weekday: $10   **Weekend:** $10
Fee 18 Holes: Weekday: $19   **Weekend:** $19
Twilight Rates: No   **Discounts:**
Cart Rental: $3/pull   **Driving Range:**
Lessons: Schools: No   **Junior Golf:** No
Membership: **Architect/Yr Open:** 1997
Other: Restaurant / Snack Bar / Bar-Lounge   **GPS:**

Popular Par 3.

	1	2	3	4	5	6	7	8	9
PAR	3	3	3	3	3	3	3	3	3
YARDS	97	185	150	105	165	65	120	124	147

PAR									
YARDS									

Directions: I-384 to Route 44. Course is on left.

Westwoods Golf Course

✪✪   46 ▶

Route 177
Farmington, CT (860) 675-2548
www.farmington.ct.org

Tees	Holes	Yards	Par	USGA	Slope
BACK					
MIDDLE	18	4407	61	60.8	93
FRONT	18	3975	61	59.5	85

Club Pro: Larry Graham, PGA
Payment: Most Major Credit Cards
Tee Times: Weekends, 7 days adv.
Fee 9 Holes: Weekday: $18   **Weekend:** $21
Fee 18 Holes: Weekday: $26.25   **Weekend:** $29.50
Twilight Rates: No   **Discounts:** Senior & Junior
Cart Rental: $29.68/18, $16.96/9 per cart   **Driving Range:** Yes
Lessons: $60/hour, $40/half hour   **Schools:** No   **Junior Golf:** July Golf Camp - Four 1-wk sessions
Membership: Yes   **Architect/Yr Open:** Geoffrey Cornish/1965
Other: Snack Bar / Bar-Lounge / Clubhouse / Restaurant / 20,000 sq. ft. Putting Green

Grass on practice range. Easy to walk, scenic.

	1	2	3	4	5	6	7	8	9
PAR	5	3	3	3	4	3	3	4	3
YARDS	494	164	135	187	315	204	159	344	235
	10	**11**	**12**	**13**	**14**	**15**	**16**	**17**	**18**
PAR	4	3	3	4	3	4	3	3	3
YARDS	420	236	121	376	211	348	163	163	132

Directions: Take I-84 to Route 72 Plainville to Washington Street (177). Take right on 177 North. Follow 3 miles, cross Route 6 and then course is 200 yards on left.

NE CT

Willimantic Country Club   ✪✪½   47

184 Club Road
Willimantic, CT (860) 456-1971
www.willigolf.com

Club Pro: Scott Potter, PGA
Payment: Visa, MC, Amex, Disc, Checks
Tee Times: M-Th, 7am-3pm
Fee 9 Holes: Weekday: $18
Fee 18 Holes: Weekday: $31
Twilight Rates: No
Cart Rental: $14pp/18, $8pp/9
Lessons: No **Schools:** No
Membership: Yes

Tees	Holes	Yards	Par	USGA	Slope
BACK	18	6271	71	70.5	121
MIDDLE	18	6003	71	69.2	119
FRONT	18	5106	71	68.5	113

Weekend: $20
Weekend: $36
Discounts: Jrs./Srs. $25/18 walking M-Th
Driving Range: No
Junior Golf: Yes
Architect/Yr Open: 1922

Other: Full Restaurant / Clubhouse / Bar-Lounge / Lockers / Showers

Open to public on weekdays and after 10am on weekends. Well worth the play. Play moves swiftly, long holes are compensated for by a number of short par 4s. Tee times required.

	1	2	3	4	5	6	7	8	9
PAR	4	4	4	4	4	5	3	4	4
YARDS	370	281	400	384	295	475	167	330	358
	10	11	12	13	14	15	16	17	18
PAR	3	4	4	5	4	5	3	4	3
YARDS	110	388	286	485	414	483	154	417	206

Directions: I-384 to Route 6 East. 11.6 miles to intersection of Route 6 and 66. Remain on Route 6 for 4.5 miles of Bypass Xpway. At end of bypass, turn left onto Route 66. Club is ½ mile on left.

Willow Brook Golf Course   ✪✪½   48

124 Brookfield St.
South Windsor, CT (860) 648-2061
www.willowbrookgc.com

Club Pro: Jeffrey Beyer, PGA
Payment: Visa, MC
Tee Times: 7 days adv.
Fee 9 Holes: Weekday: $14.50
Fee 18 Holes: Weekday: $28
Twilight Rates:
Cart Rental: $8pp/18, $4.50pp/9
Lessons: Yes **Schools:** Yes
Membership: No

Tees	Holes	Yards	Par	USGA	Slope
BACK	18	3037	60	56.2	79
MIDDLE	18	2613	60		
FRONT	18	2275	60		

Weekend: $16.50
Weekend: $30
Discounts: Senior & Junior
Driving Range: Yes
Junior Golf: Yes
Architect/Yr Open: Joe Kelly/2002
GPS:

COUPON

Other: Restaurant / Bar-Lounge / Clubhouse

Spectacular par 60 that is ideal for new golfers yet challenging to accomplished players. Public golf course in country club conditions.

	1	2	3	4	5	6	7	8	9
PAR	3	3	4	3	3	4	4	3	3
YARDS	92	119	216	67	103	197	223	106	94
	10	11	12	13	14	15	16	17	18
PAR	3	4	3	4	3	3	3	3	4
YARDS	100	233	83	281	137	100	86	75	301

Directions: I-84 to Exit 62. Left off ramp onto Sullivan Road. Follow Sullivan 4 miles. Right onto Troy Street, then right on to Brookfield Street. Course is on the right.

Wintonbury Hills GC

✪✪✪✪½ 49 ▶

206 Terry Plains Road
Bloomfield, CT (860) 242-1401
www.wintonburyhills.com

Tees	Holes	Yards	Par	USGA	Slope
BACK	18	6709	70	70.8	125
MIDDLE	18	6283	70	69.5	121
FRONT	18	5005	70	68.2	112

Club Pro: Ciaran Carr, PGA
Payment: Visa, MC, Amex, Disc
Tee Times: 7 days adv.
Fee 9 Holes: Weekday:
Fee 18 Holes: Weekday: $69
Twilight Rates: After 2pm
Cart Rental: Included
Lessons: Yes **Schools:** Yes
Membership: Yes
Other: Bloomfield Resident Rates Available / GPS-Equipped Carts
GPS: Yes

Weekend:
Weekend: $79
Discounts: Sr. wkdy, Jr. wkdy/wknd
Driving Range: Yes
Junior Golf: Yes
Architect/Yr Open: Pete Dye & Tim Liddy/2003

Resident rates available. Playing conditions better than many private clubs. "Gorgeous holes, courteous staff, excellent condition." –RW "Has joined the ranks of New England's best." –JD

	1	2	3	4	5	6	7	8	9
PAR	4	4	3	5	4	4	3	5	3
YARDS	367	365	139	512	327	400	200	543	170
	10	11	12	13	14	15	16	17	18
PAR	4	4	3	5	4	4	4	3	4
YARDS	402	400	162	521	415	397	368	190	405

Directions: From East: I-291 West toward Windsor. Take Exit 1 – CT-218 West. Turn left onto CT-218 for 4 miles. Right onto Bloomfield Avenue/CT-189. Follow 189 until it turns right at a traffic light. DO NOT GO RIGHT, go straight onto Terry Plains Road. Follow Terry Plains Road. for 1 mile. See web for more.

Woodstock Golf Course

✪✪ 50 ▶

Roseland Golf Course
South Woodstock, CT
(860) 928-4130

Tees	Holes	Yards	Par	USGA	Slope
BACK					
MIDDLE	9	2413	34	32.6	107
FRONT	9	1822	34	66.8	103

Club Pro: Eric Sarette
Payment: Visa, MC, Amex
Tee Times: 7 days
Fee 9 Holes: Weekday: $11
Fee 18 Holes: Weekday: $17
Twilight Rates: No
Cart Rental: $14pp/18, $7pp/9
Lessons: Yes **Schools:** Yes
Membership: Yes
Other: Clubhouse / Snack Bar / Lockers

Weekend: $13
Weekend: $19
Discounts: Sr. & Jr. wkdys only
Driving Range: Yes
Junior Golf: Yes
Architect/Yr Open: 1896

Great value and improved conditions. Established 1896. Challenging, hilly course with small sloping greens. Target golf. Open April - November, weather permitting

	1	2	3	4	5	6	7	8	9
PAR	3	4	4	4	4	4	3	4	4
YARDS	170	265	305	304	289	275	231	385	227
PAR									
YARDS									

Directions: I-395 to Route 44 (Exit 97). West on Route 44. Take Route 171 in Putnam, continue West. Follow 4.5 miles to Roseland Park Road, take right. Course is ¾ mile on left.

NE CT

Alling Memorial GC	1	Hawk's Landing CC	19	Portland West Golf Club	37
Banner Country Club	2	Highland Greens GC	20	Quarry Ridge GC	38
Candlewood Valley CC	3	Hop Brook GC	21	Richter Park GC	39
Chanticlair Golf Course	4	Hunter Golf Club	22	Ridgefield Golf Club	40
Crestbrook Park GC	5	Indian Springs GC	23	Short Beach Par 3 GC	41
E. Gaynor Brennan GC	6	Laurel View CC	24	Sleeping Giant GC	42
East Mountain GC	7	Longshore GC	25	South Pine Creek Par 3 GC	43
Eastwood CC	8	Lyman Orchards GC (Jones)	26	Southington CC	44
Fairchild Wheeler GC (Black)	9	Lyman Orchards GC (Player)	27	Sterling Farms GC	45
Fairchild Wheeler GC (Red)	10	Miner Hills GC	28	Stonybrook GC	46
Farmingbury Hills CC	11	Oak Hills Park GC	29	Sunset Hill GC	47
Fox Hopyard Golf Club	12	Orange Hills CC	30	Tashua Knolls CC	48
Gainfield Farms GC	13	Orchards Golf Course, The	31	Tradition GC at Wallingford	49
Grassy Hill Country Club	14	Oxford Greens, The GC at	32	Twin Lakes GC	50
Great River Golf Club	15	Pequabuck Golf Course	33	Western Hills GC	51
Griffith E. Harris GC	16	Pine Valley Golf Course	34	Whitney Farms	52
Guilford Lakes GC	17	Pomperaug Golf Club	35	Woodhaven CC	53
H. Smith Richardson GC	18	Portland Golf Club	36		

KEY TO THE STAR RATINGS:
5✪ = Outstanding **4✪** = Excellent **3✪** = Very Good **2✪** = Good **1✪** = Average **NR** = Not Rated

Alling Memorial Golf Course

NR

35 Eastern Street
New Haven, CT (203) 946-8014
www.allingmemorialgolfclub.com

Club Pro: Larry Thornhill, PGA
Payment: Cash, Visa, MC
Tee Times: Weekends, 3 days adv.

Tees	Holes	Yards	Par	USGA	Slope
BACK	18	6283	72	71.9	129
MIDDLE	18	5911	72	69.3	127
FRONT	18	5107	72	71.0	129

Fee 9 Holes: Weekday: $18
Fee 18 Holes: Weekday: $27
Twilight Rates: After 5:30pm
Cart Rental: $14pp/18, $8pp/9
Lessons: Yes **Schools:** No
Membership: Yes
Other: Lockers / Showers / Restaurant / Bar-Lounge

Weekend: $19
Weekend: $32
Discounts: Senior & Junior
Driving Range: No
Junior Golf: Yes
Architect/Yr Open: McDonald/1929

Appreciated by old, young, and new golfers alike. Excellent value for the money. Host to numerous CT state golf events. Resident rates.

	1	2	3	4	5	6	7	8	9
PAR	4	4	3	5	4	4	4	4	4
YARDS	380	313	168	474	231	344	366	274	305
	10	11	12	13	14	15	16	17	18
PAR	3	5	3	4	4	5	4	3	5
YARDS	158	475	180	337	408	493	331	203	471

Directions: I-91 to Exit 8, bear right to second light (Eastern Street), right ¾ mile. Course is on left.

Banner Country Club

○○ 2

10 Banner Road
Moodus, CT (860) 873-9075
www.bannercountryclub.com

Club Pro:
Payment: Cash, Check, MC, Visa, Amex, Disc
Tee Times: Yes

Tees	Holes	Yards	Par	USGA	Slope
BACK					
MIDDLE	18	6015	72	67.8	123
FRONT	18	5776	74	70.8	121

Fee 9 Holes: Weekday: $14
Fee 18 Holes: Weekday: $25
Twilight Rates:
Cart Rental: $17pp/18, $12pp/9
Lessons: Yes **Schools:** No
Membership: Yes
Other: Clubhouse / Snack Bar / Restaurant

Weekend: $14
Weekend: $25
Discounts: Senior & Junior
Driving Range: $5/bucket
Junior Golf: 15 and under
Architect/Yr Open: Frank Gamberdella
GPS:

COUPON

Course renamed in 2006. Management indicates many plans afoot including improved tees, fairways, and greens. Call for weekend and weekday special rates.

	1	2	3	4	5	6	7	8	9
PAR	4	4	4	4	3	5	5	3	4
YARDS	395	320	409	317	120	482	485	146	344
	10	11	12	13	14	15	16	17	18
PAR	5	4	4	4	4	3	5	3	4
YARDS	481	318	363	286	419	147	496	146	341

Directions: CT Route 9 to Exit 7; follow Route 82 East to Route 149 North. Continue to center of Moodus. Follow signs to course.

**SW
CT**

Candlewood Valley Country Club ✪✪

401 Danbury Road
New Milford, CT (860) 354-9359
www.candlewoodvalleygolf.com

Tees	Holes	Yards	Par	USGA	Slope
BACK	18	6441	71	72.1	127
MIDDLE	18	6033	71	70.7	122
FRONT	18	5080	71	72.5	123

Club Pro: Ed Slattery
Payment: Most Major
Tee Times: 7 days adv.
Fee 9 Holes: Weekday: **Weekend:**
Fee 18 Holes: Weekday: $38   **Weekend:** $45
Twilight Rates: After 3pm   **Discounts:** Senior & Junior
Cart Rental: $30/18, $16/9 per cart   **Driving Range:** No
Lessons: $45/half hour   **Schools:** Yes   **Junior Golf:** Yes
Membership: Yes - Men's Club, Ladies' Club, Senior League
Architect/Yr Open: Cornish, Kay, & McNeil/1961
Other: Clubhouse / Lockers / Showers / Snack Bar / Restaurant / Bar-Lounge / Banquet Facilities

Take advantage of the Monday & Wednesday special - cart, 18 holes, lunch.

	1	2	3	4	5	6	7	8	9
PAR	5	4	3	3	4	5	4	4	4
YARDS	457	363	153	175	404	530	350	476	402
	10	11	12	13	14	15	16	17	18
PAR	4	4	3	4	4	4	4	4	4
YARDS	310	317	210	413	390	418	371	386	316

Directions: I-84 to Exit 7. Turn right at light onto Route 7 North. Follow 4.1 miles to CVCC on the right.

Chanticlair Golf Course

NR 4

Old Hebron Road
Colchester, CT (860) 537-3223
www.chanticlair.com

Tees	Holes	Yards	Par	USGA	Slope
BACK					
MIDDLE	9	3061	35	69.8	117
FRONT	9	2501	35	69.1	112

Club Pro:
Payment: Cash, Visa, MC
Tee Times: 1 week adv.
Fee 9 Holes: Weekday: $17   **Weekend:** $18
Fee 18 Holes: Weekday: $26   **Weekend:** $27
Twilight Rates: No   **Discounts:** Senior & Junior
Cart Rental: $12pp/18, $6pp/9   **Driving Range:** No
Lessons: No   **Schools:** No   **Junior Golf:** Yes
Membership: Yes   **Architect/Yr Open:** Hymie Stoloman/1973
Other: Clubhouse / Snacks / Beer / Soda   **GPS:**

The 4th hole has an elevated island green. Fairly flat; a good walking course.

	1	2	3	4	5	6	7	8	9
PAR	3	4	4	3	4	4	4	4	5
YARDS	205	390	375	138	387	385	350	380	451
PAR									
YARDS									

Directions: Route 2 to State Police Barracks exit; take left off ramp and go up hill. Make left onto Old Hebron Road at firehouse. Course is ¼ mile on right.

Crestbrook Park Golf Course ✪✪½ 5

834 Northfield Road
Watertown, CT (860) 945-5249
www.crestbrookpark.com

Tees	Holes	Yards	Par	USGA	Slope
BACK	18	6915	71	73.6	128
MIDDLE	18	6098	71	69.9	121
FRONT	18	5696	75	73.8	128

Club Pro: Kenneth Gemmell, PGA
Payment: Cash, Visa, MC
Tee Times: Weekends, 2 days adv.
Fee 9 Holes: Weekday: $21 **Weekend:** $23
Fee 18 Holes: Weekday: $37 **Weekend:** $40
Twilight Rates: No **Discounts:** Senior & Junior M-F
Cart Rental: $29/18, $17/9 per cart **Driving Range:** $6.50/lg, $5/md, $3.50/sm
Lessons: $35/half hour **Schools:** No **Junior Golf:** Yes
Membership: Yes **Architect/Yr Open:** Geoffrey Cornish/1970
Other: Clubhouse / Snack Bar / Restaurant / Bar-Lounge / Pool / Tennis / Picnic

Player Comments: "Totally different 9s, front 9 tight, back 9 open and angled fairways." Cornish design. Resident rates.

	1	2	3	4	5	6	7	8	9
PAR	4	4	4	5	3	4	4	3	5
YARDS	370	447	411	515	152	384	405	194	536
	10	11	12	13	14	15	16	17	18
PAR	4	4	3	4	4	5	3	4	4
YARDS	357	401	160	337	333	463	210	308	393

Directions: Route 8 to Echo Lake Road (turn left). Take right at 2nd light (Buckingham); another right at stop sign (Northfield). Course is ¼ mile on right on Northfield Road.

E. Gaynor Brennan Golf Course ✪½ 6

451 Stillwater Road
Stamford, CT (203) 324-4185
www.brennangolf.com

Tees	Holes	Yards	Par	USGA	Slope
BACK	18	5931	71	69.5	121
MIDDLE	18	5814	71	68.0	118
FRONT	18	5180	73	72.3	124

Club Pro: V. Levin, A. Aulenti, Dir. of Golf
Payment: Cash, Visa, MC
Tee Times: 7 days adv.
Fee 9 Holes: Weekday: $26 **Weekend:**
Fee 18 Holes: Weekday: $40 **Weekend:** $45
Twilight Rates: After 4pm **Discounts:** Sr. & Jr., residents only
Cart Rental: $12.50pp/18, $8.50pp/9 **Driving Range:** No
Lessons: (203) 324-6507 **Schools:** No **Junior Golf:** Yes
Membership: Yes **Architect/Yr:** McCarthy, Gerrish/1925, Mungeum/1998
Other: Snack Bar / Restaurant / Bar-Lounge / Showers

The greens are usually in excellent condition. Course is a bit hilly. Open year round. Resident discounts and resident weekend lottery.

	1	2	3	4	5	6	7	8	9
PAR	4	4	3	5	4	5	4	4	3
YARDS	364	385	147	418	366	486	373	367	105
	10	11	12	13	14	15	16	17	18
PAR	4	4	4	3	4	3	4	5	4
YARDS	301	323	341	225	385	177	278	454	319

Directions: I-95 to Exit 7 (Atlantic Street). Go straight. Right onto Washington Boulevard, left onto Broad Street. Go to Stillwater Road. Course is on right.

SW CT

East Mountain Golf Course

171 East Mountain Road
Waterbury, CT (203) 753-1425
www.golfwaterbury.com

Club Pro: Dave Giacondino
Payment: Cash, Visa, MC, Amex, Disc
Tee Times: Weekends, 3 days adv.
Fee 9 Holes: Weekday: $20
Fee 18 Holes: Weekday: $31
Twilight Rates: After 5:30pm
Cart Rental: $30/18, $20/9 per cart
Lessons: Yes **Schools:** No
Membership: Yes, Yearly Season Pass
Other: Restaurant

Tees	Holes	Yards	Par	USGA	Slope
BACK	18	6012	70	68.6	118
MIDDLE	18	5801	70	67.5	116
FRONT	18	5366	70	71.7	121

Weekend: $20
Weekend: $31
Discounts: Senior & Junior
Driving Range: Yes
Junior Golf: Yes
Architect/Yr Open: Wayne Stiles/1932
GPS:

COUPON

Redesigned in 2007 with new drainage. Great classic layout with very well conditioned greens.

	1	2	3	4	5	6	7	8	9
PAR	4	4	4	3	4	6	3	3	4
YARDS	396	399	397	191	305	512	214	142	368
	10	11	12	13	14	15	16	17	18
PAR	4	4	5	4	3	4	4	3	5
YARDS	360	273	473	365	181	368	385	200	483

Directions: I-84 to Hamilton Avenue (Exit 23). Follow Route 69 West (1.5 miles). Right onto East Mountain at Church.

Eastwood Country Club

1301 Torringford West Street
Torrington, CT (860) 489-2630
www.eastwoodcountryclub.net

Club Pro: Greg Miller, PGA
Payment: Visa, MC, Amex
Tee Times: None
Fee 9 Holes: Weekday: $18
Fee 18 Holes: Weekday: $28
Twilight Rates: No
Cart Rental: $14pp/18, $8pp/9
Lessons: Yes **Schools:** No
Membership: Yes
Other: Restaurant / Clubhouse / Bar-Lounge

Tees	Holes	Yards	Par	USGA	Slope
BACK	9	2933	36	67.8	113
MIDDLE	9	2791	36	66.5	111
FRONT	9	2359	36		

Weekend: $20
Weekend: $30
Discounts: Srs & Jrs, weekdays
Driving Range: No
Junior Golf: Yes
Architect/Yr Open: 1963
GPS:

Open April - January. Greens in the best shape ever. "Course is in great condition and much improved." –SR Bunker renovation and new golf cart fleet. Course is in great shape and is much fun to play.

	1	2	3	4	5	6	7	8	9
PAR	4	4	4	5	4	3	4	3	5
YARDS	363	309	348	411	275	131	286	137	531
PAR									
YARDS									

Directions: Route 8 to Exit 45. Go right off exit to Kennedy Drive. After 1 mile up hill to 4-way intersection. Left onto Torringford Street. Course is 1 mile on left.

Fairchild Wheeler GC (Black) ✪✪ ▶ 9

2390 Eastern Turnpike
Fairfield, CT (203) 373-5911
www.fairchildwheelergolf.com

Tees	Holes	Yards	Par	USGA	Slope
BACK	18	6559	71	72	128
MIDDLE	18	6322	71	71.0	119
FRONT	18	5234	72	70.0	119

Club Pro: Stephen Roach
Payment: Visa, MC, Amex, Disc
Tee Times: 7 days adv.
Fee 9 Holes: Weekday: $20, $31 w/cart   **Weekend:** $28, $39 w/cart
Fee 18 Holes: Weekday: $29, $44w/cart   **Weekend:** $41, $56 w/cart
Twilight Rates: After 5:30pm   **Discounts:** Residents
Cart Rental: $15pp/18, $12pp/9   **Driving Range:** Yes
Lessons: Yes, inquire **Schools:** No   **Junior Golf:** Yes
Membership: Yes   **Architect/Yr Open:** Robert White/1932
Other: Clubhouse / Snack Bar / Restaurant / Bar-Lounge / Lockers / Showers

Player Comments: "Solid course at relative bargain fees." "Remarkable improvements." Challenging
course with some of the toughest par-4s around. Residents discount. Open year round.

	1	2	3	4	5	6	7	8	9
PAR	4	4	3	4	4	4	3	5	5
YARDS	405	377	128	367	321	432	212	431	500
	10	11	12	13	14	15	16	17	18
PAR	4	3	4	4	4	4	5	3	4
YARDS	417	153	407	421	314	418	512	191	396

Directions: Take Merritt Parkway (Route 15) Exit 46 to Route 59 South (Easton Turnpike). ½ mile
on left.

Fairchild Wheeler GC (Red) ✪✪½ ▶ 10

2390 Eastern Turnpike
Fairfield, CT (203) 373-5911
www.fairchildwheelergolf.com

Tees	Holes	Yards	Par	USGA	Slope
BACK	18	6568	72	72	125
MIDDLE	18	6126	72	71.3	124
FRONT	18	5330	72	68.7	117

Club Pro: Stephen Roach
Payment: Visa, MC, Amex, Disc
Tee Times: 7 days adv.
Fee 9 Holes: Weekday: $20, $31 w/cart   **Weekend:** $28, $39 w/cart
Fee 18 Holes: Weekday: $29, $44 w/cart   **Weekend:** $41, $56 w/cart
Twilight Rates: After 5:30pm   **Discounts:** Residents
Cart Rental: $15pp/18, $12pp/9   **Driving Range:** Yes
Lessons: Yes, inquire **Schools:** No   **Junior Golf:** Yes
Membership: Yes   **Architect/Yr Open:** Robert White/1932
Other: Clubhouse / Snack Bar / Restaurant / Bar-Lounge / Lockers / Showers

Flat open course, good for beginners and seniors. Reduced rates for residents and other CT public course
passholders. Open all year. Links-style course. Lessons available from First Tee Corp.

	1	2	3	4	5	6	7	8	9
PAR	4	4	5	3	4	4	4	3	4
YARDS	440	402	480	127	308	412	337	190	387
	10	11	12	13	14	15	16	17	18
PAR	5	4	3	4	4	3	4	5	5
YARDS	504	419	105	422	334	202	340	501	472

Directions: Take Merritt Parkway (Route 15) Exit 46 to Route 59 South (Easton Turnpike). ¼ mile
on left.

**SW
CT**

Farmingbury Hills Country Club   NR   11 ▶

141 East Street
Wolcott, CT (203) 879-8038
www.farmingburyhillsgolf.com

Tees	Holes	Yards	Par	USGA	Slope
BACK					
MIDDLE	9	2996	35	68.7	117
FRONT	9	2678	36	71.0	120

Club Pro: Craig Kealey, PGA
Payment: Cash, Visa, MC
Tee Times: Weekends, 7 days adv.
Fee 9 Holes: Weekday: $19   **Weekend:** $21
Fee 18 Holes: Weekday: $28   **Weekend:** $30
Twilight Rates: **Discounts:** Senior & Junior
Cart Rental: $19pp/18, $10pp/9   **Driving Range:** Yes
Lessons: $30/half hour **Schools:** No   **Junior Golf:** Yes
Membership: No   **Architect/Yr Open:**
Other: Bar-Lounge / Restaurant   **GPS:**

9-hole special: 7-8am, 12-1:30pm weekdays; 1-5:30pm weekends. Course is in great shape!

	1	2	3	4	5	6	7	8	9
PAR	4	4	4	4	4	3	4	3	5
YARDS	340	419	310	373	321	102	401	190	510
PAR									
YARDS									

Directions: I-84 to Cheshire Exit 28. Route 322 West, left up Southington Mountain. Right at top of hill, blinking light (East Street). Course is 1 mile on right.

Fox Hopyard Golf Club   ✪✪✪✪½   12 ▶

1 Hopyard Road
East Haddam, CT (860) 434-6644
www.golfthefox.com

Tees	Holes	Yards	Par	USGA	Slope
BACK	18	6512	71	72.6	131
MIDDLE	18	6109	71	70.7	124
FRONT	18	5111	71	70.7	123

Club Pro: Ron Beck, PGA
Payment: Visa, MC, Amex, Disc, Checks, Cash
Tee Times: 6 days adv.
Fee 9 Holes: Weekday: $49   **Weekend:** $54
Fee 18 Holes: Weekday: $94   **Weekend/Holidays:** $104
Twilight Rates: Yes   **Discounts:** Junior
Cart Rental: $21pp/18, $12pp/9   **Driving Range:** Yes
Lessons: $50/half hour **Schools:** Yes   **Junior Golf:** Yes
Membership: Yes   **Architect/Yr Open:** Roger Rulewich, 2001
Other: Restaurant / Bar-Lounge / Clubhouse / Showers / Lockers

COUPON

Player Comments: " Great layout in unspoiled surroundings. Many memorable holes." "Sister course to Crumpin-Fox in MA. Wide fairways. Shots to the greens are high on risk and reward." –RW

	1	2	3	4	5	6	7	8	9
PAR	4	4	5	3	5	4	4	3	4
YARDS	356	358	457	172	464	320	366	160	350
	10	11	12	13	14	15	16	17	18
PAR	4	3	4	4	3	5	3	4	5
YARDS	382	153	372	408	188	508	189	399	507

Directions: From I-95 North, take Exit 70 (Old Lyme). Go left onto Route 156 for 9 miles. Right onto Route 82 and take first left onto Hopyard. Accessible from I-91 to Route 2 to Route 11. Call for directions from I-95 South and Route 9.

Gainfield Farms Golf Course

255 Old Field Road
Southbury, CT (203) 262-1100
www.gainfieldfarmsgolf.com

Club Pro: Maurice Vossello, USGTF
Payment: Cash, Check, Credit
Tee Times: Yes
Fee 9 Holes: Weekday: $16
Fee 18 Holes: Weekday: $26
Twilight Rates: No
Cart Rental: $14pp/18, $7pp/9
Lessons: Yes **Schools:** No
Membership:
Other: Snacks

Tees	Holes	Yards	Par	USGA	Slope
BACK					
MIDDLE	9	1384	28		
FRONT	9	1203	27		

Weekend: $17
Weekend: $28
Discounts: Senior, Junior, Ladies
Driving Range: Mat and net
Junior Golf: Yes
Architect/Yr Open: Al Zikorus/1993
GPS:

Executive style, resident discounts.

	1	2	3	4	5	6	7	8	9
PAR	3	4	3	3	3	3	3	3	3
YARDS	155	261	188	123	113	94	195	127	128
PAR									
YARDS									

Directions: I-84 to Exit 15, follow signs.

Grassy Hill Country Club

441 Clark Lane
Orange, CT (203)795-1422
www.grassyhillgolf.com

Club Pro: Brian Fitzgibbons, PGA
Payment: Visa, MC
Tee Times: 7 days/wkdys, 3 days/wknds
Fee 9 Holes: Weekday: $21
Fee 18 Holes: Weekday: $36
Twilight Rates: No
Cart Rental:
Lessons: $65/45 min. **Schools:**
Membership: Men/Women Association
Other: Full Restaurant / Clubhouse / Bar-Lounge / Lockers / Showers

Tees	Holes	Yards	Par	USGA	Slope
BACK	18	6118	70	70.5	122
MIDDLE	18	5849	70	69.4	119
FRONT	18	5209	71	71.1	118

Weekend: $25
Weekend: $45
Discounts: Senior (M-F)
Driving Range: $5/lg
Junior Golf: Yes
Architect/Yr Open: 1927

Working to restore excellent conditions of fairways and greens.

	1	2	3	4	5	6	7	8	9
PAR	4	4	3	4	5	3	4	4	5
YARDS	385	410	158	301	563	145	363	360	432
	10	11	12	13	14	15	16	17	18
PAR	3	4	4	3	4	4	5	3	4
YARDS	169	384	277	175	319	421	496	165	326

Directions: I-95 to exit 39A. Turn right, pass Howard Johnson's. At second dual traffic light, turn right. 2½ miles to Clark Lane. Turn right to Grassy Hill.

**SW
CT**

Great River Golf Club

130 Coram Lane
Milford, CT (203) 876-8051
www.greatrivergolfclub.com

Club Pro: Tom Rosati, PGA
Payment: Visa, MC, Disc, Amex
Tee Times: 5 days adv.

Tees	Holes	Yards	Par	USGA	Slope
BACK	18	6901	72	73.8	149
MIDDLE	18	6475	72	71.6	137
FRONT	18	5865	72	69.4	124

Fee 9 Holes: Weekday: $50 after 5pm only **Weekend:** $50 after 5pm only
Fee 18 Holes: Weekday: $120 M-TH **Weekend:** $140 F/S/S
Twilight Rates: Yes **Discounts:** None
Cart Rental: Included **Driving Range:** Yes
Lessons: Yes **Schools:** Yes **Junior Golf:** Yes
Membership: Yes **Architect/Yr Open:** Tommy Fazio/2000
Other: Restaurant / Outdoor Dining / Beverage Cart / Snack Bar/ Clubhouse / Lockers / Showers / Bar-Lounge / Indoor Learning Center / Conference Room, Banquet Facility 150+

Player Comments: "Excellent player's course." "2 times on vacations, everything was perfect." "Best public course I've played in CT." Semi-private. Golf Academy open all year. White tees.

	1	2	3	4	5	6	7	8	9
PAR	3	4	4	5	4	3	4	5	4
YARDS	144	363	374	452	362	129	378	508	344
	10	11	12	13	14	15	16	17	18
PAR	4	3	5	4	4	5	4	3	4
YARDS	329	175	490	372	350	473	382	170	353

Directions: I-95 to Exit 38 bearing right, go to Wheeler Farms Road, turn left. Turn left at Herbert Street. Turn left on Coram Lane, course is at end of lane. Call for directions from Hartford or NY via Wilbur Cross/Merritt Parkway and from 95 North.

Griffith E. Harris Golf Course

1300 King Street
Greenwich, CT (203) 531-7261
www.greenwichct.org

Club Pro: Joe Felder, PGA
Payment: Visa, MC, Checks
Tee Times: Same day for non-members

Tees	Holes	Yards	Par	USGA	Slope
BACK	18	6512	71	71.0	125
MIDDLE	18	6093	71	69.0	122
FRONT	18	5671	73	67.1	114

Fee 9 Holes: Weekday: $50 **Weekend:** $50
Fee 18 Holes: Weekday: $50 **Weekend:** $50
Twilight Rates: After 5pm **Discounts:** Senior & Junior
Cart Rental: $14pp/18, $9.50pp/9 **Driving Range:** $10/lg., $5/sm.
Lessons: Yes **Schools:** Yes **Junior Golf:** Yes
Membership: Town residents **Architect/Yr Open:** Robert Trent Jones/1965
Other: Full Restaurant / Clubhouse / Bar / Lockers / Showers

Restaurant renovated. Open to residents of town who are members and guests only. Front side fairly open and flat. Back side narrow and hilly. Open April 1 - December 1. Resident fee offered. New irrigation system.

	1	2	3	4	5	6	7	8	9
PAR	4	4	5	4	3	4	3	5	4
YARDS	407	365	503	378	169	437	138	519	323
	10	11	12	13	14	15	16	17	18
PAR	4	3	4	4	5	3	4	4	4
YARDS	291	198	310	380	448	140	251	426	310

Directions: Merritt Parkway South to King Street. Right turn approximately 3 miles to golf course on right. Any questions, call (203) 531-7200.

Guilford Lakes Golf Course ✪✪½

200 North Madison Road
Guilford, CT (203) 453-8214
www.guilfordlakesgc.com

Tees	Holes	Yards	Par	USGA	Slope
BACK	9	1370	28		
MIDDLE	9	1165	27		
FRONT	9	739	27		

Club Pro:
Payment: Visa, MC, Disc
Tee Times: 3 days adv.
Fee 9 Holes: Weekday: $14   **Weekend:** $16
Fee 18 Holes: Weekday: $28   **Weekend:** $32
Twilight Rates: No   **Discounts:** Senior & Junior
Cart Rental: $3/pull   **Driving Range:** No
Lessons: Yes **Schools:** No   **Junior Golf:** Park and Rec.
Membership: Yes   **Architect/Yr Open:** Al Zikorus/1999
Other: Snacks / New Clubhouse Now Open   **GPS:** Yes

COUPON

Player Comments: "Polished and professionally designed." –RW Reduced resident fees. Heavily tree-lined, gentle and hilly. Challenging for both beginner and intermediate. New Par 4.

	1	2	3	4	5	6	7	8	9
PAR	3	3	3	3	3	4	3	3	3
YARDS	135	111	130	122	105	260	155	79	148
PAR									
YARDS									

Directions: I-95, Exit 58 onto Route 77. North on Route 77, turn right onto Stepstone Hill Road. Straight to North Madison Road. Course is on the left.

H. Smith Richardson GC ✪✪✪

2425 Morehouse Highway
Fairfield, CT (203) 255-7300
www.hsrgolf.com

Tees	Holes	Yards	Par	USGA	Slope
BACK	18	6676	72	71.0	127
MIDDLE	18	6323	72	70.2	124
FRONT	18	5764	73	73.9	127

Club Pro: Jim Alexander, PGA
Payment: Most Major Credit Cards
Tee Times: Weekends, 7 days adv.
Fee 9 Holes: Weekday: $28   **Weekend:** $28
Fee 18 Holes: Weekday: $42   **Weekend:** $54
Twilight Rates: No   **Discounts:** Senior & Junior
Cart Rental: $15pp/18, $11pp/9   **Driving Range:** Yes
Lessons: Yes **Schools:** No   **Junior Golf:** Yes
Membership: Yes   **Architect/Yr Open:** Hal Purdy/1972
Other: Lockers / Showers / Restaurant / Bar-Lounge / Clubhouse

This scenic, hilly course has a majestic view of Long Island Sound. Slopes on greens make putting challenging. Closed March. Discounted rates for shared carts.

	1	2	3	4	5	6	7	8	9
PAR	4	4	3	4	4	5	4	3	5
YARDS	375	310	160	339	397	503	383	180	486
	10	11	12	13	14	15	16	17	18
PAR	4	4	3	5	4	4	3	4	5
YARDS	373	351	176	502	405	350	140	373	520

SW CT

Directions: From North: Merritt Parkway to Exit 44 to Black Rock Turnpike, take right on Congress Road, second left onto Morehouse. Course is ½ mile up the road.
From South: Merritt Parkway to Exit 46, take left onto Congress Road, right on Morehouse Road.

Hawk's Landing Country Club ✪✪

201 Pattonwood Drive
Southington, CT (860) 793-6000
www.hawkslandingcc.com

Tees	Holes	Yards	Par	USGA	Slope
BACK	18	6000	70	68.6	124
MIDDLE	18	5355	70	66.4	119
FRONT	18	4015	71	63.9	106

Club Pro: John Vitale
Payment: Visa, MC, Disc, Check
Tee Times: Weekends, 7 days adv.
Fee 9 Holes: Weekday: $19.50   **Weekend:** $23
Fee 18 Holes: Weekday: $33.50   **Weekend:** $37.50
Twilight Rates: After 6pm   **Discounts:** Senior & Junior
Cart Rental: $15.50pp/18, $8.75pp/9   **Driving Range:** Yes, grass tee
Lessons: Yes **Schools:** No   **Junior Golf:** Yes
Membership: Yes   **Architect/Yr Open:** Cornish/1967
Other: Clubhouse / Bar-Lounge / Restaurant / Snack Bar

COUPON

A full-service restaurant, a chipping and putting practice area, and a pavillion area perfect for meetings and weddings. Climate-controlled banquet facility for up to 250 people.

	1	2	3	4	5	6	7	8	9
PAR	4	3	5	4	4	4	3	4	3
YARDS	265	170	420	290	340	280	220	325	175
	10	11	12	13	14	15	16	17	18
PAR	4	4	3	5	4	5	3	5	3
YARDS	385	275	150	450	385	450	160	450	165

Directions: I-84 to Exit 32. South to Route 10. Left on Laning Street to top of hill; take left to stay on Laning Street. Left on Flanders Road to first left on Pattonwood Drive.

Highland Greens Golf Course

122 Cooke Road
Prospect, CT (203) 758-4022
www.highlandgreens.com

Tees	Holes	Yards	Par	USGA	Slope
BACK					
MIDDLE	9	1398	27		
FRONT	9	1322	27		

Club Pro:
Payment: Cash, Visa, MC
Tee Times: Same day
Fee 9 Holes: Weekday: $13   **Weekend:** $14
Fee 18 Holes: Weekday: $21   **Weekend:** $22
Twilight Rates: After 6:30pm   **Discounts:** Senior
Cart Rental: $3/pull   **Driving Range:** No
Lessons: Yes **Schools:** No   **Junior Golf:** Yes
Membership: Yes   **Architect/Yr Open:** Al Zikorus/1967
Other: Snack Bar / Restaurant / Pub   **GPS:**

Completely lighted for night play. Nightly rate after 6:30pm $15 for 9 holes. Slightly hilly. A lot of improvement made to the grounds. A challenging par 3, open April - first frost.

	1	2	3	4	5	6	7	8	9
PAR	3	3	3	3	3	3	3	3	3
YARDS	132	192	115	135	188	185	157	128	166
PAR									
YARDS									

Directions: Take I-84 to Exit 26 to Route 70 East to Route 68 West. At top of hill, left onto Cooke Road. Course is 1.6 miles on right.

Hop Brook Golf Course

615 North Church Street
Naugatuck, CT (203) 729-8013

Tees	Holes	Yards	Par	USGA	Slope
BACK	9	3047	36	68.2	116
MIDDLE	9	2862	36	66.6	112
FRONT	9	2413	36	67.0	114

Club Pro: Bob Clark Jr., PGA
Payment: Cash, Check, Credit Card
Tee Times: Weekends, 2 days adv.
Fee 9 Holes: Weekday: $20   **Weekend:** $24
Fee 18 Holes: Weekday: $27   **Weekend:** $32
Twilight Rates: No   **Discounts:** Sr. & Jr. Daily Specials
Cart Rental: $15pp/18, $10pp/9 **Driving Range:** No
Lessons: Yes **Schools:** No   **Junior Golf:** Yes
Membership: Yes   **Architect/Yr Open:** 1927
Other: Clubhouse / Restaurant **GPS:**

COUPON

The course is short and turns hilly near the end. Substantial discounts for residents. Open March - December. Senior tees now on every hole. Women's senior tees on 4 holes (Blue and White). PGA Professional now on staff.

	1	2	3	4	5	6	7	8	9
PAR	5	4	4	4	3	5	3	4	4
YARDS	452	325	320	304	135	476	170	382	298
PAR									
YARDS									

Directions: I-84 to Exit 17 to Route 63 South. Course is 3 miles down on left, across from Xpress Fuel.

Hunter Golf Club

⭐⭐⭐ 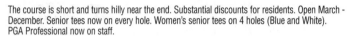 22

685 Westfield Road
Meriden, CT (203) 634-3366
www.huntergolfshop.com

Tees	Holes	Yards	Par	USGA	Slope
BACK	18	6604	71	71.9	124
MIDDLE	18	6198	71	70.2	121
FRONT	18	5569	72	72.7	131

Club Pro: Bob Tiedermann
Payment: Cash, Credit
Tee Times: Yes
Fee 9 Holes: Weekday: $20   **Weekend:** $21
Fee 18 Holes: Weekday: $35   **Weekend:** $39 ($32 resident)
Twilight Rates: 90 minutes before dusk **Discounts:** Sr. & Jr. weekdays
Cart Rental: $15pp/18, $9pp/9 **Driving Range:** Irons only
Lessons: Yes **Schools:** No   **Junior Golf:** Yes
Membership: Season Pass   **Architect/Yr Open:** Robert Pryde
Other: Clubhouse / Lockers / Showers / Snack Bar / Restaurant / Bar-Lounge

Open year round, weather permitting. Resident rates. "Greens and bunkers in great shape. If you haven't been here in awhile, it's worth a revisit." –DA

	1	2	3	4	5	6	7	8	9
PAR	4	3	4	4	5	3	4	4	4
YARDS	352	183	395	326	497	147	415	400	353
	10	11	12	13	14	15	16	17	18
PAR	5	3	4	4	4	4	4	3	5
YARDS	516	163	357	336	364	374	361	172	487

Directions: From I-91 South: Exit 19. Right off ramp to first stop sign. Right on Bee Street, course is ½ mile on left. From I-91 North or Merritt Parkway North: Take East Main Street exit. Go straight through light onto Bee Street. Course is 2 miles on left.

**SW
CT**

Indian Springs Golf Course NR 23

132 Mack Road
Middlefield, CT (860) 349-8109
www.indiansprings-golf.com

Club Pro:
Payment: Cash, Credit Cards
Tee Times: Anyday

Tees	Holes	Yards	Par	USGA	Slope
BACK					
MIDDLE	9	3000	36	68.9	116
FRONT	9	2616	36	73.0	127

Fee 9 Holes: Weekday: $18
Fee 18 Holes: Weekday: $31
Twilight Rates: No
Cart Rental: $16pp/18, $8pp/9
Lessons: Yes **Schools:** Yes
Membership: Yes
Other: Snack Bar / Bar-Lounge / Restaurant

Weekend: $20
Weekend: $36
Discounts: Senior & Junior
Driving Range: $9/lg, $5/sm
Junior Golf: Yes
Architect/Yr Open: 1964
GPS:

COUPON

Family-run golf course where you'll feel welcome. Well-maintained with immaculate greens. Clubhouse and bar, with outdoor patio, remodeled in 2013. Driving range, new putting greens. New tee box on hole #2.

	1	2	3	4	5	6	7	8	9
PAR	4	5	3	4	5	4	3	4	4
YARDS	345	455	130	370	560	300	170	355	315
PAR									
YARDS									

Directions: I-91 North to Exit 18 (Route 66) toward Middletown. At light, take a right onto Route 147. Take 1st left onto Way Road. Follow signs to course. Take I-91 South to Exit 19, left at stop sign. Take a right at light onto Route 147. Go 2 miles to Way Road and follow signs to course on Mack Road.

Laurel View Country Club ✪✪✪ 24

West Shepard Avenue
Hamden, CT (203) 287-2656
www.laurelviewcc.com

Club Pro: Edward Grant, PGA
Payment: Visa, MC
Tee Times: Weekends, 3 days adv.

Tees	Holes	Yards	Par	USGA	Slope
BACK	18	6899	72	74.3	135
MIDDLE	18	6372	72	72.1	131
FRONT	18	5558	73	71.8	130

Fee 9 Holes: Weekday: $20
Fee 18 Holes: Weekday: $31
Twilight Rates: No
Cart Rental: $15pp/18, $9pp/9
Lessons: $40/half hour **Schools:** No
Membership: Yes, residents

Weekend: $22
Weekend: $35
Discounts: Senior & Junior
Driving Range: $5/lg
Junior Golf: Yes
Architect/Yr Open: Cornish & Robinson/1969
Other: Clubhouse / Lockers / Showers / Snack Bar / Restaurant / Bar-Lounge

This Cornish course requires smart course managaement; hilly terrain provides interesting challenge. Open April 1 - December 1. Many favorable comments. Greatly improved fairways, greens, bunkers and tees.

	1	2	3	4	5	6	7	8	9
PAR	4	3	4	5	4	4	3	5	4
YARDS	330	132	390	505	435	310	230	510	420
	10	11	12	13	14	15	16	17	18
PAR	4	5	3	4	5	4	4	3	4
YARDS	320	560	155	280	470	380	390	160	395

Directions: I-91 to Exit 10, take left at the end of the ramp. At first light take left, right at next light (Dixwell Avenue). Through center of town, pass Town Hall on the right. ¾ mile, take right (Shephard Avenue). Through 5 lights, take left (W. Shephard). Course ¾ mile on left.

Longshore Golf Course

South Compo Road
Westport, CT (203) 341-1833
www.longshoregolf.com

Tees	Holes	Yards	Par	USGA	Slope
BACK	18	5845	69	67.4	115
MIDDLE	18	5676	69	66.7	113
FRONT	18	5227	73	69.9	119

Club Pro: John Cooper, PGA
Payment: Visa, MC, Cash, Check
Tee Times: 3 days adv.
Fee 9 Holes: Weekday: $32 M-Th
Fee 18 Holes: Weekday: $44 M-Th
Twilight Rates: No
Cart Rental: $15pp/18, $7.50pp/9
Lessons: Yes **Schools:** No
Membership: No
Other: Snack Bar / Restaurant / Bar-Lounge

Weekend: $37 F/S/S/H
Weekend: $50 F/S/S/H
Discounts: None
Driving Range: Yes
Junior Golf: Yes
Architect/Yr Open: Orrin E. Smith
GPS:

Good course for beginners and intermediates. Course has been completely renovated.

	1	2	3	4	5	6	7	8	9
PAR	4	3	4	4	4	4	5	3	4
YARDS	341	146	390	287	296	413	520	127	346
	10	11	12	13	14	15	16	17	18
PAR	5	3	4	3	4	3	4	4	4
YARDS	459	192	289	189	401	166	383	344	397

Directions: I-95 to Exit 18 to U.S. Route 1, left at 2nd light, Green Farms Road. Follow to next light, take left onto Compo. Course is on right.

Lyman Orchards GC (Player)

Route 157
Middlefield, CT (860) 349-6031
www.lymangolf.com

Tees	Holes	Yards	Par	USGA	Slope
BACK	18	6725	71	72.9	134
MIDDLE	18	6325	71	71.2	132
FRONT	18	5890	71	68.8	129

Club Pro: Dan Valk
Payment: Visa, MC, Amex, Disc
Tee Times: 7 days adv. (888) 99Lyman
Fee 9 Holes: Weekday: $33 w/cart
Fee 18 Holes: Weekday: $64 w/cart
Twilight Rates: After 1:30pm
Cart Rental: Included
Lessons: Yes **Schools:** Yes
Membership: Yes
Other: Clubhouse / Lockers / Showers / Snack Bar / Restaurant / Bar-Lounge

Weekend: $33 w/cart
Weekend: $66 w/cart
Discounts: Senior & Junior M-Th
Driving Range: $7/lg., $4/md.
Junior Golf: Yes
Architect/Yr Open: Gary Player/1994

Player Comments: "Beautiful layout, stresses good shot making." "Great variety. Demands that you maintain focus for all 18 holes." –JD
Designed by Gary Player. Play all 36—make a day of it. M-Th Early Bird before 8am. Open March - November.

	1	2	3	4	5	6	7	8	9
PAR	4	4	4	3	4	4	3	5	4
YARDS	400	367	374	173	386	342	191	578	381
	10	11	12	13	14	15	16	17	18
PAR	4	3	4	3	5	4	3	5	5
YARDS	348	211	427	181	473	306	165	520	502

Directions: I-91 to Exit 15 (Route 68 East). Left onto Route 157. Course is 1 mile on the right.

SW CT

Lyman Orchards GC (Jones) ✪✪✪½

70 Lyman Road
Middlefield, CT (860) 349-6031
www.lymanorchards.com

Tees	Holes	Yards	Par	USGA	Slope
BACK	18	7011	72	73.3	132
MIDDLE	18	6614	72	69.6	128
FRONT	18	6200	72	72.0	124

Club Pro: Dan Yalk
Payment: All
Tee Times: 7 days adv.
Fee 9 Holes: Weekday: $35 w/cart
Fee 18 Holes: Weekday: $56 w/cart
Twilight Rates: After 1:30pm
Cart Rental: Included
Lessons: Yes **Schools:** Yes
Membership: Yes
Other: Clubhouse / Lockers / Showers / Snack Bar / Restaurant / Bar-Lounge

Weekend: $37 w/cart
Weekend: $69 w/cart
Discounts: Senior & Junior M-F
Driving Range: Yes
Junior Golf: Yes
Architect/Yr Open: Robert Trent Jones Jr./1967

Each hole designed by Robert Trent Jones Jr. to be a demanding par or a comfortable bogey. Bent grass fairways and Penn Cross tees and greens. M-Th Early Bird before 7:30am.

	1	2	3	4	5	6	7	8	9
PAR	4	3	4	5	4	4	3	4	5
YARDS	416	175	374	552	390	350	175	373	548
	10	11	12	13	14	15	16	17	18
PAR	4	3	5	4	4	4	4	3	5
YARDS	399	152	490	370	388	382	403	162	515

Directions: I-91 to Exit 15 (Route 68 East). Left onto Route 157. Course is 1 mile on the right.

Miner Hills Golf Course ✪✪

80 Miner Hills Drive
Middletown, CT (860) 635-0051
www.minerhillsgolf.com

Tees	Holes	Yards	Par	USGA	Slope
BACK					
MIDDLE	9	1769	30	59.1	97
FRONT	9	1292	30	59.5	80

Club Pro: George Claffey
Payment: Cash, Check, MC, Visa
Tee Times: Available
Fee 9 Holes: Weekday: $12
Fee 18 Holes: Weekday: $20
Twilight Rates: Yes
Cart Rental: $12pp/18, $6pp/9
Lessons: Yes **Schools:** No
Membership: Season Passes
Other: Clubhouse / Snack Bar / Tournament & Banquet Facilities

Weekend: $14
Weekend: $20
Discounts: Senior/Junior-Mon/Sat
Driving Range: Yes
Junior Golf: No
Architect/Yr Open: John S. Ott/1993

"A delightful surprise with several interesting holes. A great executive layout and well-maintained" –AP Open March 25 until weather permits. Middletown, CT's only golf course! Just minutes from downtown Hartford and New Haven, CT.

	1	2	3	4	5	6	7	8	9
PAR	3	3	4	4	3	3	4	3	3
YARDS	160	150	298	253	173	210	260	120	130
PAR									
YARDS									

Directions: I-91 to Exit 20. Westfield district of Middletown, CT.

Oak Hills Park Golf Course

NR 29

165 Fillow Street
Norwalk, CT (203) 853-8400
www.oakhillsgc.com

Club Pro: Vincent Grillo, PGA
Payment: Cash, Visa, MC, Amex
Tee Times: 7 days adv.
Fee 9 Holes: Weekday: $30
Fee 18 Holes: Weekday: $46
Twilight Rates: After 4pm
Cart Rental: $16pp/18, $10pp/9
Lessons: Yes **Schools:** Yes
Membership: For residents
Other: Snack Bar / Restaurant

Tees	Holes	Yards	Par	USGA	Slope
BACK	18	6317	71	70.3	133
MIDDLE	18	5920	71	68.5	128
FRONT	18	5221	72	70.7	124

Weekend: $30
Weekend: $50
Discounts: Sr. & Jr. residents M-F
Driving Range: No
Junior Golf: No
Architect/Yr Open: Alfred Tull/1969
GPS:

New clubhouse opened in May 2005.

	1	2	3	4	5	6	7	8	9
PAR	4	4	3	4	3	4	4	5	4
YARDS	374	295	109	307	174	284	336	484	440
	10	11	12	13	14	15	16	17	18
PAR	5	4	5	3	4	3	4	4	4
YARDS	528	365	501	154	386	205	342	336	300

Directions: I-95, Exit 13. Right turn onto Route 1. Left onto Richards Avenue; right turn onto Fillow Street to Oak Hills Park.

Orange Hills Country Club

✪✪½ 30

389 Racebrook Road
Orange, CT (203) 795-4161
www.orangehillscountryclub.com

Club Pro: Kevin Mahaffy
Payment: Visa, MC, Disc
Tee Times: M-F 7 days adv., S/S 3 days adv.
Fee 9 Holes: Weekday: $22
Fee 18 Holes: Weekday: $38
Twilight Rates: No
Cart Rental: $15pp/18, $8pp/9
Lessons: Yes **Schools:** Yes
Membership: No
Other: Clubhouse / Snack Bar / Bar-Lounge / Restaurant

Tees	Holes	Yards	Par	USGA	Slope
BACK	18	6511	71	72.3	126
MIDDLE	18	6115	71	70.6	119
FRONT	18	5616	74	72.7	122

Weekend: $26
Weekend: $48
Discounts: Senior & Junior
Driving Range: No
Junior Golf: Yes
Architect/Yr Open: Cornish/1961

Course is hilly with a tight back 9. Call for directions from Hartford. Collared shirts and soft spikes required. No denim allowed. Newly lengthened 16th tee.

	1	2	3	4	5	6	7	8	9
PAR	4	5	3	4	4	4	4	4	3
YARDS	390	481	148	435	349	365	399	300	134
	10	11	12	13	14	15	16	17	18
PAR	3	5	4	3	4	4	4	4	5
YARDS	207	466	365	153	377	339	331	413	459

SW
CT

Directions: Merritt Parkway: Exit 57, 2 lights to Route 114, right onto Route 114, 1.75 miles on left. From NYC: I-95 North, Exit 41, left off ramp. 4 lights to U.S. 1. Right onto U.S. 1, 1 block to Racebrook Road. Left onto Racebrook Road. ¼ mile on right.

The Orchards Golf Course ✪✪ ▶31

137 Kozlowski Road
Milford, CT (203) 877-8200
www.theorchardsgolfclub.com

Club Pro:
Payment: Cash Only
Tee Times: 6 days adv.
Fee 9 Holes: Weekday: $9.45
Fee 18 Holes: Weekday: $16.70
Twilight Rates: Yes
Cart Rental: $14 for 2 people
Lessons: Yes **Schools:** No
Membership: No
Other: Snacks

Tees	Holes	Yards	Par	USGA	Slope
BACK					
MIDDLE	9	1625	32		
FRONT	9	1433	32		

Weekend: $10.86
Weekend: $17.75
Discounts: Senior & Junior
Driving Range: Yes (Net)
Junior Golf: Yes
Architect/Yr Open:
GPS:

Resident discounts. New groundskeeper.

	1	2	3	4	5	6	7	8	9
PAR	4	3	4	4	4	3	3	3	4
YARDS	242	93	222	207	217	120	167	91	266
PAR									
YARDS									

Directions: I-95 to Exit 39, go west on US Route 1. Go 2 miles to Route 121 North. Right on Route 121 for 2 miles. Course is on the right.

Oxford Greens, The Golf Club at ✪✪✪½ ▶32

99 Country Club Drive
Oxford, CT (203) 888-1600
www.oxfordgreens.com

Club Pro: Steve Landi, PGA/GM
Payment: Most Major Credit Cards
Tee Times: 7 days adv.
Fee 9 Holes: Weekday:
Fee 18 Holes: Weekday: $65 M-Th (w/cart)
Twilight Rates: After 2pm
Cart Rental:
Lessons: Yes **Schools:** Yes
Membership: Yes
Other: Restaurant

Tees	Holes	Yards	Par	USGA	Slope
BACK	18	6665	72	72.3	133
MIDDLE	18	6324	72	70.5	131
FRONT	18	5188	72	69.9	122

Weekend:
Weekend: $69 (w/cart)
Discounts: Junior
Driving Range: Yes
Junior Golf:
Architect/Yr Open: Mark Mungeam/2005
GPS:

COUPON

Also black tees at 7186 yards, 75.4/135. #3 is the longest hole in CT: 630 yards. Carved through 600 acres of stunning countryside. "Fast greens. Maturing nicely—definitely worth a visit." –JD *Golf World* Top 5 in CT.

	1	2	3	4	5	6	7	8	9
PAR	4	3	5	4	4	4	4	5	3
YARDS	345	165	535	405	370	300	365	510	175
	10	**11**	**12**	**13**	**14**	**15**	**16**	**17**	**18**
PAR	5	4	4	3	4	4	3	5	4
YARDS	517	330	370	147	405	363	132	485	405

Directions: I-84 to Exit 15 Southbury/Seymour. Follow Route 67 South for 6 miles to Riggs Street in Oxford. Left onto Riggs. Follow for approximately 2 miles to The Golf Club at Oxford Greens on right. The Course is located at 99 Country Club Drive.

Pequabuck Golf Course ✪✪ ▶ 33

56 School Street
Pequabuck, CT (860) 583-7307
www.pequabuckgolf.com

Tees	Holes	Yards	Par	USGA	Slope
BACK	18	6015	69	70.2	118
MIDDLE	18	5692	69	68.7	115
FRONT	18	5388	72	70.3	118

Club Pro: Richard Toner, PGA
Payment: Visa, MC, Disc
Tee Times: Yes
Fee 9 Holes: Weekday: $21   **Weekend:** $21
Fee 18 Holes: Weekday: $42   **Weekend:** $42
Twilight Rates: No   **Discounts:** None
Cart Rental: $14pp/18, $8pp/9   **Driving Range:** Yes
Lessons: Call for rates **Schools:** No   **Junior Golf:** Yes
Membership: Yes   **Architect/Yr Open:** 1902
Other: Restaurant / Clubhouse / Bar-Lounge / Snack Bar

Front 9 open, back 9 tree-lined with difficult greens. Known for fairways and greens. Groups up to 16 guests. Dress code.

	1	2	3	4	5	6	7	8	9
PAR	4	4	5	3	4	3	5	3	4
YARDS	286	424	470	169	322	155	465	174	371
	10	11	12	13	14	15	16	17	18
PAR	3	4	4	4	4	4	3	4	4
YARDS	190	406	377	329	401	337	155	328	333

Directions: I-84 to Route Exit 72. Follow Route 72 into Terryville. Go under railroad bridge. Take right onto School Street. Follow to club.

Pine Valley Golf Course ✪✪½ ▶ 34

300 Welch Road
Southington, CT (860) 628-0879
www.pinevalleygolfct.com

Tees	Holes	Yards	Par	USGA	Slope
BACK	18	6325	71	70.6	123
MIDDLE	18	6043	71	70.1	117
FRONT	18	5482	73	72.0	122

Club Pro: Jack McConachie, PGA
Payment: Cash, Visa, MC
Tee Times: M-F 7 days adv., S/S 4 days adv.
Fee 9 Holes: Weekday: $20   **Weekend:** $22
Fee 18 Holes: Weekday: $36   **Weekend:** $41
Twilight Rates: No   **Discounts:** Senior
Cart Rental: $17pp/18, $8.50pp/9   **Driving Range:** No
Lessons: Yes **Schools:** No   **Junior Golf:** Yes
Membership: No   **Architect/Yr Open:** Al Zikorus, Orrin Smith/1960
Other: Clubhouse / Lockers / Showers / Snack Bar / Restaurant / Bar-Lounge / Practice Sand Trap
GPS: Yes

Hilly front 9, while the back 9 are more level with water holes and very tight greens. Accuracy is essential. Dress code. New tees.

	1	2	3	4	5	6	7	8	9
PAR	5	4	3	4	4	4	5	3	4
YARDS	497	404	125	345	345	291	505	141	405
	10	11	12	13	14	15	16	17	18
PAR	3	4	5	4	4	3	5	4	3
YARDS	170	366	510	426	353	160	476	340	180

Directions: I-84 to Exit 31 (Route 229 North). Go 1.5 miles. Take a left onto Welch Road. Course is ½ mile on left.

SW CT

Pomperaug Golf Club

NR 35

522 Heritage Road
Southbury, CT (203) 264-9484
www.pomperauggolfclub.com

Club Pro: Dave Cook
Payment: Cash, Credit Cards
Tee Times: 3 days adv.

Tees	Holes	Yards	Par	USGA	Slope
BACK	9	2985	35	34.6	121
MIDDLE	9	2772	35	33.6	118
FRONT	9	2234	36	35.0	113

Fee 9 Holes: Weekday: $25   **Weekend:** $27
Fee 18 Holes: Weekday: $37   **Weekend:** $40
Twilight Rates: 90 minutes until dark   **Discounts:** None
Cart Rental: $14pp/18, $10pp/9   **Driving Range:** Practice green
Lessons: $45/half hour **Schools:**   **Junior Golf:** Yes
Membership: Yes   **Architect/Yr Open:**
Other: Hotel / Cooler / Beverage Cart / Stay & Play Packages

Semi-private course. Heritage International Hotel on premises. Dress code. Fun and challenging 9-hole course with water on every hole.

	1	2	3	4	5	6	7	8	9
PAR	4	4	4	5	3	4	4	3	4
YARDS	330	356	263	457	174	346	375	166	305
PAR									
YARDS									

Directions: I-84 to Route 67, Southbury, Exit 15. At 2nd light, take left onto Heritage Road. Course is 1 mile ahead on right.

Portland Golf Club

✪✪✪ 36

169 Bartlett Street
Portland, CT (860) 342-6107
www.portlandgolfcourse.com

Club Pro: Mark Sloan, PGA
Payment: Cash, Visa
Tee Times: 7 days adv.

Tees	Holes	Yards	Par	USGA	Slope
BACK	18	6213	71	70.5	127
MIDDLE	18	5802	71	68.7	123
FRONT	18	5039	71	68.6	118

Fee 9 Holes: Weekday: $19   **Weekend:** $22
Fee 18 Holes: Weekday: $38-$48   **Weekend:** $42-$55
Twilight Rates: After 12pm, weekends   **Discounts:** Senior & Junior
Cart Rental: $16pp/18, $9pp/9   **Driving Range:** No
Lessons: yes **Schools:** Yes   **Junior Golf:** Yes
Membership: Yes   **Architect/Yr Open:** Cornish & Robinson/1974
Other: Clubhouse / Lockers / Showers / Snack Bar / Restaurant / Bar-Lounge

Player Comments: "Lots of doglegs." "Excellent conditions." "Worth playing, I'll be back." "Hilly." Open March 15th - January 1st.

	1	2	3	4	5	6	7	8	9
PAR	4	5	4	3	4	4	4	3	4
YARDS	365	485	350	166	270	287	351	140	301
	10	11	12	13	14	15	16	17	18
PAR	4	4	5	4	3	4	5	3	4
YARDS	303	373	489	377	177	360	471	165	372

Directions: Route 2 to 17 South (left at exit); 9.5 miles down take left on Bartlett; course is less than 1 mile. Call for directions from Route 9.

Portland West Golf Club ✪✪✪ ▶ 37

105 Gospel Lane
Portland, CT (860) 342-6111
www.portlandwestgolf.com

Club Pro: Gerald J. D'Amora, PGA
Payment: Cash, Visa, MC
Tee Times: 7 days adv.

Tees	Holes	Yards	Par	USGA	Slope
BACK	18	4012	60	60.5	102
MIDDLE	18	3620	60	59.3	100
FRONT	18	3154	60	58.4	87

Fee 9 Holes: Weekday: $14   **Weekend:** $16.50
Fee 18 Holes: Weekday: $27   **Weekend:** $30
Twilight Rates: After 6pm $10, M-F 11-3pm $20pp/18, $10pp/9
Discounts: Senior & Junior
Cart Rental: $26pp/18, $16pp/9   **Driving Range:** Yes
Lessons: $45/half hour **Schools:** No   **Junior Golf:** Yes
Membership: No   **Architect/Yr Open:** 1985
Other: Restaurant / Bar-Lounge / Snack Bar   **GPS:**

Player Comments: "Excellent greens and fairways." "The 18th hole proves to be a difficult finish."
"A challenging executive par 60 course." "Nice scenery and fair prices."

	1	2	3	4	5	6	7	8	9
PAR	3	3	3	4	3	4	3	3	4
YARDS	148	130	145	264	140	339	113	137	351
	10	**11**	**12**	**13**	**14**	**15**	**16**	**17**	**18**
PAR	4	3	3	3	3	3	4	4	3
YARDS	341	135	161	114	185	122	319	293	183

Directions: I-91 to Route 9 to Route 66; left onto Route 17 (Gospel Lane); course is ½ mile on right.

Quarry Ridge Golf Course ✪✪✪½ ▶ 38

9 Rose Hill Road
Portland, CT (860) 342-6113
www.quarryridge.com

Club Pro: John Lucas Jr., PGA
Payment: Cash, Visa, MC, Amex
Tee Times: 1 week adv.

Tees	Holes	Yards	Par	USGA	Slope
BACK	18	6389	72	70.9	124
MIDDLE	18	6049	72	69.5	119
FRONT	18	4852	72	68.7	117

Fee 9 Holes: Weekday: $30   **Weekend:** $32
Fee 18 Holes: Weekday: $54   **Weekend:** $59
Twilight Rates: After 1pm, weekends   **Discounts:** Sr. & Jr., wkdys only
Cart Rental: Included   **Driving Range:** No
Lessons: Yes **Schools:** No   **Junior Golf:** No
Membership: Yes   **Architect/Yr Open:** Al Zikorus/1993
Other: Restaurant / Bar-Lounge   **GPS:**

COUPON

Player Comments: "Challenging, with tight fairways and small greens. Scenic views of Connecticut River
Valley." "Difficult, but popular. Well maintained." "Great layout." Faster greens, 10-minute tee times, faster
play. Great restaurant open Fri., Sat., Sun. night.

	1	2	3	4	5	6	7	8	9
PAR	4	3	4	5	4	5	4	4	3
YARDS	350	155	383	463	337	448	346	392	178
	10	**11**	**12**	**13**	**14**	**15**	**16**	**17**	**18**
PAR	4	5	4	4	3	4	3	5	4
YARDS	326	447	442	293	154	337	144	459	395

Directions: From Hartford: Route 2 to Route 17 (left Exit 7). Go 9 miles; take left onto Bartlett Street,
go to end. Cross road to driveway of golf course.

**SW
CT**

Richter Park Golf Course ✪✪✪✪

100 Aunt Hack Road
Danbury, CT (203) 792-2550
www.richterpark.com

Club Pro: Brian Gehan
Payment: MC, Visa, Cash
Tee Times: 8 days adv. (866) 856-9219
Fee 9 Holes: Weekday: Twilight only
Fee 18 Holes: Weekday: $68 including cart
Twilight Rates: Yes
Cart Rental: Included
Lessons: Yes **Schools:** Yes
Membership: No

Tees	Holes	Yards	Par	USGA	Slope
BACK	18	6744	72	73.6	139
MIDDLE	18	6304	72	71.6	136
FRONT	18	5114	72	70.7	124

Weekend: Twilight only
Weekend: $78 including cart
Discounts: Senior & Junior
Driving Range: No
Junior Golf: Yes
Architect/Yr Open: Ed Ryder/1971

COUPON

Other: Clubhouse / Lockers / Showers / Snack Bar / Restaurant / Bar-Lounge

Player Comments: "Very challenging and difficult." Course keeps a reputation for making even the most skillful golfers work hard: narrow fairways, approach shots require precision; water on 14 fairways.

	1	2	3	4	5	6	7	8	9
PAR	4	5	3	4	3	4	5	4	4
YARDS	372	495	150	386	170	387	508	337	308
	10	11	12	13	14	15	16	17	18
PAR	4	4	5	3	4	4	5	3	4
YARDS	345	367	479	142	395	319	570	152	422

Directions: I-84 West to Exit 2B or I-84 East to Exit 2. Take right off ramp (Mill Plain Road); take second left onto Aunt Hack Road to course.

Ridgefield Golf Club ✪✪½

545 Ridgebury Road
Ridgefield, CT (203) 748-7008
www.ridgefieldgc.com

Club Pro: Frank Sergiovanni, PGA
Payment: Cash, Check, Visa, MC
Tee Times: Yes
Fee 9 Holes: Weekday:
Fee 18 Holes: Weekday: $45
Twilight Rates: Seasonal
Cart Rental: $15pp/18, $8pp/9
Lessons: Yes **Schools:** No
Membership: Yes
Other: Snack Bar / Bar-Lounge

Tees	Holes	Yards	Par	USGA	Slope
BACK	18	6444	71	71.8	129
MIDDLE	18	6019	71	69.7	127
FRONT	18	5071	73	70.3	120

Weekend:
Weekend: $50
Discounts: Sr. & Jr. weekdays
Driving Range: $10/lg., $7/med., $4/sm.
Junior Golf: Yes
Architect/Yr Open: Tom & George Fazio/1975
GPS: Mapped for GPS

Excellent condition.

	1	2	3	4	5	6	7	8	9
PAR	4	4	3	4	3	5	4	4	4
YARDS	391	367	150	320	139	518	345	381	371
	10	11	12	13	14	15	16	17	18
PAR	5	4	3	4	5	4	4	3	4
YARDS	533	311	147	351	469	402	311	127	386

Directions: I-84 to Exit 1; Saw Mill Road to Ridgebury Road. Course entrance is on Ridgebury Road.

Short Beach Par 3 Golf Course NR

1 Dorne Drive
Stratford, CT (203) 381-2070

Tees	Holes	Yards	Par	USGA	Slope
BACK	9	1369	27		
MIDDLE	9	1270	27		
FRONT	9	1162	27		

Club Pro: Don Samatulski
Payment: Cash, Visa, MC, Disc
Tee Times: 6 days adv. wknds
Fee 9 Holes: Weekday: $14 ($9 resident)   **Weekend:** $16 ($10 resident)
Fee 18 Holes: Weekday: **Weekend:**
Twilight Rates: No   **Discounts:** Senior & Junior
Cart Rental: $8pp/9   **Driving Range:** No
Lessons: Yes **Schools:** No   **Junior Golf:** Yes
Membership: **Architect/Yr Open:** Geoffrey Cornish
Other: Snack Bar/ Mini Golf Course   **GPS:**

Par 3, 9 holes on beachfront. Proper attire required. Resident discounts. Open March - January.

	1	2	3	4	5	6	7	8	9
PAR	3	3	3	3	3	3	3	3	3
YARDS	125	154	98	170	88	130	218	162	125
PAR									
YARDS									

Directions: Call for directions.

Sleeping Giant Golf Course NR 42

3931 Whitney Avenue
Hamden, CT (203) 281-9456
www.sleepinggiantgc.com

Tees	Holes	Yards	Par	USGA	Slope
BACK	9	2671	35	65.4	99
MIDDLE	9	2572	35	63.4	96
FRONT	9	2216	37	64.6	106

Club Pro: Carl Swanson, PGA
Payment: Cash Only
Tee Times: No
Fee 9 Holes: Weekday: $17   **Weekend:** $19
Fee 18 Holes: Weekday: $30   **Weekend:** $34
Twilight Rates: No   **Discounts:** Senior
Cart Rental: $13pp/18, $8pp/9   **Driving Range:** Yes
Lessons: $30/half hour, $50/hour **Schools:** No **Junior Golf:** No
Membership: No   **Architect/Yr Open:** Ralph Barton
Other: Restaurant nearby   **GPS:**

COUPON

"A nice little well-maintained course that is pure fun. The views of Sleeping Giant Mountain enhance the aesthetics. #3 is a nice par 3 to a punchbowl green" –AP Open year round, weather permitting.

	1	2	3	4	5	6	7	8	9
PAR	3	4	3	4	5	4	4	4	4
YARDS	125	399	170	355	440	331	199	217	336
PAR									
YARDS									

Directions: I-91 to Exit 10. Right onto Whitney Avenue. Course is 3 miles on the right.

SW
CT

South Pine Creek Par 3 Golf Course NR ▶ 43

Old Dam Road
Fairfield, CT (203) 255-7356
www.fairfieldct.org

Club Pro: Sean Garrity, PGA
Payment: Cash Only
Tee Times: 5 days adv.

Tees	Holes	Yards	Par	USGA	Slope
BACK					
MIDDLE	9	1242	27		
FRONT	9	1073	27		

Fee 9 Holes: Weekday: $14 **Weekend:** $18
Fee 18 Holes: Weekday: **Weekend:**
Twilight Rates: No **Discounts:** Senior & Junior
Cart Rental: $4/pull **Driving Range:**
Lessons: No **Schools:** No **Junior Golf:** No
Membership: No **Architect/Yr Open:**
Other: **GPS:**

Residents half price. Great place to learn the game. H. Richardson affiliate course.

	1	2	3	4	5	6	7	8	9
PAR	3	3	3	3	3	3	3	3	3
YARDS	143	145	120	166	153	117	121	187	90
PAR									
YARDS									

Directions: I-95 to Exit 21, Mill Plain Road. Turn left onto Post Road. At first set of lights take left. Course is ½ mile on left.

Southington Country Club NR ▶ 44

150 Savage Street
Plantsville, CT (860) 628-7032
www.southingtoncountryclub.com

Tees	Holes	Yards	Par	USGA	Slope
BACK	18	5932	71	68.7	124
MIDDLE	18	5675	71	67.6	122
FRONT	18	5037	71	64.1	111

Club Pro: Paul Brown, PGA
Payment: Visa, MC
Tee Times: Sat/Sun am, 5 days adv.
Fee 9 Holes: Weekday: $20 **Weekend:** $23
Fee 18 Holes: Weekday: $36 **Weekend:** $40
Twilight Rates: After 5pm
Discounts: Sr. & Jr. wkdays before 3pm, wknds after 3pm
Cart Rental: $16pp/18, $9pp/9 **Driving Range:** No
Lessons: No **Schools:** No **Junior Golf:** No
Membership: Yes **Architect/Yr Open:** 1922
Other: Full Service Tavern / Pizza Oven / Banquet Room / Locker Rooms

Front 9 hilly, Back 9 narrow. Full service bar and grill. Putting and chipping practice greens. Back Nine Tavern open year round.

	1	2	3	4	5	6	7	8	9
PAR	4	4	3	5	4	5	3	4	4
YARDS	377	297	144	481	387	508	192	338	324
	10	11	12	13	14	15	16	17	18
PAR	4	4	3	4	5	3	4	3	5
YARDS	300	316	96	323	453	202	323	160	445

Directions: I-84 to Exit 28. Take right onto Route 322. Travel about 3 miles. Take a left onto South End Road. Take first right onto Savage Street.

Sterling Farms Golf Course ✪✪✪½ 45 ▶

1349 Newfield Avenue
Stamford, CT (203) 461-9090
www.sterlingfarmsgc.com

Tees	Holes	Yards	Par	USGA	Slope
BACK	18	6310	72	70.7	127
MIDDLE	18	6082	72	69.7	123
FRONT	18	5500	73	71.7	125

Club Pro: Angela Aulenti, PGA
Payment: Cash Only
Tee Times: 1 week adv.
Fee 9 Holes: Weekday: $30 (6-7:30am)   **Weekend:** $30 (6-7:30am)
Fee 18 Holes: Weekday: $50   **Weekend:** $50
Twilight Rates: After 4pm   **Discounts:** Sr. & Jr. weekdays
Cart Rental: $14pp/18, $8pp/9   **Driving Range:** Yes
Lessons: Call (203) 329-7888   **Schools:** Yes   **Junior Golf:** Yes
Membership: No   **Architect/Yr Open:** Geoffrey Cornish/1969
Other: Restaurant   **GPS:**

Course has hilly front 9; more level back 9. 2 of the course's five lakes come into play on the 14th hole. Resident rates.

	1	2	3	4	5	6	7	8	9
PAR	4	5	4	4	3	5	4	3	4
YARDS	331	489	316	350	191	465	382	179	326
	10	11	12	13	14	15	16	17	18
PAR	4	4	4	5	4	3	4	3	5
YARDS	397	307	341	477	393	147	301	215	475

Directions: Merritt Parkway South to Exit 35. Right onto High Ridge Road. Left onto Vine (5 lights). Left at end to Newfield Avenue. Club is ¼ mile on right.

Stonybrook Golf Course NR 46 ▶

263 Milton Road
Litchfield, CT (860) 567-9977
www.stonybrookgc.com

Tees	Holes	Yards	Par	USGA	Slope
BACK	9	2986	35	70.4	115
MIDDLE	9	2878	35	69.0	111
FRONT	9	2669	36	71.6	123

Club Pro: Rich Bredice, Pro
Payment: Visa, MC
Tee Times: Weekends
Fee 9 Holes: Weekday: $18   **Weekend:** $20
Fee 18 Holes: Weekday: $34   **Weekend:** $38
Twilight Rates: No   **Discounts:** Junior
Cart Rental: $18pp/18, $9pp/9   **Driving Range:** No
Lessons: Available   **Schools:** No   **Junior Golf:** Yes
Membership: Yes   **Architect/Yr Open:** Al Zikorus/1965
Other: Clubhouse / Snack Bar / Bar-Lounge / Lockers

Terrain is rolling; greens contoured (medium/fast). Outstanding course conditions, considered the best in the area.

	1	2	3	4	5	6	7	8	9
PAR	5	4	3	4	4	4	4	4	3
YARDS	530	374	150	366	325	300	375	295	163
PAR									
YARDS									

Directions: Route 8 to Exit 42; Route 118 West to 202 West to Milton Road.

SW CT

Sunset Hill Golf Club

NR **47**▶

18 Sunset Hill Road
Brookfield, CT (203) 740-7800
www.sunsethillgolfclub.com

Club Pro: Gary Cilfone, PGA
Payment: Cash, Check
Tee Times: No
Fee 9 Holes: Weekday: $19
Fee 18 Holes: Weekday: $25
Twilight Rates: After 4pm
Cart Rental: $18pp/18, $9pp/9
Lessons: Yes **Schools:** Yes, inquire
Membership: Yes
Other: Clubhouse / Snack Bar / Bar-Lounge

Tees	Holes	Yards	Par	USGA	Slope
BACK					
MIDDLE	9	2394	35	62.6	100
FRONT	9	2346	35	66.3	100

Weekend: $23
Weekend: $29
Discounts: Senior & Junior
Driving Range: No
Junior Golf: Yes
Architect/Yr Open: 1897
GPS:

COUPON

Ongoing improvements. New tee on hole #3. Sister golf course is Eastwood CC. Open April - November.

	1	2	3	4	5	6	7	8	9
PAR	5	3	3	4	4	4	5	4	3
YARDS	452	145	116	278	304	270	426	278	125
PAR									
YARDS									

Directions: I-84 to Exit 9; follow Route 25 North 3 miles; take left onto Sunset Hill Road to course.

Tashua Knolls Country Club

✪✪✪ **48**▶

40 Tashua Knolls Lane
Trumbull, CT (203) 452-5171
www.tashuaknolls.com

Club Pro: Jon Janik, PGA
Payment: Cash, Check, Credit
Tee Times: 7 days adv.
Fee 9 Holes: Weekday: $23
Fee 18 Holes: Weekday: $42
Twilight Rates: No
Cart Rental: $16pp/18, $11pp/9
Lessons: Yes **Schools:** Yes
Membership: No
Other: Snack Bar / Restaurant / Bar-Lounge / Lockers / Showers

Tees	Holes	Yards	Par	USGA	Slope
BACK	18	6540	72	71.9	125
MIDDLE	18	6119	72	70.0	121
FRONT	18	5454	72	71.7	124

Weekend: $27
Weekend: $46
Discounts: Sr. & Jr. residents M-F
Driving Range: $5/bucket
Junior Golf: Yes
Architect/Yr Open: Al Zikorus/1976

"Second 9 holes opened 2005, less daunting than the first 9." –RV

	1	2	3	4	5	6	7	8	9
PAR	5	4	3	4	4	3	5	4	4
YARDS	532	317	151	342	353	192	480	354	356
	10	**11**	**12**	**13**	**14**	**15**	**16**	**17**	**18**
PAR	4	4	3	4	5	4	5	3	4
YARDS	349	367	154	262	495	373	506	145	391

Directions: Take Merritt Parkway (Route 15) to Exit 49 (Route 25); go straight, take left onto Tashua Knolls Lane. Course is at top of hill.

Tradition GC at Wallingford, The ✪✪✪

36 Harrison Road
Wallingford, CT (203) 269-6023
www.wallingfordtradition.com

Club Pro: Nick Lykowski, Dir. of Golf
Payment: Most Major Credit Cards
Tee Times: 7 days adv.
Fee 9 Holes: Weekday: $25 w/cart
Fee 18 Holes: Weekday: $47 w/cart
Twilight Rates: After 2pm
Cart Rental: $8pp/9
Lessons: Yes **Schools:** Yes
Membership: Yes
Other: Bar-Lounge / Snack Bar / Banquet Facility

Tees	Holes	Yards	Par	USGA	Slope
BACK	18	5772	70	68.8	121
MIDDLE	18	5398	70	66.9	119
FRONT	18	4458	70	68.0	121

Weekend: $25 w/cart
Weekend: $57 w/cart
Discounts: Senior & Junior
Driving Range: Yes
Junior Golf: Yes
Architect/Yr Open: Alfred Tull/1972
GPS:

Player Comments: "Well-manicured greens. Great staff. Fairly priced." Dress code. Variety of special rates. Renovated club house.

	1	2	3	4	5	6	7	8	9
PAR	4	4	3	4	4	5	4	3	4
YARDS	347	320	106	370	342	518	281	152	389
	10	11	12	13	14	15	16	17	18
PAR	4	5	3	4	5	3	4	4	3
YARDS	256	447	131	431	409	139	380	275	105

Directions: I-91 to Exit 14. Take right onto Route 150 toward Wallingford. Take right onto Harrison Road.

Twin Lakes Golf Course

NR

241 Twin Lakes Road
North Branford, CT (203) 481-3776
www.twinlakesgolfnb.com

Club Pro: Edward Grant, PGA
Anthony Celone, Manager
Payment: Cash Only
Tee Times:
Fee 9 Holes: Weekday: $8
Fee 18 Holes: Weekday: $13
Twilight Rates: No
Cart Rental: Yes
Lessons: Yes **Schools:** Yes
Membership: No
Other: Snack Bar

Tees	Holes	Yards	Par	USGA	Slope
BACK					
MIDDLE	9	1047	27		
FRONT					

Weekend: $10
Weekend: $16
Discounts: Junior 1st tee
Driving Range: No
Junior Golf: Yes
Architect/Yr Open:
GPS:

Open March 15-October 15. This is a very short, 9-hole, par 3 course good for family fun. Season passes for unlimited play.

	1	2	3	4	5	6	7	8	9
PAR	3	3	3	3	3	3	3	3	3
YARDS	130	123	95	92	116	92	138	141	120
PAR									
YARDS									

Directions: I-95 to Exit 55 on left. Take a left at first light. Follow 2 miles, Twin Lakes Road on left.

SW
CT

Western Hills Golf Course NR ▶ 51

600 Park Road
Waterbury, CT (203) 756-1211
www.westernhillsgolfcourse.com

Club Pro: Jim Dean
Payment: Visa, MC
Tee Times: 3 days adv.

Tees	Holes	Yards	Par	USGA	Slope
BACK	18	6356	72	69.5	120
MIDDLE	18	6136	72	68.5	118
FRONT	18	5237	72	69.5	127

Fee 9 Holes: Weekday: $20   **Weekend:** $21
Fee 18 Holes: Weekday: $31   **Weekend:** $33
Twilight Rates: After 6pm M-F, after 12pm S/S **Discounts:** Senior & Junior
Cart Rental: $29/18, $19/9 per cart   **Driving Range:** No
Lessons: Yes **Schools:** No   **Junior Golf:** Yes
Membership: Yes   **Architect/Yr:** Wiliam & David Gordon/1962
Other: Clubhouse / Snack Bar / Restaurant / Bar-Lounge / Banquet / Lockers / Showers

COUPON

Scenic New England golf course with a variety of terrain and vistas. A good test of golf. The course is in the best shape ever! Much more difficult than rated.

	1	2	3	4	5	6	7	8	9
PAR	4	5	4	4	3	4	5	4	3
YARDS	354	458	356	340	162	374	527	387	145
	10	11	12	13	14	15	16	17	18
PAR	4	3	4	5	4	5	3	4	4
YARDS	363	138	305	495	391	480	153	381	327

Directions: I-84 to Exit 17. Follow Route 63 North to Park Road. Right on Park Road to stop sign. Left at stop sign to clubhouse.

Whitney Farms Golf Course ✪✪ ▶ 52

175 Shelton Road (Route 110)
Monroe, CT (203) 268-0707
www.whitneyfarmsgc.com

Club Pro: Paul McGuire, PGA
Payment: Visa, MC, Amex
Tee Times: Yes

Tees	Holes	Yards	Par	USGA	Slope
BACK	18	6628	72	72.4	134
MIDDLE	18	6262	72	70.9	129
FRONT	18	5832	73	72.9	135

Fee 9 Holes: Weekday: $32   **Weekend:** $36
Fee 18 Holes: Weekday: $55   **Weekend:** $69
Twilight Rates: After 4pm   **Discounts:** Srs. rate: $45 w/cart, M-Th
Cart Rental: Included   **Driving Range:** $6
Lessons: $50/half hour **Schools:** No   **Junior Golf:** No
Membership: No   **Architect/Yr Open:** Hal Purdy/1982
Other: Clubhouse / Lockers / Showers / Snack Bar / Restaurant / Bar-Lounge

All bunkers recently redone with new sand and new cart paths.

	1	2	3	4	5	6	7	8	9
PAR	4	4	5	3	4	5	3	5	3
YARDS	399	381	508	161	324	533	210	469	168
	10	11	12	13	14	15	16	17	18
PAR	4	5	3	4	4	3	5	4	4
YARDS	341	522	132	329	324	164	547	335	415

Directions: Merritt Parkway Exit 49 North to Route 25. Take right on Route 111 and follow for 4 miles. Take right at intersection of Route 110. Course is 1 mile on left.

Woodhaven Country Club

NR **53** ▶

275 Miller Road
Bethany, CT (203) 393-3230
www.woodhavengolf.net

Tees	Holes	Yards	Par	USGA	Slope
BACK	9	6774	72	72.7	128
MIDDLE	9	6294	72	70.6	123
FRONT	9	5370	72	72.0	125

Club Pro: Dale Humphrey, PGA
Payment: Cash, Check, MC, Visa, Disc
Tee Times: 7 days adv.
Fee 9 Holes: Weekday: $21
Fee 18 Holes: Weekday: $32
Twilight Rates: Yes
Cart Rental: $17pp/18, $9pp/9
Lessons: Yes **Schools:** No
Membership: No
Other: Snack Bar / Restaurant

Weekend: $24
Weekend: $40
Discounts: Sr. & Jr. wkdys before 2pm
Driving Range: Yes
Junior Golf: Yes
Architect/Yr Open: Al Zikorus/1968
GPS:

A family owned "hidden gem." Beautifully maintaned in a secluded setting.

	1	2	3	4	5	6	7	8	9
PAR	5	3	4	4	4	5	4	3	4
YARDS	517	156	331	375	342	542	350	152	382
PAR									
YARDS									

Directions: Route 8 to Exit 22. East on Route 67. Left on Bear Hill Road. Bear left onto Miller Road.

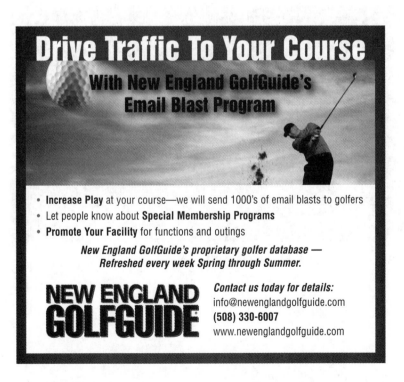
SW
CT

Directory of Coupons

Southers Marsh Golf Club, Plymouth, MA

Baker's Golf Center

- **Type of Discount:**
  Frequent Golf Card available for large baskets. Buy 9 & the 10th is free.
- **Days of the Week:**
  7 days a week
- **Hours of the Day:**

658 South Main Street
Lanesborough, MA
(413) 443-6102
www.bakersgolfcenter.com

Pro: Dennis Perrone, PGA

Coupon expires 12/14. Cannot be combined with any other offer.

Bill Pappas Indoor Golf & Batting Cages

- **Type of Discount:**
  Free half hour practice with paid half hour
- **Days of the Week:**
  7 days a week
- **Hours of the Day:**

75 Princeton Street
North Chelmsford, MA
(978) 251-3933
www.egolfschool.net

Pro: Bill Pappas, PGA

Clinics: Yes

Coupon expires 12/14. Cannot be combined with any other offer.

Callahan's Sportech Golf @ The Mammoth Green Family Golf Center

- **Type of Discount:**
  $10 off one hour lesson
- **Days of the Week:**
  7 days a week
- **Hours of the Day:**

135 Nashua Road, Route 102
Londonderry, NH
(603) 888-1976

Pro: Jim Callahan, PGA
jcallahanpga@aol.com

Clinics: Yes

Coupon expires 12/14. Cannot be combined with any other offer.

Callahan's Sportech Golf Indoor Lessons

- **Type of Discount:**
  $10 off one hour lesson
- **Days of the Week:**
  7 days a week
- **Hours of the Day:**
  Any time

1 Bittersweet Road
Nashua, NH
(603) 888-1976

Pro: Jim Callahan, PGA
jcallahanpga@aol.com

Clinics: Yes

Coupon expires 12/14. Cannot be combined with any other offer.

Driving Range Coupons

NEW ENGLAND GOLFGUIDE

2 0 1 4

NEW ENGLAND GOLFGUIDE

2 0 1 4

NEW ENGLAND GOLFGUIDE

2 0 1 4

NEW ENGLAND GOLFGUIDE

2 0 1 4

Driving Range Coupons

NEW ENGLAND
GOLFGUIDE

2 0 1 4

NEW ENGLAND
GOLFGUIDE

2 0 1 4

NEW ENGLAND
GOLFGUIDE

2 0 1 4

NEW ENGLAND
GOLFGUIDE

2 0 1 4

Driving Range Coupons

NEW ENGLAND GOLFGUIDE

2 0 1 4

NEW ENGLAND GOLFGUIDE

2 0 1 4

NEW ENGLAND GOLFGUIDE

2 0 1 4

NEW ENGLAND GOLFGUIDE

2 0 1 4

NEW ENGLAND GOLFGUIDE

Sarkisian Farms Driving Range

- **Type of Discount:**
  $1 off any size bucket
- **Days of the Week:**
  7 days a week
- **Hours of the Day:**
  All day

159 Chandler Road
Andover, MA
(978) 688-5522

Pro: Mark Fedorehuk, PGA
Clinics: Junior & Adult

Coupon expires 12/14.
Cannot be combined
with any other offer.

NEW ENGLAND GOLFGUIDE

Sonny's Driving Range & Par 3

- **Type of Discount:**
  1 small bucket free;
  2 players for price of 1
- **Days of the Week:**
  Tuesday-Sunday
- **Hours of the Day:**
  Closed Mondays

130 Cove Road
Winterport, ME
(207) 223-5242
www.sonnysrange.com
Pro: Sonny Reynolds, USGTF

Coupon expires 12/14.
Cannot be combined
with any other offer.

NEW ENGLAND GOLFGUIDE

Southborough Golf Driving Range

- **Type of Discount:**
  $10 off 1 hour lesson
- **Days of the Week:**
  7 days a week
- **Hours of the Day:**

20 Turnpike Road (Route 9E)
Southborough, MA
(508) 380-3786
www.southboroughgolf.com
Pro: Kevin Sullivan
Clinics: Yes

Coupon expires 12/14.
Cannot be combined
with any other offer.

NEW ENGLAND GOLFGUIDE

Southborough Golf Driving Range

- **Type of Discount:**
  $2 off large bucket
- **Days of the Week:**
  Monday through
  Thursday
- **Hours of the Day:**

20 Turnpike Road (Route 9E)
Southborough, MA
(508) 480-9992
www.southboroughgolf.com
Pro: Kevin Sullivan
Clinics: Yes

Coupon expires 12/14.
Cannot be combined
with any other offer.

Driving Range Coupons

NEW ENGLAND GOLFGUIDE

2 0 1 4

NEW ENGLAND GOLFGUIDE

2 0 1 4

NEW ENGLAND GOLFGUIDE

2 0 1 4

NEW ENGLAND GOLFGUIDE

2 0 1 4

NEW ENGLAND GOLFGUIDE

2 0 1 4

NEW ENGLAND GOLFGUIDE

2 0 1 4

NEW ENGLAND GOLFGUIDE

2 0 1 4

NEW ENGLAND GOLFGUIDE

2 0 1 4

Airways Golf Course
West Suffield, CT (860) 668-4973

- **Type of Discount**
  $40 for 2 players including cart (weekdays)
  $60 for 2 players including cart (weekends)

- **Days of the Week**
  7 days a week (except holidays)

- **Hours of the Day**
  All day

Coupon expires 5/31/15. Cannot be combined with any other offer.

Banner Country Club
Moodus, CT (860) 873-9075

- **Type of Discount**
  Free golf cart with 2 paid greens fees

- **Days of the Week**
  Weekdays only (except holidays)

- **Hours of the Day**
  All day

Coupon expires 5/31/15. Cannot be combined with any other offer.

Blackledge Country Club - Anderson's Glen
Hebron, CT (860) 228-0250

- **Type of Discount**
  Free golf cart with 2 paid greens fees

- **Days of the Week**
  Monday through Thursday (except holidays)

- **Hours of the Day**
  All day

Coupon expires 5/31/15. Cannot be combined with any other offer.

Blackledge Country Club - Gilead Highlands
Hebron, CT (860) 228-0250

- **Type of Discount**
  Free golf cart with 2 paid greens fees

- **Days of the Week**
  Monday through Thursday (except holidays)

- **Hours of the Day**
  All day

Coupon expires 5/31/15. Cannot be combined with any other offer.

Golf Course Coupons

NEW ENGLAND GOLFGUIDE

2 0 1 4 / 2 0 1 5

NEW ENGLAND GOLFGUIDE

2 0 1 4 / 2 0 1 5

NEW ENGLAND GOLFGUIDE

2 0 1 4 / 2 0 1 5

NEW ENGLAND GOLFGUIDE

2 0 1 4 / 2 0 1 5

CT

Cedar Ridge Golf Course
East Lyme, CT (860) 691-4568

- **Type of Discount**
  2 players for the price of 1
- **Days of the Week**
  Weekdays only (except holidays)
- **Hours of the Day**
  All day

Coupon expires 5/31/15. Cannot be combined with any other offer.

Connecticut National Golf Club
Putnam, CT (860) 928-7748

- **Type of Discount**
  4 players for the price of 3
- **Days of the Week**
  Weekdays only (except holidays)
- **Hours of the Day**
  All day

Coupon expires 5/31/15. Cannot be combined with any other offer.

Copper Hill Golf Club
East Granby, CT (860) 653-6191

- **Type of Discount**
  2 players for the price of 1
- **Days of the Week**
  Weekdays only (except holidays)
- **Hours of the Day**
  All day

Coupon expires 5/31/15. Cannot be combined with any other offer.

Elmridge Golf Course
Pawcatuck, CT (860) 599-2248

- **Type of Discount**
  Free golf cart with 2 paid greens fees
- **Days of the Week**
  Weekdays only (except holidays)
- **Hours of the Day**
  All day. Subject to availability of cart.
  No facsimilies.

Coupon expires 5/31/15. Cannot be combined with any other offer.

Golf Course Coupons

NEW ENGLAND GOLFGUIDE   **Golf Course Coupons 455**

NEW ENGLAND GOLFGUIDE

2 0 1 4 / 2 0 1 5

NEW ENGLAND GOLFGUIDE

2 0 1 4 / 2 0 1 5

NEW ENGLAND GOLFGUIDE

2 0 1 4 / 2 0 1 5

NEW ENGLAND GOLFGUIDE

2 0 1 4 / 2 0 1 5

East Mountain Golf Course
Waterbury, CT (203) 753-1425

- **Type of Discount for Foursomes**
  9 holes – $21pp (includes cart)
  18 holes – $30pp (includes cart)

- **Days of the Week**
  Weekdays only (except holidays)

- **Hours of the Day**
  7am - 1pm

Coupon expires 5/31/15. Cannot be combined with any other offer.

Fox Hopyard Golf Club
East Haddam, CT (860) 434-6644

- **Type of Discount**
  4 players for the price of 3

- **Days of the Week**
  Monday through Thursday (except holidays)

- **Hours of the Day**
  All day. Must call for tee time
  no more than 3 days in advance.

Coupon expires 5/31/15. Cannot be combined with any other offer.

Gainfield Farms Golf Course
Southbury, CT (203) 262-1100

- **Type of Discount**
  $2 off 9 holes with coupon

- **Days of the Week**
  7 days a week

- **Hours of the Day**
  All day

Coupon expires 5/31/15. Cannot be combined with any other offer.

Goodwin Golf Course
Hartford, CT (860) 956-3601

- **Type of Discount**
  Buy 1 greens fee get 1 free with purchase of cart

- **Days of the Week**
  Monday through Friday.
  Saturday/Sunday/Holidays after 12pm.

- **Hours of the Day**
  Cannot be used toward tournament
  and/or league play.

Coupon expires 5/31/15. Cannot be combined with any other offer.

Golf Course Coupons

NEW ENGLAND GOLFGUIDE

2 0 1 4 / 2 0 1 5

NEW ENGLAND GOLFGUIDE

2 0 1 4 / 2 0 1 5

NEW ENGLAND GOLFGUIDE

2 0 1 4 / 2 0 1 5

NEW ENGLAND GOLFGUIDE

2 0 1 4 / 2 0 1 5

Guilford Lakes Golf Course
Guilford, CT (203) 453-8214

- **Type of Discount**
  2 players for the price of 1
- **Days of the Week**
  7 days a week
- **Hours of the Day**
  All day

Coupon expires 5/31/15. Cannot be combined with any other offer.

Harrisville Golf Course
Woodstock, CT (860) 928-6098

- **Type of Discount**
  $3 off greens fees for up to 2 players
- **Days of the Week**
  Weekdays only (except holidays)
- **Hours of the Day**
  All day

Coupon expires 5/31/15. Cannot be combined with any other offer.

Hawk's Landing Country Club
Southington, CT (860) 793-6000

- **Type of Discount**
  $2 off a round or golf cart
- **Days of the Week**
  7 days a week
- **Hours of the Day**
  All day. Saturday and Sunday only after 1pm.

Coupon expires 5/31/15. Cannot be combined with any other offer.

Hop Brook Golf Course
Naugatuck, CT (203) 729-8013

- **Type of Discount**
  $5 off greens fee and cart
- **Days of the Week**
  7 days a week
- **Hours of the Day**
  M-F 7am - 2:45pm; S-S after 1pm for 9 holes
  M-F 7am - 12pm; S-S after 1pm for 18 holes

Coupon expires 5/31/15. Cannot be combined with any other offer.

NEW ENGLAND GOLFGUIDE

2014 / 2015

NEW ENGLAND GOLFGUIDE

2014 / 2015

NEW ENGLAND GOLFGUIDE

2014 / 2015

NEW ENGLAND GOLFGUIDE

2014 / 2015

Hotchkiss School Golf Club
Lakeville, CT (860) 435-4400

- **Type of Discount**
  2 players for the price of 1 greens fees.
  Cart rental required.

- **Days of the Week**
  Weekdays only (except holidays)

- **Hours of the Day**
  All day

Coupon expires 5/31/15. Cannot be combined with any other offer.

Indian Springs Golf Club
Middlefield, CT (860) 349-8109

- **Type of Discount**
  Free golf cart with 2 paid greens fees

- **Days of the Week**
  Weekdays before 3pm

- **Hours of the Day**
  Before 3pm

Coupon expires 5/31/15. Cannot be combined with any other offer.

Keney Golf Club
Hartford, CT (860) 525-3656

- **Type of Discount**
  2 players for the price of 1

- **Days of the Week**
  Weekdays only (except holidays)

- **Hours of the Day**
  All day. Cart rental required.

Coupon expires 5/31/15. Cannot be combined with any other offer.

Long Hill Country Club
East Hartford, CT (860) 528-5082

- **Type of Discount**
  2 players for the price of 1 w/rental of power cart

- **Days of the Week**
  Weekdays only (except holidays). From 10/1
  to end of season.

- **Hours of the Day**
  All day

Coupon expires 5/31/15. Cannot be combined with any other offer.

Golf Course Coupons

NEW ENGLAND GOLFGUIDE

2 0 1 4 / 2 0 1 5

NEW ENGLAND GOLFGUIDE

2 0 1 4 / 2 0 1 5

NEW ENGLAND GOLFGUIDE

2 0 1 4 / 2 0 1 5

NEW ENGLAND GOLFGUIDE

2 0 1 4 / 2 0 1 5

Manchester Country Club
Manchester, CT (860) 646-0226

- **Type of Discount**
  Buy 1 greens fee get 1 free (cart rental required)
- **Days of the Week**
  Monday through Thursday (except holidays)
- **Hours of the Day**
  All day

Coupon expires 5/31/15. Cannot be combined with any other offer.

Miner Hills Golf Course
Middletown, CT (860) 635-0051

- **Type of Discount**
  $14 per person
- **Days of the Week**
  Monday through Thursday
- **Hours of the Day**
  Before 1pm

Coupon expires 5/31/15. Cannot be combined with any other offer.

Oxford Greens, The Golf Club at
Oxford, CT (203) 888-1600

- **Type of Discount**
  $5 off per player (up to 4 players)
- **Days of the Week**
  Weekdays (except holidays)
- **Hours of the Day**
  Before 5pm

Coupon expires 5/31/15. Cannot be combined with any other offer.

Pequot Golf Club
Wheeler Road, Stonington, CT (860) 535-1898

- **Type of Discount**
  4 players for the price of 3.
  Cart rental required.
- **Days of the Week**
  7 days a week
- **Hours of the Day**
  All day

Coupon expires 5/31/15. Cannot be combined with any other offer.

Golf Course Coupons

NEW ENGLAND GOLFGUIDE

2 0 1 4 / 2 0 1 5

NEW ENGLAND GOLFGUIDE

2 0 1 4 / 2 0 1 5

NEW ENGLAND GOLFGUIDE

2 0 1 4 / 2 0 1 5

NEW ENGLAND GOLFGUIDE

2 0 1 4 / 2 0 1 5

Pomperaug Golf Club
Southbury, CT (203) 264-9484

- **Type of Discount**
  Free golf cart with 2 paid greens fees
- **Days of the Week**
  Weekdays only (except holidays)
- **Hours of the Day**
  All day

Coupon expires 5/31/15. Cannot be combined with any other offer.

Portland Golf Club
Portland, CT (860) 342-6107

- **Type of Discount**
  Free golf cart with 2 paid 18 hole greens fees
- **Days of the Week**
  Weekdays only (except holidays)
- **Hours of the Day**
  7-10am weekdays

Coupon expires 5/31/15. Cannot be combined with any other offer.

Quarry Ridge Golf Course
Portland, CT (860) 342-6113

- **Type of Discount**
  $35 per person (includes cart)
- **Days of the Week**
  Weekdays only (except holidays)
- **Hours of the Day**
  All day. Expires 11/15/14.

Coupon expires 11/15/14. Cannot be combined with any other offer.

Richter Park Golf Course
Danbury, CT (203) 792-2550

- **Type of Discount**
  Danbury resident rates
- **Days of the Week**
  Monday through Thursday (except holidays)
- **Hours of the Day**
  All day

Coupon expires 5/31/15. Cannot be combined with any other offer.

Golf Course Coupons

NEW ENGLAND GOLFGUIDE

2 0 1 4 / 2 0 1 5

✂ -

NEW ENGLAND GOLFGUIDE

2 0 1 4 / 2 0 1 5

✂ -

NEW ENGLAND GOLFGUIDE

2 0 1 4 / 2 0 1 5

✂ -

NEW ENGLAND GOLFGUIDE

2 0 1 4 / 2 0 1 5

Rolling Meadows Country Club
Ellington, CT (860) 870-5328

- **Type of Discount**
  2 players for price of 1. Cart rental required.
- **Days of the Week**
  Weekdays only (except holidays)
- **Hours of the Day**
  10am - 1pm

Coupon expires 5/31/15. Cannot be combined with any other offer.

Shennecosset Golf Club
Groton, CT (860) 445-0262

- **Type of Discount**
  Free cart with 2 paid greens fees
- **Days of the Week**
  Weekdays only (except holidays)
- **Hours of the Day**
  All day

Coupon expires 5/31/15. Cannot be combined with any other offer.

Simsbury Farms Golf Club
West Simsbury, CT (860) 658-6246

- **Type of Discount**
  2 players for the price of 1.
  Cart rental required.
- **Days of the Week**
  Weekdays only (except holidays)
- **Hours of the Day**
  All day

Coupon expires 5/31/15. Cannot be combined with any other offer.

Skungamaug River Golf Club
Coventry, CT (860) 742-9348

- **Type of Discount**
  Free golf cart with 2 paid greens fees
- **Days of the Week**
  7 days a week
- **Hours of the Day**
  Weekday mornings, weekend afternoons

Coupon expires 5/31/15. Cannot be combined with any other offer.

Golf Course Coupons

NEW ENGLAND GOLFGUIDE

2014 / 2015

NEW ENGLAND GOLFGUIDE

2014 / 2015

NEW ENGLAND GOLFGUIDE

2014 / 2015

NEW ENGLAND GOLFGUIDE

2014 / 2015

Sleeping Giant Golf Course
Hamden, CT (203) 281-9456

- **Type of Discount**
  2 players for the price of 1
- **Days of the Week**
  7 days a week
- **Hours of the Day**
  All day

Coupon expires 5/31/15. Cannot be combined with any other offer.

Sunset Hill Golf Club
Brookfield, CT (203) 740-7800

- **Type of Discount**
  2 players for the price of 1 (cart rental required)
- **Days of the Week**
  Monday through Thursday (except holidays)
- **Hours of the Day**
  All day

Coupon expires 5/31/15. Cannot be combined with any other offer.

Timberlin Golf Club
Berlin, CT (860) 828-3228

- **Type of Discount**
  $31 for 18 holes (cart included)
- **Days of the Week**
  Monday through Friday (except holidays)
- **Hours of the Day**
  All day

Coupon expires 5/31/15. Cannot be combined with any other offer.

Tower Ridge Golf Course
Simsbury, CT (860) 658-9767

- **Type of Discount**
  4 players for the price of 2.
  Cart rental required.
- **Days of the Week**
  Weekdays only (except holidays)
- **Hours of the Day**
  All day

Coupon expires 5/31/15. Cannot be combined with any other offer.

Golf Course Coupons

NEW ENGLAND GOLFGUIDE

2 0 1 4 / 2 0 1 5

NEW ENGLAND GOLFGUIDE

2 0 1 4 / 2 0 1 5

NEW ENGLAND GOLFGUIDE

2 0 1 4 / 2 0 1 5

NEW ENGLAND GOLFGUIDE

2 0 1 4 / 2 0 1 5

Twin Hills Country Club
Coventry, CT (860) 742-9705

- **Type of Discount**
  Free golf cart with 2 paid greens fees
- **Days of the Week**
  Monday through Thursday (except holidays)
- **Hours of the Day**
  All day

Coupon expires 5/31/15. Cannot be combined with any other offer.

Western Hills Golf Course
Waterbury, CT (203) 756-1211

- **Type of Discount**
  2 players for the price of 1.
  Cart rental required.
- **Days of the Week**
  Weekdays only (except holidays)
- **Hours of the Day**
  Before 12pm

Coupon expires 5/31/15. Cannot be combined with any other offer.

Willow Brook Golf Course
South Windsor, CT (860) 648-2061

- **Type of Discount**
  4 players for the price of 3
- **Days of the Week**
  Monday through Thursday (except holidays)
- **Hours of the Day**
  All day

Coupon expires 5/31/15. Cannot be combined with any other offer.

Wintonbury Hills Golf Course
Bloomfield, CT (860) 242-1401

- **Type of Discount**
  25% discount for 2-4 players
- **Days of the Week**
  Weekdays only (except holidays)
- **Hours of the Day**
  6am–4:50pm

Coupon expires 5/31/15. Cannot be combined with any other offer.

Golf Course Coupons

NEW ENGLAND GOLFGUIDE

2 0 1 4 / 2 0 1 5

NEW ENGLAND GOLFGUIDE

2 0 1 4 / 2 0 1 5

NEW ENGLAND GOLFGUIDE

2 0 1 4 / 2 0 1 5

NEW ENGLAND GOLFGUIDE

2 0 1 4 / 2 0 1 5

Woodhaven Country Club
Bethany, CT (203) 393-3230

- **Type of Discount**
  4 players for price of 3
- **Days of the Week**
  7 days a week
- **Hours of the Day**
  All day

Coupon expires 5/31/15. Cannot be combined with any other offer.

Woodstock Golf Course
South Woodstock, CT (860) 928-4130

- **Type of Discount**
  2 players for price of 1
- **Days of the Week**
  7 days a week
- **Hours of the Day**
  All day

Coupon expires 5/31/15. Cannot be combined with any other offer.

Apple Valley Golf Course
Lewiston, ME (207) 784-9773

- **Type of Discount**
  Free golf cart with 2 paid greens fees
- **Days of the Week**
  7 days a week
- **Hours of the Day**
  All day

Coupon expires 5/31/15. Cannot be combined with any other offer.

Aroostook Valley Country Club
Fort Fairfield, ME (207) 476-8083

- **Type of Discount**
  2 players for the price of 1
- **Days of the Week**
  7 days a week
- **Hours of the Day**
  All day

Coupon expires 5/31/15. Cannot be combined with any other offer.

Golf Course Coupons

NEW ENGLAND GOLFGUIDE

2 0 1 4 / 2 0 1 5

NEW ENGLAND GOLFGUIDE

2 0 1 4 / 2 0 1 5

NEW ENGLAND GOLFGUIDE

2 0 1 4 / 2 0 1 5

NEW ENGLAND GOLFGUIDE

2 0 1 4 / 2 0 1 5

Bar Harbor Golf Course
Route 204, Trenton, ME (207) 667-7505

- **Type of Discount**
  Free golf cart with 2 paid greens fees
- **Days of the Week**
  7 days a week
- **Hours of the Day**
  All day

Coupon expires 5/31/15. Cannot be combined with any other offer.

Barnes Brook Golf Course
Lincoln, ME (207) 732-3006

- **Type of Discount**
  25% discount for 2-4 players
- **Days of the Week**
  7 days a week
- **Hours of the Day**
  All day

Coupon expires 5/31/15. Cannot be combined with any other offer.

Bethel Inn Resort
Bethel, ME (207) 824-6276

- **Type of Discount**
  2nd greens fees at 50% off
- **Days of the Week**
  Weekdays only (except holidays)
- **Hours of the Day**
  All day. Must make tee time no more than
  48 hours in advance.

Coupon expires 5/31/15. Cannot be combined with any other offer.

Boothbay Harbor Country Club
Boothbay, ME (207) 633-3673

- **Type of Discount**
  2 players for the price of 1
- **Days of the Week**
  7 days a week
- **Hours of the Day**
  All day. Valid from opening through May 31
  and October 1 through closing.

Coupon expires 5/31/15. Cannot be combined with any other offer.

Golf Course Coupons

NEW ENGLAND GOLFGUIDE

2 0 1 4 / 2 0 1 5

NEW ENGLAND GOLFGUIDE

2 0 1 4 / 2 0 1 5

NEW ENGLAND GOLFGUIDE

2 0 1 4 / 2 0 1 5

NEW ENGLAND GOLFGUIDE

2 0 1 4 / 2 0 1 5

Bridgton Highlands Country Club
Bridgton, ME (207) 647-3491

- **Type of Discount**
  25% discount for 2-4 players
- **Days of the Week**
  7 days a week
- **Hours of the Day**
  After 1pm

Coupon expires 5/31/15. Cannot be combined with any other offer.

Brunswick Golf Club
River Road, Brunswick, ME (207) 725-8224

- **Type of Discount**
  4 players for the price of 3
- **Days of the Week**
  7 days a week
- **Hours of the Day**
  All day

Coupon expires 5/31/15. Cannot be combined with any other offer.

Bucksport Golf Club
Route 46, Bucksport, ME (207) 469-7612

- **Type of Discount**
  4 players for the price of 3
- **Days of the Week**
  7 days a week, not valid in July and August
- **Hours of the Day**
  All day

Coupon expires 5/31/15. Cannot be combined with any other offer.

Cape Neddick Country Club
Ogunquit, ME (207) 361-2011

- **Type of Discount**
  4 players for the price of 3
- **Days of the Week**
  Monday through Thursday (except holidays)
- **Hours of the Day**
  All day

Coupon expires 5/31/15. Cannot be combined with any other offer.

Golf Course Coupons

NEW ENGLAND GOLFGUIDE

2 0 1 4 / 2 0 1 5

NEW ENGLAND GOLFGUIDE

2 0 1 4 / 2 0 1 5

NEW ENGLAND GOLFGUIDE

2 0 1 4 / 2 0 1 5

NEW ENGLAND GOLFGUIDE

2 0 1 4 / 2 0 1 5

Caribou Country Club
Caribou, ME (207) 493-3933

- **Type of Discount**
  4 players for the price of 3
- **Days of the Week**
  7 days a week
- **Hours of the Day**
  All day. Call in advance.

Coupon expires 5/31/15. Cannot be combined with any other offer.

Castine Golf Club
Castine, ME (207) 326-8844

- **Type of Discount**
  4 players for the price of 3
- **Days of the Week**
  7 days a week
- **Hours of the Day**
  All day

Coupon expires 5/31/15. Cannot be combined with any other offer.

Cedar Springs Golf Course
Albion, ME (207) 437-2073

- **Type of Discount**
  2 players for the price of 1
- **Days of the Week**
  Weekdays only (except holidays)
- **Hours of the Day**
  All day

Coupon expires 5/31/15. Cannot be combined with any other offer.

Cobbossee Colony Golf Course
Monmouth, ME (207) 268-4182

- **Type of Discount**
  4 players for the price of 3
- **Days of the Week**
  Weekdays only (except holidays)
- **Hours of the Day**
  All day

Coupon expires 5/31/15. Cannot be combined with any other offer.

Golf Course Coupons

NEW ENGLAND GOLFGUIDE

2 0 1 4 / 2 0 1 5

NEW ENGLAND GOLFGUIDE

2 0 1 4 / 2 0 1 5

NEW ENGLAND GOLFGUIDE

2 0 1 4 / 2 0 1 5

NEW ENGLAND GOLFGUIDE

2 0 1 4 / 2 0 1 5

Country View Golf Course
Route 7, Brooks, ME (207) 722-3161

- **Type of Discount**
  1/2 price golf cart with 2 paid greens fees
- **Days of the Week**
  7 days a week
- **Hours of the Day**
  All day

Coupon expires 5/31/15. Cannot be combined with any other offer.

Deep Brook Golf Course
Saco, ME (207) 283-3500

- **Type of Discount**
  4 players for the price of 3
- **Days of the Week**
  7 days a week
- **Hours of the Day**
  All day

Coupon expires 5/31/15. Cannot be combined with any other offer.

Dunegrass Golf Club
Old Orchard Beach, ME (207) 934-4513

- **Type of Discount**
  4 players for the price of 3
- **Days of the Week**
  7 days a week
- **Hours of the Day**
  All day

Coupon expires 5/31/15. Cannot be combined with any other offer.

Dutch Elm Golf Course
Arundel, ME (207) 282-9850

- **Type of Discount**
  4 players for the price of 3
- **Days of the Week**
  7 days a week
- **Hours of the Day**
  After 12pm

Coupon expires 5/31/15. Cannot be combined with any other offer.

Golf Course Coupons

NEW ENGLAND GOLFGUIDE

2 0 1 4 / 2 0 1 5

NEW ENGLAND GOLFGUIDE

2 0 1 4 / 2 0 1 5

NEW ENGLAND GOLFGUIDE

2 0 1 4 / 2 0 1 5

NEW ENGLAND GOLFGUIDE

2 0 1 4 / 2 0 1 5

Evergreen Golf Club
Rangeley, ME (207) 240-5248

- **Type of Discount**
  10% off everything
- **Days of the Week**
  Weekdays only (except holidays)
- **Hours of the Day**
  All day

Coupon expires 5/31/15. Cannot be combined with any other offer.

Fort Kent Golf Club
Fort Kent, ME (207) 834-3149

- **Type of Discount**
  1 player at 9 hole price for 18 holes
- **Days of the Week**
  7 days a week
- **Hours of the Day**
  All day. Valid 4/1/14 to 10/20/14.

Valid 4/1/14 to 10/20/14. Cannot be combined with any other offer.

Foxcroft Golf Club
Dover-Foxcroft, ME (207) 564-8887

- **Type of Discount**
  $99 for 4 players with carts
- **Days of the Week**
  Weekdays only (except holidays)
- **Hours of the Day**
  All day

Coupon expires 5/31/15. Cannot be combined with any other offer.

Fox Ridge Golf Club
Auburn, ME (207) 777-GOLF(4653)

- **Type of Discount**
  4 players for the price of 3. Cart rental required.
- **Days of the Week**
  7 days a week
- **Hours of the Day**
  All day. Fri/Sat/Sun/Holiday after 1pm.

Coupon expires 5/31/15. Cannot be combined with any other offer.

Golf Course Coupons

NEW ENGLAND GOLFGUIDE

2 0 1 4 / 2 0 1 5

✂ -

NEW ENGLAND GOLFGUIDE

2 0 1 4 / 2 0 1 5

✂ -

NEW ENGLAND GOLFGUIDE

2 0 1 4 / 2 0 1 5

✂ -

NEW ENGLAND GOLFGUIDE

2 0 1 4 / 2 0 1 5

Freeport Country Club
Freeport, ME (207) 865-0711

- **Type of Discount**
  $29 for 18 holes (includes cart)
- **Days of the Week**
  Monday through Thursday (except holidays)
- **Hours of the Day**
  All day

Coupon expires 5/31/15. Cannot be combined with any other offer.

Frye Island Golf Course
Raymond, ME (207) 655-3551

- **Type of Discount**
  $5 off greens fees for up to 2 players
- **Days of the Week**
  Weekdays only (except holidays)
- **Hours of the Day**
  All day. Valid May through June and
  September through October.

Coupon expires 5/31/15. Cannot be combined with any other offer.

Goose River Golf Club
Rockport, ME (207) 236-8488

- **Type of Discount**
  4 players for the price of 3
- **Days of the Week**
  Weekdays only (except holidays)
- **Hours of the Day**
  All day

Coupon expires 5/31/15. Cannot be combined with any other offer.

Hampden Country Club
Hampden, ME (207) 862-9999

- **Type of Discount**
  All you can play for $15. Cart not included.
- **Days of the Week**
  Wednesday
- **Hours of the Day**
  All day

Coupon expires 5/31/15. Cannot be combined with any other offer.

Golf Course Coupons

NEW ENGLAND GOLFGUIDE

2 0 1 4 / 2 0 1 5

NEW ENGLAND GOLFGUIDE

2 0 1 4 / 2 0 1 5

NEW ENGLAND GOLFGUIDE

2 0 1 4 / 2 0 1 5

NEW ENGLAND GOLFGUIDE

2 0 1 4 / 2 0 1 5

Hermon Meadow Golf Club
Bangor, ME (207) 848-3741

- **Type of Discount**
  Free golf cart with 2 regular 18 hole greens fees
- **Days of the Week**
  Weekdays only (except holidays)
- **Hours of the Day**
  All day

Coupon expires 5/31/15. Cannot be combined with any other offer.

Hidden Meadows Golf Course
Old Town, ME (207) 827-4779

- **Type of Discount**
  Free golf cart with 2 paid greens fees
- **Days of the Week**
  7 days a week
- **Hours of the Day**
  All day

Coupon expires 5/31/15. Cannot be combined with any other offer.

Highland Green Golf Club
Topsham, ME (207) 725-8066

- **Type of Discount**
  $29 for 18 holes (includes cart)
- **Days of the Week**
  Monday through Thursday (except holidays)
- **Hours of the Day**
  All day

Coupon expires 5/31/15. Cannot be combined with any other offer.

Houlton Community Golf Course
Houlton, ME (207) 532-2662

- **Type of Discount**
  4 players for the price of 3
- **Days of the Week**
  7 days a week
- **Hours of the Day**
  All day. Call for tee times.

Coupon expires 5/31/15. Cannot be combined with any other offer.

Golf Course Coupons

NEW ENGLAND GOLFGUIDE

2 0 1 4 / 2 0 1 5

NEW ENGLAND GOLFGUIDE

2 0 1 4 / 2 0 1 5

NEW ENGLAND GOLFGUIDE

2 0 1 4 / 2 0 1 5

NEW ENGLAND GOLFGUIDE

2 0 1 4 / 2 0 1 5

Jato Highlands Golf Course
Lincoln, ME (207) 794-2433

- **Type of Discount**
  4 players for the price of 3
- **Days of the Week**
  7 days a week
- **Hours of the Day**
  All day

Coupon expires 5/31/15. Cannot be combined with any other offer.

Johnson W. Parks Golf Course
Pittsfield, ME (207) 487-5545

- **Type of Discount**
  2 players for the price of 1.
  Cart rental required.
- **Days of the Week**
  7 days a week
- **Hours of the Day**
  All weekdays, weekends and holidays after 1pm

Coupon expires 5/31/15. Cannot be combined with any other offer.

Kebo Valley Golf Club
Bar Harbor, ME (207) 288-3000

- **Type of Discount**
  15% off greens fees
- **Days of the Week**
  7 days a week
- **Hours of the Day**
  Not valid for afternoon or twilight rates

Coupon expires 5/31/15. Cannot be combined with any other offer.

Kenduskeag Golf & Country Club
Kenduskeag, ME (207) 884-7330

- **Type of Discount**
  Free golf cart with 2 paid greens fees
- **Days of the Week**
  Weekdays only (except holidays)
- **Hours of the Day**
  All day

Coupon expires 5/31/15. Cannot be combined with any other offer.

NEW ENGLAND GOLFGUIDE

2 0 1 4 / 2 0 1 5

NEW ENGLAND GOLFGUIDE

2 0 1 4 / 2 0 1 5

NEW ENGLAND GOLFGUIDE

2 0 1 4 / 2 0 1 5

NEW ENGLAND GOLFGUIDE

2 0 1 4 / 2 0 1 5

Lake Kezar Country Club
Lovell, ME (207) 925-2462

- **Type of Discount**
  4 players for price of 3
- **Days of the Week**
  7 days a week
- **Hours of the Day**
  After 1pm

Coupon expires 5/31/15. Cannot be combined with any other offer.

Lakeview Golf Course
Burnham, ME (207) 948-5414

- **Type of Discount**
  4 greens fees for the price of 3
- **Days of the Week**
  Monday through Thursday (except holidays)
- **Hours of the Day**
  All day

Coupon expires 5/31/15. Cannot be combined with any other offer.

Lakewood Golf Course
Madison, ME (207) 474-5955

- **Type of Discount**
  4 players for the price of 3
- **Days of the Week**
  7 days a week
- **Hours of the Day**
  All day

Coupon expires 5/31/15. Cannot be combined with any other offer.

Ledges Golf Club, The
York, ME (207) 351-3000

- **Type of Discount**
  Free golf cart with 2 paid greens fees
- **Days of the Week**
  7 days a week
- **Hours of the Day**
  All day

Coupon expires 5/31/15. Cannot be combined with any other offer.

Golf Course Coupons

NEW ENGLAND GOLFGUIDE

2 0 1 4 / 2 0 1 5

NEW ENGLAND GOLFGUIDE

2 0 1 4 / 2 0 1 5

NEW ENGLAND GOLFGUIDE

2 0 1 4 / 2 0 1 5

NEW ENGLAND GOLFGUIDE

2 0 1 4 / 2 0 1 5

Limestone Country Club
Limestone, ME (207) 328-7277

- **Type of Discount**
  $5 off greens fees. Cart rental required.

- **Days of the Week**
  Weekdays only (except holidays)

- **Hours of the Day**
  All day

Coupon expires 5/31/15. Cannot be combined with any other offer.

Links at Outlook, The
South Berwick, ME (207) 384-4653

- **Type of Discount**
  Free golf cart with 2 paid greens fees

- **Days of the Week**
  7 days a week

- **Hours of the Day**
  All day

Coupon expires 5/31/15. Cannot be combined with any other offer.

Long Lake Country Club
Madawaska, ME (207) 895-6957

- **Type of Discount**
  Free golf cart with 2 paid greens fees

- **Days of the Week**
  7 days a week

- **Hours of the Day**
  All day. Valid June 1 through September 15.

Coupon expires 5/31/15. Cannot be combined with any other offer.

Lucerne-in-Maine Golf Course
Dedham, ME (207) 843-6282

- **Type of Discount**
  Free golf cart with 2 paid greens fees

- **Days of the Week**
  Weekdays only (except holidays)

- **Hours of the Day**
  Before 3pm

Coupon expires 5/31/15. Cannot be combined with any other offer.

Golf Course Coupons

NEW ENGLAND GOLFGUIDE

2 0 1 4 / 2 0 1 5

NEW ENGLAND GOLFGUIDE

2 0 1 4 / 2 0 1 5

NEW ENGLAND GOLFGUIDE

2 0 1 4 / 2 0 1 5

NEW ENGLAND GOLFGUIDE

2 0 1 4 / 2 0 1 5

Maple Lane Inn and Golf Club
Livermore, ME (207) 897-3770

- **Type of Discount**
  18 holes of golf, golf cart & lunch for $30
- **Days of the Week**
  Weekdays only (except holidays)
- **Hours of the Day**
  All day

Coupon expires 5/31/15. Cannot be combined with any other offer.

Mars Hill Country Club
Mars Hill, ME (207) 425-4802

- **Type of Discount**
  $32 for 18 holes including cart
- **Days of the Week**
  7 days a week
- **Hours of the Day**
  All day

Coupon expires 5/31/15. Cannot be combined with any other offer.

Martindale Country Club
Auburn, ME (207) 782-1107

- **Type of Discount**
  4 players for the price of 3
- **Days of the Week**
  Monday through Thursday (except holidays)
- **Hours of the Day**
  All day

Coupon expires 5/31/15. Cannot be combined with any other offer.

Meadows Golf Club, The
Litchfield, ME (207) 268-3000

- **Type of Discount**
  25% discount for 2 to 4 players
- **Days of the Week**
  7 days a week
- **Hours of the Day**
  Saturday and Sunday after 12pm

Coupon expires 5/31/15. Cannot be combined with any other offer.

Golf Course Coupons

NEW ENGLAND GOLFGUIDE

2 0 1 4 / 2 0 1 5

NEW ENGLAND GOLFGUIDE

2 0 1 4 / 2 0 1 5

NEW ENGLAND GOLFGUIDE

2 0 1 4 / 2 0 1 5

NEW ENGLAND GOLFGUIDE

2 0 1 4 / 2 0 1 5

Mere Creek Golf Course
Brunswick, ME (207) 721-9995

- **Type of Discount**
  $29 for 18 holes (includes cart)
- **Days of the Week**
  Monday through Thursday (except holidays)
- **Hours of the Day**
  All day

Coupon expires 5/31/15. Cannot be combined with any other offer.

Merriland Farm Par 3 Golf
Wells, ME (207) 646-0508

- **Type of Discount**
  2 players for the price of 1
- **Days of the Week**
  Weekdays only (except holidays)
- **Hours of the Day**
  All day. Valid April, May, June, September, and October.

Coupon expires 5/31/15. Cannot be combined with any other offer.

Mt. Kineo Golf Course
Kineo Island Township, ME (207) 534-9012

- **Type of Discount**
  Free golf cart with 2 paid greens fees
- **Days of the Week**
  7 days a week
- **Hours of the Day**
  All day

Coupon expires 5/31/15. Cannot be combined with any other offer.

Naples Golf and Country Club
Route 114, Naples, ME (207) 693-6424

- **Type of Discount**
  25% discount for 2-4 players
- **Days of the Week**
  Weekdays only (except holidays)
- **Hours of the Day**
  After 1pm

Coupon expires 5/31/15. Cannot be combined with any other offer.

Golf Course Coupons

NEW ENGLAND GOLFGUIDE

2 0 1 4 / 2 0 1 5

✂ --

NEW ENGLAND GOLFGUIDE

2 0 1 4 / 2 0 1 5

✂ --

NEW ENGLAND GOLFGUIDE

2 0 1 4 / 2 0 1 5

✂ --

NEW ENGLAND GOLFGUIDE

2 0 1 4 / 2 0 1 5

Nonesuch River Golf Club
Scarborough, ME (888) 256-2717

- **Type of Discount**
  4 players for the price of 3. Cart rental required.
- **Days of the Week**
  Monday through Thursday
- **Hours of the Day**
  All day

Coupon expires 5/31/15. Cannot be combined with any other offer.

Northport Golf Club
Northport, ME (207) 338-2270

- **Type of Discount**
  $25 per person (includes cart) for 18 holes
- **Days of the Week**
  Weekdays only (except holidays)
- **Hours of the Day**
  All day

Coupon expires 5/31/15. Cannot be combined with any other offer.

Oakdale Country Club
Mexico, ME (207) 364-3951

- **Type of Discount**
  4 players for the price of 3
- **Days of the Week**
  7 days a week
- **Hours of the Day**
  All day

Coupon expires 5/31/15. Cannot be combined with any other offer.

Old Marsh Country Club
Wells, ME (207) 251-4653

- **Type of Discount**
  4 players for the price of 3 (18 holes including cart)
- **Days of the Week**
  Monday through Thursday (except holidays)
- **Hours of the Day**
  All day

Coupon expires 5/31/15. Cannot be combined with any other offer.

Golf Course Coupons

NEW ENGLAND GOLFGUIDE

2 0 1 4 / 2 0 1 5

NEW ENGLAND GOLFGUIDE

2 0 1 4 / 2 0 1 5

NEW ENGLAND GOLFGUIDE

2 0 1 4 / 2 0 1 5

NEW ENGLAND GOLFGUIDE

2 0 1 4 / 2 0 1 5

Palmyra Golf Course
Palmyra, ME (207) 938-4947

- **Type of Discount**
  2 players for the price of 1
- **Days of the Week**
  7 days a week
- **Hours of the Day**
  All day

Coupon expires 5/31/15. Cannot be combined with any other offer.

Paris Hill Country Club
Paris Hill Road, Paris, ME (207) 743-2371

- **Type of Discount**
  2 players for the price of 1
- **Days of the Week**
  Weekdays only (except holidays)
- **Hours of the Day**
  All day

Coupon expires 5/31/15. Cannot be combined with any other offer.

Penobscot Valley Country Club
Orono, ME (207) 866-2423

- **Type of Discount**
  4 players for the price of 3 (18 holes
  including cart)
- **Days of the Week**
  Monday through Thursday (except holidays)
- **Hours of the Day**
  All day

Coupon expires 5/31/15. Cannot be combined with any other offer.

Point Sebago Golf Club
Casco, ME (207) 655-2747

- **Type of Discount**
  2 players for the price of 1
- **Days of the Week**
  Monday through Thursday (except holidays)
- **Hours of the Day**
  After 11am

Coupon expires 5/31/15. Cannot be combined with any other offer.

Golf Course Coupons

NEW ENGLAND GOLFGUIDE

2 0 1 4 / 2 0 1 5

NEW ENGLAND GOLFGUIDE

2 0 1 4 / 2 0 1 5

NEW ENGLAND GOLFGUIDE

2 0 1 4 / 2 0 1 5

NEW ENGLAND GOLFGUIDE

2 0 1 4 / 2 0 1 5

Poland Spring Country Club
Route 26, Poland Spring, ME (207) 998-6002

- **Type of Discount**
  4 players for the price of 3
- **Days of the Week**
  Monday through Thursday (except holidays)
- **Hours of the Day**
  All day

Coupon expires 5/31/15. Cannot be combined with any other offer.

Portage Hills Country Club
Route 11, Portage, ME (207) 435-8221

- **Type of Discount**
  2 players for the price of 1
- **Days of the Week**
  7 days a week
- **Hours of the Day**
  All day

Coupon expires 5/31/15. Cannot be combined with any other offer.

Presque Isle Country Club
Presque Isle, ME (207) 764-0430

- **Type of Discount**
  Play 18 holes at 9 hole rate. Cart rental required.
- **Days of the Week**
  7 days a week
- **Hours of the Day**
  All day. Valid through October 31, 2014.

Coupon expires 10/31/14. Cannot be combined with any other offer.

Province Lake Golf Club
Route 153, Parsonfield, ME (800) 325-4434

- **Type of Discount**
  4 players for price of 3
- **Days of the Week**
  7 days a week
- **Hours of the Day**
  After 1pm

Coupon expires 5/31/15. Cannot be combined with any other offer.

NEW ENGLAND GOLFGUIDE

2 0 1 4 / 2 0 1 5

NEW ENGLAND GOLFGUIDE

2 0 1 4 / 2 0 1 5

NEW ENGLAND GOLFGUIDE

2 0 1 4 / 2 0 1 5

NEW ENGLAND GOLFGUIDE

2 0 1 4 / 2 0 1 5

Rockland Golf Club
Rockland, ME (207) 594-9322

- **Type of Discount**
  $50 per player (includes cart)
- **Days of the Week**
  7 days a week
- **Hours of the Day**
  All day

Coupon expires 5/31/15. Cannot be combined with any other offer.

Rocky Knoll Country Club
Orrington, ME (207) 989-0109

- **Type of Discount**
  2 players for the price of 1
- **Days of the Week**
  7 days a week
- **Hours of the Day**
  All day

Coupon expires 5/31/15. Cannot be combined with any other offer.

Sable Oaks Golf Club
South Portland, ME (207) 775-6257

- **Type of Discount**
  4 players for the price of 3
- **Days of the Week**
  7 days a week
- **Hours of the Day**
  All day

Coupon expires 5/31/15. Cannot be combined with any other offer.

Salmon Falls Golf Course
Hollis, ME (207) 929-5233 or (800) 734-1616

- **Type of Discount**
  $60 for 2 players and golfcart for 18 holes
- **Days of the Week**
  7 days a week
- **Hours of the Day**
  All day

Coupon expires 5/31/15. Cannot be combined with any other offer.

Golf Course Coupons

NEW ENGLAND GOLFGUIDE

2 0 1 4 / 2 0 1 5

- -

NEW ENGLAND GOLFGUIDE

2 0 1 4 / 2 0 1 5

- -

NEW ENGLAND GOLFGUIDE

2 0 1 4 / 2 0 1 5

- -

NEW ENGLAND GOLFGUIDE

2 0 1 4 / 2 0 1 5

Samoset Resort Golf Club
Rockport, ME (207) 594-1431

- **Type of Discount**
  4 players for the price of 3

- **Days of the Week**
  7 days a week

- **Hours of the Day**
  All day

Coupon expires 5/31/15. Cannot be combined with any other offer.

Sanford Country Club
Route 4, Sanford, ME (207) 324-5462

- **Type of Discount**
  2 players for the price of 1

- **Days of the Week**
  Weekdays only (except holidays)

- **Hours of the Day**
  All day

Coupon expires 5/31/15. Cannot be combined with any other offer.

Searsport Pines Golf Course
Searsport, ME (207) 548-2854

- **Type of Discount**
  $5 off greens fees for up to 4 players

- **Days of the Week**
  7 days a week

- **Hours of the Day**
  All day

Coupon expires 5/31/15. Cannot be combined with any other offer.

Sebasco Harbor Resort Golf Club
Sebasco Estates, ME (207) 389-9060

- **Type of Discount**
  $35 per person (includes cart) up to 4 players

- **Days of the Week**
  Weekdays only (except holidays)

- **Hours of the Day**
  All day

Coupon expires 5/31/15. Cannot be combined with any other offer.

Golf Course Coupons

NEW ENGLAND GOLFGUIDE

2014 / 2015

NEW ENGLAND GOLFGUIDE

2014 / 2015

NEW ENGLAND GOLFGUIDE

2014 / 2015

NEW ENGLAND GOLFGUIDE

2014 / 2015

Sheepscot Links Golf Club
Whitefield, ME (207) 549-7060

- **Type of Discount**
  2 players for the price of 1
- **Days of the Week**
  7 days a week
- **Hours of the Day**
  All day

Coupon expires 5/31/15. Cannot be combined with any other offer.

Spring Meadows Golf Course
Gray, ME (207) 657-2586

- **Type of Discount**
  4 players for the price of 3
- **Days of the Week**
  Monday through Thursday (except holidays)
- **Hours of the Day**
  All day

Coupon expires 5/31/15. Cannot be combined with any other offer.

Sugarloaf Golf Club
Carrabassett Valley, ME (207) 237-2000

- **Type of Discount**
  Free golf cart with 2 paid greens fees
- **Days of the Week**
  Weekdays only (except holidays)
- **Hours of the Day**
  All day

Coupon expires 5/31/15. Cannot be combined with any other offer.

Sunday River Golf Club
Bethel, ME (207) 824-4653

- **Type of Discount**
  4 players for the price of 3 (18 holes
  including cart)
- **Days of the Week**
  Monday through Thursday (except holidays)
- **Hours of the Day**
  All day

Coupon expires 5/31/15. Cannot be combined with any other offer.

Golf Course Coupons

NEW ENGLAND GOLFGUIDE

2 0 1 4 / 2 0 1 5

NEW ENGLAND GOLFGUIDE

2 0 1 4 / 2 0 1 5

NEW ENGLAND GOLFGUIDE

2 0 1 4 / 2 0 1 5

NEW ENGLAND GOLFGUIDE

2 0 1 4 / 2 0 1 5

Toddy Brook Golf Course
North Yarmouth, ME (207) 829-5100

- **Type of Discount**
  4 players for the price of 3
- **Days of the Week**
  7 days a week
- **Hours of the Day**
  All day

Coupon expires 5/31/15. Cannot be combined with any other offer.

Traditions Golf Club
Holden, ME (207) 989-9909

- **Type of Discount**
  Free bucket of range balls
- **Days of the Week**
  7 days a week
- **Hours of the Day**
  All day

Coupon expires 5/31/15. Cannot be combined with any other offer.

Turner Highlands Golf Course
Turner, ME (207) 224-7060

- **Type of Discount**
  $35 with a cart
- **Days of the Week**
  7 days a week
- **Hours of the Day**
  All day

Coupon expires 5/31/15. Cannot be combined with any other offer.

Va-Jo-Wa Golf Club
Island Falls, ME (207) 463-2128

- **Type of Discount**
  2 players for the price of 1. Cart rental required.
- **Days of the Week**
  Weekdays only (except holidays)
- **Hours of the Day**
  All day

Coupon expires 5/31/15. Cannot be combined with any other offer.

Golf Course Coupons

NEW ENGLAND GOLFGUIDE

2 0 1 4 / 2 0 1 5

NEW ENGLAND GOLFGUIDE

2 0 1 4 / 2 0 1 5

NEW ENGLAND GOLFGUIDE

2 0 1 4 / 2 0 1 5

NEW ENGLAND GOLFGUIDE

2 0 1 4 / 2 0 1 5

Wawenock Country Club
Walpole, ME (207) 563-3938

- **Type of Discount**
  $30 per player for 18 holes with cart
- **Days of the Week**
  7 days a week
- **Hours of the Day**
  All day. Please call ahead for tee time.

Coupon expires 5/31/15. Cannot be combined with any other offer.

Webhannet Golf Club
Kennebunk, ME (207) 967-3951

- **Type of Discount**
  4 players for the price of 3
- **Days of the Week**
  7 days a week
- **Hours of the Day**
  All day. Valid May, June, September,
  and October.

Coupon expires 5/31/15. Cannot be combined with any other offer.

Western View Golf Club
Augusta, ME (207) 622-5309

- **Type of Discount**
  2 players for the price of 1 (greens fees).
  Cart rental for 2 required.
- **Days of the Week**
  7 days a week
- **Hours of the Day**
  All day

Coupon expires 5/31/15. Cannot be combined with any other offer.

Whitetail Golf Course
Charleston, ME (207) 285-7730

- **Type of Discount**
  18 holes for 9 hole price with cart/per person
- **Days of the Week**
  Sundays
- **Hours of the Day**
  7am–11am

Coupon expires 5/31/15. Cannot be combined with any other offer.

Golf Course Coupons

NEW ENGLAND GOLFGUIDE

2 0 1 4 / 2 0 1 5

NEW ENGLAND GOLFGUIDE

2 0 1 4 / 2 0 1 5

NEW ENGLAND GOLFGUIDE

2 0 1 4 / 2 0 1 5

NEW ENGLAND GOLFGUIDE

2 0 1 4 / 2 0 1 5

Wilson Lake Country Club
Wilton, ME (207) 645-2016

- **Type of Discount**
  $29 for 18 holes (includes cart)

- **Days of the Week**
  Monday through Thursday (except holidays)

- **Hours of the Day**
  All day

Coupon expires 5/31/15. Cannot be combined with any other offer.

Acushnet River Valley Golf Course
Acushnet, MA (508) 998-7777

- **Type of Discount**
  Free golf cart with 4 paid greens fees

- **Days of the Week**
  Weekdays only (except holidays)

- **Hours of the Day**
  All day

Coupon expires 5/31/15. Cannot be combined with any other offer.

Allendale Country Club
Dartmouth, MA (508) 992-8682

- **Type of Discount**
  $100 for 2 players (including cart)
  $200 for 4 players (including cart)

- **Days of the Week**
  7 days a week

- **Hours of the Day**
  After 1pm. Must call for tee time.

Coupon expires 5/31/15. Cannot be combined with any other offer.

Amherst Golf Club
Amherst, MA (413) 256-6894

- **Type of Discount**
  2 players for the price of 1 (golf cart required).
  Please call ahead when using coupon.

- **Days of the Week**
  Weekdays only (except holidays)

- **Hours of the Day**
  All day

Coupon expires 5/31/15. Cannot be combined with any other offer.

Golf Course Coupons

NEW ENGLAND GOLFGUIDE

2 0 1 4 / 2 0 1 5

NEW ENGLAND GOLFGUIDE

2 0 1 4 / 2 0 1 5

NEW ENGLAND GOLFGUIDE

2 0 1 4 / 2 0 1 5

NEW ENGLAND GOLFGUIDE

2 0 1 4 / 2 0 1 5

Ashfield Community Golf Club
Ashfield, MA (413) 628- 4413

- **Type of Discount**
  $5 off greens fees
- **Days of the Week**
  Weekends and holidays only
- **Hours of the Day**
  All day

Coupon expires 5/31/15. Cannot be combined with any other offer.

Atlantic Country Club
Plymouth, MA (508) 759-6644

- **Type of Discount**
  $5 off greens fees
- **Days of the Week**
  Monday through Thursday
- **Hours of the Day**
  All day (excludes twilight hours)

Coupon expires 5/31/15. Cannot be combined with any other offer.

Back Nine Club, The
Lakeville, MA (508) 947-9991

- **Type of Discount**
  Free cart with 2 paid greens fees
- **Days of the Week**
  Weekdays only (except holidays)
- **Hours of the Day**
  All day

Coupon expires 5/31/15. Cannot be combined with any other offer.

Bas Ridge Golf Course
Plunkett Street, Hinsdale, MA (413) 655-2605

- **Type of Discount**
  2 greens fees for the price of 1.
  Cart rental required.
- **Days of the Week**
  Weekdays only (except holidays)
- **Hours of the Day**
  8am–3pm; not valid July & August

Coupon expires 5/31/15. Cannot be combined with any other offer.

NEW ENGLAND
GOLFGUIDE

2 0 1 4 / 2 0 1 5

NEW ENGLAND
GOLFGUIDE

2 0 1 4 / 2 0 1 5

NEW ENGLAND
GOLFGUIDE

2 0 1 4 / 2 0 1 5

NEW ENGLAND
GOLFGUIDE

2 0 1 4 / 2 0 1 5

Bayberry Hills Golf Course
South Yarmouth, MA (508) 394-5597

- **Type of Discount**
  $25 greens fee
- **Days of the Week**
  Weekdays only (except holidays)
- **Hours of the Day**
  All day. November through March.
  Cart rental required.

Coupon expires 5/31/15. Cannot be combined with any other offer.

Bay Path Golf Course
East Brookfield, MA (508) 867-8161

- **Type of Discount**
  4 players for price of 3
- **Days of the Week**
  7 days a week
- **Hours of the Day**
  10am–2pm (excludes league play)

Coupon expires 5/31/15. Cannot be combined with any other offer.

Bay Pointe Country Club
Onset, MA (508) 759-8802, 1-800-24T-TIME

- **Type of Discount**
  4 players for the price of 3 (includes cart)
- **Days of the Week**
  Monday through Friday, year-round
- **Hours of the Day**
  Until 1pm

Coupon expires 5/31/15. Cannot be combined with any other offer.

Beaver Brook Country Club
Main Street, Haydenville, MA (413) 268-7229

- **Type of Discount**
  2 players for the price of 1. Cart rental required.
- **Days of the Week**
  7 days a week
- **Hours of the Day**
  Before 12pm

Coupon expires 5/31/15. Cannot be combined with any other offer.

Golf Course Coupons

NEW ENGLAND GOLFGUIDE

2014 / 2015

NEW ENGLAND GOLFGUIDE

2014 / 2015

NEW ENGLAND GOLFGUIDE

2014 / 2015

NEW ENGLAND GOLFGUIDE

2014 / 2015

Bedrock Golf Club
Rutland, MA (508) 886-0202

- **Type of Discount**
  4 players for the price of 3
- **Days of the Week**
  7 days a week
- **Hours of the Day**
  All day

Coupon expires 5/31/15. Cannot be combined with any other offer.

Berlin Country Club
Berlin, MA (978) 838-2733

- **Type of Discount**
  Buy 1 greens fee get 1 free
- **Days of the Week**
  Weekdays only (except holidays)
- **Hours of the Day**
  Until 2pm

Coupon expires 5/31/15. Cannot be combined with any other offer.

Beverly Golf & Tennis
Beverly, MA (978) 922-9072

- **Type of Discount**
  2 players for the price of 1.
  Cart rental required.
- **Days of the Week**
  Monday through Thursday
- **Hours of the Day**
  All day

Coupon expires 5/31/15. Cannot be combined with any other offer.

Blackstone National Golf Club
Sutton, MA (508) 865-2111

- **Type of Discount**
  4 players for the price of 3. Cart rental required.
- **Days of the Week**
  Monday through Thursday
- **Hours of the Day**
  All day

Coupon expires 5/31/15. Cannot be combined with any other offer.

Golf Course Coupons

NEW ENGLAND
GOLFGUIDE

2 0 1 4 / 2 0 1 5

NEW ENGLAND
GOLFGUIDE

2 0 1 4 / 2 0 1 5

NEW ENGLAND
GOLFGUIDE

2 0 1 4 / 2 0 1 5

NEW ENGLAND
GOLFGUIDE

2 0 1 4 / 2 0 1 5

Blissful Meadows Golf Club
Uxbridge, MA (508) 278-6113

- **Type of Discount**
  4 players for the price of 3
- **Days of the Week**
  Weekdays only (except holidays)
- **Hours of the Day**
  All day

Coupon expires 5/31/15. Cannot be combined with any other offer.

Blue Rock Golf Course
South Yarmouth, MA (508) 398-9295

- **Type of Discount**
  Links & Lunch – Complement your round with lunch at the Blue Rock Grill for only $5
- **Days of the Week**
  7 days a week
- **Hours of the Day**
  All day

Coupon expires 5/31/15. Cannot be combined with any other offer.

Bradford Country Club
Bradford, MA (978) 372-8587

- **Type of Discount**
  2 players, $80 for 18 holes with cart
- **Days of the Week**
  Weekdays only (except holidays)
- **Hours of the Day**
  All day. Must bring coupon.

Coupon expires 5/31/15. Cannot be combined with any other offer.

The Brookside Club
Bourne, MA (508) 743-4653

- **Type of Discount**
  4 players for the price of 3
- **Days of the Week**
  Monday through Thursday (except holidays)
- **Hours of the Day**
  All day

Coupon expires 5/31/15. Cannot be combined with any other offer.

Golf Course Coupons

NEW ENGLAND GOLFGUIDE

2 0 1 4 / 2 0 1 5

NEW ENGLAND GOLFGUIDE

2 0 1 4 / 2 0 1 5

NEW ENGLAND GOLFGUIDE

2 0 1 4 / 2 0 1 5

NEW ENGLAND GOLFGUIDE

2 0 1 4 / 2 0 1 5

Bungay Brook Golf Club
Bellingham, MA (508) 883-1600

- **Type of Discount**
  Free golf cart with 2 paid greens fees.
  Free small pail range balls with paid greens fees.
- **Days of the Week**
  7 days a week
- **Hours of the Day**
  All day

Coupon expires 5/31/15. Cannot be combined with any other offer.

Captains Golf Course, The
Brewster, MA (508) 896-1716

- **Type of Discount**
  $5 off greens fees
- **Days of the Week**
  7 days a week
- **Hours of the Day**
  After 12pm

Coupon expires 5/31/15. Cannot be combined with any other offer.

Cedar Glen Golf Club
Saugus, MA (781) 233-3609

- **Type of Discount**
  4 players for price of 3
- **Days of the Week**
  Weekdays only (except holidays)
- **Hours of the Day**
  Before 2pm

Coupon expires 5/31/15. Cannot be combined with any other offer.

Cedar Hill Golf Club
Stoughton, MA (781) 344-8913

- **Type of Discount**
  4 players for price of 3
- **Days of the Week**
  Weekdays only (except holidays)
- **Hours of the Day**
  Before 2pm

Coupon expires 5/31/15. Cannot be combined with any other offer.

Golf Course Coupons

NEW ENGLAND GOLFGUIDE

2 0 1 4 / 2 0 1 5

NEW ENGLAND GOLFGUIDE

2 0 1 4 / 2 0 1 5

NEW ENGLAND GOLFGUIDE

2 0 1 4 / 2 0 1 5

NEW ENGLAND GOLFGUIDE

2 0 1 4 / 2 0 1 5

Chelmsford Country Club
Chelmsford, MA (978) 256-1818

- **Type of Discount**
  Free golf cart with 2 paid greens fees
- **Days of the Week**
  7 days a week
- **Hours of the Day**
  All day

Coupon expires 5/31/15. Cannot be combined with any other offer.

Chequessett Golf Club
Wellfleet, MA (508) 349-3704

- **Type of Discount**
  20% off greens fees
- **Days of the Week**
  7 days a week
- **Hours of the Day**
  After 1pm

Coupon expires 5/31/15. Cannot be combined with any other offer.

Cherry Hill Golf Course
Amherst, MA (413) 256-4071

- **Type of Discount**
  2 players for the price of 1
- **Days of the Week**
  7 days a week
- **Hours of the Day**
  All day

Coupon expires 5/31/15. Cannot be combined with any other offer.

Clearview Golf Course
Millbury, MA (508) 754-5654

- **Type of Discount**
  2 players for the price of 1
- **Days of the Week**
  Monday through Friday
- **Hours of the Day**
  All day. Not valid during leagues and
  tournaments.

Coupon expires 5/31/15. Cannot be combined with any other offer.

NEW ENGLAND GOLFGUIDE

2 0 1 4 / 2 0 1 5

NEW ENGLAND GOLFGUIDE

2 0 1 4 / 2 0 1 5

NEW ENGLAND GOLFGUIDE

2 0 1 4 / 2 0 1 5

NEW ENGLAND GOLFGUIDE

2 0 1 4 / 2 0 1 5

Cold Spring Country Club
Belchertown, MA (413) 323-4888

- **Type of Discount**
  Free golf cart with 2 paid greens fees
- **Days of the Week**
  Monday through Thursday (except holidays)
- **Hours of the Day**
  All day

Coupon expires 5/31/15. Cannot be combined with any other offer.

Country Club of Billerica
Billerica, MA (978) 667-9121 ext. 22

- **Type of Discount**
  4 players for the price of 3
- **Days of the Week**
  Weekdays only (except holidays)
- **Hours of the Day**
  9am–2pm. Riding carts not included.

Coupon expires 5/31/15. Cannot be combined with any other offer.

Country Club of Greenfield
Greenfield, MA (413) 773 -7530

- **Type of Discount**
  4 players for $120 with cart
- **Days of the Week**
  Weekdays only (except holidays)
- **Hours of the Day**
  All day

Coupon expires 5/31/15. Cannot be combined with any other offer.

Cranwell Resort, Spa, and Golf Course
Lenox, MA (413) 637-2563

- **Type of Discount**
  2 players for the price of 1.
  Cart rental required.
- **Days of the Week**
  7 days a week
- **Hours of the Day**
  All day. Not valid July and August.

Coupon expires 5/31/15. Cannot be combined with any other offer.

Golf Course Coupons

NEW ENGLAND GOLFGUIDE

2 0 1 4 / 2 0 1 5

✂ -

NEW ENGLAND GOLFGUIDE

2 0 1 4 / 2 0 1 5

✂ -

NEW ENGLAND GOLFGUIDE

2 0 1 4 / 2 0 1 5

✂ -

NEW ENGLAND GOLFGUIDE

2 0 1 4 / 2 0 1 5

Crestview Country Club
Agawam, MA (413) 786-2593

- **Type of Discount**
  4 players for the price of 3.
  Cart rental required.
- **Days of the Week**
  Monday through Thursday (except holidays)
- **Hours of the Day**
  10am–2pm

Coupon expires 5/31/15. Cannot be combined with any other offer.

Crosswinds Golf Club
Plymouth, MA (508) 830-1199

- **Type of Discount**
  4 players for the price of 3
- **Days of the Week**
  Monday through Thursday (except holidays)
- **Hours of the Day**
  After 1pm. Rates subject to change.

Coupon expires 5/31/15. Cannot be combined with any other offer.

Crumpin-Fox Club
Bernardston, MA (413) 648-9101

- **Type of Discount**
  $25 off per guide holder or coupon holder
- **Days of the Week**
  Monday through Thursday (except holidays)
- **Hours of the Day**
  All day. Valid May 15 - October 15.

Coupon expires 5/31/15. Cannot be combined with any other offer.

Crystal Lake Golf Club
Haverhill, MA (978) 374-9621

- **Type of Discount**
  $39 per person (includes cart)
- **Days of the Week**
  7 days a week
- **Hours of the Day**
  All day

Coupon expires 5/31/15. Cannot be combined with any other offer.

Golf Course Coupons

NEW ENGLAND GOLFGUIDE

2014 / 2015

✂ -

NEW ENGLAND GOLFGUIDE

2014 / 2015

✂ -

NEW ENGLAND GOLFGUIDE

2014 / 2015

✂ -

NEW ENGLAND GOLFGUIDE

2014 / 2015

Dennis Highlands Golf Course
Dennis, MA (508) 385-8347

- **Type of Discount**
  2 players for the price of 1. Cart rental required.
- **Days of the Week**
  Monday through Thursday (except holidays)
- **Hours of the Day**
  All day. Not valid July and August.

Coupon expires 5/31/15. Cannot be combined with any other offer.

Dennis Pines Golf Course
East Dennis, MA (508) 385-8347

- **Type of Discount**
  2 players for the price of 1. Cart rental required.
- **Days of the Week**
  Monday through Thursday (except holidays)
- **Hours of the Day**
  All day. Not valid July and August.

Coupon expires 5/31/15. Cannot be combined with any other offer.

Dunroamin Country Club
Gilbertville, MA (413) 477-0004

- **Type of Discount**
  2 players for the price of 1
- **Days of the Week**
  Weekdays only (except holidays)
- **Hours of the Day**
  All day. Call for tee times.

Coupon expires 5/31/15. Cannot be combined with any other offer.

D.W. Field Golf Course
Brockton, MA (508) 580-7855

- **Type of Discount**
  4 players for the price of 3. Cart rental required.
- **Days of the Week**
  Monday through Thursday (except holidays)
- **Hours of the Day**
  All day

Coupon expires 5/31/15. Cannot be combined with any other offer.

Golf Course Coupons

NEW ENGLAND GOLFGUIDE

2 0 1 4 / 2 0 1 5

NEW ENGLAND GOLFGUIDE

2 0 1 4 / 2 0 1 5

NEW ENGLAND GOLFGUIDE

2 0 1 4 / 2 0 1 5

NEW ENGLAND GOLFGUIDE

2 0 1 4 / 2 0 1 5

Easton Country Club
South Easton, MA (508) 238-2500

- **Type of Discount**
  4 players for the price of 3

- **Days of the Week**
  7 days a week

- **Hours of the Day**
  All day - weekdays (except holidays).
  After 11:30am (Saturday, Sunday, holidays)

Coupon expires 5/31/15. Cannot be combined with any other offer.

Edge Hill Golf Club
Ashfield, MA (413) 625-6018

- **Type of Discount**
  4 players for the price of 3

- **Days of the Week**
  Weekdays only (except holidays)

- **Hours of the Day**
  All day

Coupon expires 5/31/15. Cannot be combined with any other offer.

Egremont Country Club
Great Barrington, MA (413) 528-4222

- **Type of Discount**
  2 players for the price of 1. Cart rental required.

- **Days of the Week**
  Weekdays only (except holidays)

- **Hours of the Day**
  Tee off by 2pm

Coupon expires 5/31/15. Cannot be combined with any other offer.

Ellinwood Country Club
Athol, MA (978) 249-7460

- **Type of Discount**
  2 players for the price of 1. Cart rental required.

- **Days of the Week**
  Weekdays only (except holidays)

- **Hours of the Day**
  All day

Coupon expires 5/31/15. Cannot be combined with any other offer.

Golf Course Coupons

NEW ENGLAND GOLFGUIDE

2 0 1 4 / 2 0 1 5

NEW ENGLAND GOLFGUIDE

2 0 1 4 / 2 0 1 5

NEW ENGLAND GOLFGUIDE

2 0 1 4 / 2 0 1 5

NEW ENGLAND GOLFGUIDE

2 0 1 4 / 2 0 1 5

Falmouth Country Club
Falmouth, MA (508) 548-3211

- **Type of Discount**
  $10 off each player, up to 4 players (resident prices)
- **Days of the Week**
  Monday through Thursday (except holidays)
- **Hours of the Day**
  Before 2pm. Must have coupon.

Coupon expires 5/31/15. Cannot be combined with any other offer.

Fire Fly Country Club
Seekonk, MA (508) 336-6622

- **Type of Discount**
  4 players for the price of 3
- **Days of the Week**
  7 days a week
- **Hours of the Day**
  All day

Coupon expires 5/31/15. Cannot be combined with any other offer.

Fore Kicks Golf Course & Sports Complex
Norfolk, MA (508) 384-4433

- **Type of Discount**
  1 player at 1/2 price
- **Days of the Week**
  7 days a week
- **Hours of the Day**
  All day

Coupon expires 5/31/15. Cannot be combined with any other offer.

Forest Park Country Club
Adams, MA (413) 743-3311

- **Type of Discount**
  2 players for the price of 1
- **Days of the Week**
  7 days a week
- **Hours of the Day**
  Please call ahead on weekends for availability

Coupon expires 5/31/15. Cannot be combined with any other offer.

NEW ENGLAND GOLFGUIDE

2 0 1 4 / 2 0 1 5

NEW ENGLAND GOLFGUIDE

2 0 1 4 / 2 0 1 5

NEW ENGLAND GOLFGUIDE

2 0 1 4 / 2 0 1 5

NEW ENGLAND GOLFGUIDE

2 0 1 4 / 2 0 1 5

Foxborough Country Club
Foxborough, MA (508) 543-4661

- **Type of Discount**
  4 players for the price of 3. Cart rental required.

- **Days of the Week**
  Monday through Thursday

- **Hours of the Day**
  Call Pro Shop for availability:
  (508) 543-4661 ext. 4

Coupon expires 5/31/15. Cannot be combined with any other offer.

Fresh Pond Golf Club
Cambridge, MA (617) 349-6282

- **Type of Discount**
  2 players for the price of 1

- **Days of the Week**
  Weekdays only (except holidays)

- **Hours of the Day**
  All day. Excludes league play.

Coupon expires 5/31/15. Cannot be combined with any other offer.

Garrison Golf Center
Haverhill, MA (978) 374-9380

- **Type of Discount**
  $2 off 9 holes when accompanied
  by 1 full-paying customer

- **Days of the Week**
  Weekdays only (except holidays)

- **Hours of the Day**
  All day

Coupon expires 5/31/15. Cannot be combined with any other offer.

Glen Ellen Country Club
Route 115, Millis, MA (508) 376-2775

- **Type of Discount**
  Free golf cart with 2 paid greens fees

- **Days of the Week**
  7 days a week

- **Hours of the Day**
  Monday through Friday all day.
  Weekends and Holidays after 11am.

Coupon expires 5/31/15. Cannot be combined with any other offer.

Golf Course Coupons

NEW ENGLAND GOLFGUIDE

2 0 1 4 / 2 0 1 5

NEW ENGLAND GOLFGUIDE

2 0 1 4 / 2 0 1 5

NEW ENGLAND GOLFGUIDE

2 0 1 4 / 2 0 1 5

NEW ENGLAND GOLFGUIDE

2 0 1 4 / 2 0 1 5

Groton Pool & Golf Center
Groton, MA (978) 448-2564

- **Type of Discount**
  2 players for the price of 1. Cart rental required.
- **Days of the Week**
  7 days a week
- **Hours of the Day**
  All day. Call for availability.

Coupon expires 5/31/15. Cannot be combined with any other offer.

Heather Hill Country Club
Plainville, MA (508) 695-0309

- **Type of Discount**
  4 players for the price of 3. Cart rental required.
- **Days of the Week**
  Monday through Friday (except holidays)
- **Hours of the Day**
  Before 1pm. Tee time required.

Coupon expires 5/31/15. Cannot be combined with any other offer.

Heritage Country Club
Charlton, MA (508) 248-5111

- **Type of Discount**
  25% discount for 2-4 players
- **Days of the Week**
  Monday through Friday (except holidays)
- **Hours of the Day**
  11am–3pm. No holidays. No tournaments.

Coupon expires 5/31/15. Cannot be combined with any other offer.

Hickory Ridge Country Club
South Amherst, MA (413) 253-9320

- **Type of Discount**
  Free golf cart with 2 paid greens fees
- **Days of the Week**
  Weekdays only (except holidays)
- **Hours of the Day**
  All day. Seasonal fees do not apply.

Coupon expires 5/31/15. Cannot be combined with any other offer.

Golf Course Coupons

NEW ENGLAND GOLFGUIDE

2014 / 2015

NEW ENGLAND GOLFGUIDE

2014 / 2015

NEW ENGLAND GOLFGUIDE

2014 / 2015

NEW ENGLAND GOLFGUIDE

2014 / 2015

Highfields Golf & Country Club
Grafton, MA (508) 839-1945

- **Type of Discount**
  4 players for the price of 3
- **Days of the Week**
  Weekdays only (except holidays)
- **Hours of the Day**
  All day

Coupon expires 5/31/15. Cannot be combined with any other offer.

Hillside Country Club
Rehoboth, MA (508) 252-9761

- **Type of Discount**
  Play 18 holes, get 18 holes free the next time
  you play. Must bring in this coupon.
- **Days of the Week**
  Monday through Friday
- **Hours of the Day**
  All day

Coupon expires 5/31/15. Cannot be combined with any other offer.

Holly Ridge Golf Club
South Sandwich, MA (508) 428-5577

- **Type of Discount**
  $5 off each 18-hole greens fee
  for up to 4 players
- **Days of the Week**
  7 days a week
- **Hours of the Day**
  7am–3pm. Expires 9/30/14.

Coupon expires 9/30/14. Cannot be combined with any other offer.

Hyannis Golf Club
Hyannis, MA (508) 362-2606

- **Type of Discount**
  4 players for the price of 3
- **Days of the Week**
  Monday through Thursday (except holidays)
- **Hours of the Day**
  All day

Coupon expires 5/31/15. Cannot be combined with any other offer.

Golf Course Coupons

NEW ENGLAND GOLFGUIDE

2 0 1 4 / 2 0 1 5

NEW ENGLAND GOLFGUIDE

2 0 1 4 / 2 0 1 5

NEW ENGLAND GOLFGUIDE

2 0 1 4 / 2 0 1 5

NEW ENGLAND GOLFGUIDE

2 0 1 4 / 2 0 1 5

MA

Indian Meadows Golf Club
Westboro, MA (508) 836-5460

- **Type of Discount**
  4 players for the price of 3
- **Days of the Week**
  7 days a week
- **Hours of the Day**
  All day

Coupon expires 5/31/15. Cannot be combined with any other offer.

John F. Parker Municipal GC
Taunton, MA (508) 822-1797

- **Type of Discount**
  4 players for the price of 3.
  2 cart rentals required.
- **Days of the Week**
  Weekdays only (except holidays) 10am–5pm.
  Weekends 3–6pm.
- **Hours of the Day**

Coupon expires 5/31/15. Cannot be combined with any other offer.

Lakeview Golf Club
Wenham, MA (978) 468-6676

- **Type of Discount**
  4 players for the price of 3
- **Days of the Week**
  7 days a week
- **Hours of the Day**
  All day. Call for starting time.

Coupon expires 5/31/15. Cannot be combined with any other offer.

Ledges Golf Club
South Hadley, MA (413) 532-2307

- **Type of Discount**
  Free golf cart with 2 paid greens fees
- **Days of the Week**
  7 days, must make tee time
- **Hours of the Day**
  All day M-F; after 1pm Saturday/Sunday

Coupon expires 5/31/15. Cannot be combined with any other offer.

Golf Course Coupons

**NEW ENGLAND
GOLFGUIDE**

2 0 1 4 / 2 0 1 5

**NEW ENGLAND
GOLFGUIDE**

2 0 1 4 / 2 0 1 5

**NEW ENGLAND
GOLFGUIDE**

2 0 1 4 / 2 0 1 5

**NEW ENGLAND
GOLFGUIDE**

2 0 1 4 / 2 0 1 5

Leicester Country Club
Leicester, MA (508) 892-1390 Ext. 12

- **Type of Discount**
  25% discount for 2 to 4 players.
  Cart rental required.

- **Days of the Week**
  Monday through Thursday

- **Hours of the Day**
  7am–1pm

Coupon expires 5/31/15. Cannot be combined with any other offer.

Links at Lancaster Golf, The
Lancaster, MA (978) 537-8922

- **Type of Discount**
  2 players for the price of 1

- **Days of the Week**
  7 days a week

- **Hours of the Day**
  All day

Coupon expires 5/31/15. Cannot be combined with any other offer.

Little Harbor Country Club
Wareham, MA (508) 295-2617

- **Type of Discount**
  $4 off regular greens fees

- **Days of the Week**
  Weekdays only (except holidays and
  Wednesdays)

- **Hours of the Day**
  Before 3pm

Coupon expires 5/31/15. Cannot be combined with any other offer.

Maplegate Country Club
Bellingham, MA (508) 966-4040

- **Type of Discount**
  4 players for the price of 3

- **Days of the Week**
  Weekdays only (except holidays)

- **Hours of the Day**
  All day. Valid April - October, 2014.

Coupon expires 5/31/15. Cannot be combined with any other offer.

Golf Course Coupons

NEW ENGLAND GOLFGUIDE

2014 / 2015

NEW ENGLAND GOLFGUIDE

2014 / 2015

NEW ENGLAND GOLFGUIDE

2014 / 2015

NEW ENGLAND GOLFGUIDE

2014 / 2015

Marion Golf Course
Marion, MA (508) 748-0199

- **Type of Discount**
  2 players for the price of 1

- **Days of the Week**
  Weekdays only (except holidays)

- **Hours of the Day**
  All day. With coupon only.

Coupon expires 5/31/15. Cannot be combined with any other offer.

Marlborough Country Club
Marlborough, MA (508) 485-1660

- **Type of Discount**
  $110 for 2 players (including cart)
  $220 for 4 players (including cart)

- **Days of the Week**
  Monday and Tuesday

- **Hours of the Day**
  All day. Must call for tee time.

Coupon expires 5/31/15. Cannot be combined with any other offer.

The Meadows Golf Club
Greenfield, MA (413) 773-9047

- **Type of Discount**
  Free golf cart with 2 paid greens fees
  for 18 holes

- **Days of the Week**
  Weekdays only (except holidays)

- **Hours of the Day**
  Before 3pm

Coupon expires 5/31/15. Cannot be combined with any other offer.

Middleton Golf Course
Middleton, MA (978) 774-4075

- **Type of Discount**
  $5 off each greens fee for up to 4 players

- **Days of the Week**
  7 days a week

- **Hours of the Day**
  All day

Coupon expires 5/31/15. Cannot be combined with any other offer.

Golf Course Coupons

NEW ENGLAND GOLFGUIDE

2 0 1 4 / 2 0 1 5

NEW ENGLAND GOLFGUIDE

2 0 1 4 / 2 0 1 5

NEW ENGLAND GOLFGUIDE

2 0 1 4 / 2 0 1 5

NEW ENGLAND GOLFGUIDE

2 0 1 4 / 2 0 1 5

Mill Valley Golf Links
Belchertown, MA (413) 323-4079

- **Type of Discount**
  $10 greens fee

- **Days of the Week**
  Weekdays only (except holidays)

- **Hours of the Day**
  All day

Coupon expires 5/31/15. Cannot be combined with any other offer.

New England Country Club
Bellingham, MA (508) 883-2300

- **Type of Discount**
  4 players for the price of 3.
  Not valid for senior rates.

- **Days of the Week**
  Monday through Thursday (except holidays)

- **Hours of the Day**
  9am–12pm

Coupon expires 5/31/15. Cannot be combined with any other offer.

New Meadows Golf Club
Topsfield, MA (978) 887-9307

- **Type of Discount**
  4 players for the price of 3

- **Days of the Week**
  7 days a week

- **Hours of the Day**
  All day

Coupon expires 5/31/15. Cannot be combined with any other offer.

Newton Commonwealth Golf Course
Newton, MA (617) 630-1971

- **Type of Discount**
  Free golf cart with 2 paid greens fees

- **Days of the Week**
  Monday through Friday

- **Hours of the Day**
  Monday through Thursday all day,
  Friday before 10am

Coupon expires 5/31/15. Cannot be combined with any other offer.

Golf Course Coupons

NEW ENGLAND GOLFGUIDE

2 0 1 4 / 2 0 1 5

NEW ENGLAND GOLFGUIDE

2 0 1 4 / 2 0 1 5

NEW ENGLAND GOLFGUIDE

2 0 1 4 / 2 0 1 5

NEW ENGLAND GOLFGUIDE

2 0 1 4 / 2 0 1 5

North Adams Country Club
Clarksburg, MA (413) 664-7149

- **Type of Discount**
  2 players for the price of 1.
  Cart rental required.
- **Days of the Week**
  Weekdays only (except holidays)
- **Hours of the Day**
  All day.

Coupon expires 5/31/15. Cannot be combined with any other offer.

Norton Country Club
Norton, MA (508) 285-2400

- **Type of Discount**
  $49.95 Lunch Special
- **Days of the Week**
  Tuesday and Wednesday
- **Hours of the Day**
  All day

Coupon expires 5/31/15. Cannot be combined with any other offer.

Norwood Country Club
Norwood, MA (781) 769-5880

- **Type of Discount**
  2 players for the price of 1
- **Days of the Week**
  Weekdays only (except holidays)
- **Hours of the Day**
  Before 2pm. 18 hole cart rental at regular
  weekday prices is required.

Coupon expires 5/31/15. Cannot be combined with any other offer.

Olde Barnstable Fairgrounds Golf Course
Marstons Mills, MA (508) 420-1141

- **Type of Discount**
  4 players for the price of 3
- **Days of the Week**
  Monday through Thursday (except holidays)
- **Hours of the Day**
  All day. Valid Jan. 1 - May 20 and Sept. 13 - Dec. 31.

Coupon expires 5/31/15. Cannot be combined with any other offer.

Golf Course Coupons

NEW ENGLAND GOLFGUIDE

2 0 1 4 / 2 0 1 5

NEW ENGLAND GOLFGUIDE

2 0 1 4 / 2 0 1 5

NEW ENGLAND GOLFGUIDE

2 0 1 4 / 2 0 1 5

NEW ENGLAND GOLFGUIDE

2 0 1 4 / 2 0 1 5

Olde Salem Greens
Salem, MA (978) 744-2149

- **Type of Discount**
  $40 for 18 holes with cart. Tee time required.
- **Days of the Week**
  7 days a week
- **Hours of the Day**
  All day

Coupon expires 5/31/15. Cannot be combined with any other offer.

Olde Scotland Links
Bridgewater, MA (508) 279-3344

- **Type of Discount**
  Free golf cart with 2 paid greens fees
- **Days of the Week**
  Monday through Thursday (except holidays)
- **Hours of the Day**
  All day. Not to be used during league, group, or tournament play.

Coupon expires 5/31/15. Cannot be combined with any other offer.

Paul Harney Golf Club
East Falmouth, MA (508) 563-3454

- **Type of Discount**
  10 play card – play 9 times and get 10th free
- **Days of the Week**
  7 days a week
- **Hours of the Day**
  All day

Coupon expires 5/31/15. Cannot be combined with any other offer.

Pinecrest Golf Club
Holliston, MA (508) 429-9871

- **Type of Discount**
  Free golf cart with 2 paid greens fees
- **Days of the Week**
  Weekdays only (except holidays)
- **Hours of the Day**
  All day

Coupon expires 5/31/15. Cannot be combined with any other offer.

Golf Course Coupons

NEW ENGLAND GOLFGUIDE

2014 / 2015

NEW ENGLAND GOLFGUIDE

2014 / 2015

NEW ENGLAND GOLFGUIDE

2014 / 2015

NEW ENGLAND GOLFGUIDE

2014 / 2015

Pinehills Golf Club (Jones & Nicklaus)
Plymouth, MA (508) 209-3000

- **Type of Discount**
  4 players for the price of 3 (includes carts)
- **Days of the Week**
  Monday through Thursday
- **Hours of the Day**
  All day

Coupon expires 5/31/15. Cannot be combined with any other offer.

Pine Grove Golf Club
Northampton, MA (413) 584-4570

- **Type of Discount**
  $28 per person for 18 holes with cart
- **Days of the Week**
  Weekdays only (except holidays)
- **Hours of the Day**
  Before 1pm. No singles.

Coupon expires 5/31/15. Cannot be combined with any other offer.

Pine Knoll Par 3 Golf Course
East Longmeadow, MA (413) 525-4444

- **Type of Discount**
  2 players for the price of 1
- **Days of the Week**
  Weekdays only (except holidays)
- **Hours of the Day**
  All day. Maximum 1 free per coupon.

Coupon expires 5/31/15. Cannot be combined with any other offer.

Pine Oaks Golf Course
South Easton, MA (508) 238-2320

- **Type of Discount**
  2 players for price of 1
- **Days of the Week**
  7 days a week
- **Hours of the Day**
  All day

Coupon expires 5/31/15. Cannot be combined with any other offer.

Golf Course Coupons

NEW ENGLAND GOLFGUIDE

2 0 1 4 / 2 0 1 5

NEW ENGLAND GOLFGUIDE

2 0 1 4 / 2 0 1 5

NEW ENGLAND GOLFGUIDE

2 0 1 4 / 2 0 1 5

NEW ENGLAND GOLFGUIDE

2 0 1 4 / 2 0 1 5

Pine Ridge Country Club
North Oxford, MA (508) 892-9188

- **Type of Discount**
  4 players for the price of 3

- **Days of the Week**
  7 days a week

- **Hours of the Day**
  6am–12pm. Excludes league play,
  tournaments or special offers.

Coupon expires 5/31/15. Cannot be combined with any other offer.

Pontoosuc Lake Country Club
Pittsfield, MA (413) 445-4217

- **Type of Discount**
  Buy 1 greens fee, get second greens fee
  at one-half off with cart rental

- **Days of the Week**
  Weekdays only (except holidays)

- **Hours of the Day**
  All day

Coupon expires 5/31/15. Cannot be combined with any other offer.

Poquoy Brook Golf Course
Lakeville, MA (508) 947-5261

- **Type of Discount**
  20% off non-sale golf apparel

- **Days of the Week**
  7 days a week

- **Hours of the Day**
  All day

Coupon expires 5/31/15. Cannot be combined with any other offer.

Quaboag Country Club
Monson, MA (413) 267-5294

- **Type of Discount**
  Free golf cart with 2 paid greens fees

- **Days of the Week**
  Weekdays only (except holidays)

- **Hours of the Day**
  All day

Coupon expires 5/31/15. Cannot be combined with any other offer.

Golf Course Coupons

NEW ENGLAND GOLFGUIDE

2 0 1 4 / 2 0 1 5

NEW ENGLAND GOLFGUIDE

2 0 1 4 / 2 0 1 5

NEW ENGLAND GOLFGUIDE

2 0 1 4 / 2 0 1 5

NEW ENGLAND GOLFGUIDE

2 0 1 4 / 2 0 1 5

Quail Ridge Country Club
Acton, MA (978) 264-0399

- **Type of Discount**
  $40 including cart per person (18 holes)
  $30 including cart per person (9 holes)

- **Days of the Week**
  Monday through Friday (except holidays)

- **Hours of the Day**
  All day

Coupon expires 5/31/15. Cannot be combined with any other offer.

Quashnet Valley Country Club
Mashpee, MA (508) 477-4412

- **Type of Discount**
  $5 off greens fees for up to 4 players

- **Days of the Week**
  Monday through Thursday (except holidays)

- **Hours of the Day**
  All day

Coupon expires 5/31/15. Cannot be combined with any other offer.

Ranch Golf Club, The
Southwick, MA (413) 569-9333

- **Type of Discount**
  $65 per player (includes cart)

- **Days of the Week**
  Monday through Wednesday (except holidays)

- **Hours of the Day**
  All day

Coupon expires 5/31/15. Cannot be combined with any other offer.

Reedy Meadow Golf Course
Lynnfield, MA (781) 334-9877

- **Type of Discount**
  $40 for 2 players with cart

- **Days of the Week**
  Weekdays (except holidays)

- **Hours of the Day**
  Monday and Friday 11:30am–5:30pm
  Tues/Wed/Thur 11:30am–2pm

Coupon expires 5/31/15. Cannot be combined with any other offer.

Golf Course Coupons

NEW ENGLAND GOLFGUIDE

2 0 1 4 / 2 0 1 5

NEW ENGLAND GOLFGUIDE

2 0 1 4 / 2 0 1 5

NEW ENGLAND GOLFGUIDE

2 0 1 4 / 2 0 1 5

NEW ENGLAND GOLFGUIDE

2 0 1 4 / 2 0 1 5

Rowley Country Club
Rowley, MA (978) 948-2731

- **Type of Discount**
  4 players with carts for price of 3
- **Days of the Week**
  Monday through Thursday
- **Hours of the Day**
  Before 3pm

Coupon expires 5/31/15. Cannot be combined with any other offer.

Sagamore Spring Golf Club
Lynnfield, MA (781) 334-3151

- **Type of Discount**
  Free bucket of ball with greens fee
- **Days of the Week**
  7 days a week
- **Hours of the Day**
  All day

Coupon expires 5/31/15. Cannot be combined with any other offer.

Sandwich Hollows Golf Club
East Sandwich, MA (508) 888-3384 x0

- **Type of Discount**
  Greens fee for 18 holes $29.95
- **Days of the Week**
  7 days a week
- **Hours of the Day**
  After 2pm

Coupon expires 5/31/15. Cannot be combined with any other offer.

Sassamon Trace Golf Course
Natick, MA (508) 655-1330

- **Type of Discount**
  Free golf cart with 2 paid greens fees
- **Days of the Week**
  7 days a week
- **Hours of the Day**
  All day

Coupon expires 5/31/15. Cannot be combined with any other offer.

Golf Course Coupons

NEW ENGLAND GOLFGUIDE

2 0 1 4 / 2 0 1 5

NEW ENGLAND GOLFGUIDE

2 0 1 4 / 2 0 1 5

NEW ENGLAND GOLFGUIDE

2 0 1 4 / 2 0 1 5

NEW ENGLAND GOLFGUIDE

2 0 1 4 / 2 0 1 5

Settlers Crossing Golf Course
Lunenburg, MA (978) 582-6694

- **Type of Discount**
  $36 for 2 players and a cart for 9 holes
- **Days of the Week**
  Weekdays only (except holidays)
- **Hours of the Day**
  11:30am - 2pm

Coupon expires 5/31/15. Cannot be combined with any other offer.

Shaker Farms Country Club
Westfield, MA (413) 562-2770

- **Type of Discount**
  1 free greens fee. 1 per person/1 time only.
- **Days of the Week**
  Weekdays only (except holidays)
- **Hours of the Day**
  All day

Coupon expires 5/31/15. Cannot be combined with any other offer.

Shaker Hills Country Club
Harvard, MA (978) 772-2227

- **Type of Discount**
  4 players for the price of 3.
  Monday through Thursday greens fee only.
- **Days of the Week**
  Monday through Thursday only (except holidays)
- **Hours of the Day**
  Before 2pm

Coupon expires 5/31/15. Cannot be combined with any other offer.

Skyline Country Club
Route 7, Lanesborough, MA (413) 445-5584

- **Type of Discount**
  25% discount for 2 to 4 players
- **Days of the Week**
  7 days a week
- **Hours of the Day**
  All day

Coupon expires 5/31/15. Cannot be combined with any other offer.

Golf Course Coupons

NEW ENGLAND GOLFGUIDE

2 0 1 4 / 2 0 1 5

NEW ENGLAND GOLFGUIDE

2 0 1 4 / 2 0 1 5

NEW ENGLAND GOLFGUIDE

2 0 1 4 / 2 0 1 5

NEW ENGLAND GOLFGUIDE

2 0 1 4 / 2 0 1 5

Southers Marsh Golf Club
Plymouth, MA (508) 830-3535

- **Type of Discount**
  Free golf cart with 2 paid greens fees
- **Days of the Week**
  7 days a week
- **Hours of the Day**
  All day

Coupon expires 5/31/15. Cannot be combined with any other offer.

Southwick Country Club
Southwick, MA (413) 569-0136

- **Type of Discount**
  1 player with cart $25; Senior with cart $21
- **Days of the Week**
  Weekdays only (except holidays)
- **Hours of the Day**
  All day

Coupon expires 5/31/15. Cannot be combined with any other offer.

St. Mark's Golf Club
Southborough, MA (508) 460-0946

- **Type of Discount**
  Free golf cart with 2 paid greens fees
- **Days of the Week**
  Monday through Thursday (except holidays)
- **Hours of the Day**
  Before 2pm

Coupon expires 5/31/15. Cannot be combined with any other offer.

Squirrel Run Golf Course
Plymouth, MA (508) 746-5001

- **Type of Discount**
  2 players with cart for $60
- **Days of the Week**
  Weekdays only (except holidays)
- **Hours of the Day**
  After 10am

Coupon expires 5/31/15. Cannot be combined with any other offer.

Golf Course Coupons

NEW ENGLAND GOLFGUIDE

2 0 1 4 / 2 0 1 5

NEW ENGLAND GOLFGUIDE

2 0 1 4 / 2 0 1 5

NEW ENGLAND GOLFGUIDE

2 0 1 4 / 2 0 1 5

NEW ENGLAND GOLFGUIDE

2 0 1 4 / 2 0 1 5

Stony Brook Golf Course
Southboro, MA (508) 485-3151

- **Type of Discount**
  2 players for the price of 1
- **Days of the Week**
  Weekdays only (except holidays)
- **Hours of the Day**
  All day

Coupon expires 5/31/15. Cannot be combined with any other offer.

Sun Valley Golf Course
Rehoboth, MA (508) 336-8686

- **Type of Discount**
  4 players for the price of 3
- **Days of the Week**
  Weekdays only (except holidays)
- **Hours of the Day**
  7am–1pm

Coupon expires 5/31/15. Cannot be combined with any other offer.

Swansea Country Club
Swansea, MA (508) 379-9886

- **Type of Discount**
  Golf, cart, 2 hot dogs, soda, and chips - $44.95
- **Days of the Week**
  Weekdays only (except holidays)
- **Hours of the Day**
  11am–1pm

Coupon expires 5/31/15. Cannot be combined with any other offer.

Tekoa Country Club
Westfield, MA (413) 568-1064

- **Type of Discount**
  2 players for the price of 1.
  Cart rental required.
- **Days of the Week**
  Weekdays only
- **Hours of the Day**
  Before 1pm

Coupon expires 5/31/15. Cannot be combined with any other offer.

Golf Course Coupons

NEW ENGLAND GOLFGUIDE

2 0 1 4 / 2 0 1 5

NEW ENGLAND GOLFGUIDE

2 0 1 4 / 2 0 1 5

NEW ENGLAND GOLFGUIDE

2 0 1 4 / 2 0 1 5

NEW ENGLAND GOLFGUIDE

2 0 1 4 / 2 0 1 5

Templewood Golf Course
Templeton, MA (978) 939-5031

- **Type of Discount**
  2 players for the price of 1.
  Cart rental required.
- **Days of the Week**
  Weekdays only (except holidays)
- **Hours of the Day**
  All day. Tee time required.

Coupon expires 5/31/15. Cannot be combined with any other offer.

The International (The Oaks)
Bolton, MA (978) 779-6910

- **Type of Discount**
  $25 off per player up to 4 players
- **Days of the Week**
  7 days a week
- **Hours of the Day**
  All day

Coupon expires 5/31/15. Cannot be combined with any other offer.

Thomas Memorial Golf & CC
Turners Falls, MA (413) 863-8003

- **Type of Discount**
  2 players for the price of 1
- **Days of the Week**
  7 days a week
- **Hours of the Day**
  All day

Coupon expires 5/31/15. Cannot be combined with any other offer.

Touisset Country Club
Swansea, MA (508) 679-9577

- **Type of Discount**
  2 players for the price of 1
- **Days of the Week**
  7 days a week
- **Hours of the Day**
  All day. Not valid for league or tournament play.

Coupon expires 5/31/15. Cannot be combined with any other offer.

Golf Course Coupons

NEW ENGLAND GOLFGUIDE

2 0 1 4 / 2 0 1 5

NEW ENGLAND GOLFGUIDE

2 0 1 4 / 2 0 1 5

NEW ENGLAND GOLFGUIDE

2 0 1 4 / 2 0 1 5

NEW ENGLAND GOLFGUIDE

2 0 1 4 / 2 0 1 5

Townsend Ridge Country Club
Townsend, MA (978) 597-8400

- **Type of Discount**
  2 players for the price of 1. Cart rental required.
- **Days of the Week**
  7 days a week
- **Hours of the Day**
  All day

Coupon expires 5/31/15. Cannot be combined with any other offer.

Twin Brooks Golf Course
Hyannis, MA (508) 862-6980

- **Type of Discount**
  4 players for the price of 3
- **Days of the Week**
  Monday - Thursday (except holidays)
- **Hours of the Day**
  All day

Coupon expires 5/31/15. Cannot be combined with any other offer.

Twin Springs Golf Club
Bolton, MA (978) 779-5020

- **Type of Discount**
  2 players for the price of 1
- **Days of the Week**
  Monday through Thursday (except holidays)
- **Hours of the Day**
  6:30am to 3pm

Coupon expires 5/31/15. Cannot be combined with any other offer.

Village Links
Plymouth, MA (508) 830-4653

- **Type of Discount**
  2 players with cart for $50
- **Days of the Week**
  Weekdays only (except holidays)
- **Hours of the Day**
  After 10am. Valid April - October, 2014.

Coupon expires 5/31/15. Cannot be combined with any other offer.

Golf Course Coupons

NEW ENGLAND GOLFGUIDE

2 0 1 4 / 2 0 1 5

✂ -

NEW ENGLAND GOLFGUIDE

2 0 1 4 / 2 0 1 5

✂ -

NEW ENGLAND GOLFGUIDE

2 0 1 4 / 2 0 1 5

✂ -

NEW ENGLAND GOLFGUIDE

2 0 1 4 / 2 0 1 5

Wampanoag Golf Club
North Swansea, MA (508) 379-9832

- **Type of Discount**
  $31 per person for 18 holes w/cart
- **Days of the Week**
  7 days a week (except holidays)
- **Hours of the Day**
  7am-1pm weekdays/after 12pm weekends.
  Valid through September 2014.

Coupon expires 5/31/15. Cannot be combined with any other offer.

Waubeeka Golf Links
South Williamstown, MA (413) 458-8355

- **Type of Discount**
  4 players for the price of 3
- **Days of the Week**
  Weekdays only (except holidays)
- **Hours of the Day**
  All day

Coupon expires 5/31/15. Cannot be combined with any other offer.

Waverly Oaks Golf Club
Plymouth, MA (508) 224-6016

- **Type of Discount**
  $5 off greens fees for up to 2 players
- **Days of the Week**
  7 days a week
- **Hours of the Day**
  All day

Coupon expires 5/31/15. Cannot be combined with any other offer.

Wenham Country Club
Wenham, MA (978) 468-4714

- **Type of Discount**
  25% discount for 2 to 4 players
- **Days of the Week**
  Weekdays only (except holidays)
- **Hours of the Day**
  All day

Coupon expires 5/31/15. Cannot be combined with any other offer.

MA

Golf Course Coupons

NEW ENGLAND GOLFGUIDE

2 0 1 4 / 2 0 1 5

NEW ENGLAND GOLFGUIDE

2 0 1 4 / 2 0 1 5

NEW ENGLAND GOLFGUIDE

2 0 1 4 / 2 0 1 5

NEW ENGLAND GOLFGUIDE

2 0 1 4 / 2 0 1 5

Wentworth Hills Country Club
Plainville, MA (508) 316-0240

- **Type of Discount**
  4 players for the price of 3. Cart rental required.
- **Days of the Week**
  Monday through Thursday (except holidays)
- **Hours of the Day**
  Before 1pm. Tee time required.

Coupon expires 5/31/15. Cannot be combined with any other offer.

Westborough Country Club
Westborough, MA (508) 366-9947

- **Type of Discount**
  2 players for the price of 1
- **Days of the Week**
  Monday through Friday (except holidays)
- **Hours of the Day**
  All day. Call for availability.
  Not valid for league play.

Coupon expires 5/31/15. Cannot be combined with any other offer.

Westminster Country Club
Westminster, MA (978) 874-5938

- **Type of Discount**
  25% discount for 4 players. Cart rental required.
  $38 for lunch, cart, and 18 holes
- **Days of the Week**
  Weekend after 2pm
- **Hours of the Day**
  6am–12pm. Not to be combined with any
  league, player's pass, or any other offers.

Coupon expires 5/31/15. Cannot be combined with any other offer.

Winchendon School Country Club
Winchendon, MA (978) 297-9897

- **Type of Discount**
  2 players for the price of 1. Cart rental required.
- **Days of the Week**
  Weekdays only (except holidays).
  Weekends after 12pm
- **Hours of the Day**
  All day

Coupon expires 5/31/15. Cannot be combined with any other offer.

Golf Course Coupons

NEW ENGLAND GOLFGUIDE

2 0 1 4 / 2 0 1 5

NEW ENGLAND GOLFGUIDE

2 0 1 4 / 2 0 1 5

NEW ENGLAND GOLFGUIDE

2 0 1 4 / 2 0 1 5

NEW ENGLAND GOLFGUIDE

2 0 1 4 / 2 0 1 5

Widow's Walk Golf Course
Scituate, MA (781) 544-7777

- **Type of Discount**
  4 players for the price of 3
- **Days of the Week**
  7 days a week
- **Hours of the Day**
  Weekends and holidays after 11am

Coupon expires 5/31/15. Cannot be combined with any other offer.

Woods of Westminster Country Club
Westminster, MA (978) 874-0500

- **Type of Discount**
  $29 for 18 holes, cart, and lunch
- **Days of the Week**
  Weekdays only (except holidays)
- **Hours of the Day**
  Monday-Friday before 12 noon.
  Excludes league play.

Coupon expires 5/31/15. Cannot be combined with any other offer.

Worthington Golf Course
Worthington, MA (413) 238-4464

- **Type of Discount**
  $25 for 18 holes with cart
- **Days of the Week**
  Weekdays only (except holidays)
- **Hours of the Day**
  All day

Coupon expires 5/31/15. Cannot be combined with any other offer.

Androscoggin Valley Country Club
Route 2, Gorham, NH (603) 466-9468

- **Type of Discount**
  $70 for 2 players (includes cart)
- **Days of the Week**
  7 days a week
- **Hours of the Day**
  All day with tee times only. Must bring
  in coupon in NE GolfGuide.

Coupon expires 5/31/15. Cannot be combined with any other offer.

Golf Course Coupons

NEW ENGLAND GOLFGUIDE

2014 / 2015

✂ -

NEW ENGLAND GOLFGUIDE

2014 / 2015

✂ -

NEW ENGLAND GOLFGUIDE

2014 / 2015

✂ -

NEW ENGLAND GOLFGUIDE

2014 / 2015

Apple Hill Golf Club
East Kingston, NH (603) 642-4414

- **Type of Discount**
  $5 off greens fees for up to 2 players
- **Days of the Week**
  Weekdays only (except holidays)
- **Hours of the Day**
  All day

Coupon expires 5/31/15. Cannot be combined with any other offer.

Atkinson Resort and Country Club
Atkinson, NH (603) 362-8700

- **Type of Discount**
  4 players for the price of 3 (greens fees only).
  Cart rental required.
- **Days of the Week**
  Monday through Thursday (except holidays)
- **Hours of the Day**
  All day

Coupon expires 5/31/15. Cannot be combined with any other offer.

Beaver Meadow Golf Club
Concord, NH (603) 228-8954

- **Type of Discount**
  2 greens fees and cart for $80
- **Days of the Week**
  Monday through Wednesday (except holidays)
- **Hours of the Day**
  After 12pm

Coupon expires 5/31/15. Cannot be combined with any other offer.

Bethlehem Country Club
Bethlehem, NH (603) 869-5745

- **Type of Discount**
  $30 w/cart M - Th (except holidays)
  $35 w/cart F/S/S/H
- **Days of the Week**
  See above
- **Hours of the Day**
  All day. Not valid holidays.

Coupon expires 5/31/15. Cannot be combined with any other offer.

NEW ENGLAND GOLFGUIDE

2 0 1 4 / 2 0 1 5

NEW ENGLAND GOLFGUIDE

2 0 1 4 / 2 0 1 5

NEW ENGLAND GOLFGUIDE

2 0 1 4 / 2 0 1 5

NEW ENGLAND GOLFGUIDE

2 0 1 4 / 2 0 1 5

Blackmount Country Club
North Haverhill, NH (603) 787-6564

- **Type of Discount**
  $3 off power cart rental with paid greens fee

- **Days of the Week**
  Weekdays only (except holidays)

- **Hours of the Day**
  All day

Coupon expires 5/31/15. Cannot be combined with any other offer.

Breakfast Hill Golf Club
Greenland, NH (603) 436-5001

- **Type of Discount**
  25% discount for 2-4 players

- **Days of the Week**
  Monday through Thursday (except holidays)

- **Hours of the Day**
  All day

Coupon expires 5/31/15. Cannot be combined with any other offer.

Campbell's Scottish Highlands
Salem, NH (603) 894-4653

- **Type of Discount**
  18 holes, cart, & bag lunch for 2 golfers - $96

- **Days of the Week**
  Monday through Thursday (except holidays)

- **Hours of the Day**
  All day. Valid March 31 - May 22
  and October 14 - November 20.

Coupon expires 5/31/15. Cannot be combined with any other offer.

Canterbury Woods Country Club
Canterbury, NH (603) 783-9400

- **Type of Discount**
  2 players for the price of 1

- **Days of the Week**
  Weekdays only (except holidays)

- **Hours of the Day**
  All day. Cart rental required.

Coupon expires 5/31/15. Cannot be combined with any other offer.

Golf Course Coupons

NEW ENGLAND
GOLFGUIDE

2 0 1 4 / 2 0 1 5

✂ -

NEW ENGLAND
GOLFGUIDE

2 0 1 4 / 2 0 1 5

✂ -

NEW ENGLAND
GOLFGUIDE

2 0 1 4 / 2 0 1 5

✂ -

NEW ENGLAND
GOLFGUIDE

2 0 1 4 / 2 0 1 5

Colebrook Country Club
Colebrook, NH (603) 237-5566

- **Type of Discount**
  2 players for the price of 1.
  18-hole power cart required.

- **Days of the Week**
  Weekdays only (except holidays)

- **Hours of the Day**
  All day

Coupon expires 5/31/15. Cannot be combined with any other offer.

Country Club of New Hampshire
North Sutton, NH (603) 927-4246

- **Type of Discount**
  Mondays – $35 for 18 holes with cart

- **Days of the Week**
  Mondays

- **Hours of the Day**
  All day

Coupon expires 5/31/15. Cannot be combined with any other offer.

Countryside Golf Club
Dunbarton, NH (603) 774-5031

- **Type of Discount**
  2 players for $32 (before 11am)

- **Days of the Week**
  Weekdays only (except holidays)

- **Hours of the Day**
  Before 11am

Coupon expires 5/31/15. Cannot be combined with any other offer.

Crotched Mountain Golf Course
Route 47, Francestown, NH (603) 588-2923

- **Type of Discount**
  $5 off 2-4 players

- **Days of the Week**
  7 day a week

- **Hours of the Day**
  All day. Cart not included.

Coupon expires 5/31/15. Cannot be combined with any other offer.

Golf Course Coupons

NEW ENGLAND GOLFGUIDE

2 0 1 4 / 2 0 1 5

NEW ENGLAND GOLFGUIDE

2 0 1 4 / 2 0 1 5

NEW ENGLAND GOLFGUIDE

2 0 1 4 / 2 0 1 5

NEW ENGLAND GOLFGUIDE

2 0 1 4 / 2 0 1 5

Den Brae Golf Course
Sanbornton, NH (603) 934-9818

- **Type of Discount**
  25% discount for 2-4 players
- **Days of the Week**
  Weekdays only (except holidays)
- **Hours of the Day**
  All day

Coupon expires 5/31/15. Cannot be combined with any other offer.

Derryfield Country Club
Manchester, NH (603) 669-0235

- **Type of Discount**
  2 players for price of 1. Cart rental required.
- **Days of the Week**
  Weekdays only (except holidays)
- **Hours of the Day**
  M-Th all day. Fri-Sat-Sun-Holiday after 1pm.
  1 coupon per visit.

Coupon expires 5/31/15. Cannot be combined with any other offer.

Duston Country Club
Hopkinton, NH (603) 746-4234

- **Type of Discount**
  Free sandwich after round (up to $5 value)
- **Days of the Week**
  Weekdays only (except holidays)
- **Hours of the Day**
  All day

Coupon expires 5/31/15. Cannot be combined with any other offer.

Eastman Golf Links
Grantham, NH (603) 863-4500

- **Type of Discount**
  $45 per person including cart
- **Days of the Week**
  7 days a week
- **Hours of the Day**
  M-Th all day; Fri/Sat/Sun after 12pm.
  Please call ahead.

Coupon expires 5/31/15. Cannot be combined with any other offer.

Golf Course Coupons

NEW ENGLAND
GOLFGUIDE

2 0 1 4 / 2 0 1 5

✂ -

NEW ENGLAND
GOLFGUIDE

2 0 1 4 / 2 0 1 5

✂ -

NEW ENGLAND
GOLFGUIDE

2 0 1 4 / 2 0 1 5

✂ -

NEW ENGLAND
GOLFGUIDE

2 0 1 4 / 2 0 1 5

NH

Exeter Country Club
Exeter, NH (603) 772-4752

- **Type of Discount**
  2 players for the price of 1
- **Days of the Week**
  Weekdays only (except holidays)
- **Hours of the Day**
  All day

Coupon expires 5/31/15. Cannot be combined with any other offer.

Hales Location Golf Course
North Conway, NH (603) 356-2140

- **Type of Discount**
  $5 off 9 holes; $10 off $18 holes
- **Days of the Week**
  Monday through Thursday (except holidays)
- **Hours of the Day**
  All day

Coupon expires 5/31/15. Cannot be combined with any other offer.

Hanover Country Club
Hanover, NH (603) 646-2000

- **Type of Discount**
  4 players for the price of 3
- **Days of the Week**
  Weekends
- **Hours of the Day**
  After 1pm

Coupon expires 5/31/15. Cannot be combined with any other offer.

Hidden Valley Golf Course
Derry, NH (603) 887-7888

- **Type of Discount**
  2 players for the price of 1.
  Cart rental not included.
- **Days of the Week**
  7 days a week
- **Hours of the Day**
  All day

Coupon expires 5/31/15. Cannot be combined with any other offer.

Golf Course Coupons

NEW ENGLAND GOLFGUIDE

2014 / 2015

NEW ENGLAND GOLFGUIDE

2014 / 2015

NEW ENGLAND GOLFGUIDE

2014 / 2015

NEW ENGLAND GOLFGUIDE

2014 / 2015

Highlands Links Golf Club
Plymouth, NH (603) 536-3452

- **Type of Discount**
  2 players for the price of 1 (at regular adult fee)
- **Days of the Week**
  7 days a week
- **Hours of the Day**
  All day

Coupon expires 5/31/15. Cannot be combined with any other offer.

Hoodkroft Country Club
Derry, NH (603) 434-0651

- **Type of Discount**
  4 players for the price of 3
- **Days of the Week**
  Weekdays only (except holidays)
- **Hours of the Day**
  All day

Coupon expires 5/31/15. Cannot be combined with any other offer.

Indian Mound Golf Club
Center Ossippee, NH (603) 539-7733

- **Type of Discount**
  4 players for the price of 3.
  Golf cart rental required.
- **Days of the Week**
  Weekdays; weekends (after 2pm)
- **Hours of the Day**
  All day

Coupon expires 5/31/15. Cannot be combined with any other offer.

Jack O'Lantern Resort
Woodstock, NH (603) 745-3636

- **Type of Discount**
  4 players for the price of 3
- **Days of the Week**
  Weekdays only (except holidays)
- **Hours of the Day**
  Until 4pm (mid-May to mid-October)

Coupon expires 5/31/15. Cannot be combined with any other offer.

NEW ENGLAND GOLFGUIDE

2 0 1 4 / 2 0 1 5

NEW ENGLAND GOLFGUIDE

2 0 1 4 / 2 0 1 5

NEW ENGLAND GOLFGUIDE

2 0 1 4 / 2 0 1 5

NEW ENGLAND GOLFGUIDE

2 0 1 4 / 2 0 1 5

Kingswood Golf Course
Wolfeboro, NH (603) 569-3569

- **Type of Discount**
  2 players for the price of 1. Cart rental required.
- **Days of the Week**
  7 days a week
- **Hours of the Day**
  After 2pm on weekends in July/August

Coupon expires 5/31/15. Cannot be combined with any other offer.

Lisbon Village Country Club
Bishop Road, Lisbon, NH (603) 838-6004

- **Type of Discount**
  Free golf cart with 2 paid greens fees
- **Days of the Week**
  Weekdays only (except holidays)
- **Hours of the Day**
  All day

Coupon expires 5/31/15. Cannot be combined with any other offer.

Loudon Country Club
Loudon, NH (603) 783-3372

- **Type of Discount**
  $38 per player with cart
- **Days of the Week**
  Weekdays only (except holidays)
- **Hours of the Day**
  All day

Coupon expires 5/31/15. Cannot be combined with any other offer.

Maplewood Golf Club
Bethlehem, NH (603) 869-3335

- **Type of Discount**
  $5 off greens fee
- **Days of the Week**
  Weekdays only (except holidays)
- **Hours of the Day**
  7am-6pm. 18 holes only, cart rental required.

Coupon expires 5/31/15. Cannot be combined with any other offer.

Golf Course Coupons

NEW ENGLAND GOLFGUIDE

2 0 1 4 / 2 0 1 5

NEW ENGLAND GOLFGUIDE

2 0 1 4 / 2 0 1 5

NEW ENGLAND GOLFGUIDE

2 0 1 4 / 2 0 1 5

NEW ENGLAND GOLFGUIDE

2 0 1 4 / 2 0 1 5

Mojalaki Country Club
Franklin, NH (603) 934-3033

- **Type of Discount**
  $5 off greens fees for up to 2 players
  for 18 holes
- **Days of the Week**
  Weekdays only (except holidays)
- **Hours of the Day**
  Before 2pm

Coupon expires 5/31/15. Cannot be combined with any other offer.

Mountain View Grand Resort & Spa
Whitefield, NH (866) 484-3843

- **Type of Discount**
  Free golf cart with 2 paid greens fees
- **Days of the Week**
  7 days a week
- **Hours of the Day**
  All day

Coupon expires 5/31/15. Cannot be combined with any other offer.

Mount Washington Golf Club
Bretton Woods, NH (603) 278-4653

- **Type of Discount**
  2 players for the price of 1
- **Days of the Week**
  Mondays only
- **Hours of the Day**
  All day

Coupon expires 5/31/15. Cannot be combined with any other offer.

Newport Golf Club
Newport, NH (603) 863-7787

- **Type of Discount**
  4 players for the price of 3
- **Days of the Week**
  Weekdays only (except holidays)
- **Hours of the Day**
  All day. Not valid on discount rates or holidays.

Coupon expires 5/31/15. Cannot be combined with any other offer.

Golf Course Coupons

NEW ENGLAND GOLFGUIDE

2 0 1 4 / 2 0 1 5

NEW ENGLAND GOLFGUIDE

2 0 1 4 / 2 0 1 5

NEW ENGLAND GOLFGUIDE

2 0 1 4 / 2 0 1 5

NEW ENGLAND GOLFGUIDE

2 0 1 4 / 2 0 1 5

Nippo Lake Golf Club
Barrington, NH (603) 664-7616

- **Type of Discount**
  $80 for 2 players and a cart (18 holes)

- **Days of the Week**
  Weekdays (except holidays).
  Weekends/Holidays after 12pm.

- **Hours of the Day**
  All day

Coupon expires 5/31/15. Cannot be combined with any other offer.

North Conway Country Club
North Conway, NH (603) 356-9391

- **Type of Discount**
  10% off with coupon after 12pm

- **Days of the Week**
  7 days a week

- **Hours of the Day**
  After 12pm

Coupon expires 5/31/15. Cannot be combined with any other offer.

Oak Hill Golf Course
Meredith, NH (603) 279-4438

- **Type of Discount**
  2 players for the price of 1. Cart rental required.

- **Days of the Week**
  7 days a week (except holiday weekends)

- **Hours of the Day**
  All day

Coupon expires 5/31/15. Cannot be combined with any other offer.

Owl's Nest Golf Club
Campton, NH (603) 726-3076

- **Type of Discount**
  2 players for the price of 1

- **Days of the Week**
  Weekdays (except holidays)

- **Hours of the Day**
  After 11am

Coupon expires 5/31/15. Cannot be combined with any other offer.

Golf Course Coupons

NEW ENGLAND GOLFGUIDE

2 0 1 4 / 2 0 1 5

NEW ENGLAND GOLFGUIDE

2 0 1 4 / 2 0 1 5

NEW ENGLAND GOLFGUIDE

2 0 1 4 / 2 0 1 5

NEW ENGLAND GOLFGUIDE

2 0 1 4 / 2 0 1 5

Passaconaway Country Club
Litchfield, NH (603) 424-4653

- **Type of Discount**
  4 seniors with carts – $40 each for 18 holes.
  All players must be present.
- **Days of the Week**
  Monday though Thursday
- **Hours of the Day**
  Monday through Thursday till 11pm

Coupon expires 5/31/15. Cannot be combined with any other offer.

Pease Golf Course
Portsmouth, NH (603) 433-1331

- **Type of Discount**
  Free golf cart with 2 paid greens fees
- **Days of the Week**
  7 days a week
- **Hours of the Day**
  All day weekdays; after 1pm weekends and
  holidays

Coupon expires 5/31/15. Cannot be combined with any other offer.

Pembroke Pines Country Club
Pembroke, NH (603) 210-1365

- **Type of Discount**
  4 players for the price of 3
- **Days of the Week**
  Weekdays Only (except holidays)
- **Hours of the Day**
  All day

Coupon expires 5/31/15. Cannot be combined with any other offer.

Pine Grove Springs Country Club
Route 9A, Spofford, NH (603) 363-4433

- **Type of Discount**
  2 players for the price of 1
- **Days of the Week**
  7 days a week
- **Hours of the Day**
  All day (excludes Sunday AM)

Coupon expires 5/31/15. Cannot be combined with any other offer.

Golf Course Coupons

NEW ENGLAND GOLFGUIDE

2 0 1 4 / 2 0 1 5

NEW ENGLAND GOLFGUIDE

2 0 1 4 / 2 0 1 5

NEW ENGLAND GOLFGUIDE

2 0 1 4 / 2 0 1 5

NEW ENGLAND GOLFGUIDE

2 0 1 4 / 2 0 1 5

Pine Valley Golf Links
Pelham, NH (603) 635-7979, (603) 635-8305

- **Type of Discount**
  4 players for the price of 3
- **Days of the Week**
  7 days a week
- **Hours of the Day**
  All day

Coupon expires 5/31/15. Cannot be combined with any other offer.

Portsmouth Country Club
Greenland, NH (603) 436-9719

- **Type of Discount**
  4 players for the price of 3
- **Days of the Week**
  Monday through Thursday (except holidays)
- **Hours of the Day**
  After 10am. Valid before Memorial Day, after Labor Day only.

Coupon expires 5/31/15. Cannot be combined with any other offer.

Ridgewood Country Club
Moultonborough, NH (603) 476-5930

- **Type of Discount**
  4 players for the price of 3
- **Days of the Week**
  Monday through Thursday (except holidays)
- **Hours of the Day**
  All day

Coupon expires 5/31/15. Cannot be combined with any other offer.

Rochester Country Club
Rochester, NH (603) 332-9892

- **Type of Discount**
  $80 for 2 players and cart (18 holes)
- **Days of the Week**
  7 days a week
- **Hours of the Day**
  Weekends/holidays after 12pm

Coupon expires 5/31/15. Cannot be combined with any other offer.

NEW ENGLAND GOLFGUIDE

2 0 1 4 / 2 0 1 5

NEW ENGLAND GOLFGUIDE

2 0 1 4 / 2 0 1 5

NEW ENGLAND GOLFGUIDE

2 0 1 4 / 2 0 1 5

NEW ENGLAND GOLFGUIDE

2 0 1 4 / 2 0 1 5

NH

Sagamore-Hampton Golf Club
North Hampton, NH (603) 964-5341

- **Type of Discount**
  25% discount for 2-4 players (cart included)
  18 holes only

- **Days of the Week**
  Weekdays (except holidays)

- **Hours of the Day**
  10am–2:30pm. Not valid for league play.

Coupon expires 5/31/15. Cannot be combined with any other offer.

Shattuck Golf Course, The
Jaffrey, NH (603) 532-4300

- **Type of Discount**
  2 players for $80 for 18 holes with cart

- **Days of the Week**
  7 days a week

- **Hours of the Day**
  All day

Coupon expires 5/31/15. Cannot be combined with any other offer.

Souhegan Woods Golf Club
Amherst, NH (603) 673-0200

- **Type of Discount**
  $5 off 18-hole greens fees. Cart rental required.

- **Days of the Week**
  Monday through Thursday only (except holidays)

- **Hours of the Day**
  All day

Coupon expires 5/31/15. Cannot be combined with any other offer.

Stonebridge Country Club
Goffstown, NH (603) 497-8633

- **Type of Discount**
  4 players for 18 holes and 2 carts for $169

- **Days of the Week**
  Monday through Thursday (excludes holidays)

- **Hours of the Day**
  All day

Coupon expires 5/31/15. Cannot be combined with any other offer.

Golf Course Coupons

NEW ENGLAND
GOLFGUIDE

2 0 1 4 / 2 0 1 5

NEW ENGLAND
GOLFGUIDE

2 0 1 4 / 2 0 1 5

NEW ENGLAND
GOLFGUIDE

2 0 1 4 / 2 0 1 5

NEW ENGLAND
GOLFGUIDE

2 0 1 4 / 2 0 1 5

Sunset Hill Golf Course
Sugar Hill, NH (603) 823-7244

- **Type of Discount**
  $22.50 per person for 9 or 18 holes (with cart)
- **Days of the Week**
  7 days a week (except July 4th weekend)
- **Hours of the Day**
  All day

Coupon expires 5/31/15. Cannot be combined with any other offer.

Waterville Valley Golf Club
Waterville, NH (603) 236-4805

- **Type of Discount**
  Unlimited golf with cart for $25
- **Days of the Week**
  Monday through Thursday (except holidays)
- **Hours of the Day**
  All day

Coupon expires 5/31/15. Cannot be combined with any other offer.

Waukewan Golf Club
Center Harbor, NH (603) 279-6661

- **Type of Discount**
  4 players for the price of 3.
  18-hole greens fee only.
- **Days of the Week**
  7 days a week
- **Hours of the Day**
  All day

Coupon expires 5/31/15. Cannot be combined with any other offer.

Waumbek Golf Club
Jefferson, NH (603) 586-7777

- **Type of Discount**
  $10 off 2 players with cart
- **Days of the Week**
  Monday through Friday (except holidays)
- **Hours of the Day**
  Before 3pm

Coupon expires 5/31/15. Cannot be combined with any other offer.

Golf Course Coupons

NEW ENGLAND GOLFGUIDE

2014 / 2015

NEW ENGLAND GOLFGUIDE

2014 / 2015

NEW ENGLAND GOLFGUIDE

2014 / 2015

NEW ENGLAND GOLFGUIDE

2014 / 2015

Wentworth Resort Golf Club
Rt. 16, Jackson, NH (603) 383-9641

- **Type of Discount**
  $5 off each greens fee for up to 2 players

- **Days of the Week**
  Monday through Thursday

- **Hours of the Day**
  After 1pm. Must call ahead. Must mention coupon when reserving tee time.

Coupon expires 5/31/15. Cannot be combined with any other offer.

White Mountain Country Club
Ashland, NH (603) 536-2227

- **Type of Discount**
  $5 off 18-hole greens fee.
  Cart rental required.

- **Days of the Week**
  Monday through Thursday (except holidays)

- **Hours of the Day**
  All day.

Coupon expires 5/31/15. Cannot be combined with any other offer.

Windham Country Club
Windham, NH (603) 434-2093

- **Type of Discount**
  Free bucket of balls per player

- **Days of the Week**
  Weekdays only (except holidays)

- **Hours of the Day**
  All day

Coupon expires 5/31/15. Cannot be combined with any other offer.

Beaver River Golf Club
Richmond, RI (401) 539-2100

- **Type of Discount**
  $42 with cart (Seniors/Military - $39 with cart)

- **Days of the Week**
  Monday through Thursday

- **Hours of the Day**
  8am–1pm

Coupon expires 5/31/15. Cannot be combined with any other offer.

Golf Course Coupons

NEW ENGLAND GOLFGUIDE

2 0 1 4 / 2 0 1 5

NEW ENGLAND GOLFGUIDE

2 0 1 4 / 2 0 1 5

NEW ENGLAND GOLFGUIDE

2 0 1 4 / 2 0 1 5

NEW ENGLAND GOLFGUIDE

2 0 1 4 / 2 0 1 5

Country View Golf Club
Harrisville, RI (401) 568-7157

- **Type of Discount**
  2 players for the price of 1.
  Cart rental required.

- **Days of the Week**
  Weekdays only (except holidays)

- **Hours of the Day**
  All day

Coupon expires 5/31/15. Cannot be combined with any other offer.

Cranston Country Club
Cranston, RI (401) 826-1683

- **Type of Discount**
  $35 with cart (18 holes)

- **Days of the Week**
  Monday through Friday (before 12pm)

- **Hours of the Day**
  All day. Valid July 7 - 31, 2014.

Valid July 7 - 31, 2014. Cannot be combined with any other offer.

Crystal Lake Golf Club
Mapleville, RI (401) 567-4500

- **Type of Discount**
  4 players for the price of 3. Carts not included.

- **Days of the Week**
  Monday though Thursday (except holidays)

- **Hours of the Day**
  All day

Coupon expires 5/31/15. Cannot be combined with any other offer.

Fairlawn Golf Course
Lincoln, RI (401) 334-3937

- **Type of Discount**
  2 players for the price of 1

- **Days of the Week**
  7 days a week

- **Hours of the Day**
  All day

Coupon expires 5/31/15. Cannot be combined with any other offer.

Golf Course Coupons

NEW ENGLAND GOLFGUIDE

2 0 1 4 / 2 0 1 5

NEW ENGLAND GOLFGUIDE

2 0 1 4 / 2 0 1 5

NEW ENGLAND GOLFGUIDE

2 0 1 4 / 2 0 1 5

NEW ENGLAND GOLFGUIDE

2 0 1 4 / 2 0 1 5

Laurel Lane Country Club
West Kingston, RI (401) 783-3844

- **Type of Discount**
  4 players for the price of 3

- **Days of the Week**
  Weekdays (except holidays).
  Weekends after 12pm.

- **Hours of the Day**
  All day

Coupon expires 5/31/15. Cannot be combined with any other offer.

Midville Country Club
West Warwick, RI (401) 828-9215

- **Type of Discount**
  Free golf cart with 2 paid greens fees

- **Days of the Week**
  Weekdays only (except holidays)

- **Hours of the Day**
  All day. Valid from 9/6/14 to 12/31/14.

Coupon expires 5/31/15. Cannot be combined with any other offer.

North Kingstown Muni. Golf Course
North Kingstown, RI (401) 294-0684

- **Type of Discount**
  Foursome special if you have 4 players–
  $38 per player

- **Days of the Week**
  M-Th; April, May, September, October

- **Hours of the Day**
  Until 12pm

Coupon expires 5/31/15. Cannot be combined with any other offer.

Pinecrest Golf Course
Carolina, RI (401) 364-8600

- **Type of Discount**
  $5 off greens fees for up to 2 players

- **Days of the Week**
  Weekdays only (except holidays)

- **Hours of the Day**
  Tee times 10am–2pm

Coupon expires 5/31/15. Cannot be combined with any other offer.

Golf Course Coupons

NEW ENGLAND GOLFGUIDE

2 0 1 4 / 2 0 1 5

NEW ENGLAND GOLFGUIDE

2 0 1 4 / 2 0 1 5

NEW ENGLAND GOLFGUIDE

2 0 1 4 / 2 0 1 5

NEW ENGLAND GOLFGUIDE

2 0 1 4 / 2 0 1 5

Rose Hill Golf Club
Wakefield, RI (401) 788-1088

- **Type of Discount**
  4 greens fees for the price of 3
- **Days of the Week**
  Weekdays only (except holidays)
- **Hours of the Day**
  7am–2pm

Coupon expires 5/31/15. Cannot be combined with any other offer.

Windmill Hill Golf Course
Warren, RI (401) 245-1463

- **Type of Discount**
  4 players for the price of 3
- **Days of the Week**
  7 days a week
- **Hours of the Day**
  12pm–3pm

Coupon expires 5/31/15. Cannot be combined with any other offer.

Wood River Golf
Hope Valley, RI (401) 364-0700

- **Type of Discount**
  Free golf cart with 2 paid greens fees
- **Days of the Week**
  Weekdays only (except holidays)
- **Hours of the Day**
  All day

Coupon expires 5/31/15. Cannot be combined with any other offer.

Alburg Golf Links
Alburg, VT (802) 796-4248

- **Type of Discount**
  4 players for the price of 3
- **Days of the Week**
  7 days a week
- **Hours of the Day**
  All day

Coupon expires 5/31/15. Cannot be combined with any other offer.

Golf Course Coupons

NEW ENGLAND GOLFGUIDE

2 0 1 4 / 2 0 1 5

NEW ENGLAND GOLFGUIDE

2 0 1 4 / 2 0 1 5

NEW ENGLAND GOLFGUIDE

2 0 1 4 / 2 0 1 5

NEW ENGLAND GOLFGUIDE

2 0 1 4 / 2 0 1 5

Barton Golf Club
Barton, VT (802) 525-1126

- **Type of Discount**
  2 players for the price of 1.
  Cart rental required.

- **Days of the Week**
  7 days a week

- **Hours of the Day**
  All day

Coupon expires 5/31/15. Cannot be combined with any other offer.

Bellows Falls Country Club
Route 103, Bellows Falls, VT (802) 463-9809

- **Type of Discount**
  2 players for the price of 1

- **Days of the Week**
  Weekdays only (except holidays)

- **Hours of the Day**
  All day

Coupon expires 5/31/15. Cannot be combined with any other offer.

Blush Hill Country Club
Waterbury, VT (802) 244-8974

- **Type of Discount**
  2 players for the price of 1

- **Days of the Week**
  7 days a week

- **Hours of the Day**
  All day

Coupon expires 5/31/15. Cannot be combined with any other offer.

Brattleboro Country Club
Brattleboro, VT (802) 257-7380

- **Type of Discount**
  2 players for the price of 1. Cart rental required.

- **Days of the Week**
  7 days a week

- **Hours of the Day**
  Monday through Friday after 10am
  Saturday and Sunday after 1pm

Coupon expires 5/31/15. Cannot be combined with any other offer.

Golf Course Coupons

NEW ENGLAND GOLFGUIDE

2 0 1 4 / 2 0 1 5

NEW ENGLAND GOLFGUIDE

2 0 1 4 / 2 0 1 5

NEW ENGLAND GOLFGUIDE

2 0 1 4 / 2 0 1 5

NEW ENGLAND GOLFGUIDE

2 0 1 4 / 2 0 1 5

Catamount Golf Club
Williston, VT (802) 878-7227

- **Type of Discount**
  $2 off large bucket of balls
- **Days of the Week**
  7 days a week
- **Hours of the Day**
  All day. Valid through October 31.

Coupon expires 10/31/14. Cannot be combined with any other offer.

Champlain Country Club
Swanton, VT (802) 527-1187

- **Type of Discount**
  Free golf cart with 2 paid greens fees
- **Days of the Week**
  Weekdays only (except holidays)
- **Hours of the Day**
  All day

Coupon expires 5/31/15. Cannot be combined with any other offer.

Country Club of Barre
Plainsfield Road, Barre, VT (802) 476-7658

- **Type of Discount**
  2 players for the price of 1.
  Cart rental required.
- **Days of the Week**
  Mon, Tues, Wed, Fri, all day; Sat/Sun after 12pm
- **Hours of the Day**
  Not valid holidays

Coupon expires 5/31/15. Cannot be combined with any other offer.

Crown Point Country Club
Springfield, VT (802) 885-1010

- **Type of Discount**
  2 players for the price of 1.
  Cart rental required.
- **Days of the Week**
  7 days a week
- **Hours of the Day**
  All day

Coupon expires 5/31/15. Cannot be combined with any other offer.

Golf Course Coupons

NEW ENGLAND
GOLFGUIDE

2 0 1 4 / 2 0 1 5

NEW ENGLAND
GOLFGUIDE

2 0 1 4 / 2 0 1 5

NEW ENGLAND
GOLFGUIDE

2 0 1 4 / 2 0 1 5

NEW ENGLAND
GOLFGUIDE

2 0 1 4 / 2 0 1 5

Enosburg Falls Country Club
Enosburg Falls, VT (802) 933-2296

- **Type of Discount**
  2 players for the price of 1.
  Cart rental required.

- **Days of the Week**
  7 days a week

- **Hours of the Day**
  All day

Coupon expires 5/31/15. Cannot be combined with any other offer.

Equinox Golf Club
Manchester, VT (802) 362-7870

- **Type of Discount**
  2 players for the price of 1

- **Days of the Week**
  Every day (except Saturday)

- **Hours of the Day**
  All day

Coupon expires 5/31/15. Cannot be combined with any other offer.

Green Mountain National Golf Course
Killington, VT (802) 422-GOLF

- **Type of Discount**
  2 players for the price of 1 (excludes groups
  of 12 or more)

- **Days of the Week**
  Monday though Thursday (includes holidays)

- **Hours of the Day**
  All day

Coupon expires 5/31/15. Cannot be combined with any other offer.

Hermitage Golf Club
Wilmington, VT (802) 464-8301

- **Type of Discount**
  4 players for the price of 3

- **Days of the Week**
  Sun. through Thurs. after 12pm (non-holiday)

- **Hours of the Day**
  After 12pm

Coupon expires 5/31/15. Cannot be combined with any other offer.

Golf Course Coupons

NEW ENGLAND GOLFGUIDE

2 0 1 4 / 2 0 1 5

NEW ENGLAND GOLFGUIDE

2 0 1 4 / 2 0 1 5

NEW ENGLAND GOLFGUIDE

2 0 1 4 / 2 0 1 5

NEW ENGLAND GOLFGUIDE

2 0 1 4 / 2 0 1 5

Jay Peak Resort Golf Course
Jay, VT (802) 988-2611

- **Type of Discount**
  Free golf cart with 2 paid greens fees
- **Days of the Week**
  7 days a week
- **Hours of the Day**
  All day

Coupon expires 5/31/15. Cannot be combined with any other offer.

Killington Golf Course
Killington, VT (802) 422-6700

- **Type of Discount**
  $49 + tax per person. Includes greens fee + cart.
  Coupon good for up to 4 players.
- **Days of the Week**
  Weekdays (except holidays). Sunday after 1pm.
- **Hours of the Day**
  Weekdays all day. Sunday after 1pm.

Coupon expires 5/31/15. Cannot be combined with any other offer.

Lake Morey Country Club
Fairlee, VT (802) 333-4800

- **Type of Discount**
  2 players for the price of 1
- **Days of the Week**
  Monday through Thursday (except holidays)
- **Hours of the Day**
  All day

Coupon expires 5/31/15. Cannot be combined with any other offer.

Montague Golf Club
Randolph, VT (802) 728-3806

- **Type of Discount**
  $35 greens fee (cart included)
- **Days of the Week**
  7 days a week
- **Hours of the Day**
  All day. Not to be used for tournament entry.

Coupon expires 5/31/15. Cannot be combined with any other offer.

Golf Course Coupons

NEW ENGLAND
GOLFGUIDE
2 0 1 4 / 2 0 1 5

NEW ENGLAND
GOLFGUIDE
2 0 1 4 / 2 0 1 5

NEW ENGLAND
GOLFGUIDE
2 0 1 4 / 2 0 1 5

NEW ENGLAND
GOLFGUIDE
2 0 1 4 / 2 0 1 5

Mt. Anthony Country Club
Bennington, VT (802) 447-7079

- **Type of Discount**
  4 players for the price of 3 (cart rental required)
- **Days of the Week**
  Monday through Thursday (except holidays)
- **Hours of the Day**
  All day

Coupon expires 5/31/15. Cannot be combined with any other offer.

Mount Snow
Mount Snow, VT (802) 464-4254

- **Type of Discount**
  4 players for the price of 3 (cart included)
- **Days of the Week**
  7 days a week
- **Hours of the Day**
  All day

Coupon expires 5/31/15. Cannot be combined with any other offer.

Neshobe Golf Club
Brandon, VT (802) 247-3611

- **Type of Discount**
  25% discount for 2-4 players
- **Days of the Week**
  7 days a week
- **Hours of the Day**
  All day (Monday - Friday; except holidays).
  After 12pm (Saturday, Sunday, holidays).

Coupon expires 5/31/15. Cannot be combined with any other offer.

Newport Country Club
Newport, VT (802) 334-2391

- **Type of Discount**
  2 players for the price of 1. Cart rental required.
- **Days of the Week**
  Weekdays only (except holidays)
- **Hours of the Day**
  After 11am.
  Valid April/May/June/September/October.

Coupon expires 5/31/15. Cannot be combined with any other offer.

Golf Course Coupons

NEW ENGLAND GOLFGUIDE

2 0 1 4 / 2 0 1 5

NEW ENGLAND GOLFGUIDE

2 0 1 4 / 2 0 1 5

NEW ENGLAND GOLFGUIDE

2 0 1 4 / 2 0 1 5

NEW ENGLAND GOLFGUIDE

2 0 1 4 / 2 0 1 5

Okemo Valley Golf Club
Ludlow, VT (802) 228-1396

- **Type of Discount**
  2 players for the price of 1 (greens fee only)
- **Days of the Week**
  Monday through Thursday (except holidays)
- **Hours of the Day**
  After 11am

Coupon expires 5/31/15. Cannot be combined with any other offer.

Orleans Country Club
Orleans, VT (802) 754-2333

- **Type of Discount**
  2 players for the price of 1. Cart rental required.
- **Days of the Week**
  Weekdays only (except holidays)
- **Hours of the Day**
  All day

Coupon expires 5/31/15. Cannot be combined with any other offer.

Proctor Pittsford Country Club
Pittsford, VT (802) 483-9379

- **Type of Discount**
  $40 for 18 holes with cart
- **Days of the Week**
  7 days a week
- **Hours of the Day**
  Weekends and holidays after 12pm

Coupon expires 5/31/15. Cannot be combined with any other offer.

Ralph Myhre Golf Course
Middlebury, VT (802) 443-5125

- **Type of Discount**
  Free golf cart with 2 paid greens fees
- **Days of the Week**
  7 days a week
- **Hours of the Day**
  All day

Coupon expires 5/31/15. Cannot be combined with any other offer.

Golf Course Coupons

NEW ENGLAND GOLFGUIDE

2 0 1 4 / 2 0 1 5

NEW ENGLAND GOLFGUIDE

2 0 1 4 / 2 0 1 5

NEW ENGLAND GOLFGUIDE

2 0 1 4 / 2 0 1 5

NEW ENGLAND GOLFGUIDE

2 0 1 4 / 2 0 1 5

Richford Country Club
Richford, VT (802) 848-3527

- **Type of Discount**
  4 players with carts for $75

- **Days of the Week**
  Monday through Thursday (except holidays)

- **Hours of the Day**
  All day

Coupon expires 5/31/15. Cannot be combined with any other offer.

Rocky Ridge Golf Club
St. George, VT (802) 482-2191

- **Type of Discount**
  2 players for the price of 1.
  Cart rental required.

- **Days of the Week**
  7 days a week

- **Hours of the Day**
  After 12pm

Coupon expires 5/31/15. Cannot be combined with any other offer.

Ryder Brook Golf Club
Morrisville, VT (802) 888-3525

- **Type of Discount**
  25% discount for 2-4 players.
  Cart rental required.

- **Days of the Week**
  Weekdays only (except holidays)

- **Hours of the Day**
  All day

Coupon expires 5/31/15. Cannot be combined with any other offer.

Sitzmark Golf Course
Wilmington, VT (802) 464-3384

- **Type of Discount**
  2 players for the price of 1

- **Days of the Week**
  Monday through Thursday (except holidays)

- **Hours of the Day**
  All day

Coupon expires 5/31/15. Cannot be combined with any other offer.

Golf Course Coupons

NEW ENGLAND GOLFGUIDE

2 0 1 4 / 2 0 1 5

NEW ENGLAND GOLFGUIDE

2 0 1 4 / 2 0 1 5

NEW ENGLAND GOLFGUIDE

2 0 1 4 / 2 0 1 5

NEW ENGLAND GOLFGUIDE

2 0 1 4 / 2 0 1 5

St. Johnsbury Country Club
Route 5, St. Johnsbury, VT (802) 748-9894

- **Type of Discount**
  2 players for the price of 1. Cart rental required.

- **Days of the Week**
  Weekdays (except holidays).
  Must present coupon.

- **Hours of the Day**
  After 12pm – call for times

Coupon expires 5/31/15. Cannot be combined with any other offer.

Stratton Mountain
Stratton Mountain, VT (802) 297-4114

- **Type of Discount**
  2 players for the price of 1

- **Days of the Week**
  Weekdays only (except holidays)

- **Hours of the Day**
  After 1pm

Coupon expires 5/31/15. Cannot be combined with any other offer.

Sugarbush Resort Golf Club
Warren, VT (802) 583-6725

- **Type of Discount**
  Foursome with cart $160 M-Th
  Foursome with cart $200 Friday

- **Days of the Week**
  Monday through Friday (except holidays)

- **Hours of the Day**
  All day. Coupon Code: 1016283223.

Coupon expires 5/31/15. Cannot be combined with any other offer.

Tater Hill Golf Club
North Windham, VT (802) 875-2517

- **Type of Discount**
  50% off greens fees for up to 4 players

- **Days of the Week**
  Weekdays only (except holidays)

- **Hours of the Day**
  After 11am

Coupon expires 5/31/15. Cannot be combined with any other offer.

Golf Course Coupons

NEW ENGLAND GOLFGUIDE

2 0 1 4 / 2 0 1 5

NEW ENGLAND GOLFGUIDE

2 0 1 4 / 2 0 1 5

NEW ENGLAND GOLFGUIDE

2 0 1 4 / 2 0 1 5

NEW ENGLAND GOLFGUIDE

2 0 1 4 / 2 0 1 5

White River Golf Club
Rt. 100, Rochester, VT (802) 767-4653

- **Type of Discount**
  Free golf cart with 2 paid greens fees

- **Days of the Week**
  Weekdays only (except holidays)

- **Hours of the Day**
  All day. Tee times required.

Coupon expires 5/31/15. Cannot be combined with any other offer.

Wilcox Cove Golf Course
Highway 314, Grand Isle, VT (802) 372-8343

- **Type of Discount**
  2 players for the price of 1

- **Days of the Week**
  Weekdays only (except holidays)

- **Hours of the Day**
  All day. Not available July 1 through Labor Day.

Coupon expires 5/31/15. Cannot be combined with any other offer.

Williston Golf Club
Williston, VT (802) 878-3747

- **Type of Discount**
  Free golf cart with 2 paid greens fees

- **Days of the Week**
  7 days a week

- **Hours of the Day**
  All day

Coupon expires 5/31/15. Cannot be combined with any other offer.

Woodbury Golf Course
South Woodbury, VT (802) 456-7421

- **Type of Discount**
  2 players for the price of 1

- **Days of the Week**
  7 days a week

- **Hours of the Day**
  All day

Coupon expires 5/31/15. Cannot be combined with any other offer.

Golf Course Coupons

NEW ENGLAND GOLFGUIDE

2 0 1 4 / 2 0 1 5

NEW ENGLAND GOLFGUIDE

2 0 1 4 / 2 0 1 5

NEW ENGLAND GOLFGUIDE

2 0 1 4 / 2 0 1 5

NEW ENGLAND GOLFGUIDE

2 0 1 4 / 2 0 1 5

NEW ENGLAND GOLFGUIDE

BCNE33114

Offer excludes PING, Titleist, FootJoy, ECCO, Mizuno, Scotty Cameron, and select TaylorMade and Callaway products. Cannot be combined with other coupons or discounts. Not valid on previous purchases or gift cards. Additional exclusions may apply, see store for complete details.

NEW ENGLAND GOLFGUIDE

BCNE43014

Offer excludes PING, Titleist, FootJoy, ECCO, Mizuno, Scotty Cameron, and select TaylorMade and Callaway products. Cannot be combined with other coupons or discounts. Not valid on previous purchases or gift cards. Additional exclusions may apply, see store for complete details.

NEW ENGLAND GOLFGUIDE

BCNE53114

Offer excludes PING, Titleist, FootJoy, ECCO, Mizuno, Scotty Cameron, and select TaylorMade and Callaway products. Cannot be combined with other coupons or discounts. Not valid on previous purchases or gift cards. Additional exclusions may apply, see store for complete details.

NEW ENGLAND GOLFGUIDE

BCNE63014

Offer excludes PING, Titleist, FootJoy, ECCO, Mizuno, Scotty Cameron, and select TaylorMade and Callaway products. Cannot be combined with other coupons or discounts. Not valid on previous purchases or gift cards. Additional exclusions may apply, see store for complete details.

NEW ENGLAND GOLFGUIDE

BCNE73114

Offer excludes PING, Titleist, FootJoy, ECCO, Mizuno, Scotty Cameron, and select TaylorMade and Callaway products. Cannot be combined with other coupons or discounts. Not valid on previous purchases or gift cards. Additional exclusions may apply, see store for complete details.

NEW ENGLAND GOLFGUIDE

BCNE13115

Offer excludes PING, Titleist, FootJoy, ECCO, Mizuno, Scotty Cameron, and select TaylorMade and Callaway products. Cannot be combined with other coupons or discounts. Not valid on previous purchases or gift cards. Additional exclusions may apply, see store for complete details.

NEW ENGLAND GOLFGUIDE

BCNE22815

Offer excludes PING, Titleist, FootJoy, ECCO, Mizuno, Scotty Cameron, and select TaylorMade and Callaway products. Cannot be combined with other coupons or discounts. Not valid on previous purchases or gift cards. Additional exclusions may apply, see store for complete details.

NEW ENGLAND GOLFGUIDE

BCNE33115

Offer excludes PING, Titleist, FootJoy, ECCO, Mizuno, Scotty Cameron, and select TaylorMade and Callaway products. Cannot be combined with other coupons or discounts. Not valid on previous purchases or gift cards. Additional exclusions may apply, see store for complete details.

NEW ENGLAND GOLFGUIDE

BCNE43015

Offer excludes PING, Titleist, FootJoy, ECCO, Mizuno, Scotty Cameron, and select TaylorMade and Callaway products. Cannot be combined with other coupons or discounts. Not valid on previous purchases or gift cards. Additional exclusions may apply, see store for complete details.

NEW ENGLAND GOLFGUIDE

BCNE53115

Offer excludes PING, Titleist, FootJoy, ECCO, Mizuno, Scotty Cameron, and select TaylorMade and Callaway products. Cannot be combined with other coupons or discounts. Not valid on previous purchases or gift cards. Additional exclusions may apply, see store for complete details.

Chris Cote's
GOLF
SHOP

750 Portland-Cobalt Road
Portland, CT
(860) 342-2226

$15 OFF
ANY PULL CART

www.chriscotegolf.com

Chris Cote's
GOLF
SHOP

750 Portland-Cobalt Road
Portland, CT
(860) 342-2226

$15 OFF
ANY WEDGE

www.chriscotegolf.com

Chris Cote's
GOLF
SHOP

750 Portland-Cobalt Road
Portland, CT
(860) 342-2226

$15 OFF
ANY PUTTER

www.chriscotegolf.com

Chris Cote's
GOLF
SHOP

750 Portland-Cobalt Road
Portland, CT
(860) 342-2226

$3 OFF
ANY GOLF GLOVE

www.chriscotegolf.com

NEW ENGLAND GOLFGUIDE

2 0 1 4 / 2 0 1 5

Cannot be used with any other offers or discounts. Offer expires 5/31/15.

NEW ENGLAND GOLFGUIDE

2 0 1 4 / 2 0 1 5

Cannot be used with any other offers or discounts. Offer expires 5/31/15.

NEW ENGLAND GOLFGUIDE

2 0 1 4 / 2 0 1 5

Cannot be used with any other offers or discounts. Offer expires 5/31/15.

NEW ENGLAND GOLFGUIDE

2 0 1 4 / 2 0 1 5

Cannot be used with any other offers or discounts. Offer expires 5/31/15.

$10 OFF
ANY GOLF BAG
OR TRAVEL COVER

Hyannis, MA
1019 Iyannough Road
(508) 771-4653

www.capeandislandsgolf.com

$10 OFF
ANY PAIR OF SHOES

Hyannis, MA
1019 Iyannough Road
(508) 771-4653

www.capeandislandsgolf.com

FREE LABOR
ON CLUB RE-GRIPPING

Hyannis, MA
1019 Iyannough Road
(508) 771-4653

www.capeandislandsgolf.com

20% OFF
ANY ONE APPAREL ITEM
(NON SALE ITEMS)

Hyannis, MA
1019 Iyannough Road
(508) 771-4653

www.capeandislandsgolf.com

NEW ENGLAND GOLFGUIDE

2 0 1 4 / 2 0 1 5

Cannot be used with any other offers or discounts. Offer expires 5/31/15.

NEW ENGLAND GOLFGUIDE

2 0 1 4 / 2 0 1 5

Cannot be used with any other offers or discounts. Offer expires 5/31/15.

NEW ENGLAND GOLFGUIDE

2 0 1 4 / 2 0 1 5

Cannot be used with any other offers or discounts. Offer expires 5/31/15.

NEW ENGLAND GOLFGUIDE

2 0 1 4 / 2 0 1 5

Cannot be used with any other offers or discounts. Offer expires 5/31/15.

NEW ENGLAND GOLFGUIDE

2 0 1 4 / 2 0 1 5

Cannot be used with any other offers or discounts. Offer expires 5/31/15.

NEW ENGLAND GOLFGUIDE

2 0 1 4 / 2 0 1 5

Cannot be used with any other offers or discounts. Offer expires 5/31/15.

NEW ENGLAND GOLFGUIDE

2 0 1 4 / 2 0 1 5

Cannot be used with any other offers or discounts. Offer expires 5/31/15.

NEW ENGLAND GOLFGUIDE

2 0 1 4 / 2 0 1 5

Cannot be used with any other offers or discounts. Offer expires 5/31/15.

20% Off
Apparel and Accessories*

Route 12A West Lebanon, NH 603-298-8282
Route 33 Greenland, NH 603-433-8585
Route 3A Hudson, NH 603-595-8484
Payne Road Scarborough, ME 207-883-4343
Open Daily • No NH Sales Tax
www.golfskiwarehouse.com

$20 Off
Any Golf Bag or Pair of Golf Shoes Over $100*

Route 12A West Lebanon, NH 603-298-8282
Route 33 Greenland, NH 603-433-8585
Route 3A Hudson, NH 603-595-8484
Payne Road Scarborough, ME 207-883-4343
Open Daily • No NH Sales Tax
www.golfskiwarehouse.com

$2.00 off per grip
Plus FREE Installation*

Route 12A West Lebanon, NH 603-298-8282
Route 33 Greenland, NH 603-433-8585
Route 3A Hudson, NH 603-595-8484
Payne Road Scarborough, ME 207-883-4343
Open Daily • No NH Sales Tax
www.golfskiwarehouse.com

NEW ENGLAND
GOLFGUIDE

2 0 1 4 / 2 0 1 5

Cannot be used with any other offers or discounts. Offer expires 5/31/15.

NEW ENGLAND
GOLFGUIDE

2 0 1 4 / 2 0 1 5

Cannot be used with any other offers or discounts. Offer expires 5/31/15.

NEW ENGLAND
GOLFGUIDE

2 0 1 4 / 2 0 1 5

Cannot be used with any other offers or discounts. Offer expires 5/31/15.

NEW ENGLAND GOLFGUIDE

2 0 1 4 / 2 0 1 5

Cannot be used with any other offers or discounts. Offer expires 5/31/15.

NEW ENGLAND GOLFGUIDE

2 0 1 4 / 2 0 1 5

Cannot be used with any other offers or discounts. Offer expires 5/31/15.

NEW ENGLAND GOLFGUIDE

2 0 1 4 / 2 0 1 5

Cannot be used with any other offers or discounts. Offer expires 5/31/15.

NEW ENGLAND GOLFGUIDE

2 0 1 4 / 2 0 1 5

Cannot be used with any other offers or discounts. Offer expires 5/31/15.

NEW ENGLAND GOLFGUIDE

2 0 1 4 / 2 0 1 5

Cannot be used with any other offers or discounts. Offer expires 5/31/15.

NEW ENGLAND GOLFGUIDE

2 0 1 4 / 2 0 1 5

Cannot be used with any other offers or discounts. Offer expires 5/31/15.

NEW ENGLAND GOLFGUIDE

2 0 1 4 / 2 0 1 5

Cannot be used with any other offers or discounts. Offer expires 5/31/15.

The Ledges | York, ME

The Ledges Golf Club (York, ME) is clearly the gateway to any memorable Maine golf trip. Conveniently located minutes from I-95 and the Maine/NH border, it's an easy ride from both Boston and Portland. Breathtaking views of the rugged Maine landscape make The Ledges a true escape from your daily routine. Rated 4 stars by *NE GolfGuide* and 4.5 stars by *Golf Digest,* The Ledges Golf Club is sure to exceed expectations.

The Ledges has four sets of tees ranging from 6,981 to 5,000 yards and widely known as the finest public golf experience on the seacoast. The fair but challenging layout gives players of all abilities the opportunity to hit every club in the bag. Those who frequent The Ledges know their work isn't done once they reach the green. The Ledges consistently has first rate putting surfaces that have challenged tour players and weekend warriors alike!

When you're finished with your round you can enjoy fantastic pub food at our newly renovated 19th hole. Perfect for small corporate outings and large charity events the staff at The Ledges will ensure your post round festivities rival your on-course experience. Check out The Ledges Golf Club on-line at www.ledgesgolf.com. Book tee-times, see the various "Stay and Play" packages, the latest Ledges news and much more.